Helen Gordon-Smith

CONTACTS® 2003

92nd edition published in October by The Spotlight, 7 Leicester Place, London WC2H 7RJ
Tel: 020-7437 7631 Fax: 020-7437 5881 e-mail: info@spotlightcd.com www.spotlightcd.com

Dear Reader,

Contacts is known as the most comprehensive and essential handbook in the industry. Readership is now in excess of 100,000. Published every October, a dedicated team devote the utmost care to produce and publish the UK's number one theatrical handbook.

If you are a drama school graduate, a seasoned veteran, at stage or drama school or work in the tv, radio, theatre and film arena, we guarantee that you will find *Contacts* packed with information for all your needs.

Your suggestions from last year have provided for a new photographers category and also a new colour mid-section.

We hope that you have a successful year and hope that *Contacts* helps you find the information you are looking for.

Best Wishes

THE SPOTLIGHT®

D0293130

Editor: Kate Poynton   Production: Kathy Norrish

CONTENTS

INDEX TO ADVERTISERS   320

CONTENTS

ABBOT MEAD VICKERS BBDO Ltd
151 Marylebone Road
London NW1 5QE
Fax: 020-7616 3600   Tel: 020-7616 3500

AKA
Gloucester Mansions
140A Shaftesbury Avenue, London WC2H 8HD
Website: www.akauk.com
e-mail: aka@akauk.com
Fax: 020-7836 8787   Tel: 020-7836 4747

BANKS HOGGINS O'SHEA FCB
55 Newman Street, London W1T 3EB
Fax: 020-7947 8001   Tel: 020-7947 8000

BARTLE BOGLE HEGARTY
60 Kingly Street
London W1B 5DS
Fax: 020-7437 3666   Tel: 020-7734 1677

BATES TAVNER RESOURCES INTERNATIONAL Ltd
International House, World Trade Centre,
1 St Katherine's Way, London E1W 1UN
Fax: 020-7702 2271   Tel: 020-7481 2000

BATES UK Ltd
121-141 Westbourne Terrace
London W2 6JR
Fax: 020-7258 3757   Tel: 020-7262 5077

BDH/TBWA
St Paul's, 781 Wilmslow Road
Didsbury Village, Manchester M20 2RW
Website: www.bdhtbwa.co.uk
e-mail: info@bdhtbwa.co.uk
Fax: 0161-908 8601   Tel: 0161-908 8600

BMP DDB Ltd
12 Bishops Bridge Road
London W2 6AA
Fax: 020-7402 4871   Tel: 020-7258 3979

BURNETT Leo Ltd
60 Sloane Avenue, London SW3 3XB
Fax: 020-7591 9126   Tel: 020-7591 9111

CDP TRAVIS SULLY
9 Lower John Street, London W1F 9DZ
Fax: 020-7437 5445   Tel: 020-7437 4224

COGENT
Heath Farm, Hampton Lane, Meriden
West Midlands CV7 7LL
Fax: 0121-627 5038   Tel: 0121-627 5040

D'ARCY
Warwick Building, Kensington Village
Avonmore Road, London W14 8HQ
Fax: 020-7348 3855   Tel: 020-7751 1800

DEWYNTERS Plc
48 Leicester Square, London WC2H 7QD
Fax: 020-7321 0104   Tel: 020-7321 0488

DONER CARDWELL HAWKINS
26-34 Emerald Street
London WC1N 3QA
Fax: 020-7437 3961   Tel: 020-7734 0511

EURO RSCG WNEK GOSPER
11 Great Newport Street
London WC2H 7JA
Fax: 020-7465 0552   Tel: 020-7240 4111

FAULDS ADVERTISING Ltd
Sutherland House
108 Dundas Street
Edinburgh EH3 5DQ
Fax: 0131-557 2261   Tel: 0131-557 6003

GOLLEY SLATER & PARTNERS (LONDON) Ltd
St George's House, 3 St George's Place
Church Street, Twickenham TW1 3NE
Fax: 020-8892 4451   Tel: 020-8744 2630

GREY WORLDWIDE
215-227 Great Portland Street
London W1W 5PN
Fax: 020-7637 7473   Tel: 020-7636 3399

HARDSELL Ltd
(Advertising, Marketing, Design)
Lafone House
The Leathermarket, Weston Street
London SE1 3HN
e-mail: bigideas@hardsell.co.uk
Fax: 020-7403 5381   Tel: 020-7403 4037

HAYMARKET ADVERTISING Ltd
(See M+H COMMUNICATIONS Ltd)

Advertising Agents

A

laura woolnough 07941 018957 / 020 86743078

camilla rutherford

David Potter Photography

07973 579988

www. davidpotterphoto.com

or

See my portfolio at Spotlight

Emma Woolliams

HOLMAN ADVERTISING Ltd
Holman House, 30 Maple Street, London W1T 6HA
e-mail: holman.house@lineone.net
Fax: 020-7631 5283 Tel: 020-7637 3533

KANE Peter & COMPANY Ltd
12 Burleigh Street
Covent Garden, London WC2E 7PX
Fax: 020-7836 4073 Tel: 020-7836 4561

LEAGAS DELANEY LONDON Ltd
1 Alfred Place
London WC1E 7EB
Website: www.leagusdelaney.com
Fax: 020-7758 1760 Tel: 020-7758 1758

LEITH AGENCY The
37 The Shore, Edinburgh EH6 6QU
Fax: 0131-561 8601 Tel: 0131-561 8600

LOWE
Bowater House, 68-114 Knightsbridge
London SW1X 7LT
Website: www.loweworldwide.com
Fax: 020-7584 9557 Tel: 020-7584 5033

M+H COMMUNICATIONS Ltd
(Advertising, Marketing)
36 Lexington Street, London W1F 0LJ
Website: www.mandh.co.uk
e-mail: info@mandh.co.uk
Fax: 020-7412 2020 Tel: 020-7412 2000

McCANN-ERICKSON ADVERTISING Ltd
7-11 Herbrand Street, London WC1N 1EX
Fax: 020-7837 3773 Tel: 020-7837 3773

MEDIA ED CIA
1 Paris Garden
London SE1 8NU Tel: 020-7633 9999

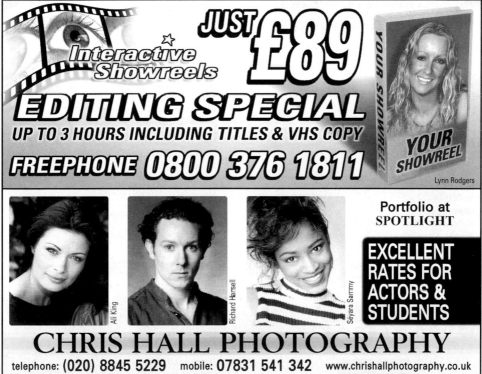

Interactive Showreels JUST £89 EDITING SPECIAL UP TO 3 HOURS INCLUDING TITLES & VHS COPY FREEPHONE 0800 376 1811

YOUR SHOWREEL

Lynn Rodgers

Portfolio at SPOTLIGHT

EXCELLENT RATES FOR ACTORS & STUDENTS

Ali King Richard Harsell Séyara Sammy

CHRIS HALL PHOTOGRAPHY
telephone: (020) 8845 5229 mobile: 07831 541 342 www.chrishallphotography.co.uk

5

MEDIACOM
180 North Gower Street
London NW1 2NB
Fax: 020-7874 5999   Tel: 020-7874 5500

MOUNTAIN VIEW Ltd
279 Tottenham Court Road
London W1T 7RJ
Fax: 020-7670 3672   Tel: 020-7670 3670

MUSTOE MERRIMAN HERRING LEVY
2-4 Bucknall Street
London WC2H 8LA
Fax: 020-7379 8487   Tel: 020-7379 9999

OGILVY & MATHER Ltd
10 Cabot Square, Canary Wharf
London E14 4QB
Fax: 020-7345 9000   Tel: 020-7345 3000

PARTNERS BDDH
Cupola House
London WC1E 7EB
Fax: 020-7467 9210   Tel: 020-7467 9200

PUBLICIS Ltd
82 Baker Street
London W1U 6AE
Fax: 020-7487 5351   Tel: 020-7935 4426

RAINEY KELLY CAMPBELL ROALFE Y & R
Greater London House
Hampstead Road, London NW1 7QP
Fax: 020-7611 6011   Tel: 020-7404 2700

RED CELL ADVERTISING Ltd
12-16 Clerkenwell Road, London EC1M 5PQ
Website: www.redcellnetwork.com
Fax: 020-7324 6314   Tel: 020-7240 4949

RICHMOND TOWERS Ltd
26 Fitzroy Square, London W1T 6BT
Fax: 020-7388 7761   Tel: 020-7388 7421

ROOSE & PARTNERS
Holborn Hall, 100 Gray's Inn Road
London WC1X 8AU
Fax: 020-7831 8761   Tel: 020-7831 7400

RPM 3
William Blake House
8 Marshall Street, London W1V 2AJ
Fax: 020-7439 8884   Tel: 020-7434 4343

SAATCHI & SAATCHI
80 Charlotte Street, London W1A 1AQ
Fax: 020-7637 8489   Tel: 020-7636 5060

SMEE'S ADVERTISING Ltd
3-5 Duke Street
London W1U 3BA
Fax: 020-7935 8588   Tel: 020-7486 6644

SWK & PARTNERS Ltd
52-54 Broadwick Street
London W1F 7AQ
e-mail: firstname.surname@swk.co.uk
Fax: 020-7534 0808   Tel: 020-7534 0800

TBWA LONDON
76-80 Whitfield Street
London W1T 4EZ
Fax: 020-7573 6667   Tel: 020-7573 6666

TBWA/GGT DIRECT
82 Dean Street
London W1D 3HA
Fax: 020-7434 2925   Tel: 020-7439 4282

THOMPSON J Walter CO Ltd
1 Knightsbridge Green
London SW1X 7NW
e-mail: firstname.lastname@jwt.com
Fax: 020-7656 7010   Tel: 020-7656 7000

TMP WORLDWIDE
Chancery House
53-64 Chancery Lane
London WC2A 1QS   Tel: 020-7406 5000

TV MANAGEMENTS
Brink House, Avon Castle
Ringwood
Hants BH24 2BL   Tel: 01425 475544

WCRS
5 Golden Square
London W1F 9BS
Fax: 020-7806 5099   Tel: 020-7806 5000

YOUNG & RUBICAM Ltd
Greater London House, Hampstead Road
London NW1 7QP
Fax: 020-7611 6570   Tel: 020-7387 9366

KREATE
PROMOTIONS · PRODUCTIONS
KREATE PRODUCTIONS
Unit 201 30 Great Guildford Street
Great Guildford Business Centre
London SE1 0HS
T - 020 7401 9007/8   F - 020 7401 3003

Reynolds Performing Arts Academy

Incorporating

The Reynolds Agency

"Professionally Trained Children & Adults"
Available for:
TV, Film, Theatre, Commercials & Modelling
We can also supply
Dancers, Choreographers, Singers & Presenters

01322 277200   WESTGATE HOUSE,
SPITAL STREET,
DARTFORD KENT

Key to areas of specialization:
C Cabaret **F** Films **G** General **M** Musicals **Md** Models **PM** Personal Managers **S** Singing **TV** Television **V** Variety
For information regarding membership of the Personal Managers' Association please contact:
Personal Managers' Association Ltd, Rivercroft, 1 Summer Road, East Molesey, Surrey KT8 9LX
Tel: 020-8398 9796   *** Denotes PMA Membership**
For information regarding membership of the Co-operative Personal Managers' Association please contact:
Secretary, CPMA, c/o 1 Mellor Road, Leicester LE3 6HN
Tel: 0116-233 8432
e-mail: cpmauk@yahoo.co.uk   **• Denotes CPMA Membership**

1984 PERSONAL MANAGEMENT Ltd
Suite 508, Davina House
137 Goswell Road, London EC1V 7ET
e-mail: onenine@eightfour.freeserve.co.uk
Fax: 020-7250 3031   Tel: 020-7251 8046

1ST FRAMEWORK
Fulcrum, 19 Great Guildford Street, London SE1 9EZ
Website: www.1stframework.org
Fax: 020-7803 0531   Tel: 020-7803 0530

21ST CENTURY ACTORS MANAGEMENT
Co-operative
E10 Panther House, 38 Mount Pleasant, London WC1X 0AN
e-mail: twentyfirstcenturyactors@yahoo.co.uk
Fax: 020-7833 1158   Tel: 020-7278 3438

21ST CENTURY VAUX CASTING
The Corn Exchange, Fenwick Street, Liverpool L2 7QS
e-mail: 21stcenturyvaux@beeb.net
Fax: 0151-231 1068   Tel: 0151-258 1679

2MA
(Sports & Stunts)
Spring Vale, Tutland Road
North Baddesley, Hants SO52 9FL
Website: www.2ma.co.uk
e-mail: mo@2ma.co.uk
Fax: 023-8074 1355   Tel: 023-8074 1354

41 MANAGEMENT*
4th Floor
41 St Vincent Place, Glasgow G1 2ER
e-mail: mhunwick@41man.co.uk
Fax: 0141-248 6307   Tel: 0141-248 3891

A-LIST
(Lookalikes & Entertainments)
29 New Line
Greengates, Bradford BD10 9AS
Website: www.alistlookalikes.co.uk
e-mail: enquiries@alistlookalikes.co.uk
Mobile: 07866 583106   Tel: 01274 618309

A PLUS
(16-26 year olds)
54 Grove Park, London SE5 8LG
Website: www.kidsplusuk.com
e-mail: janekidsplus@aol.com
Mobile: 07759 944215   Tel/Fax: 020-7737 3901

A & B PERSONAL MANAGEMENT Ltd*
PM Write
Paurelle House
91 Regent Street, London W1B 4EL
e-mail: billellis@aandb.co.uk
Fax: 020-7734 6318   Tel: 020-7734 6047

ABBOTT JUNE ASSOCIATES
The Courtyard, 10 York Way, King's Cross
London N1 9AA
Website: www.thecourtyard.org.uk
e-mail: thecourtyard@btclick.com
Fax: 020-7833 0870   Tel: 020-7837 7826

ACCESS ASSOCIATES
PO Box 39925
London EC1V 0WN
e-mail: access.mail@virgin.net   Tel: 020-8505 1094

ACROBAT PRODUCTIONS
(Artists & Advisors)
The Circus Space, Coronet Street, London N1 6HD
Website: www.acrobatsunlimited.com
e-mail: info@acrobatproductions.co.uk
    Tel: 020-7613 5259

ACT ONE DRAMA STUDIO & AGENCY
31 Dobbin Hill, Sheffield S11 7JA
e-mail: info@actonedrama.co.uk
Fax: 07971 112153   Tel: 0114-266 7209

ACT OUT AGENCY
22 Greek Street, Stockport
Cheshire SK3 8AB
e-mail: ab22@supanet.com   Tel/Fax: 0161-429 7413

ACTING ASSOCIATES
PM
71 Hartham Road, London N7 9JJ
Website: www.actingassociates.co.uk
e-mail: fiona@actingassociates.co.uk
    Tel/Fax: 020-7607 3562

ACTIVATE DRAMA SCHOOL
Priestman Cottage
Sea View Road, Sunderland SR2 7UP
Website: website.lineone.net/~lesley.mcdonough
e-mail: activate_agcy@hotmail.com
Fax: 0191-551 2051   Tel: 0191-565 2345

ACTORS AGENCY
1 Glen Street
Tollcross, Edinburgh EH3 9JD
Website: www.stivenchristie.co.uk
Fax: 0131-228 4645   Tel: 0131-228 4040

ACTORS ALLIANCE •
Co-operative
Disney Place House
14 Marshalsea Road, London SE1 1HL
e-mail: actors@actorsalliance.fsnet.co.uk
    Tel/Fax: 020-7407 6028

ACTORS' CREATIVE TEAM
Co-operative
Albany House
82-84 South End
Croydon CR0 1DQ
Website: www.actorscreativeteam.co.uk
e-mail: actorscreativeteam@ukonline.co.uk
Fax: 020-8239 8818   Tel: 020-8239 8892

ACTORS DIRECT Ltd
Gainsborough House
109 Portland Street, Manchester M1 6DN
Fax: 0161-237 9993   Tel: 0161-237 1904

ACTORS FILE The
PM Co-operative
Spitfire Studios
63-71 Collier Street, London N1 9BE
e-mail: mail@theactorsfile.co.uk
Fax: 020-7278 0364   Tel: 020-7278 0087

ACTORS' GROUP The (TAG)
PM Co-operative
21-31 Oldham Street, Manchester M1 1JG
e-mail: agent@tagactors.co.uk
Fax: 0161-834 5588   Tel: 0161-843 4466

ACTORS IN SCANDINAVIA
Vuorimiehenkatu 20D, 00150 Helsinki, Finland
Website: www.actors.fi
e-mail: lauram@actors.fi
Fax: 00 358 9 68 404 422   Tel: 00 358 9 68 40440

Brannkyvhog 39, Stockholm, Sweden 11822

ACTORS INTERNATIONAL Ltd
Conway Hall
25 Red Lion Square, London WC1R 4RL
e-mail: actors-international@talk21.com
Fax: 020-7831 8319   Tel: 020-7242 9300

**ACTORS IRELAND INCORPORATING
ASHDOWN ASSOCIATES**
Crescent Arts Centre
2-4 University Road, Belfast BT7 1NH
e-mail: ashdown.cbn.@artservicesireland.com
                              Tel/Fax: 028-9024 8861

ACTORS LIST The
Half Moon Chambers, Chapel Walks
Manchester M2 1HN
e-mail: elizabeth@actorslist.co.uk
Fax: 0161-832 5219   Tel: 0161-833 1605

ACTORUM Ltd
PM Co-operative
3rd Floor
21 Foley Street, London W1W 6DR
Website: www.actorum.com
e-mail: actorum2@ukonline.co.uk
Fax: 020-7636 6975   Tel: 020-7636 6978

ACTUAL MANAGEMENT
Website: www.actualmanagement.co.uk
e-mail: agents@actualmanagement.co.uk
Fax: 020-7631 4433   Tel: 020-7631 4422

AFFINITY MANAGEMENT
Jessops Farm, Tonbridge Road
Bough Beech
Kent TN8 7AU
e-mail: crbird2310@mistral.co.uk   Tel: 01892 870067

AGENCY The
(Teri Hayden)
47 Adelaide Road, Dublin 2, Eire
e-mail: info@tagency.ie
Fax: 00 353 1 6760052   Tel: 00 353 1 6618535

AHA
(See HOWARD Amanda ASSOCIATES Ltd)

**AIM (ASSOCIATED INTERNATIONAL
MANAGEMENT)***
Nederlander House
7 Great Russell Street, London WC1B 3NH
Website: www.a-i-m.net
e-mail: info@aim.demon.co.uk
Fax: 020-7637 8666   Tel: 020-7637 1700

AIR-O-BATS
(Acrobatic & Aerial Agency)
84 Laburnum Avenue, Hornchurch
Essex RM12 4HA
e-mail: kda@air-o-bats.com   Tel: 01708 705601

A & J MANAGEMENT
551 Green Lanes, London N13 4DR
Website: www.ajmanagement.co.uk
e-mail: ajmanagement@bigfoot.com
Fax: 020-8882 5983   Tel: 020-8882 7716

ALANDER AGENCY
TV F S V
135 Merrion Avenue, Stanmore
Middlesex HA7 4RZ   Tel: 020-8954 7685

ALEXANDER PERSONAL MANAGEMENT Ltd
16 Roughdown Avenue
Hemel Hempstead, Herts HP3 9BH
e-mail: apm@onetel.net.uk
Fax: 01442 241099   Tel: 01442 252907

ALEXANDER Suzanne MANAGEMENT
170 Town Lane, Higher Bebington, Wirral CH63 8LG
e-mail: suzyalex@hotmail.com
                         Tel/Fax: 0151-608 9655

ALL STAR SPEAKERS
(After Dinner Speakers)
100 Farm Lane
Fulham, London SW6 1QH
e-mail: laura@allstarspeakers.co.uk
Fax: 020-7385 6647   Tel: 020-7381 4693

ALLGOOD ASSOCIATES
24 South Road, Bisley
Surrey GU24 9ES   Tel: 01483 487831

ALLSORTS
(Drama for Children) (Sasha Leslie, Melissa Healy)
2 Pember Road, London NW10 5LP
e-mail: enquiries@allsorts.ltd.uk
                         Tel/Fax: 020-8969 3249

ALLSORTS THE AGENCY Ltd
1 Cathedral Street, London SE1 9DE
Website: www.allsortstheagency.co.uk
e-mail: joannaallsorts@aol.com
Fax: 020-7403 1656   Tel: 020-7403 4834

ALPHA PERSONAL MANAGEMENT Ltd
PM Co-operative
Studio B4, 3 Bradbury Street, London N16 8JN
Website: www.alpham.moonfruit.com
e-mail: alphamanagement3@aol.com
Fax: 020-7241 2410   Tel: 020-7241 0077

ALRAUN Anita REPRESENTATION*
5th Floor
28 Charing Cross Road
London WC2H 0DB
e-mail: anita@cjagency.demon.co.uk
Fax: 020-7379 6865   Tel: 020-7379 6840

ALTARAS Jonathan ASSOCIATES Ltd*
11 Garrick Street, Covent Garden
London WC2E 9AT
e-mail: (whoever)@jaa.ndirect.co.uk
Fax: 020-7836 6066   Tel: 020-7836 8722

ALVAREZ MANAGEMENT
86 Muswell Road London N10 2BE
e-mail: sga@alvarezmanagement.fsnet.co.uk
Fax:020-8444 2646   Tel: 020-8883 2206

ALW ASSOCIATES
1 Grafton Chambers
Grafton Place, London NW1 1LN
e-mail: alweurope@onetel.net.uk
Fax: 020-7813 1398   Tel: 020-7388 7018

AMBER PERSONAL MANAGEMENT Ltd
PM
189 Wardour Street, London W1F 8ZD
Website: www.amberltd.co.uk
e-mail: info@amberltd.co.uk
Fax: 020-7734 9883   Tel: 020-7734 7887

28 St Margaret's Chambers
5 Newton Street, Manchester M1 1HL
Fax: 0161-228 0235   Tel: 0161-228 0236

AMERICAN AGENCY The
14 Bonny Street, London NW1 9PG
Fax: 020-7482 0856   Tel: 020-7485 8883

ANA (Actors Network Agency) •
PM Co-operative
55 Lambeth Walk, London SE11 6DX
Website: www.ana-actors.co.uk
e-mail: info@ana-actors.co.uk
Fax: 020-7735 8177   Tel: 020-7735 0999

ANDERSSEN'S
4 Rothmans Avenue
Chelmsford CM2 9UE   Tel/Fax: 01245 476187

ANDREW'S MANAGEMENT
203 Links Road, London SW17 9EP
e-mail: atj@andrewsman.fsnet.co.uk
Fax: 020-8677 8973   Tel: 020-8769 7416

ANGEL Susan & FRANCIS Kevin Ltd*
Write, no e-mails
1st Floor, 12 D'Arblay Street, London W1F 8DU
e-mail: angelpair@freeuk.com
Fax: 020-7437 1712   Tel: 020-7439 3086

ANOTHER FACE
48 Dean Street, London W1V 5HL
Website: www.anotherface.com
e-mail: mia@anotherface.com
Fax: 020-7494 3300   Tel: 020-7287 1223

A.P.M. ASSOCIATES (Linda French)
(See ALEXANDER PERSONAL MANAGEMENT Ltd)

ARAENA/COLLECTIVE
10 Bramshaw Gardens, South Oxhey, Herts WD1 6XP
e-mail: patricia@araena.watford.net
                         Tel/Fax: 020-8428 0037

ARCH CREATIVE MANAGEMENT Ltd
No. 4, 2 St Stephen's Crescent
London W2 5QT
e-mail: md@arch123.com   Tel/Fax: 020-7727 2910

ARENA ENTERTAINMENT CONSULTANTS
(Corporate Entertainment)
Regent's Court, 39 Harrogate Road, Leeds LS7 3PD
Website: www.arenaentertainments.co.uk
e-mail: stars@arenaentertainments.co.uk
Fax: 0113-239 2016   Tel: 0113-239 2222

ARENA PERSONAL MANAGEMENT Ltd
Co-operative
Room 11, East Block, Panther House,
38 Mount Pleasant, London WC1X 0AP
e-mail: arenapmltd@aol.com
                    Tel/Fax: 020-7278 1661

A R G (ARTISTS RIGHTS GROUP Ltd)
4 Great Portland Street, London W1W 8PA
e-mail: argall@argtalent.com
Fax: 020-7436 6700   Tel: 020-7436 6400

ARGYLE ASSOCIATES
PM (Richard Linford) (No Unsolicited Mail)
St. John's Buildings
43 Clerkenwell Road, London EC1M 5RS
e-mail: argyle.associates@virgin.net
Fax: 020-7608 1642   Tel: 020-7608 2095

ARRAN ASSOCIATES
6 Greenland Quay, Surrey Quays, London SE16 7RN
e-mail: info@tk1management.com
Fax: 020-7740 3119   Tel: 020-7252 3402

ARTISTS INDEPENDENT NETWORK
32 Tavistock Street, London WC2E 7PB
Fax: 020-7240 9029   Tel: 020-7257 8727

ARTS MANAGEMENT
Pinewood Studios
Iver, Bucks SLO 0NH
Fax: 01753 785443   Tel: 01753 785444

ARTSWORLD INTERNATIONAL MANAGEMENT Ltd
1 Farrow Road
Whaplode Drove, Nr. Spalding PE12 0TS
e-mail: bob@artsworld.freeserve.co.uk
Fax: 01406 331147   Tel: 01406 330099

ASH PERSONAL MANAGEMENT
3 Spencer Road
Mitcham Common, Surrey CR4 1SG
e-mail: ash_personal_mgmt@yahoo.co.uk
                    Tel/Fax: 020-8646 0050

ASHCROFT Sharron MANAGEMENT Ltd
Dean Clough, Halifax HX3 5AX
Website: www.sharronashcroft.com
e-mail: info@sharronashcroft.com
Fax: 01422 343417   Tel: 01422 343949

ASQUITH & HORNER
PM Write with SAE
The Studio, 14 College Road, Bromley, Kent BR1 3NS
Fax: 020-8313 0443   Tel: 020-8466 5580

ASSOCIATED ARTS
(Directors, Designers, Lighting Designers)
8 Shrewsbury Lane, London SE18 3JF
Website: www.associated-arts.co.uk
e-mail: karen@associated-arts.co.uk
Fax: 020-8856 8189   Tel: 020-8856 4958

ASSOCIATED SPEAKERS
(Lecturers & Celebrity Speakers)
24A Park Road, Hayes
Middlesex UB4 8JN   Tel: 020-8848 9048

AVALON MANAGEMENT GROUP Ltd
4A Exmoor Street, London W10 6BD
Fax: 020-7598 7300   Tel: 020-7598 8000

AVENUE ARTISTES Ltd
C G TV
8 Winn Road, Southampton SO17 1EN
Fax: 023-8090 5703   Tel: 023-8055 1000

Bill Nighy

David Koppel

Portraits & Production
Photography

Tel: **020 8349 0001**
Mobile: **07831 838378**

Lara Belmont

DIRECT LINE

LONDON	Personal Management	LEEDS
St. John's House	Personal Manager: Daphne Franks	Park House
16 St. John's Vale		62 Lidgett Lane
London SE8 4EN	e-mail: daphne.franks@dline.org.uk	Leeds LS8 1PL
Tel/fax 020 8694 1788	website: www.dline.org.uk	Tel/fax 0113 266 4036

AWA - ANDREA WILDER AGENCY
23 Cambrian Drive, Colwyn Bay, Conwy LL28 4SL
Website: www.awagency.co.uk
e-mail: casting@awagency.co.uk
Fax: 07092 249314   Tel: 01492 547542

AXM
Actors' Exchange Management
PM Co-operative
206 Great Guildford Business Square
30 Great Guildford Street
London SE1 0HS
Website: www.axmgt.com
e-mail: info@axmgt.com
Fax: 020-7261 0408   Tel: 020-7261 0400

AZA ARTISTES
(Existing Clients only)
652 Finchley Road
London NW11 7NT   Tel: 020-8458 7288

BALLROOM, LONDON THEATRE OF
(Ballroom/Social Dancers for Film/TV/Theatre)
24 Ovett Close, Upper Norwood, London SE19 3RX
e-mail: paulharrisdance@hotmail.com
Mobile: 07958 784462   Tel: 020-8771 4274

B A M ASSOCIATES
41 Bloomfield Road
Bristol BS4 3QA
e-mail: bamassociates@aol.com
                    Tel/Fax: 0117-971 0636

BARKER Gavin ASSOCIATES Ltd*
(Gavin Barker, Michelle Burke)
2D Wimpole Street, London W1G 0EB
e-mail: gbarker@dircon.co.uk
Fax: 020-7499 3777   Tel: 020-7499 4777

B.A.S.I.C./JD AGENCY
C V S
3 Rushden House
Tatlow Road, Glenfield
Leicester LE3 8ND   Tel/Fax: 0116-287 9594

BECKER Paul Ltd
223A Portobello Road
London W11 1LU
e-mail: info@paulbeckerltd.com
Fax: 020-7221 5030   Tel: 020-7221 3050

BELCANTO LONDON ACADEMY MANAGEMENT
(Children & Young Adults)
Performance House
20 Passey Place, Eltham, London SE9 5DQ
Fax: 020-8850 9944   Tel: 020-8850 9888

BELFRAGE Julian ASSOCIATES
46 Albemarle Street, London W1S 4DF
Fax: 020-7493 5460   Tel: 020-7491 4400

BELL Olivia Ltd
189 Wardour Street
London W1F 8ZD
Website: www.olivia-bell.co.uk
e-mail: info@olivia-bell.co.uk
Fax: 020-7439 3485   Tel: 020-7439 3270

BENJAMIN Audrey AGENCY
278A Elgin Avenue
Maida Vale, London W9 1JR
e-mail: aud@elginavenue.fs.business.co.uk
Fax: 020-7266 5480   Tel: 020-7289 7180

BETTS Jorg ASSOCIATES
Gainsborough House
81 Oxford Street, London W1D 2EU
e-mail: jorgbetts@aol.com
Fax: 020-7903 5301   Tel: 020-7903 5300

Xavier Carrington

Gail Haighton

Simon Lys

JAMES GILL 020 7735 5632 *Photographer with Attitude & Imagination*

Victoria Smurfit 2001

Photography by

PETER SIMPKIN

020 8883 2727
Mobile: 07973 224 084
e-mail: petersimpkin@aol.com

Hugo Speer 2001

Michael Leader

BEXFIELD Glenn PERSONAL MANAGEMENT
Brighton Media Centre, Friese-Greene House
15-17 Middle Street, Brighton BN1 1AL
Fax: 01273 201118   Tel: 01273 201104

BILL & CHRISTIAN @JB AGENCY ONLINE Ltd
(Extras, Walk-on's and Theatre)
7 Stonehills Mansions
8 Streatham High Road, London SW16 1DD
Website: www.jb-agency.com
e-mail: christian@jb-agency.com
Fax: 020-8769 9567   Tel: 020-8769 0123

BILLBOARD PERSONAL MANAGEMENT
Co-operative
The Co-op Centre
11 Mowll Street, London SW9 6BG
Website: www.billboardpm.com
e-mail: billboardpm@easynet.co.uk
Fax: 020-7793 0426   Tel: 020-7735 9956

BIRD AGENCY
(Personal Performance Management)
Birkbeck Centre
Birkbeck Road, Sidcup, Kent DA14 4DE
Fax: 020-8308 1370   Tel: 020-8300 6004

BLACKBURN Debra MANAGEMENT
Oak Lodge Studio
Arkley Lane, Arkley, Herts EN5 3JR
e-mail: dbm2@freeuk.com
Fax: 020-8440 7674   Tel: 020-8440 4532

BLACKBURN SACHS ASSOCIATES
88-90 Crawford Street
London W1H 2BS
Website: www.blackburnsachsassociates.com
e-mail: presenters@blackburnsachsassociates.com
Fax: 020-7258 6162   Tel: 020-7258 6158

BLOND Rebecca ASSOCIATES
69A Kings Road
London SW3 4NX
e-mail: rebecca.blond@lineone.net
Fax: 020-7351 4600   Tel: 020-7351 4100

BLUE WAND PRODUCTIONS Ltd
PM TV F G
2nd Floor
12 Weltje Road, London W6 9TG
e-mail: lino@bluewand.co.uk
Mobile: 07885 528743   Tel/Fax: 020-8741 2038

BMA MODELS
The Stables
5 Norcott Hall Barns
Norcott Hill, Berkhamsted, Herts HP4 1RB
Website: www.bmamodels.com
e-mail: bmamodels@bmamodels.com
Fax: 01442 879879   Tel: 01442 878878

BODEN AGENCY
PM
99 East Barnet Road
New Barnet, Herts EN4 8RF
Website: www.bodenstudios.com
e-mail: bodens2692@aol.com
Fax: 020-8449 5212   Tel: 020-8447 0909

BOOKERS UK
7 Green Avenue, Mill Hill
London NW7 4PX   Tel/Fax: 020-8201 1400

BOOKHOUSE GROUP The
2 Gill's Cottages, Rochester, Kent ME1 1BY
e-mail: mr.barnes@virgin.net   Tel/Fax: 01634 812672

BOSS MODEL MANAGEMENT Ltd
Half Moon Chambers
Chapel Walks, Manchester M2 1HN
e-mail: julie@bossagencies.co.uk
Fax: 0161-832 5219   Tel: 0161-834 3403

Sam Kindred

Suzanne McAthy

Natasha Greenberg

020 8677 8753
07932 618111

Lindsay Duncan

Alan Rickman

Fatimah Namdar **020 8341 1332**

BOURNE Sheila MANAGEMENT*
14 Crown Road
Shoreham, Kent TN14 7TL
e-mail: sheila@bourne-uk.freeserve.co.uk
Fax: 01959 524529   Tel: 01959 524528

BOYCE Sandra MANAGEMENT*
1 Kingsway House
Albion Road, London N16 0TA
e-mail: info@sandraboyce.com
Fax: 020-7241 2313   Tel: 020-7923 0606

BRAIDMAN Michelle ASSOCIATES*
3rd Floor Suite
10-11 Lower John Street
London W1F 9EB
e-mail: info@braidman.com
Fax: 020-7439 3600   Tel: 020-7437 0817

BRAITHWAITE'S THEATRICAL AGENCY
8 Brookshill Avenue, Harrow Weald
Middlesex HA3 6RZ   Tel: 020-8954 5638

BREAK A LEG MANAGEMENT
Units 2/3 The Precinct
Packington Square
London N1 7UP
Website: www.geocities.com/precincttheatre
e-mail: reima@breakalegmangmt.fsnet.co.uk
Fax: 020-7359 3660   Tel: 020-7359 3594

BRITT MANAGEMENT
59 Plains of Waterloo
Ramsgate, Kent CT11 8JE
Website: www.msmallbritt@aol.com
    Tel/Fax: 01843 850586

BROADCASTING COMPANY
Unit 23, Canalot Studios
222 Kensal Road, London W10 5BN
Fax: 020-7460 5223   Tel: 020-7460 5222

BROOK Dolly AGENCY
PO Box 5436, Dunmow CM6 1WW
Fax: 01371 875996   Tel: 01371 875767

BROOK Valerie AGENCY
10 Sandringham Road
Cheadle Hulme, Cheshire SK8 5NH
e-mail: colinbrook@freenetname.co.uk
Fax: 0161-488 4206   Tel: 0161-486 1631

BROOKS Claude ENTERTAINMENTS
1 Burlington Avenue
Slough, Berks SL1 2JY
Fax: 01753 520424   Tel: 01753 520717

BROOKS Neil MANAGEMENT
153 Rathgar Road
Rathgar, Dublin 6
Website: www.neilbrooksmanagement.com
e-mail: nbm2@eircom.net
    Tel/Fax: 00 353 1 496 6470

BROWN & SIMCOCKS*
PM Write
1 Bridgehouse Court
109 Blackfriars Road
London SE1 8HW
e-mail: barryandcarrie@lineone.net
Fax: 020-7928 1909   Tel: 020-7928 1229

BRUNSKILL MANAGEMENT Ltd
PM M S TV Write
Suite 8A
169 Queen's Gate, London SW7 5HE
Website: www.brunskill.com
e-mail: contact@brunskill.com
Fax: 020-7589 9460   Tel: 020-7581 3388
The Courtyard, Edenhall, Penrith, Cumbria CA11 8ST
Fax: 01768 881850   Tel: 01768 881430

BSA Ltd
(See HARRISON Penny BSA Ltd)

BSL
1 Hinde Street, London W1U 2AY
e-mail: bslperry@aol.com
Fax: 020-7224 1567   Tel: 020-7935 8788

BUCHANAN ASSOCIATES
PO Box 27559
London SE4 1XH
Website: www.buchanan-associates.co.uk
e-mail: info@buchanan-associates.co.uk
Fax: 020-8691 4264   Tel: 020-8692 0718

BURN David
(Formerly THE SINGERS' AGENCY) PM M G
16 Harris Lane
Shenley, Radlett, Herts WD7 9EB
e-mail: davidburn@btinternet.com
Fax: 01923 859636   Tel: 01923 852175

Real people with genuine acting talent trained in our own workshops and experienced in theatre, television, films and commercials.

54 Princess St. Manchester M1 6HS
fax : 0161 236 7557
Director : Nigel Martin-Smith

BURNETT GRANGER ASSOCIATES
(Barry Burnett, Lindsay Granger)
Prince of Wales Theatre
31 Coventry Street, London W1D 6AS
e-mail: associates@burnettgranger.co.uk
Fax: 020-7839 0438   Tel: 020-7839 0202

BURT Ben ASSOCIATES (BBA)
162A Springfield Road
Brighton, East Sussex BN1 6DG
e-mail: ben@benburt.com   Tel/Fax: 01273 565114

C.A. ARTISTES MANAGEMENT
Md Featured Commercials
153 Battersea Rise, London SW11 1HP
e-mail: casting@caartistes.com
Fax: 020-7924 2334   Tel: 020-7223 7827

CADS MANAGEMENT
209 Abbey Road, Bearwood, Birmingham B67 5NG
Website: www.cadsmanagement.co.uk
e-mail: admin@cadsmanagement.co.uk
Fax: 0121-434 4909   Tel: 0121-420 1996

C.A.L.S. CASTING
(Children & Teenagers)
Unit E2
Bellevale Shopping Centre, Liverpool L25 2RG
Mobile: 07904 551914   Tel/Fax: 0151-487 8500

CAM
PM Write
19 Denmark Street, London WC2H 8NA
Website: www.cam.co.uk
e-mail: info@cam.co.uk
Fax: 020-7240 7384   Tel: 020-7497 0448

CAMBELL JEFFREY MANAGEMENT
(Set, Costume, Lighting Designers)
11A Greystone Court
South Street, Eastbourne BN21 4LP
e-mail: cambell@theatricaldesigners.co.uk
Fax: 01323 411373   Tel: 01323 411444

**CAMPBELL ALISON MODEL & PROMOTION
AGENCY**
381 Beersbridge Road, Belfast BT5 5DT
Website: www.alisoncampbellmodels.com
e-mail: info@alisoncampbellmodels.com
Fax: 028-9080 9808   Tel: 028-9080 9809

CAMPBELL ASSOCIATES
Campbell Park
Fernhurst Road
Milland, Nr Liphook, Hants GU30 7LU
Fax: 01428 741648

2 Chelsea Cloisters, Sloane Avenue
Chelsea, London SW3 3DW
e-mail: campbell.associates@btinternet.com
Fax: 020-7584 8799   Tel: 020-7584 5586

CAPITAL ARTS THEATRICAL AGENCY
Wyllyotts Centre
Darkes Lane
Potters Bar, Herts EN6 2HN
e-mail: capitalartstheatre@genie.co.uk
Mobile: 07885 232414   Tel/Fax: 020-8449 2342

CAPITAL VOICES
(Anne Skates. Session Singers, Studio, Stage & TV)
Brook House
8 Rythe Road
Claygate, Surrey KT10 9DF
Website: www.capitalvoices.com
e-mail: capvox@aol.com
Fax: 01372 466229   Tel: 01372 466228

CARDIFF CASTING
Co-operative Actors Management
Chapter Arts Centre
Market Road, Cardiff CF5 1QE
Website: www.cardiffcasting.co.uk
e-mail: admin@cardiffcasting.co.uk
Fax: 029-2023 3380   Tel: 029-2023 3321

CAREY Roger ASSOCIATES*
PM
7 St George's Square
London SW1V 2HX
e-mail: rogercarey@freeuk.com
Fax: 020-7630 0029   Tel: 020-7630 6301

CARNEY Jessica ASSOCIATES*
PM Write
Suite 90-92
87 Regent Street
London W1B 4EH
e-mail: info@jcarneyassociates.co.uk
Fax: 020-7434 4173   Tel: 020-7434 4143

Lucy Smith *photographer*

Jane Hayward

Solomon Maudarbocus

Lizzie France

Tel 020 7498 6182

www.thatlucy.co.uk

www.harrispearson.co.uk

14 - 16 Guilford St   T: 020 7430 9890
London   F: 020 7430 9229
WC1N 1DW   E: agent@harrispearson.co.uk

Personal Representation   **Film**   **Television**   **Theatre**   **Commercials**

CAROUSEL ENTERTAINMENT & EVENT MANAGEMENT
(Acts for Corporate & Private Events)
18 Westbury Lodge Close
Pinner, Middlesex HA5 3FG
Website: www.carouselentertainments.co.uk
e-mail: acts@carouselentertainments.co.uk
Fax: 020-8933 1614   Tel: 020-8866 8816

CARTEURS
170A Church Road, Hove, East Sussex BN3 2DJ
Website: www.stonelandsschool.co.uk
Fax: 01273 770444   Tel: 01273 770445

CASAROTTO MARSH Ltd
(Film Technicians)
National House
60-66 Wardour Street, London W1V 4ND
e-mail: casarottomarsh@casarotto.uk.com
Fax: 020-7287 5644   Tel: 020-7287 4450

CASTAWAY ACTORS AGENCY
30-31 Wicklow Street, Dublin 2, Ireland
Website: www.irish-actors.com
e-mail: castaway@clubi.ie
Fax: 00 353 1 6719133   Tel: 00 353 1 6719264

CASTCALL & CASTFAX
(Casting & Consultancy Service)
106 Wilsden Avenue, Luton LU1 5HR
Website: www.castcall.co.uk
e-mail: casting@castcall.co.uk
Fax: 01582 480736   Tel: 01582 456213

CASTING COMPANY ARTISTS The (Spain)
Pasaje Ramos Puente no 4, Edificio Sol bajo b,
29620 Torremolinos, Malaga, Spain
Website: www.thecastingcompanyspain.com
e-mail: theteam@thecastingcompanyspain.com
Tel/Fax: +34 952 382 106

CASTING COUCH PRODUCTIONS Ltd
Canalot Production Studios
222 Kensal Road, London W10 5BN
e-mail: moiratownsend@yahoo.co.uk
Fax: 020-8208 2373   Tel: 020-8438 9679

CASTING DEPARTMENT The
10 Tiverton Road, London NW10 3HL
Fax: 020-8960 0410   Tel: 020-8960 0055

CASTING UK
88-90 Grays Inn Road, London WC1X 8AA
Website: www.castinguk.com
e-mail: info@castinguk.com
Fax: 020-7430 1155   Tel: 020-7430 1122

C B A INTERNATIONAL (CINDY BRACE)
31 rue Milton, 75009 Paris, France,
e-mail: c_b_a@club-internet.fr
Fax: 33 148 74 51 42   Tel: 33 145 26 33 42

166 Waverley Avenue, Twickenham TW2 6DL

C C A MANAGEMENT*
PM Write (Actors and Technicians)
7 St George's Square
London SW1V 2HX
e-mail: ccamanagement@btclick.com
Fax: 020-7630 7376   Tel: 020-7630 6303

CCM
Co-operative
Panther House
38 Mount Pleasant
London WC1X 0AP
Website: www.ccmaa.co.uk
e-mail: ccmaa@bigfoot.com
Fax: 020-7813 3103   Tel: 020-7278 0507

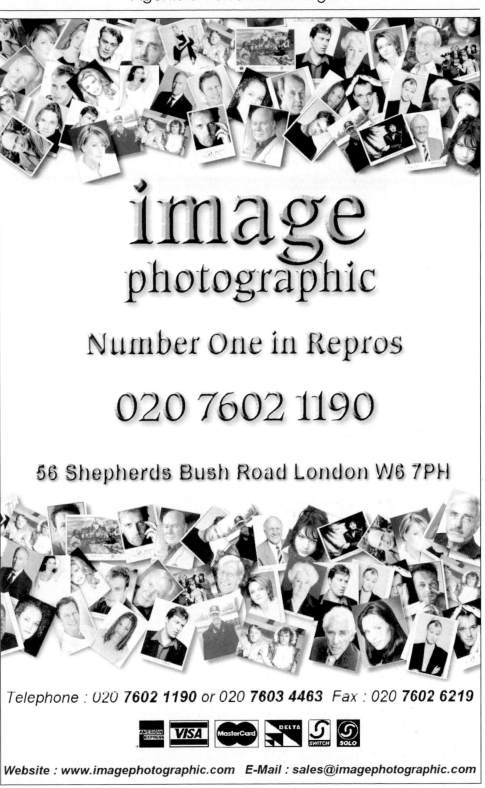

CDA
(See DAWSON Caroline ASSOCIATES)

CELEBRITY MANAGEMENT Ltd
12 Nottingham Place
London W1M 3FA
Website: www.celebrity.co.uk
e-mail: info@celebrity.co.uk
Fax: 020-7224 6060   Tel: 020-7224 5050

CELEX CASTING
(Anne Sweeting)
11 Glencroft Drive
Stenson Fields, Derby DE24 3LS
Website: www.celex.co.uk
e-mail: anne@celex.co.uk
Fax: 01332 232115   Tel: 01332 232445

CENTRAL AGENCY The
PM
112 Gunnersbury Avenue, London W5 4HB
Website: www.thedormgroup.com
e-mail: info@dorm.co.uk
Fax: 020-8992 9993   Tel: 020-8993 7441

CENTRAL LINE •
PM Co-operative
11 East Circus Street, Nottingham NG1 5AF
Website: www.the-central-line.co.uk
e-mail: mailact@the-central-line.co.uk
Fax: 0115-950 8087   Te: 0115-941 2937

CENTRE STAGE AGENCY
7 Rutledge Terrace, South Circular Road, Dublin 8
e-mail: geraldinecenterstage@eircom.net
    Tel/Fax: 00 353 1 4533599

Simon Dutton

Donna King

David de Keyser

ric bacon
07970 970799

CFA MANAGEMENT
East Trevelmond Farm
Trevelmond, Liskeard, Cornwall PL14 4LY
e-mail: frances@cornwall-film-agency.fsnet.co.uk
Tel/Fax: 01579 321858

CHANCE David A. ASSOCIATES
(See CINEL GABRAN MANAGEMENT)

CHAPMAN AGENCY
The Link Building
Paradise Place, Birmingham B3 3HJ
e-mail: chapman.agency@virgin.net
Fax: 0121-262 6801   Tel: 0121-262 6807

CHARACTERS MANAGEMENT Ltd
110 Stoke Newington Church Street
London N16 0JX   Tel: 020-7502 0203

CHARLESWORTH Peter & ASSOCIATES
68 Old Brompton Road, London SW7 3LQ
e-mail: petercharlesworth@tiscali.co.uk
Fax: 020-7589 2922   Tel: 020-7581 2478

CHATTO & LINNIT Ltd
123A Kings Road, London SW3 4PL
Fax: 020-7352 3450   Tel: 020-7352 7722

CHURCHILL Hetty PERSONAL MANAGEMENT
9 Daleside Road, London SW16 6SN
e-mail: actors@hettychurchill.com
Fax: 020-8679 2868   Tel: 020-8677 8870

CINEL GABRAN MANAGEMENT*
The Coach House
Cog Road, Sully, Penarth CF64 5UD
Website: www.cinelgabran.co.uk
e-mail: enquiries@cinelgabran.co.uk
Fax: 029-2053 1613   Tel: 029-2053 1655

CIRCUIT PERSONAL MANAGEMENT Ltd
Suite 71 S.E.C., Bedford Street
Shelton, Stoke-on-Trent, Staffs ST1 4PZ
Website: www.circuitpm.co.uk
e-mail: mail@circuitpm.co.uk
Fax: 01782 206821   Tel: 01782 285388

CIRCUS MANIACS
(Physical Artistes & Corporate Events)
Office 8A, The Kingswood Foundation
Britannia Road, Kingswood, Bristol BS15 8DB
e-mail: agency@circusmaniacs.com
Mobile: 07977 247287   Tel/Fax: 0117-947 7042

CITY ACTORS' MANAGEMENT Ltd
PM Co-operative
24 Rivington Street, London EC2A 3DU
Website: www.city-actors.freeserve.co.uk
e-mail: info@city-actors.freeserve.co.uk
Fax: 020-7613 2656   Tel: 020-7613 2636

CITY LITES
(Performing Arts School & Casting Agency)
PO Box 29673, London E8 3FH
Mobile: 07773 865025   Tel/Fax: 020-7683 9016

C.K.K. ENTERTAINMENT
PO Box 24550, London E17 9FG
e-mail: ckk.entertainment@virgin.net
Fax: 020-8923 0983   Tel: 020-8923 0977

CLAPPERBOARD CASTING
PO Box 153, Manchester M7 4YU
Website: www.clapperboard-casting.co.uk
Fax: 0161-792 4285   Tel: 0161-792 2277

HUGO SPEER

tamsin skan

BERWICK KALER   RICHARD WILSON FOR 'SHELTER'   MADELEINE HOWARD

CLARKE Jean & BROOK Jeremy MANAGEMENT
International House
223 Regent Street, London W1R 7DB
Fax: 020-7495 7742   Tel: 020-7495 2424

CLARKE Rose MANAGEMENT
51 Shooters Hill
Blackheath, London SE18 3RL
e-mail: roseclarkemanagement@hotmail.com
                                Tel/Fax: 020-8856 2536

CLASS ACT
11 Thorn Road, Farnham, Surrey GU10 4TV
e-mail: classact93@hotmail.com
                                Tel/Fax: 01252 792078

CLAYPOLE MANAGEMENT
PO Box 123, DL3 7WA
e-mail: claypole_1@hotmail.com
Fax: 0870 1334784   Tel: 0845 6501777

CLOUD NINE AGENCY
96 Tiber Gardens
Treaty Street, London N1 0XE
e-mail: cloudnineagency@blueyonder.co.uk
                                Tel/Fax: 020-7278 0029

CMA (COULTER MANAGEMENT AGENCY)
(Anne Coulter)
74 Victoria Crescent Road
Glasgow G12 9JN
e-mail: cmaglasgow@aol.com
Fax: 0141-579 4700   Tel: 0141-579 1400

CMP MANAGEMENT
Tandy House
30-40 Dalling Road, London W6 0JB
e-mail: ravenscourt@hotmail.com
Fax: 020-8741 1786   Tel: 020-8741 3400

COCHRANE Elspeth PERSONAL MANAGEMENT*
PM
14/2, 2nd Floor, South Bank Commercial Centre
140 Battersea Park Road, London SW11 4NB
e-mail: elspethc@dircon.co.uk
Fax: 020-7622 5815   Tel: 020-7622 0314

COHEN MAYER Charlie
(UK and USA Talent) (Incorporating
Jimmy D. Literary/Screenplay Agency)
PM
121 Brecknock Road, London N19 5AE
Mobile: 07979 856199   Tel: 020-7813 9892

COLLINS Shane ASSOCIATES*
39-41 New Oxford Street
Bloomsbury, London WC1A 1BN
Website: www.shanecollins.co.uk
e-mail: info@shanecollins.co.uk
Fax: 020-7836 9388   Tel: 020-7836 9377

COLLIS MANAGEMENT
182 Trevelyan Road, London SW17 9LW
e-mail: marilyn@collismanagement.co.uk
Fax: 020-8682 0973   Tel: 020-8767 0196

COMEDY CLUB
165 Peckham Rye, London SE15 3HZ
Website: www.comedyclub.org.uk
e-mail: comedyclub@cwcom.net
Fax: 020-7732 9292   Tel: 020-7732 3434

CONTI Italia AGENCY Ltd
S M TV F Write or Phone
23 Goswell Road, London EC1M 7AJ
e-mail: sca@italiaconti36.freeserve.co.uk
Fax: 020-7253 1430   Tel: 020-7608 7500

CONWAY VAN GELDER *
PM
3rd Floor
18-21 Jermyn Street
London SW1Y 6HP
Fax: 020-7287 1940   Tel: 020-7287 0077

COOKE Howard ASSOCIATES*
19 Coulson Street
Chelsea, London SW3 3NA
e-mail: mail@hca1.co.uk
Fax: 020-7591 0155   Tel: 020-7591 0144

CORNER Clive ASSOCIATES
73 Gloucester Road
Hampton, Middlesex TW12 2UQ
e-mail: cornerassociates@aol.com
Fax: 020-8979 4983   Tel: 020-8287 2726

CORNISH Caroline MANAGEMENT Ltd
12 Shinfield Street
London W12 0HN
Website: www.carolinecornish.co.uk
e-mail: carolinecornish@aol.com
Fax: 020-8743 7887   Tel: 020-8743 7337

COULSON Lou*
1st Floor
37 Berwick Street
London W1F 8RS
Fax: 020-7439 7569   Tel: 020-7734 9633

CRAWFORDS
6 Brook Street, London W1S 1BB
Website: www.crawfords.tv
e-mail: cr@wfords.com
Fax: 020-7355 1084   Tel: 020-7629 6464

CREATIVE MEDIA INTERNATIONAL*
PM Write
22 Kingsbury Avenue, Dunstable
Bedfordshire LU5 4PU   Tel/Fax: 01582 510869

CREATIVE MEDIA MANAGEMENT*
(Film, TV & Theatre Technical Personnel)
Unit 3B Walpole Court
Ealing Studios, Ealing Green, London W5 5ED
e-mail: enquiries@creativemediamanagement.com
Fax: 020-8566 5554   Tel: 020-8584 5363

CREATIVE SOLUTIONS AND EVENTS
21-37 Third Avenue, London E13 8AW
e-mail: info@creativeeventsuk.com
Fax: 020-8471 2111   Tel: 020-8471 3111

CREDITS ACTORS AGENCY Ltd
29 Lorn Road, London SW9 0AB
e-mail: credits@actors29.treeserve.co.uk
Fax: 020-7274 5849   Tel: 020-7737 0735

CRESCENT MANAGEMENT*
PM Co-operative
10 Barley Mow Passage, Chiswick, London W4 4PH
e-mail: jennybenson@crescentmanagement.fsnet.co.uk
Fax: 020-8987 0207   Tel: 020-8987 0191

CROUCH ASSOCIATES*
PM Write
9-15 Neal Street, London WC2H 9PW
e-mail: crouchassociates@aol.com
Fax: 020-7379 1991   Tel: 020-7379 1684

CROUCH Sara MANAGEMENT
Suite 1, Ground Floor
1 Duchess Street, London W1W 6AN
e-mail: saracrouch@btinternet.com
Fax: 020-7436 4627   Tel: 020-7436 4626

CROWD PULLERS
(Street Performers)
14 Somerset Gardens, London SE13 7SY
e-mail: jhole@crowdpullers.co.uk
Fax: 020-8469 2147   Tel: 020-8469 3900

Heather Peace

Steve McFadden

Nicola Blackman

DANCERS

1 Charlotte Street, London W1T 1RD
Tel (020) 7636 1473   Fax (020) 7636 1657   Email: info@danceragency.com

CRUICKSHANK Harriet*
(Directors, Designers, Choreographers)
97 Old South Lambeth Road, London SW8 1XU
Fax: 020-7820 1081   Tel: 020-7735 2933

CS MANAGEMENT
The Croft, 7 Cannon Road
Southgate, London N14 7HE
Website: www.centrestageuk.com
e-mail: carole@centrestageuk.com
Fax: 020-8886 7555   Tel: 020-8886 4264

C.S.A.
(Christina Shepherd Advertising)
13 Radnor Walk, London SW3 4BP
e-mail: csa@shepherdmanagement.co.uk
Fax: 020-7352 2277   Tel: 020-7352 2255

CSM (ARTISTES)
PM
St Dunstan's Hall, East Acton Lane, London W3 7EG
e-mail: carolecdleadact@aol.com
Fax: 020-8740 6542   Tel: 020-8743 9982

CURTIS BROWN GROUP Ltd*
(Actors, Producers, Directors, Set/Costume
Designers)
Haymarket House, 28-29 Haymarket, London SW1Y 4SP
e-mail: cb@curtisbrown.co.uk
Fax: 020-7396 0110   Tel: 020-7396 6600

CYBER 2000/IN THE CAN Ltd
20 Old Steine, Brighton BN1 1EL
Website: www.cyberartists.co.uk
e-mail: cyber.1@btclick.com
Fax: 01273 571085   Tel: 01273 671234

D Lisa MANAGEMENT Ltd
Unit 5, Gun Wharf
241 Old Ford Road, London E3 5QB
e-mail: casting@lisad.co.uk
Fax: 020-8980 2211   Tel: 020-8980 0117

DALY David ASSOCIATES
586A Kings Road, London SW6 2DX
e-mail: agents@daviddaly.co.uk
Fax: 020-7610 9512   Tel: 020-7384 1036

DALY David ASSOCIATES (MANCHESTER)
(Clare Marshall)
16 King Street, Knutsford WA16 6DL
e-mail: clare@daviddaly.co.uk
Fax: 01565 755334   Tel: 01565 631999

DALZELL & BERESFORD Ltd
26 Astwood Mews, London SW7 4DE
Fax: 020-7341 9412   Tel: 020-7341 9411

DANCERS
1 Charlotte Street, London W1T 1RD
e-mail: info@dancersagency.com
Fax: 020-7636 1657   Tel: 020-7636 1473

FEATURES

1 Charlotte Street London W1T 1RD

Tel: (020) 7637 1487 Fax: (020) 7636 1657 E-mail address: info@features.co.uk

DARRELL Emma MANAGEMENT
(Producers, Directors & Existing Writers only)
North Vale, Shire Lane, Chorleywood, Herts WD3 5NH
e-mail: emma.mc@virgin.net
Fax: 01923 284064   Tel: 01923 284061

DAVID ARTISTES MANAGEMENT AGENCY Ltd The
F TV Md Write or Phone
153 Battersea Rise, London SW11 1HP
Website: www.davidagency.net
e-mail: casting@davidagency.net
Fax: 020-7924 2334   Tel: 020-7223 7720

DAVIS Dabber PRODUCTIONS
(Write or Phone)
24A Park Road, Hayes
Middlesex UB4 8JN   Tel: 020-8848 9048

DAVIS Lena, JOHN BISHOP ASSOCIATES
Cotton's Farmhouse
Whiston Road, Cogenhoe, Northants NN7 1NL
Fax: 01604 890405   Tel: 01604 891487

DAWSON Caroline ASSOCIATES*
19 Sydney Mews, London SW3 6HL
e-mail: cda@cdalondon.com
Fax: 020-7589 4800   Tel: 020-7581 8111

DD AGENCY Ltd
The South West Business Centre
Queensgate House
48 Queen Street, Exeter EX4 3SR
Website: www.casting-online.com
e-mail: ddagency@lycos.com
Mobile: 07814 791489   Tel/Fax: 0870 7442767

DEALERS AGENCY BELFAST
85 Rosebery Road, Belfast BT6 8JB
e-mail: dealers@dnet.co.uk
Mobile: 07702 183299   Tel/Fax: 028-9046 0381

DENMAN CASTING AGENCY
Burgess House
Main Street, Farnsfield
Notts NG22 8EF   Tel/Fax: 01623 882272

DENMARK STREET MANAGEMENT
PM Co-operative Write SAE
Packington Bridge Workspace
Unit 11, 1B Packington Square, London N1 7UA
e-mail: mail@denmarkstreet.net
Fax: 020-7354 8558   Tel: 020-7354 8555

DEREK'S HANDS AGENCY
153 Battersea Rise, London SW11 1HP
Website: www.derekshands.com
e-mail: casting@derekshands.com
Fax: 020-7924 2334   Tel: 020-7924 2484

DESMOND Ken AGENCY & MANAGEMENT
Tudor House, Catherine Road
Benfleet, Essex SS7 1HY   Tel/Fax: 01268 566916

de WOLFE Felix*
PM Write
Garden Offices, 51 Maida Vale, London W9 1SD
e-mail: felixdewolfe@aol.com
Fax: 020-7289 5731   Tel: 020-7289 5770

DIESTENFELD Lily
(Personal Manager for 45+ Playing Ages)
28B Alexandra Grove, London N12 8HG
e-mail: lilyd@talk21.com
Fax: 020-7485 1005   Tel: 020-8446 5379

DIMPLES MODEL & CASTING ACADEMY
Suite 2, 2nd Floor, Magnum House
33 Lord Street, Leigh, Lancs WN7 1BY
e-mail: dimples_m_c_a@btinternet.com
Fax: 01942 262232   Tel: 01942 262012

DIRECT CHOICE MANAGEMENT
5 Denmark Street, London WC2H 8LP
e-mail: agents@dircm.co.uk
Fax: 020-7379 0677   Tel: 020-7240 8490

DIRECT LINE
PM (Personal Manager: Daphne Franks)
St John's House, 16 St John's Vale, London SE8 4EN
Website: www.dline.org.uk
e-mail: daphne.franks@dline.org.uk
                                    Tel/Fax: 020-8694 1788

Park House, 62 Lidgett Lane
Leeds LS8 1PL   Tel/Fax: 0113-266 4036

DOWNES PRESENTERS AGENCY
96 Broadway, Bexleyheath, Kent DA6 7DE
e-mail: downes@presenters.com
Fax: 020-8301 5591   Tel: 020-8304 0541

DREW Bryan Ltd
PM Write
Mezzanine, Quadrant House
80-82 Regent Street, London W1B 5AU
e-mail: bryan@bryandrewltd.com
Fax: 020-7437 0561   Tel: 020-7437 2293

DSA THEATRICAL AGENCY Ltd
1 Addley Court
435 Chiswick High Road, London W4 4AU
Fax: 020-8995 1347   Tel: 020-8994 9445

EARLE Kenneth PERSONAL MANAGEMENT
214 Brixton Road, London SW9 6AP
Website: www.entertainment-kennethearle.co.uk
e-mail: kennethearle@agents-uk.com
Fax: 020-7274 9529   Tel: 020-7274 1219

EARNSHAW Susi MANAGEMENT
PM
5 Brook Place, Barnet, Herts EN5 2DL
Website: www.susiearnshaw.co.uk
e-mail: casting@susiearnshaw.co.uk
Fax: 020-8364 9618   Tel: 020-8441 5010

EDLER Debbie MANAGEMENT
15 Perfect View
Bath BA1 5JY
e-mail: dem@fsmail.net   Tel/Fax: 01225 484967

EDWARDS REPRESENTATION Joyce
PM Write
275 Kennington Road, London SE11 6BY
e-mail: joyce.edwards@virgin.net
Fax: 020-7820 1845   Tel: 020-7735 5736

ELLIOTT Annie MANAGEMENT
6 Brenchley Close
Chislehurst, Kent BR7 5NQ
e-mail: annieelliottmgmt@aol.com
                            Tel: 020-8295 1130
ELLIS Bill Ltd
(See A & B MANAGEMENT Ltd)

EMPTAGE HALLETT*
24 Poland Street
London W1F 8QL
e-mail: mail@emptagehallett.co.uk
Fax: 020-7287 4411   Tel: 020-7287 5511

2nd Floor
3-5 The Balcony
Castle Arcade, Cardiff CF10 1BU
e-mail: gwenprice@emphal.fsnet.co.uk
Fax: 029-2034 4206   Tel: 029-2034 4205

ENGLISH Doreen '95
Write or Phone
4 Selsey Avenue, Aldwick
Bognor Regis
West Sussex PO21 2QZ   Tel/Fax: 01243 825968

ENTERTAINMENT DIRECTORY The
21-37 Third Avenue
London E13 8AW
Fax: 020-8471 2111   Tel: 020-8471 3111

EPSTEIN June ASSOCIATES
Write
Flat 1, 62 Compayne Gardens, London NW6 3RY
e-mail: june@june-epstein-associates.co.uk
Fax: 020-7328 0684   Tel: 020-7328 0864

ESSANAY*
PM Write
6 Brook Street, London W1S 1BB
e-mail: info@essanay.co.uk
Fax: 020-7355 1084   Tel: 020-7409 3526

ETHNICS ARTISTE AGENCY
86 Elphinstone Road, Walthamstow, London E17 5EX
Fax: 020-8523 4523   Tel: 020-8523 4242

ET-NIK-A
PRIME MANAGEMENT AND CASTINGS Ltd
Unit 4, 1A Hollybush Place, London E2 9QX
Website: www.et-nik-a.co.uk
e-mail: info@et-nik-a.co.uk
Fax: 020-7739 6718   Tel: 020-7739 6738

ETTINGER BROS GROUP
(Representation & Management)
Gladstone House
2 Church Road, Liverpool L15 9EG
e-mail: ettinger@genie.co.uk
Fax: 0151-733 2468   Tel: 0151-734 2240

**EUROKIDS AND ADULTS INTERNATIONAL CASTING
AND MODEL AGENCY**
The Warehouse Studio
Glaziers Lane, Culcheth, Warrington WA3 4AQ
Website: www.eurokidsandadults.co.uk
e-mail: info@eurokidsandadults.co.uk
Fax: 01925 767563   Tel: 0870 7572002

EVANS Jacque MANAGEMENT Ltd
Top Floor Suite, 14 Holmesley Road, London SE23 1PJ
Fax: 020-8699 5192   Tel: 020-8699 1202

EVANS & REISS*
100 Fawe Park Road, London SW15 2EA
e-mail: marcia@evans-reiss.fsnet.co.uk
Fax: 020-8877 0307   Tel: 020-8877 3755

EVOLUTION TALENT MANAGEMENT
The Truman Brewery Building
Studio 21, 91 Brick Lane, London E1 6QB
e-mail: evolutionmng@aol.com
Fax: 020-7375 2752   Tel: 020-7053 2128

FACE FACTORY
29 Abbey Business Centre
Ingate Place, London SW8 3NS
Website: www.facefactoryuk.com
Fax: 020-7720 9871   Tel: 020-7720 9877

FACT PRESENTATIONS
Unit 123
Aberdeen House, The Aberdeen Centre
22-24 Highbury Grove, London N1 0EW
e-mail: factartists@onetel.net.uk
Fax: 020-7359 2581   Tel: 020-7359 4289

FARNES Norma MANAGEMENT
9 Orme Court, London W2 4RL
Fax: 020-7792 2110   Tel: 020-7727 1544

FASTCAST UK
PO Box 80, Middlesex UB5 6JU
Website: www.fastcastuk.co.uk
e-mail: mrblack@fastcastuk.co.uk
Mobile: 07930 612315   Tel: 020-8839 9354

FAWKES Irene MANAGEMENT
2nd Floor, 91A Rivington Street, London EC2A 3AY
e-mail: irenefawkes@fsbdial.co.uk
Fax: 020-7613 0769   Tel: 020-7729 8559

Eve Pearce 'The Last Obit'

George Sewell 'Who Killed Agatha Christie'

Mike Eddowes
Theatre Photographer

Colin Penfold

Andy Brereton

Lionel Blair

Jeremy Child
Glyn Williams

Rob Richardson

Megan Francis

Michael Berryman

London & West Sussex
Production Photography
Casting Portraits
Posters • Rehearsals • Publicity

Please visit our website or email for further information, studio locations and rates.
www.theatre-photography.co.uk

Mobile: **07970 141005**
Admin: **01903 882525**
Email: mike@photo-publicity.co.uk
Portfolio at Spotlight offices

Lime
ACTORS AGENCY & MANAGEMENT LIMITED

T 0161 237 3300 F 0161 236 7557

54 Princess Street Manchester M1 6HS
Incorporating Manchesters most elite casting suites

FBI AGENCY Ltd The
PO Box 250, Leeds LS1 2AZ
Website: www.fbi-agency.ltd.uk
e-mail: j.spencer@fbi-agency.ltd.uk
Tel/Fax: 07050 222747

FBI Ltd
4th Floor
20-24 Kirby Street, London EC1N 8TS
Website: www.fullybooked-inc.com
e-mail: fbi@dircon.co.uk
Fax: 020-7242 8125   Tel: 020-7242 5542

FEAST Kate MANAGEMENT*
10 Primrose Hill Studios
Fitzroy Road, London NW1 8TR
e-mail: katefeast@freeuk.com
Fax: 020-7586 9817   Tel: 020-7586 5502

FEATURES
1 Charlotte Street, London W1T 1RD
e-mail: info@features.co.uk
Fax: 020-7636 1657   Tel: 020-7637 1487

FENLON Colette PERSONAL MANAGEMENT
(Incorporating CHILTERN CASTING CHILDREN'S
AGENCY)
2A Eaton Road, West Derby L12 7JJ
e-mail: collettefenlon@hotmail.com
Fax: 0151-280 7998   Tel: 0151-259 2926

FILM RIGHTS Ltd
PM Write
Mezzanine, Quadrant House
80-82 Regent Street, London W1B 5AU
Fax: 020-7734 0044   Tel: 020-7734 9911

FIRST HAND MANAGEMENT
PO Box 34610
London E17 7EX
e-mail: nick@fhmgt.co.uk
Fax: 0870 1350179   Tel: 020-8521 9783

FITZGERALD Sheridan MANAGEMENT
87 Western Road, Upton Park
London E13 9JE
Fax: 020-8470 2587   Tel: 020-8471 9814

FLETCHER ASSOCIATES
(Broadcast & Media)
25 Parkway, London N20 0XN
Fax: 020-8361 8866   Tel: 020-8361 8061

**FOCUS MANAGEMENT Ltd in Association
with BAK MANAGEMENT**
PM
155 Park Road, Teddington
Middlesex TW11 0BP
e-mail: focus.mgt@virgin.net
Fax: 020-8241 2447   Tel: 020-8241 2446

FREEHAND PRODUCTIONS Ltd
33-37 Hatherley Mews
Hiltongrove Business Centre
London E17 4QP
e-mail: freehanduk@yahoo.com
Tel/Fax: 020-8520 7777

FRENCH Linda
(See ALEXANDER PERSONAL MANAGEMENT Ltd)

FRONTLINE ACTORS' AGENCY DUBLIN
Seagrove
Claremont Road
Howth, Co Dublin, Ireland
Website: www.frontlineactors.org
e-mail: frontlineactors@eircom.net
Fax: 00 353 1 839 0956   Tel: 00 353 1 893 7499

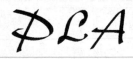

PLA

PAT LOVETT ASSOCIATES

Pat Lovett, Dolina Logan

39 Sandhurst Court, Acre Lane, London, SW2 5TX Tel: 020 7733 1110 Fax: 020 7733 4440
5 Union Street, Edinburgh, EH1 3LT Tel: 0131 478 7878 Fax: 0131 478 7070

FRONTLINE MANAGEMENT
PM Co-operative
Colombo Centre
34-68 Colombo Street, London SE1 8DP
e-mail: frontlineactor@freeuk.com
Tel/Fax: 020-7261 9466

FUSHION
27 Old Gloucester Street
London WC1N 3XX
Website: www.fushion-uk.com
e-mail: info@fushion-uk.com
Fax: 08700 111020   Tel: 08700 111100

GAGAN Hilary ASSOCIATES*
PM
187 Drury Lane
London WC2B 5QD
e-mail: hilary@hgassoc.freeserve.co.uk
Fax: 020-7430 1869   Tel: 020-7404 8794

GALLIARD'S MANAGEMENT
(Hugh Galliard)
33 Richford Street, London W6 7HJ
Website: www.galliards.net
e-mail: hugh@galliards.net   Tel: 020-8743 2201

GALLOWAYS ONE
15 Lexham Mews, London W8 6JW
e-mail: hugh@galloways.ltd.uk
Fax: 020-7376 2416   Tel: 020-7376 2288

GARDNER Kerry MANAGEMENT*
7 St George's Square, London SW1V 2HX
e-mail: kerrygardner@freeuk.com
Fax: 020-7828 7758   Tel: 020-7828 7748

GARRETT Michael ASSOCIATES*
23 Haymarket, London SW1Y 4DG
Website: www.michaelgarrett.co.uk
e-mail: enquiries@michaelgarrett.co.uk
Fax: 020-7839 4555   Tel: 020-7839 4888

Joanna Woodbridge

FRANS SMIT
PHOTOGRAPHY

07813 989 372

Ian Reddington

GARRICKS*
7 Garrick Street, London WC2E 9AR
e-mail: megan@garricks.net
Fax: 020-7240 9299   Tel: 020-7240 0660

GAY Noel ARTISTS*
19 Denmark Street, London WC2H 8NA
Website: www.noelgay.com
Fax: 020-7287 1816   Tel: 020-7836 3941

GFI MANAGEMENT
(Incorporating GO FOR IT CHILDREN'S AGENCY)
47 North Lane
Teddington, Middlesex TW11 0HU
e-mail: agency@goforit.info
Fax: 020-8287 9405   Tel: 020-8943 1120

GILBERT & PAYNE
Suite 73-74 Kent House
87 Regent Street, London W1B 4EH
e-mail: ee@successtheatrical.com
Fax: 020-7494 3787   Tel: 020-7734 7505

GLASS Eric Ltd
PM Write
25 Ladbroke Crescent, Notting Hill, London W11 1PS
e-mail: eglassltd@aol.com
Fax: 020-7229 6220   Tel: 020-7229 9500

GO ENTERTAINMENTS Ltd
(Circus Artistes, Chinese State Circus, Cirque Surreal,
Bolshoi Circus "Spirit of the Horse")
The Arts Exchange, Congleton, Cheshire CW12 1JG
Website: www.circus-online.co.uk
e-mail: phillipgandey@netcentral.co.uk
Fax: 01260 270777   Tel: 01260 276627

GOLDPUSH Ltd
38 Langham Street, London W1N 5RH
e-mail: razgold@goldpush.com
Fax: 020-7323 9526   Tel: 020-7323 9522

GORDON & FRENCH*
Write
12-13 Poland Street, London W1F 8QB
e-mail: mail@gordonandfrench.net
Fax: 020-7734 4832   Tel: 020-7734 4818

GOSS Gerald Ltd
Dudley House, 169 Piccadilly, London W1J 9EH
Fax: 020-7499 7227   Tel: 020-7499 7447

G.O.T. PERSONAL MANAGEMENT
1 Balliol Chambers, Hollow Lane, Herts SG4 9SB
Website: www.guild-of-thieves.com
e-mail: cast@guild-of-thieves.com
                                  Tel: 01462 420400

GOUGH MANAGEMENT
2A Bellevue Mews, Bellevue Road, London N11 3ET
Website: www.goughmanagement.com
e-mail: steve@goughmanagement.com
                          Tel/Fax: 020-8368 4222

GRANTHAM-HAZELDINE
5 Blenheim Street, London W1S 1L
Fax: 020-7495 3370   Tel: 020-7499 4011

GRAY Darren MANAGEMENT
(Specialising in representing/promoting Australian Artists)
2 Marston Lane, Portsmouth, Hampshire PO3 5TW
Website: www.darrengraymanagement.co.uk
e-mail: darren.gray1@virgin.net
Fax: 023-9267 7227   Tel: 023-9269 9973

GRAY Joan PERSONAL MANAGEMENT
PM F TV
29 Sunbury Court Island
Sunbury-on-Thames
Middlesex TW16 5PP   Tel/Fax: 01932 783544

GRAYS MANAGEMENT Ltd
PM
Panther House
38 Mount Pleasant, London WC1X 0AP
Website: www.graysmanagement.co.uk
e-mail: e-mail@graysmanagement.idps.co.uk
Fax: 020-7278 1091   Tel: 020-7278 1054

GREEN & UNDERWOOD
PM Write
6 Brook Street, London W1S 1BB
Website: www.greenandunderwood.com
e-mail: info@greenandunderwood.com
Fax: 020-7355 1084   Tel: 020-7493 0308

GREIG Miranda ASSOCIATES Ltd
41 Beauchamp Road
London SW11 1PG
e-mail: mail@mirandagreigassoc.co.uk
Fax: 020-7228 1400   Tel: 020-7228 1200

GRESHAM Carl GROUP
PO Box 3
Bradford, West Yorkshire BD1 4QN
Website: www.carlgresham.co.uk
e-mail: carl@carlgresham.co.uk
Fax: 01274 370313   Tel: 01274 735880

GRIFFIN Sandra MANAGEMENT
6 Ryde Place
Richmond Road
East Twickenham, Middlesex TW1 2EH
e-mail: sgmgmt@aol.com
Fax: 020-8744 1812   Tel: 020-8891 5676

GROUP 3 ASSOCIATES
PM (Henry Davies)
35D Newton Road
London W2 5JR
Tel: 020-7359 9116   Tel: 020-7221 4989

GURNETT J. PERSONAL MANAGEMENT Ltd
PM
2 New Kings Road
London SW6 4SA
Website: www.jgpm.co.uk
e-mail: mail@jgpm.co.uk
Fax: 020-7736 5455   Tel: 020-7736 7828

HALLY WILLIAMS AGENCY The
121 Grange Road
Rathfarnham, Dublin 14
e-mail: hallywilliams@eircom.net
Fax: 00 353 14933076   Tel: 00 353 14933685

HAMILTON HODELL Ltd*
24 Hanway Street
London W1T 1UH
e-mail: info@hamiltonhodell.co.uk
Fax: 020-7636 1226   Tel: 020-7636 1221

HANCOCK Roger Ltd*
4 Water Lane, London NW1 8NZ
e-mail: hancockltd@aol.com
Fax: 020-7267 0705   Tel: 020-7267 4418

HARLEY AGENCY The
Regent House, 291 Kirkdale, London SE26 4QD
e-mail: mail@theharleyagency.co.uk
Fax: 020-8659 8118   Tel: 020-8659 8147

HARRIS AGENCY Ltd The
52 Forty Avenue
Wembley Park, Middlesex HA9 8LQ
e-mail: sharrisltd@aol.com
Fax: 020-8908 4455   Tel: 020-8908 4451

HARRISON Penny BSA Ltd
Trinity Lodge, 25 Trinity Crescent, London SW17 7AG
e-mail: bsaltd@yahoo.co.uk
Fax: 020-8672 8971   Tel: 020-8672 0136

HARRISPEARSON MANAGEMENT Ltd
14-16 Guilford Street, London WC1N 1DW
Website: www.harrispearson.co.uk
e-mail: agent@harrispearson.co.uk
Fax: 020-7430 9229   Tel: 020-7430 9890

HARTFIELD MANAGEMENT
16 Hartfield Crescent
West Wickham, Kent BR4 9DN
Website: www.hartfieldentertainment.co.uk
e-mail: enquiries@hartfieldentertainment.co.uk
    Tel/Fax: 020-8462 1760

HATTON McEWAN*
(Stephen Hatton, Aileen McEwan)
PM Write
3 Chocolate Studios
7 Shepherdess Place, London N1 7LJ
e-mail: info@thetalent.biz
Fax: 020-7251 9081   Tel: 020-7253 4770

TOPSHOTS
THE FINISHING TOUCH

Mobile
07855 586177

HATTON Richard Ltd*
29 Roehampton Gate, London SW15 5JR
Fax: 020-8876 8278   Tel: 020-8876 6699

HAYDEN Teri
(See AGENCY The)

HAZEMEAD Ltd
(Entertainment Consultants)
Camellia House, 38 Orchard Road
Sundridge Park, Bromley, Kent BR1 2PS
Fax: 020-8460 5830   Tel: 0870 2402082

HEATHCOTE George MANAGEMENT
38 Great Queen Street, London WC2B 5AA
e-mail: gheathcote@freeuk.com
Fax: 020-7404 8680   Tel: 020-7404 8681

HEAVY PENCIL MANAGEMENT
PM Co-operative
BAC, Lavender Hill, London SW11 5TF
e-mail: heavy.pencil@talk21.com
Fax: 020-7924 4636   Tel: 020-7738 9574

HENRY'S AGENCY
53 Westbury, Rochford, Essex SS4 1UL
Website: www.henrysagency.co.uk
e-mail: info@henrysagency.co.uk
Fax: 01702 543654   Tel: 01702 541413

HICKS Jeremy ASSOCIATES
11-12 Tottenham Mews, London W1T 4AG
Website: www.jeremyhicks.com
e-mail: hicksworld@aol.com
Fax: 020-7636 8880   Tel: 020-7636 8008

HILL Edward MANAGEMENT
Riverbank House
1 Putney Bridge Approach, London SW6 3JD
e-mail: hill@ehillmanagement.freeserve.co.uk
Fax: 020-7371 0066   Tel: 020-7371 0666

HILLMAN THRELFALL
33 Brookfield, Highgate West Hill, London N6 6AT
e-mail: emma@hillmanthrelfall.net
Fax: 020-8340 9309   Tel: 020-8341 2207

HINDIN Dee ASSOCIATES
67 York Street, London W1H 1QA
Fax: 020-7724 0822   Tel: 020-7724 0022

HINDIN Philip
66 Melbourne Way, Bush Hill Park, Enfield
Middlesex EN1 1XQ   Tel/Fax: 020-8366 2978

HIRED HANDS
12 Cressy Road, London NW3 2LY
e-mail: models@hiredhands.freeserve.co.uk
Fax: 020-7267 1030   Tel: 020-7267 9212

HOBBS Liz GROUP Ltd
(Artist Management & Public Relations)
68 Castlegate, Newark, Notts NG24 1BG
Website: www.lizhobbsgroup.com
e-mail: info@lizhobbsgroup.com
Fax: 0870 3337009   Tel: 08700 702702

HOBSON'S ACTORS
62 Chiswick High Road
Chiswick, London W4 1SY
Website: www.hobsons-international.com
e-mail: actors@hobsons-international.com
Fax: 020-8996 5350   Tel: 020-8995 3628

HOLLAND-FORD Robert
PM Write or Phone
103 Lydyett Lane, Barnton, Northwich
Cheshire CW8 4JT   Tel: 01606 76960

HOLLOWOOD Jane ASSOCIATES Ltd
50 Copperas Street
Manchester M4 1HS
e-mail: janehollowood@ukonline.co.uk
Fax: 0161-834 8333   Tel: 0161-834 8334

Charmaine Parsons

Peter Helmer

Daniel Harwood-Stamper

Tel: 020 7930 1372   Mob: 07966 236865

Northern Lights Management

Personal representation of Actors from the North and in the North

Agents: Maureen Magee and Angie Forrest

Dean Clough Mills, Halifax, West Yorkshire HX3 5AX

Tel: 01422 382203
Fax: 01422 330101

email: NLManagement@aol.com

HOLLY Dave ARTS MEDIA SERVICES
The Annexe, 23 Eastwood Gardens
Felling, Tyne & Wear NE10 0AH
Fax: 0191-438 2722   Tel: 0191-438 2711

HOPE Sally ASSOCIATES*
108 Leonard Street, London EC2A 4XS
e-mail: casting@sallyhope.biz
Fax: 020-7613 4848   Tel: 020-7613 5353

HOWARD Amanda ASSOCIATES Ltd*
21 Berwick Street, London W1F 0PZ
Website: www.amandahowardassociates.co.uk
e-mail: mail@amandahowardassociates.co.uk
Fax: 020-7287 7785   Tel: 020-7287 9277

HOWE Janet
40 Princess Street, Manchester M1 6DE
Website: www.janethowe.co.uk
e-mail: janet@jhowecasting.fsbusiness.co.uk
Mobile: 07801 942178   Tel/Fax: 0161-233 0700

Studio 1, Whitebridge Estate, Whitebridge Lane
Stone, Staffs ST15 8LQ
Tel/Fax: 01785 818480   Tel/Fax: 01785 816888

HOWELL Philippa
(See PHPM)

HUDSON Nancy ASSOCIATES Ltd
3rd Floor
50 South Molton Street, London W1K 5SB
Website: www.vilhud.co.uk
e-mail: vilhud@freeuk.com
Fax: 020-7499 0884   Tel: 020-7499 5548

HUGHES Jane MANAGEMENT
The Coach House, PO Box 123
Knutsford, Cheshire WA16 9HX
Fax: 01565 722211   Tel: 01565 723000

HUNTER Bernard ASSOCIATES
13 Spencer Gardens
London SW14 7AH
Fax: 020-8392 9334   Tel: 020-8878 6308

I C M (International Creative Management)*
Oxford House
76 Oxford Street
London W1D 1BS
e-mail: casting@icmlondon.co.uk
Fax: 020-7323 0101   Tel: 020-7636 6565

ICON ACTORS MANAGEMENT
Tanzaro House
Ardwick Green North
Manchester M12 6FZ
Website: www.iconactors.net
e-mail: info@iconactors.net
Fax: 0161-273 4567   Tel: 0161-273 3344

IMAGIO GROUP Ltd The
(UK & India, Fashion, TV, Film & Music)
43 Colmansmoor Road
Woodley, Reading, Berkshire RG5 4DG
Website: www.imagiogroup.co.uk
e-mail: info@imagiogroup.co.uk
Mobile: 07989 33745   Tel/Fax: 0118-375 7871

I.M.L.
PM Co-operative
Oval House
52-54 Kennington Oval
London SE11 5SW
Website: www.iml.org.uk
e-mail: imllondon@hotmail.com
                                Tel/Fax: 020-7587 1080

IMPACT INTERNATIONAL MANAGEMENT
2nd Floor
16-18 Balderton Street
London W1K 6TN
e-mail: info@impactinternationalgroup.com
Fax: 020-8441 4828   Tel: 020-7495 6655

INDEPENDENT THEATRE WORKSHOP The
2 Mornington Road
Ranelagh, Dublin 6, Eire
Website: www.independent-theatre-workshop.com
e-mail: itw@satclear.ie   Tel/Fax: 00 353 1 4968808

INGMAN T.J.
PM
29 Whitcomb Street
London WC2H 7EP
Website: www.trevor.ingman.btinternet.co.uk
e-mail: tjingman@hotmail.com
Fax: 020-7930 4441   Tel: 020-7930 4442

INSPIRATION MANAGEMENT
PM Co-operative
Room 200, The Aberdeen Centre
22-24 Highbury Grove, London N5 2EA
Website: www.inspiration.ukweb.nu
e-mail: agent@inspirationmanagement.freeserve.co.uk
Fax: 020-7704 8497   Tel: 020-7704 0440

INTER-CITY CASTING
PM
Portland Tower
Portland Street, Manchester M1 3LF
Website: www.iccast.co.uk
e-mail: intercity@bigfoot.com
                                Tel/Fax: 0161-226 0103

INTERNATIONAL ARTISTES Ltd*
Mezzanine Floor
235 Regent Street, London W1B 2AX
Website: www.intart.co.uk
e-mail: (name)@intart.co.uk
Fax: 020-7409 2070   Tel: 020-7439 8401

INTERNATIONAL THEATRE & MUSIC Ltd
(Piers Chater Robinson)
Shakespeare House, Theatre Street, London SW11 5ND
e-mail: inttheatre@aol.com
Fax: 020-7801 6317   Tel: 020-7801 6316

IRISH ARTS NETWORK
Victor House
Marlborough Gardens, London N20 0SH
e-mail: rosemaryifbco@aol.com
                    Tel/Fax: 020-8361 0678

ITG ARTIST MANAGEMENT Ltd
5 Vigo Street, London W1S 3HB
Website: www.italentg.com
e-mail: camilla@italentg.com
Fax: 020-7287 3992   Tel: 020-7287 3993

JAA
(See ALTARAS Jonathan ASSOCIATES Ltd)

JAMES Julie
e-mail: juliejames@btclick.com
Mobile: 07931 219054   Tel/Fax: 020-7834 0967

JAMES Susan
(See SJ MANAGEMENT)

JAMESON Joy Ltd
PM
2.19 The Plaza, 535 Kings Road, London SW10 0SZ
Fax: 020-7352 1744   Tel: 020-7351 3971

J.A.R. LEISURE Ltd
(Formerly International World of Sport/
See International Ltd)
PO Box 14, Bognor Regis, West Sussex PO22 7JW
Fax: 01243 868907   Tel: 01243 868397

JAY Alex PERSONAL MANAGEMENT
Hawthorns, Amberely, Glos GL5 5AW
e-mail: alex@alex-jay-pm.freeserve.co.uk
                    Tel/Fax: 01453 872038

JB ASSOCIATES*
First Floor, 3 Stevenson Square, Manchester M1 1DN
e-mail: united_cities@compuserve.com
Fax: 0161-237 1809   Tel: 0161-237 1808

JEFFREY & WHITE MANAGEMENT*
PM
9-15 Neal Street, London WC2H 9PW
Fax: 020-7240 0007   Tel: 020-7240 7000

J.G.M.
15 Lexham Mews, London W8 6JW
e-mail: jgm@galloways.ltd.uk
Fax: 020-7376 2416   Tel: 020-7376 2414

JLM PERSONAL MANAGEMENT*
(Janet Lynn Malone, Sharon Henry)
259 Acton Lane, London W4 5DG
e-mail: jlm@skynow.net
Fax: 020-8747 8286   Tel: 020-8747 8223

JLS CASTINGS
(Casting Agency & Management)
14 Kings Terrace, Basford
Stoke on Trent, Staffordshire ST4 6EB
Mobile: 07957 687144   Tel/Fax: 01782 626260

J M ASSOCIATES*
(Jan Murphy)
77 Beak Street, London W1F 9ST
Fax: 020-7434 0640   Tel: 020-7434 0602

JOHNSON WHITELEY Ltd
21 Eastcastle Street, London W1W 8DD
e-mail: jwltd@freeuk.com
Fax: 020-7323 3761   Tel: 020-7323 3744

JOHNSTON & MATHERS ASSOCIATES Ltd
PO Box 3167, Barnet EN5 2WA
e-mail: johnstonmathers@aol.com
Mobile: 07976 961251   Tel/Fax: 020-8449 4968

JONES Sally AGENCY The
96 Lutton Gate
Gedney Hill, Spalding
Lincs PE12 0QH
e-mail: sjonesag@aol.com   Tel: 01406 330383

JPA MANAGEMENT
30 Daws Hill Lane, High Wycombe, Bucks HP11 1PW
Website: www.jackiepalmer.co.uk
e-mail: jackie.palmer@btinternet.com
Fax: 01494 510479   Tel: 01494 520978

KAL MANAGEMENT
Write
95 Gloucester Road, Hampton, Middlesex TW12 2UW
Website: www.kalplan-k.co.uk
e-mail: kaplan222@aol.com
Fax: 020-8979 6487   Tel: 020-8783 0039

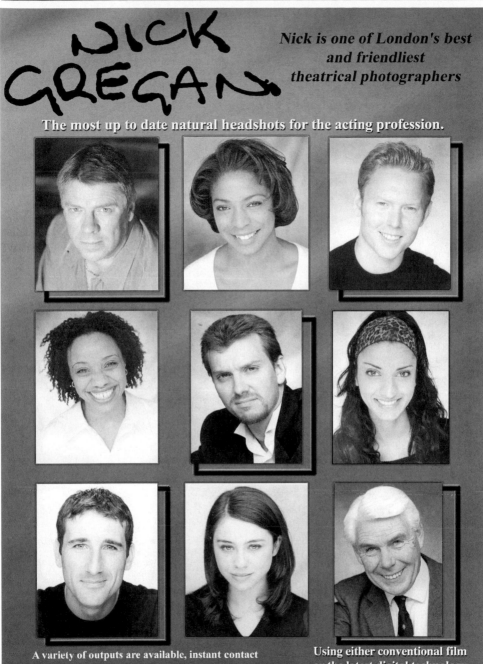

stuart **Oakley** photography

07813 813 176   oakleystuart@hotmail.com   www.oakleystuart.co.uk

KANAL Roberta AGENCY
82 Constance Road
Twickenham, Middlesex TW2 7JA
e-mail: roberta@kanal.fsnet.co.uk
Tel/Fax: 020-8894 7952   Tel: 020-8894 2277

KARUSHI MANAGEMENT
Golden Cross House
8 Duncannon Street, London WC2N 4JF
Website: www.karushi.com
e-mail: lisa@karushi.com
Fax: 020-7484 5151   Tel: 020-7484 5040

KEAN & GARRICK
PM (Existing Clients only)
PO Box 303, Hampton TW12 3TU
Fax: 020-8979 5335   Tel: 020-8979 0900

KEARNEY Dee MANAGEMENT
Rolekall Casting
1 Dunwood Bridge, Bridge Street, Shaw OL2 8BG
e-mail: dee@rolekall.fsnet.co.uk
          Tel/Fax: 01706 882442

KENIS Steve & Co*
Royalty House
72-74 Dean Street, London W1D 3SG
e-mail: sk@sknco.com
Fax: 020-7287 6328   Tel: 020-7534 6001

KENT YOUTH THEATRE & AGENCY
Pinks Hill House
Briton Road, Faversham
Kent ME13 8QH
e-mail: richard@kyt.org.uk   Tel/Fax: 01795 534395

KIDZ IN THE BIZ
The Lime House
Leaves Green Road, Keston, Kent BR2 6DQ
Website: www.kidzinthebiz.co.uk
e-mail: agency@kidzinthebiz.co.uk
Fax: 01959 576632   Tel: 01959 542552

KING Adrian ASSOCIATES
33 Marlborough Mansions, Cannon Hill, London NW6 1JS
e-mail: akassocs@aol.com
Fax: 020-7435 4100   Tel: 020-7435 4600

K M C AGENCIES
All postal submissions to Manchester office
e-mail: london@kmcagencies.co.uk
Fax: 0870 4421780   Tel: 0845 6602459

PO Box 122
48 Great Ancoats Street
Manchester M4 5AB
e-mail: casting@kmcagencies.co.uk
Fax: 0161-237 9812   Tel: 0161-237 3009

Nyland management

20 School Lane, Heaton Chapel,
Stockport SK4 5DG
Tel: 0161 442 2224
Fax: 0161 432 5406
e-mail: nylandmgmt@freenet.co.uk

KNIGHT AYTON MANAGEMENT
114 St Martin's Lane, London WC2N 4BE
Website: www.knightayton.co.uk
e-mail: info@knightayton.co.uk
Fax: 020-7836 5333   Tel: 020-7836 8333

KNIGHT Ray CASTING
21A Lambolle Place, London NW3 4PG
Website: www.rayknight.co.uk
e-mail: casting@rayknight.co.uk
Fax: 020-7722 2322   Tel: 020-7722 1551

KREATE Ltd
Unit 201, 30 Great Guildford Street, London SE1 0HS
e-mail: kreate@btconnect.com
Fax: 020-7401 3003   Tel: 020-7401 9007

KREMER ASSOCIATES
(See MARSH Billy DRAMA Ltd)

KRUGER Rolf MANAGEMENT Ltd
PM (Rachel & Rolf Kruger)
205 Chudleigh Road, London SE4 1EG
Website: www.krugeractors.com
e-mail: mail@krugeractors.com
Fax: 020-8690 7999   Tel: 020-8690 7666

LADKIN Michael PERSONAL MANAGEMENT
Suite 1, Ground Floor
1 Duchess Street, London W1W 6AN
e-mail: ladkinm@aol.com
Fax: 020-7436 4627   Tel: 020-7436 4626

LAINE MANAGEMENT
131 Victoria Road, Salford M6 8LF
e-mail: info@lainemanagement.co.uk
Fax: 0161-787 7572   Tel: 0161-789 7775

LAINE Betty MANAGEMENT
The Studios East Street, Epsom, Surrey KT17 1HH
e-mail: enquiries@betty-laine-management.co.uk
                          Tel/Fax: 01372 721815

LAMONT CASTING AGENCY
94 Harington Road, Formby, Liverpool L37 1PZ
Website: www.lamontcasting.co.uk
e-mail: diane@lamontcasting.co.uk
Fax: 01704 872422   Tel: 01704 877024

LAND Paulette
(Business Management)
48 Acacia Grove, New Malden, Surrey KT3 3BP
e-mail: pauletteland@free.uk.com
Fax: 020-8949 0840   Tel: 020-8949 5586

LANGFORD ASSOCIATES
17 Westfields Avenue, Barnes, London SW13 0AT
e-mail: langford@ctors.fsnet.co.uk
Fax: 020-8878 7078   Tel: 020-8878 7148

LAPATA
St Matthew's Church
St Petersburgh Place, London W2 4LA
e-mail: admin@lapadrama.com
Fax: 020-7727 0330   Tel: 020-7229 7339

L'BROOKE PERSONAL MANAGEMENT
7 Malt House Place
High Street, Romford, Essex RM1 1AR
e-mail: l'brookepersonalmanagement-claire@btinternet.com
                          Tel/Fax: 01708 723883

LEE Bernard MANAGEMENT
1 Heathside Place, Epsom Downs, Surrey KT18 5TX
e-mail: jon@blm1.freeserve.co.uk
                          Tel/Fax: 01737 354777

LEE Wendy MANAGEMENT
4th Floor Suite, 40 Langham Street, London W1W 7AS
e-mail: wendylee@wendyleemanagement.fsworld.co.uk
Fax: 020-7580 8700   Tel: 020-7580 4800

Julia Sawalha

Nicky Amin

LEE'S PEOPLE
60 Poland Street, London W1F 7NT
e-mail: lee@lees-people.co.uk
Fax: 020-7734 3033   Tel: 020-7734 5775

LEHRER Jane ASSOCIATES*
100A Chalk Farm Road
London NW1 8EH
e-mail: janelehrer@aol.com
Fax: 020-7482 4899   Tel: 020-7482 4898

LEIGH MANAGEMENT
14 St David's Drive, Edgware HA8 6JH
Tel/Fax: 020-8951 4449   Tel: 020-8952 5536

LEWIS Tony ENTERTAINMENTS
PO Box 11268, London SW5 0ZL
Fax: 020-7373 6427   Tel: 020-7370 0416

LIME ACTORS AGENCY & MANAGEMENT Ltd
4th Floor
54 Princess Street, Manchester M1 6HS
e-mail: debbie.pine@limemanagement.co.uk
Fax: 0161-236 7557   Tel: 0161-237 3300

LINKS MANAGEMENT
34-68 Colombo Street
London SE1 8DP
e-mail: links@eidosnet.co.uk Tel/Fax: 020-7928 0806

LINKSIDE AGENCY
21 Poplar Road, Leatherhead, Surrey KT22 8SF
e-mail: linksideagency@hotmail.com
Fax: 01372 801972   Tel: 01372 802374

LITTLE ACORNS MODELLING AGENCY
London House
271-273 King Street
Hammersmith, London W6 9LZ
Fax: 020-8408 3077   Tel: 020-8563 0773

LONDON MANAGEMENT*
2-4 Noel Street, London W1F 8GB
Fax: 020-7287 3036   Tel: 020-7287 9000

LONDON MUSICIANS Ltd
(Orchestral Contracting)
Cedar House, Vine Lane
Hillingdon, Middlesex UB10 0BX
e-mail: mail@londonmusicians.co.uk
Fax: 01895 252556   Tel: 01895 252555

LONGTIME MANAGEMENT
(Existing Clients only)
2 Devonshire Court
Devonshire Hill Lane, London N17 7NJ
e-mail: nigeladams@talk21.com
Tel/Fax: 020-8352 1467

Justin Salinger

Tracy Ann Oberman

Jamie R. Bradley

Emily Bruni

MAGNUS DOMINIC 020 7700 6475 *Student Rates*

LOOK ALIKES Ltd
17-23 Lorn Road, London SW9 0AB
e-mail: info@lookalikes.ltd.uk
Fax: 020-7274 4466   Tel: 020-7274 0666

LOOKALIKES (Susan Scott)
26 College Crescent, London NW3 5LH
Website: www.lookalikes.info
e-mail: susan@lookalikes.info
Fax: 020-7722 8261   Tel: 020-7387 9245

LOVETT Pat ASSOCIATES
(See P.L.A.)

LSW PROMOTIONS
181A Faunce House
Doddington Grove, Kennington, London SE17 3TB
Website: www.londonshakespeare.org.uk/promos
e-mail: lswpromos@hotmail.com
                    Tel/Fax: 020-7735 5911

LYNE Dennis AGENCY*
108 Leonard Street, London EC2A 4RH
e-mail: d.lyne@virgin.net
Fax: 020-7739 4101   Tel: 020-7739 6200

MAC-10 Ltd
Unit 69, 2 Hellidon Close, Ardwick, Manchester M12 4AH
Website: www.mac-10.co.uk
e-mail: info@mac-10.co.uk
Fax: 0161-275 9610   Tel: 0161-275 9510

MACNAUGHTON LORD 2000 Ltd*
(Writers, Designers, Directors,
Composers/Lyricists/Musical Directors)
Douglas House
16-18 Douglas Street, London SW1P 4PB
Website: www.ml2000.org.uk
e-mail: info@ml2000.org.uk
Fax: 020-7834 4949   Tel: 020-7834 4646

MADELEY Paul PUBLICITY
17 Valley Road, Arden Park
Bredbury, Stockport, Cheshire SK6 2EA
e-mail: madeleypublicity@talk21.com
Fax: 0161-430 4016   Tel: 0161-430 5380

MAGNET PERSONAL MANAGEMENT
Co-operative
Unit 743, The Big Peg
120 Vyse Street, Birmingham B18 6NF
Website: www.magnetactors.fsnet.co.uk
                    Tel/Fax: 0121-628 7788

MAGNOLIA MANAGEMENT*
136 Hicks Avenue, Greenford, Middlesex UB6 8HB
e-mail: jaffreymag@aol.com
Fax: 020-8575 0369   Tel: 020-8578 2899

MAITLAND MUSIC
PM (Anne Skates)
Brook House
8 Rythe Road, Claygate, Surrey KT10 9DF
Website: www.maitlandmusic.com
e-mail: maitmus@aol.com
Fax: 01372 466229   Tel: 01372 466228

MAKDEE MANAGEMENT
64A Canadian Avenue, London SE6 3BP
e-mail: donka@canad.freeserve.co.uk
Tel/Fax: 020-8425 0093   Tel: 020-8695 9522

MANAGEMENT 2000
23 Alexandra Road, Mold, Flintshire CH7 1HJ
Website: www.jcmanagement-2000.co.uk
e-mail: jcmanagement2000@aol.com
                    Tel/Fax: 01352 771231

MANS Johnny PRODUCTIONS Ltd
PO Box 196, Hoddesdon, Herts EN10 7WG
e-mail: real@legend.co.uk
Fax: 01992 470516   Tel: 01992 470907

A

MANSON Andrew PERSONAL MANAGEMENT*
288 Munster Road, London SW6 6BQ
Website: www.talentroom.com
e-mail: amanson@aol.com
Fax: 020-7381 8874   Tel: 020-7386 9158

MARCUS & McCRIMMON MANAGEMENT
4 Fitzwarren Gardens
Highgate, London N19 3TP
Website: www.marcusandmccrimmon.com
e-mail: mail@marcusandmccrimmon.com
Fax: 020-7281 3933   Tel: 020-7281 2692

MARKHAM & FROGGATT Ltd*
PM Write
4 Windmill Street, London W1P 1HF
e-mail: admin@markhamfroggatt.co.uk
Fax: 020-7637 5233   Tel: 020-7636 4412

MARKHAM John ASSOCIATES
1A Oakwood Avenue
Purley, Surrey CR8 1AR
e-mail: info@johnmarkhamassociates.co.uk
Fax: 020-8763 8942   Tel: 020-8763 8941

MARMONT MANAGEMENT Ltd*
PM
Langham House, 308 Regent Street
London W1B 3AT
e-mail: penrose@marmont.co.uk
Fax: 020-7323 4798   Tel: 020-7637 3183

MARSH Billy ASSOCIATES Ltd
174-178 North Gower Street, London NW1 2NB
e-mail: bmarsh@bmarsh.demon.co.uk
Fax: 020-7388 6848   Tel: 020-7388 6858

MARSH Billy DRAMA Ltd*
174-178 North Gower Street, London NW1 2NB
e-mail: info@billymarshdrama.co.uk
Fax: 020-7383 5514   Tel: 020-7383 5020

MARSH Sandra MANAGEMENT
(Film Technicians)
c/o Casarotto Marsh Ltd, National House
60-66 Wardour Street, London W1V 4ND
e-mail: casarottomarsh@casarotto.uk.com
Fax: 020-7287 5644   Tel: 020-7287 4450

MARSHALL Ronnie AGENCY
S F M PM TV Write or Phone
66 Ollerton Road
London N11 2LA   Tel/Fax: 020-8368 4958

MARSHALL Scott*
PM TV Write or phone
44 Perryn Road, London W3 7NA
e-mail: scott@scottmarshall.co.uk
Fax: 020-8740 7342   Tel: 020-8749 7692

MARTIN Carol PERSONAL MANAGEMENT
19 Highgate West Hill, London N6 6NP
Fax: 020-8340 4868   Tel: 020-8348 0847

MASON PERSONAL MANAGEMENT
12A Allen Road, London N16 8SD
e-mail: mason@pmanagement.freeserve.co.uk
                    Tel/Fax: 020-7254 8212

MAY John
Garden Flat
6 Westbourne Park Villas, London W2 5EA
e-mail: john@johnmayagent.freeserve.co.uk
Fax: 020-7229 9828   Tel: 020-7221 7917

MAYER Cassie Ltd*
11 Wells Mews, London W1T 3HD
e-mail: cassandra.mayer@cassiemayerltd.co.uk
Fax: 020-7462 0041   Tel: 020-7462 0040

Paul Bradley

Rania Ajami

Rupert Whickham

JONATHAN
DOCKAR ~ DRYSDALE
PHOTOGRAPHY
020 8560 1077
MOBILE 07711 006191

Student Discount ~ Portfolio at The Spotlight

THEATRICAL AGENTS

ACTORS

DANCERS

SINGERS

MODELS

PRESENTERS

CHOREOGRAPHERS

SUITE 73-74 KENT HOUSE

87 REGENT STREET

LONDON W1B 4EH

TEL: 020 7734 3356

FAX: 020 7494 3787

www.successagency.co.uk   e-mail: ee@successagency.co.uk

MBA (Formerly John Mahoney Management)
Concorde House
18 Margaret Street, Brighton BN2 1TS
Website: www.mbagency.fsnet.co.uk
e-mail: mba.concorde@virgin.net
Fax: 01273 685971   Tel: 01273 685970

McCORQUODALE Anna PERSONAL MANAGEMENT
43 St Maur Road, London SW6 4DR
e-mail: amc@netcomuk.co.uk
Fax: 020-7371 9048   Tel: 020-7731 1721

McINTOSH RAE MANAGEMENT*
Write SAE
Thornton House
Thornton Road, London SW19 4NG
e-mail: mcinrae@talk21.com
Fax: 020-8944 6624   Tel: 020-8944 6688

McKINNEY MACARTNEY MANAGEMENT Ltd
(Technicians)
The Barley Mow Centre
10 Barley Mow Passage, London W4 4PH
Website: www.mckinneymacartney.com
e-mail: fkb@mmtechsrep.demon.co.uk
Fax: 020-8995 2414   Tel: 020-8995 4747

McLEAN Bill PERSONAL MANAGEMENT Ltd
PM Write
23B Deodar Road
London SW15 2NP   Tel: 020-8789 8191

McLEAN-WILLIAMS MANAGEMENT
212 Piccadilly, London W1J 9HG
e-mail: alex@mclean-williams.com
Fax: 020-7917 2805   Tel: 020-7917 2806

McLEOD HOLDEN ENTERPRISES Ltd
Priory House, 1133 Hessle High Road, Hull HU4 6SB
Website: www.mcleod-holden.com
e-mail: peter.mcleod@mcleod-holden.com
Fax: 01482 353635   Tel: 01482 565444

McREDDIE Ken Ltd*
PM
91 Regent Street, London W1B 4EL
Fax: 020-7734 6530   Tel: 020-7439 1456

MCS AGENCY
47 Dean Street, London W1D 5BE
e-mail: info@mcs-group.freeserve.co.uk
Fax: 020-7734 9996   Tel: 020-7734 9995

MEDIA LEGAL
PM F TV Voice-overs (Existing Clients only)
83 Clarendon Road, Sevenoaks
Kent TN13 1ET
Tel: 01732 460592

MEDIA MODELLING & CASTING AGENCY
53 Astley Avenue, Dover, Kent CT16 2PP
Website: www.mediamc.co.uk
e-mail: info@mediamc.co.uk
Mobile: 07713 158355   Tel: 01304 204715

MILLENNIUM ARTISTES MANAGEMENT Ltd
(Personal Management & Event Co-ordinators)
PO Box 2001, Caterham, Surrey CR3 6UA
e-mail: mamltd@ntlworld.com
                                Tel/Fax: 01883 347790

MILNER David MANAGEMENT
1A Pollards Row, Bethnal Green, London E2 6NA
e-mail: milner.agent@btopenworld.com
Fax: 020-7613 0780   Tel: 020-7613 4041

MINT MANAGEMENT
8A Barry Road, London SE22 0HU
e-mail: lisi@mintman.co.uk
Fax: 020-8693 2976   Tel: 020-8637 0351

MK MANAGEMENT
20B Chancellors Street, London W6 9RN
Website: www.mkmanagement.co.uk
e-mail: hannah@mkmanagement.co.uk
Fax: 0870 0111970   Tel: 0870 0111205

M.K.A.
11 Russell Kerr Close, Chiswick, London W4 3HF
e-mail: mka.agency@virgin.net
Fax: 020-8994 2992   Tel: 020-8994 1619

ML 2000 Ltd
(See MACNAUGHTON LORD 2000 Ltd)

MONDI ASSOCIATES Ltd
51 Nevill Court
Edith Terrace, Chelsea
London SW10 0TL
Fax: 020-7439 9301   Mobile: 07971 958727

Agent labels

Did you know that you can order **agent** labels from us for only £10.50?
This will allow you to send your CV to UK Agents quickly and professionally.

To order:
Telephone: 020 7437 7631   Fax: 020 7287 1201   e-mail: info@spotlightcd.com

MONTAGU ASSOCIATES
3 Bretton House, 145 Fairbridge Road, London N19 3HP
Fax: 020-7263 3993   Tel: 020-7263 3883

MOORE ACTORS
71 Buttermere Road
Ashton-under-Lyne, Manchester OL7 9EW
e-mail: mooreactors@btinternet.com
Fax: 0161-330 6626   Tel: 0161-355 7341

MORE MANAGEMENT
21 Brittany Road, Worthing, West Sussex BN14 7DY
e-mail: kylanik@freeuk.com   Tel/Fax: 01903 538877

MORGAN & GOODMAN
Mezzanine, Quadrant House
80-82 Regent Street, London W1B 5RP
e-mail: mg1@btinternet.com
Fax: 020-7494 3446   Tel: 020-7437 1383

MOSS Jae ENTERPRISES
Riverside House, Feltham Avenue
Hampton Court, Surrey KT8 9BJ
Website: www.jmossent.co.uk
e-mail: jmossent@aol.com
Fax: 020-8979 9631   Tel: 020-8979 3459

MOUNTVIEW MANAGEMENT
Ralph Richardson Memorial Studios, Kingfisher Place
Clarendon Road, Wood Green, London N22 6XF
Fax: 020-8829 1050   Tel: 020-8889 8231

MOVIESTYLE ARTISTS
3 Lefroy Road, Shepherd's Bush, London W12 9LF
Website: www.moviestyle.co.uk
e-mail: mail@moviestyle.co.uk
Fax: 020-8746 2065   Tel: 020-8740 7871

MPC ENTERTAINMENT
Write or Phone
MPC House,
15-16 Maple Mews, Maida Vale, London NW6 5UZ
Website: www.mpce.com
e-mail: mpc@mpce.com
Fax: 020-7624 4220   Tel: 020-7624 1184

MR.MANAGEMENT
29 Belton Road
Brighton, East Sussex BN2 3RE
e-mail: dawespollard@aol.com
Mobile: 07785 341080   Tel/Fax: 01273 232381

MUGSHOTS AGENCY
(Amanda Ashed)
20 Greek Street
London W1D 4DU
Fax: 020-7437 0308   Tel: 020-7437 9245

MURPHY Elaine ASSOCIATES
310 Aberdeen House
22-24 Highbury Grove
London N5 2EA
e-mail: emurphy@freeuk.com
Fax: 020-7704 8039   Tel: 020-7704 9913

MUSIC INTERNATIONAL
M
13 Ardilaun Road, London N5 2QR
e-mail: music@musicint.demon.co.uk
Fax: 020-7226 9792   Tel: 020-7359 5183

MW MANAGEMENT
11 Old School Court
Drapers Road
London N17 6PZ
e-mail: the@gents.co.uk
Tel/Fax: 020-8376 2789   Tel: 020-8376 2025

MYERS MANAGEMENT
63 Fairfields Crescent
London NW9 0PR   Tel/Fax: 020-8204 8941

NARROW ROAD COMPANY*
22 Poland Street
London W1F 8QH
e-mail: agents@narrowroad.co.uk
Fax: 020-7439 1237   Tel: 020-7434 0406

Paul Ritter

Jenny Jules

Joe Renton

Eve Best

Angela Cameron

**regan
rimmer**
management

Leigh-Ann Regan   Debbie Rimmer

36-38 Glasshouse St.
London WIB 5DL

t 020 7287 9005
f 020 7287 9006
e thegirls@regan-rimmer.co.uk
www.regan-rimmer.co.uk

NASH INTERNATIONAL
135 Epping New Road
Buckhurst Hill, Essex IG9 5TZ
e-mail: patnash@btinternet.com
Fax: 020-8559 0974   Tel: 020-8559 1696

NCI MANAGEMENT Ltd
51 Queen Anne Street, London W1G 9HS
Fax: 020-7935 1258   Tel: 020-7224 3960

NCM ASSOCIATES (Nicola Clarkson Associates)
12 Kings Gate, Gosling Way, London SW9 6JX
e-mail: nikki.clarkson1@btopenworld.com
Fax: 020-7793 7053   Tel: 020-7582 7343

NEVS AGENCY
Regal House, 198 Kings Road, London SW3 5XP
Website: www.nevs.co.uk
e-mail: getamodel@nevs.co.uk
Fax: 020-7352 6068   Tel: 020-7352 4886

NEW CASEY AGENCY
The Annexe
129 Northwood Way
Middlesex HA6 1RF   Tel: 01923 823182

NICHOLSON Jackie ASSOCIATES
PM
Suite 30, 1st Floor, Kent House
87 Regent Street, London W1B 4EH
Fax: 020-7434 0445   Tel: 020-7434 0441

N M MANAGEMENT
16 St Alfege Passage, Greenwich, London SE10 9JS
e-mail: nmmanagement@hotmail.com
Tel: 020-8853 4337

NOEL CASTING
(Specialising in Character Actors and Ethnic
and Asian Actors)
Suite 501, International House
223 Regent Street, London W1B 2QD
e-mail: noelcasting@yahoo.com
Fax: 020-7544 1090   Tel: 020-7544 1010

NORTH OF WATFORD ACTORS AGENCY
Co-operative
Bridge Mill, Hebden Bridge, West Yorks HX7 8EX
Website: www.northofwatford.com
e-mail: northofwatford@btconnect.com
Fax: 01422 846503   Tel: 01422 845361

NORTH ONE MANAGEMENT
18 Ashwin Street, London E8 3DL
Website: www.northone.co.uk
e-mail: actors@northone.co.uk
Fax: 020-7249 9989   Tel: 020-7254 9093

NORTHERN DRAMA
PO Box 27, Tadcaster, North Yorks LS24 9XS
e-mail: alyson@connew.com
Tel/Fax: 01977 681949

NORTHERN LIGHTS MANAGEMENT
PM
Dean Clough Mills, Halifax, West Yorks HX3 5AX
e-mail: nlmanagement@aol.com
Fax: 01422 330101   Tel: 01422 382203

NORTHERN PROFESSIONALS
(Casting, Technicians
Action Safety, Boat & Diving Equipment Hire)
21 Cresswell Avenue
North Shields, Tyne & Wear NE29 9BQ
e-mail: bill.gerard@northpro83.freeserve.co.uk
Fax: 0191-296 3243   Tel: 0191-257 8635

NORWELL LAPLEY ASSOCIATES
Lapley Hall, Lapley, Staffs ST19 9JR
Website: www.norwelllapley.co.uk
e-mail: norwelllapley@freeuk.com
Fax: 01785 841992   Tel: 01785 841991

NSM
(Natasha Stevenson Management)
The Nightingale Centre
8 Balham Hill, London SW12 9EA
e-mail: nsm@netcomuk.co.uk
Fax: 020-8772 0111   Tel: 020-8772 0100

NUTOPIA PERSONAL MANAGEMENT
Number 8
132 Charing Cross Road, London WC2H 0LA
Website: www.nutopia.co.uk
                          Tel/Fax: 020-8882 6299

NYLAND MANAGEMENT Ltd
20 School Lane
Heaton Chapel, Stockport SK4 5DG
e-mail: nylandmgmt@freenet.co.uk
Fax: 0161-432 5406   Tel: 0161-442 2224

OFF THE KERB PRODUCTIONS
3rd Floor, Hammer House
113-117 Wardour Street
London W1F 0UN
e-mail: offthekerb@aol.com
Fax: 020-7437 0647   Tel: 020-7437 0607

22 Thornhill Crescent
London N1 1BJ
Website: www.offthekerb.co.uk
e-mail: info@offthekerb.co.uk
Fax: 020-7700 4646   Tel: 020-7700 4477

OPERA & CONCERT ARTISTS
M Opera
75 Aberdare Gardens
London NW6 3AN
Fax: 020-7372 3537   Tel: 020-7328 3097

Paul Blackthorne

Martiné McCutcheon

Peter Hall

PHOTOGRAPHER
Photography in a friendly unhurried atmosphere. Special Student Rates

0 2 0   8 9 8 1   2 8 2 2

email: peter@peterhall.fsnet.co.uk

ORDINARY PEOPLE Ltd
8 Camden Road, London NW1 9DP
Website: www.ordinarypeople.co.uk
e-mail: info@ordinarypeople.co.uk
Fax: 020-7267 5677   Tel: 020-7267 7007

O'REILLY Dee MANAGEMENT Ltd
PM
112 Gunnersbury Avenue
London W5 4HB
Website: www.thedormgroup.com
e-mail: info@dorm.co.uk
Fax: 020-8992 9993   Tel: 020-8993 7441

ORIENTAL CASTING AGENCY Ltd (Peggy Sirr)
Afro/Asian Artists Write or Phone
1 Wyatt Park Road
Streatham Hill, London SW2 3TN
Website: www.orientalcasting.com
e-mail: peggy.sirr@btconnect.com
Fax: 020-8674 9303   Tel: 020-8671 8538

ORION PRODUCTIONS & CASTING AGENCY
DBH House, Boundary Street
Liverpool L5 9YJ   Tel/Fax: 0151-482 5565

OTTO PERSONAL MANAGEMENT Ltd
PM Co-operative
The Printer's Loft
111 Arundel Lane, Sheffield S1 4RF
Website: www.ottopm.freeuk.com
e-mail: ottopm@hotmail.com
Fax: 0114-275 0550   Tel: 0114-275 2592

OUT & OUT ENTERTAINMENTS
(Actors, Entertainers & DJ's)
21-37 Third Avenue
London E13 8AW
e-mail: info@oao.co.uk
Fax: 020-8471 2111   Tel: 020-8471 3111

PAN ARTISTS AGENCY
Ingleby, 1 Hollins Grove, Sale, Cheshire M33 6RE
e-mail: bookings@panartists.freeserve.co.uk
Fax: 0161-973 9724   Tel: 0161-969 7419

PANTO PEOPLE
3 Rushden House
Tatlow Road, Glenfield
Leicester LE3 8ND   Tel/Fax: 0116-287 9594

PARAMOUNT INTERNATIONAL MANAGEMENT
Talbot House
204-226 Imperial Drive, Harrow, Middlesex HA2 7HH
Website: www.ukcomedy.com
e-mail: mail@ukcomedy.com
Fax: 020-8868 6475   Tel: 020-8429 3179

PARK MANAGEMENT Ltd
PM Co-operative
Studio 5A, Disney Place House
14 Marshalsea Road, London SE1 1HL
e-mail: park_management@hotmail.com
Fax: 020-7357 0047   Tel: 020-7357 0024

PARR & BOND
The Tom Thumb Theatre
Eastern Esplanade
Cliftonville, Kent CT9 2LB   Tel: 01843 221791

PAUL Yvonne MANAGEMENT Ltd
10 Tiverton Road, London NW10 3HL
Fax: 020-8960 0410   Tel: 020-8960 0022

P B J MANAGEMENT Ltd*
(Comedy)
7 Soho Street, London W1D 3DQ
Website: www.pbjmgt.co.uk
e-mail: general@pbjmgt.co.uk
Fax: 020-7287 1191   Tel: 020-7287 1112

THEATRICAL PHOTOGRAPHY
ACTOR/ACTRESS PORTRAITS
for all your publicity and spotlight needs

in your own home or in our fully equipped studio

with thanks to:

Richard Burton,

Brigitte Bardot,

Sophia Loren,

Kojak,

Judi Dench,

Derek Jacobi,

John Lennon,

Virginia McKenna,

Don Johnson,

Grace Jones,

Roger Moore,

Bruce Willis,

Demi Moore,

Patrick Swayze,

Sir Richard Branson,

Diana Dors,

David Bellamy.

To photograph advanced and established actors and artists	To photograph young actors, actresses and beginners	To photograph the under 15s
	Special beginners pack	
30 black and white prints 7x5 30 colour prints 7x5 2 high quality 300 DPI * - CD of all of the above	30 black and white prints OR colour photographs your choice 30 prints of the above 7x5 1 high quality 300 DPI * - CD containing all the photographs	30 black and white prints OR colour photographs your choice 30 prints of the above 7x5 1 high quality 300 DPI * - CD containing all the photographs
£120	**£90**	**£60**

*We can also produce one or more high quality hand printed 10x8 prints of any of the above for £15 each suitable for taking to any repro house

Tel/Fax: 020 8438 0202

Messages: 020 8438 0303

Mobile: 07712 669 953

Email: billy_snapper@hotmail.com

www.theukphotographerexhibition.co.uk

www.theukphotographer.com

www.billysnapper.com

photographer to the stars

PC THEATRICAL & MODEL AGENCY
(Large Database of Twins)
10 Strathmore Gardens
Edgware, Middlesex HA8 5HJ
Website: www.twinagency.com
e-mail: twinagy@aol.com
Fax: 020-8933 3418   Tel: 020-8381 2229

PELHAM ASSOCIATES
(Peter Cleall)
Pelham Associates
The Media Centre
9-12 Middle Street, Brighton BN1 1AL
Website: www.pelhamassociates.co.uk
e-mail: petercleall@pelhamassociates.co.uk
Fax: 01273 202492   Tel: 01273 323010

PEMBERTON ASSOCIATES Ltd*
Suite 35-36 Barton Arcade
Deansgate, Manchester M3 2BH
e-mail: general@pembertonassociates.com
Fax: 0161-835 3319   Tel: 0161-832 1661

193 Wardour Street, London W1F 8ZF
Fax: 020-7734 2522   Tel: 020-7734 4144

PEPPERPOT PROMOTIONS
(Bands)
Suite 20B
20-22 Orde Hall Street, London WC1N 3JW
e-mail: chris@pepperpot.co.uk
Fax: 01255 473107   Tel: 020-7405 9108

PERFORMANCE ACTORS AGENCY •
PM Co-operative
137 Goswell Road, London EC1V 7ET
Website: www.p-a-a.co.uk
e-mail: performance@p-a-a.co.uk
Fax: 020-7251 3974   Tel: 020-7251 5716

PERFORMERS DIRECTORY
(Actors, Dancers, Models and Extras)
PO Box 29942, London SW6 1FL
Website: www.performersdirectory.co.uk
e-mail: performersdirectory@yahoo.com
                            Tel: 020-7384 0445

PERFORMING ARTS*
(Directors/Designers/Choreographers/Lighting
Designers)
6 Windmill Street, London W1T 2JB
Website: www.performing-arts.co.uk
e-mail: info@performing-arts.co.uk
Fax: 020-7631 4631   Tel: 020-7255 1362

PERRY George
(See PROFILE MANAGEMENT)

PERSONAL APPEARANCES
20 North Mount
1147-1161 High Road, Whetstone N20 0PH
e-mail: pers.appearances@talk21.com
                       Tel/Fax: 020-8343 7748

PFD*
PM
Drury House, 34-43 Russell Street, London WC2B 5HA
Website: www.pfd.co.uk
e-mail: postmaster@pfd.co.uk
Fax: 020-7836 9544   Tel: 020-7344 1010

PHILLIPS Frances*
Millennium Studios
Elstree Way, Borehamwood, Herts WD6 1SF
e-mail: derekphillips@talk21.com
Fax: 020-8236 1367   Tel: 020-8236 1366

PHPM
(Philippa Howell Personal Management)
184 Bradway Road, Sheffield S17 4QX
e-mail: philippa@phpm.co.uk
                       Tel/Fax: 0114-235 3663

PHYSICALITY Ltd*
(Physical Skills Specialists)
265-267 Ilford Lane, Ilford, Essex IG1 2SD
Website: www.physicality.co.uk
e-mail: info@physicality.co.uk
Fax: 020-8491 2801   Tel: 020-8491 2800

PHYSICK Hilda
PM Write
78 Temple Sheen Road, London SW14 7RR
Fax: 020-8876 5561   Tel: 020-8876 0073

PICCADILLY MANAGEMENT
PM (Personal Manager: Juliet Russell)
23 New Mount Street, Manchester M4 4DE
e-mail: piccadilly.management@virgin.net
Fax: 0161-953 4001   Tel: 0161-953 4057

PICOT Nic ENTERTAINMENT AGENCY
25 Highfield, Carpenders Park WD19 5DY
Website: www.nicpicot.co.uk
e-mail: nic@nicpicot.co.uk
Fax: 020-8421 2700   Tel: 020-8421 2500

PINEAPPLE AGENCY
159-161 Balls Pond Road, London N1 4BG
Fax: 020-7241 3006   Tel: 020-7241 6601

P.L.A.
(LOVETT Pat ASSOCIATES)
39 Sandhurst Court, Acre Lane, London SW2 5TX
e-mail: pla.london@blueyonder.co.uk
Fax: 020-7733 4440   Tel: 020-7733 1110

5 Union Street, Edinburgh EH1 3LT
e-mail: pla.edinburgh@blueyonder.co.uk
Fax: 0131-478 7070   Tel: 0131-478 7878

PLATER Janet MANAGEMENT Ltd
D Floor
Milburn House
Dean Street, Newcastle upon Tyne NE1 1LF
e-mail: magpie@tynebridge.demon.co.uk
Fax: 0191-221 2491   Tel: 0191-221 2490

PLUNKET GREENE Ltd
(In conjunction with James Sharkey Assoc Ltd)
(Existing Clients only)
PO Box 8365, London W14 0GL
Fax: 020-7603 2221   Tel: 020-7603 2227

POLLYANNA MANAGEMENT Ltd
PO Box 30661, London E1W 3GG
Website: www.eada.demon.co.uk/pollyanna
e-mail: pollyanna-mgmt@yahoo.co.uk
Fax: 020-7480 6761   Tel: 020-7702 1937

POOLE Gordon AGENCY Ltd
The Limes, Brockley, Bristol BS48 3BB
Website: www.gordonpoole.com
e-mail: agents@gordonpoole.com
Fax: 01275 462252   Tel: 01275 463222

POWER MODEL MANAGEMENT
CASTING AGENCY
The Royal
25 Bank Plain, Norwich NR2 4SF
Website: www.powermodelmanagement.co.uk
e-mail: powermodelmanagement@btinternet.com
Fax: 01603 621101   Tel: 01603 621100

POWER PROMOTIONS
PO Box 61, Liverpool L13 0EF
Website: www.powerpromotions.co.uk
e-mail: tom@powerpromotions.co.uk
                              Tel/Fax: 0151-230 0070

PPM - Polo Piatti Management
157 Capel Road, London E7 0JT
e-mail: polo@polopiatti.com
                              Tel/Fax: 020-8478 2101

PREGNANT PAUSE AGENCY
(Pregnant Models, Dancers, Actresses)
11 Matham Road, East Molesey KT8 0SX
Website: www.pregnantpause.co.uk
e-mail: sandy@pregnantpause.co.uk
Fax: 020-8783 0337   Tel: 020-8979 8874

PRICE GARDNER MANAGEMENT
85 Shorrolds Road, London SW6 7TU
Website: www.pricegardner.com
e-mail: info@pricegardner.com
Fax: 020-7381 3288   Tel: 020-7610 2111

PRICHARD Peter AT INTERNATIONAL ARTISTES Ltd
Mezzanine Floor, 235 Regent Street, London W1B 2AX
e-mail: maria@intart.co.uk
Fax: 020-7409 2070   Tel: 020-7352 6417

PRINCIPAL ARTISTES
PM Write
4 Paddington Street, Marylebone, London W1U 5QE
Fax: 020-7486 4668   Tel: 020-7224 3414

PROFILE MANAGEMENT
(George Perry)
2nd Floor, 213 Chalk Farm Road, London NW1 8AB
e-mail: georgeperryprofile@hotmail.com
Fax: 020-7482 1447   Tel: 020-7485 0441

PROTOCOL
2/7 Harbour Yard
Chelsea Harbour, London SW10 0XD
e-mail: stars@protocoltalent.com
Fax: 020-7349 1533   Tel: 020-7349 8877

PVA MANAGEMENT Ltd
Hallow Park, Worcester WR2 6PG
e-mail: clients@pva.co.uk
Fax: 01905 641842   Tel: 01905 640663

QDOS Ltd
8 King Street, Covent Garden, London WC2E 8HN
e-mail: info@qdosentertainment.plc.uk
Fax: 020-7240 4956   Tel: 020-7240 5052

QUADRAPHOLD MANAGEMENT
(Andy Ball)
Queens Chambers
Queen Street, Blackpool, Lancashire FY1 1PD
Website: www.quadraphold.com
e-mail: info@quadraphold.com
Fax: 01253 290019   Tel: 01253 311112

QUICK Nina ASSOCIATES
(See TAYLOR Brian - QUICK Nina ASSOCIATES)

RAGE MODELS
(Young Adults Fashion)
Tigris House
256 Edgware Road, London W2 1DS
Website: www.ugly.org
e-mail: info@ugly.org
Fax: 020-7402 0507   Tel: 020-7262 0515

RAINBOW REPRESENTATION
45 Nightingale Lane, Crouch End, London N8 7RA
e-mail: rainbowrp@onetel.net.uk
Tel/Fax: 020-8341 6241

RAPPORT PROMOTIONS Ltd
(Promotional Staff)
11A Hannell Road, Fulham, London SW6 7RA
e-mail: info@rapportpromotions.co.uk
Fax: 020-7386 8522   Tel: 020-7386 7555

RATTLEBAG ACTORS AGENCY Ltd •
PM
Everyman Theatre Annexe
13-15 Hope Street, Liverpool L1 9BH
e-mail: actors@rattlebag.co.uk
Fax: 0151-709 0773   Tel: 0151-708 7273

RAVENSCOURT MANAGEMENT
Tandy House, 30-40 Dalling Road, London W6 0JB
e-mail: ravenscourt@hotmail.com
Fax: 020-8741 1786   Tel: 020-8741 0707

RAY'S NORTHERN CASTING AGENCY
7 Wince Close, Alkrington
Middleton
Manchester M24 1UJ   Tel/Fax: 0161-643 6745

RAZZAMATAZZ MANAGEMENT
Crofters, East Park Lane
New Chapel, Surrey RH7 6HS
e-mail: mcgrogan@tinyworld.co.uk
Fax: 01342 835433   Tel: 01342 835359

RBM
PM (Comedy)
3rd Floor, 18 Broadwick Street, London W1V 1FG
Website: www.rbmcomedy.com
e-mail: info@rbmcomedy.com
Fax: 020-7287 5020   Tel: 020-7287 5010

RDF MANAGEMENT
48 Princes Place, Holland Park, London W11 4QA
e-mail: debi.allen@rdfmanagement.com
Fax: 020-7908 1363   Tel: 020-7908 1238

REACTORS AGENCY
1 Eden Quay, Dublin 1
e-mail: reactors@eircom.net
Fax: 00 353 1 8783182   Tel: 00 353 1 8786833

RE.ANIMATOR MANAGEMENT
(Representation for Dancers)
Wimbledon Theatre
The Broadway, London SW19 1QG
e mail: management@reanimator.co.uk
Fax: 020-8542 8081   Tel: 020-8542 9763

REDDIN Joan
PM Write
Hazel Cottage, Frogg's Island
Wheeler End Common
Bucks HP14 3NL   Tel: 01494 882729

REDROOFS ASSOCIATES
Pinewood Studios, Iver, Bucks SL0 0NH
Fax: 01753 785443   Tel: 01753 785444

REDWAY John ASSOCIATES
(in association with A.I.M.)
Nederlander House
/ Great Russell Street, London WC1B 3NH
Website: www.a-i-m.net
e-mail: info@aim.demon.co.uk
Fax: 020-7637 8666   Tel: 020-7637 1700

REGAN RIMMER MANAGEMENT
(Leigh-Ann Regan, Debbie Rimmer)
36-38 Glasshouse Street, London W1B 5DL
e-mail: thegirls@regan-rimmer.co.uk
Fax: 020-7287 9006   Tel: 020-7287 9005

matt damon

hannah bourne

Mark Theodor

Aldo Williams

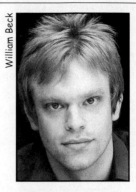

William Beck

Ricky Groves

Rebecca Jane

Jeremy Rendell Photography
Mobile: +44(0)7860 277 411
www.jeremyrendell.com
www.contact-me.net-jeremyrendell
email: jeremy@rendell-photo.demon.co.uk

REGARDEZ MODEL MANAGEMENT
Wessex House
Upper Market Street, Eastleigh, Hampshire SO50 9FD
Website: www.regardez.co.uk
e-mail: regardezltd@aol.com
Fax: 023-8065 1856   Tel: 023-8065 1855

REGENCY AGENCY
F TV
25 Carr Road, Calverley
Leeds LS28 5NE   Tel: 0113-255 8980

REPRESENTATION JOYCE EDWARDS
(See EDWARDS REPRESENTATION Joyce)

REYNOLDS Sandra MODEL & CASTING AGENTS
Md F TV
50 Fitzroy Street, London W1T 5BT
Website: www.sandrareynolds.co.uk
e-mail: tessa@sandrareynolds.co.uk
Fax: 020-7387 5848   Tel: 020-7387 5858

35 St Georges Street, Norwich NR3 1DA
Fax: 01603 219825   Tel: 01603 623842

RHINO MANAGEMENT
Oak Porch House, 5 Western Road
Nazeing, Essex EN9 2QN
Website: www.rhino-management.co.uk
e-mail: rhinomanagement@btinternet.com
Mobile: 07901 528988   Tel/Fax: 01992 893259

RICHARDS Lisa
46 Upper Baggot Street
Dublin 4
e-mail: info@lisarichards.ie
Fax: 00 353 1 6603545   Tel: 00 353 1 6603534

RICHARDS Stella MANAGEMENT
(Existing Clients only)
42 Hazlebury Road, London SW6 2ND
Fax: 020-7731 5082   Tel: 020-7736 7786

RIDGEWAY MANAGEMENT
Fairley House
Andrews Lane, Cheshunt, Herts EN7 6LB
e-mail: info@ridgewaystudios.co.uk
Fax: 01992 633844   Tel: 01992 633775

RK COMMERCIALS
G Md
205 Chudleigh Road, London SE4 1EG
Website: www.rkcommercials.com
e-mail: mail@rkcommercials.com
Fax: 020-8690 7999   Tel: 020-8690 6542

RKM
(See KRUGER Rolf MANAGEMENT Ltd)

ROBSON NEWMAN MANAGEMENT
14 Ritz Buildings, Church Road
Tunbridge Wells, Kent TN1 1HP
Website: www.newmangroup.co.uk
Fax: 01892 514173   Tel: 01892 524122

ROGUES & VAGABONDS MANAGEMENT Ltd
PM Co-operative
The Print House
18 Ashwin Street, London E8 3DL
e-mail: rogues.vagabonds@virgin.net
Fax: 020-7249 8564   Tel: 020-7254 8130

ROGUE UK Ltd
196 Broadhurst Gardens
West Hampstead, London NW6 3AY
Website: www.rogueukltd.biz
e-mail: info@rogueukltd.biz   Mobile: 07909 695492

ROLE MODELS
12 Cressy Road
London NW3 2LY
Fax: 020-7267 1030   Tel: 020-7284 4337

ROSEBERY MANAGEMENT Ltd•
PM
Diorama Arts Centre
34 Osnaburgh Street, London NW1 3ND
e-mail: roseberymgt@aol.com
Fax: 020-7692 3065   Tel: 020-7813 1026

ROSEMAN ORGANISATION The
11 Grove Park Gardens, Chiswick, London W4 3RY
Website: www.therosemanorganisation.co.uk
e-mail: info@therosemanorganisation.co.uk
Fax: 020-8742 0554   Tel: 020-8742 0552

ROSS BROWN ASSOCIATES
PM
Rosedale House
Rosedale Road, Richmond, Surrey TW9 2SZ
e-mail: rossbrownassoc@freeuk.com
Fax: 020-8398 3925   Tel: 020-8398 3984

ROSSMORE PERSONAL MANAGEMENT
Rossmore Road, Marylebone, London NW1 6NJ
e-mail: agents@rossmoremanagement.com
Fax: 020-7258 0124   Tel: 020-7258 1953

ROYCE MANAGEMENT
34A Sinclair Road, London W14 0NH
Fax: 020-7371 4985   Tel: 020-7602 4992

RUBICON MANAGEMENT
27 Inderwick Road, Crouch End
London N8 9LB   Tel/Fax: 020-8374 1836

RUBY TALENT*
Apartment 9, Goldcrest Building
1 Lexington Street, London W1F 9TA
e-mail: tara@ruby-talent.co.uk
Fax: 020-7439 1649   Tel: 020-7439 4554

RWM MANAGEMENT
The Aberdeen Centre
22-24 Highbury Grove, London N5 2EA
e-mail: rwm.mario-kate@virgin.net
Fax: 020-7226 3371   Tel: 020-7226 3311

SANDERS Loesje*
(Designers, Directors,
Choreographers, Lighting Designers)
Pound Square, 1 North Hill, Woodbridge, Suffolk IP12 1HH
Website: www.loesjesanders.com
e-mail: loesjev@aol.com
Fax: 01394 388734   Tel: 01394 385260

SARABAND ASSOCIATES
(Sara Randall, Bryn Newton)
265 Liverpool Road, London N1 1LX
Fax: 020-7609 2370   Tel: 020-7609 5313

SAYERS Nicola MANAGEMENT Ltd
2C Admirals Walk, Hoddesdon, Herts EN11 8AA
e-mail: nicki@nsmanagement.fsnet.co.uk
Mobile: 07870 644089   Tel: 01992 442223

SBS Ltd (The Casting Information Service)
Suite 1, 16 Sidmouth Road, London NW2 5JX
e-mail: casting@sbsltd.demon.co.uk
Fax: 020-8459 7442   Tel: 020-8459 2781

SCA MANAGEMENT
TV F S M Write or Phone
23 Goswell Road, London EC1M 7AJ
e-mail: sca@italiaconti36.freeserve.co.uk
Fax: 020-7253 1430   Tel: 020-7608 7500

SCHER Anna THEATRE The
PM
AST Management
70-72 Barnsbury Road, London N1 0ES
e-mail: abby@astm.co.uk
Fax: 020-7833 9467   Tel: 020-7278 2101

SCHNABL Peter
The Barn House, Cutwell
Tetbury, Gloucestershire, GL8 8EB
Fax: 01666 502998   Tel: 01666 502133

SCOT-BAKER AGENCY
35 Caithness Road, Brook Green, London W14 0JA
e-mail: info@scot-baker.com
Fax: 020-7603 7698 Tel: 020-7603 9988

SCOTT-PAUL YOUNG ENTERTAINMENTS Ltd
S.P.Y. Promotions & Productions
Northern Lights House, 110 Blandford Road
North Langley, Nr Windsor, Berks SL3 7TA
e-mail: sp.young@blueyonder.co.uk
Fax: 01753 810961 Tel: 01753 693250

SCOTT Tim
284 Grays Inn Road, London WC1X 8EB
e-mail: timscott@btinternet.com
Fax: 020-7278 9175 Tel: 020-7833 5733

SCREENLITE AGENCY
Shepperton Film Studios
Shepperton
Middlesex TW17 0QD
e-mail: screenlite@dial.pipex.com
Fax: 01932 572507 Tel: 01932 562611 Ext 2271

SCRIMGEOUR Donald ARTISTS AGENCY
(Dance)
49 Springcroft Avenue, London N2 9JH
e-mail: vwest@dircon.co.uk
Fax: 020-8883 9751 Tel: 020-8444 6248

SECOND SKIN AGENCY
50 Elmwood Road, Chiswick, London W4 3DZ
e-mail: jenny@secondskinagency.com
Tel/Fax: 020-8994 9864

SEDGWICK Dawn (MANAGEMENT)
3 Goodwins Court
Covent Garden, London WC2N 4LL
Fax: 020-7240 0415 Tel: 020-7240 0404

SEQUINS THEATRICAL AGENCY
Winsome, 8 Summerhill Grove
Bush Hill Park
Enfield EN1 2HY Tel: 020-8360 4015

SHALIT GLOBAL MANAGEMENT
Cambridge Theatre, Seven Dials
Covent Garden, London WC2H 9HU
e-mail: info@shalit.co.uk
Fax: 020-7379 3238 Tel: 020-7379 3282

SHAPER Susan MANAGEMENT
Queens House, 1 Leicester Place, London WC2H 7BP
e-mail: shapermg@dircon.co.uk
Fax: 020-7534 3317 Tel: 020-7534 3316

SHAW Vincent ASSOCIATES Ltd
51 Byron Road, London E17 4SN
Website: www.vincentshaw.com
e-mail: info@vincentshaw.com
Fax: 020-8521 1588 Tel: 020-8509 2211

SHEDDEN Malcolm MANAGEMENT
1 Charlotte Street, London W1T 1RD
Fax: 020-7636 1657 Tel: 020-7636 1876

SHEPHERD MANAGEMENT Ltd
13 Radnor Walk, London SW3 4BP
e-mail: info@shepherdmanagement.co.uk
Fax: 020-7352 2277 Tel: 020-7352 2200

SHEPHERD Elizabeth AGENCY
29 Eversley Crescent, London N21 1EL
e-mail: elizabeth.esa@bigfoot.com
Fax: 020-8364 1624 Tel: 020-8364 0598

SHOWBUSINESS ENTERTAINMENT & TELEVISION CASTING AGENCY
The Bungalow, Chatsworth Avenue
Long Eaton, Nottingham NG10 2FL
Fax: 0115-946 1831 Tel: 0115-973 5445

SHOWSTOPPERS!
(Entertainments & Management)
42 Foxglove Close, Witham, Essex CM8 2XW
Website: www.showstoppers-group.com
e-mail: mail@showstoppers-group.com
Fax: 01376 510340   Tel: 01376 518486

SILVER FOX ARTIST MANAGEMENT*
8-18 Rampart Street, London E1 2LA
Website: www.silverfoxartist.co.uk
e-mail: enquiries@silverfoxartist.co.uk
Fax: 020-7791 2842   Tel: 020-7791 2952

SILVESTER MANAGEMENT
24 Lake View, Edgware HA8 7RU
e-mail: silvestermgmt@freeuk.com
Fax: 020-8958 7711   Tel: 020-8958 5555

SIMONES INTERNATIONALE
(Model & Artistes Management & Agency)
PO Box 15154
London W5 3FW   Tel/Fax: 020-8861 3900

SIMPSON FOX ASSOCIATES Ltd*
(Directors, Designers, Choreographers)
52 Shaftesbury Avenue, London W1D 6LP
e-mail: cary@simpson-fox.demon.co.uk
Fax: 020-7494 2887   Tel: 020-7434 9167

SINGER Sandra ASSOCIATES
21 Cotswold Road, Westcliff-on-Sea, Essex SS0 8AA
Website: www.sandrasinger.com
e-mail: sandrasingeruk@aol.com
Fax: 01702 339393   Tel: 01702 331616

SIRR PEGGY
(See ORIENTAL CASTING AGENCY Ltd)

SJ MANAGEMENT
15 Maiden Lane, London WC2E 7NA
e-mail: sj@susanjames.demon.co.uk
Fax: 020-7836 5724   Tel: 020-7836 5723

SO DAM TUFF Ltd
The Coach House, 136 Westbridge Road
Battersea Square, London SW11 3PF
Website: www.sodamtuff.com
e-mail: tiger@sodamtuff.com
Fax: 020-7223 7387   Tel: 020-7223 7377

SOLOMON ARTISTES
MANAGEMENT INTERNATIONAL
30 Clarence Street
Southend-on-Sea, Essex SS1 1BD
Website: www.solomon-artistes.co.uk
e-mail: info@solomon-artistes.co.uk
Fax: 01702 392385   Tel: 01702 392370

SOMETHIN' ELSE
(Grant Michaels)
Units 1-4, 1A Old Nichol Street, London E2 7HR
e-mail: grant.michaels@somethin-else.com
Fax: 020-7739 9799   Tel: 020-7204 1969

SOPHIE'S PEOPLE
(Dancers and Choreographers)
26 Reporton Road, London SW6 7RJR
Website: www.sophiespeople.com
e-mail: sophies.people@btinternet.com
Fax: 0870 7876447   Tel: 0870 7876446

SOUTH WEST MANAGEMENT & CASTING CO Ltd
The Courtyard, Whitchurch, Ross-on-Wye HR9 6DA
Website: www.southwestcasting.co.uk
e-mail: agent@southwestcastingco.uk
Fax: 01600 891099   Tel: 01600 892005

SPARE PARTS
(Body Parts Specialists)
153 Battersea Rise, London SW11 1HP
Fax: 020-7924 2334   Tel: 020-7924 2484

Caroline Summers

Session includes make up artist

020-7223 7669

Short notice possible

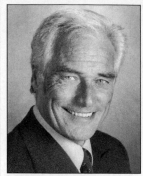

SPEAK Ltd
140 Devonshire Road, Chiswick, London W4 2AW
Website: www.speak-voices.com
e-mail: speak@dircon.co.uk
Fax: 020-8742 1333   Tel: 020-8742 1001

SPEAKERS CORNER
(Speakers, Presenters, Facilitation
and Cabaret for the Corporate Market)
Tigana House, Catlins Lane
Pinner, Middlesex HA5 2AG
Website: www.speakerscorner-uk.com
e-mail: info@speakerscorner-uk.com
Fax: 020-8868 4409   Tel: 020-8866 8967

SPETCH AND MUSKETT
20 Cherry Hills
Carpenters Meadow, Watford, Herts WD19 6DH
Website: www.spetchandmuskett.co.uk
e-mail: info@spetchandmuskett.co.uk
Mobile: 07736 539417   Tel/Fax: 020-8428 8304

**SPHINX MANAGEMENT
& ENTERTAINMENT AGENCY**
Unity House, 2 Unity Place
Westgate, Rotherham, South Yorks S60 1AR
Fax: 01709 369990   Tel: 01709 820379

SPIRE CASTING
PO Box 372
Chesterfield S41 0XW
e-mail: spirecasting@aol.com   Tel: 01246 224798

SPLITTING IMAGES LOOKALIKE AGENCY
29 Mortimer Court, Abbey Road, London NW8 9AB
Website: www.splitting-images.com
e-mail: info@splitting-images.com
Fax: 020-8809 6103   Tel: 020-7286 8300

SPORTS WORKSHOP PROMOTIONS Ltd
(Sports Models)
PO Box 878, Crystal Palace
National Sports Centre, London SE19 2BH
e-mail: info@sportspromotions.co.uk
Fax: 020-8776 7772   Tel: 020-8659 4561

SPORTABILITY Ltd
(Sporting Personalities)
Unit 2, 23 Green Lane, Dronfield, Derbyshire S18 2LL
Fax: 01246 290520   Tel: 01246 292010

SPYKER Paul MANAGEMENT
7 Garrick Street
Covent Garden, London WC2E 9AR
e-mail: info@pspy.com
Fax: 020-7379 8282   Tel: 020-7379 8181

STACEY Barrie PROMOTIONS
Apartment 8
132 Charing Cross Road, London WC2H 0LA
Fax: 020-7836 2949   Tel: 020-7836 4128

STAFFORD Helen MANAGEMENT
14 Park Avenue
Bush Hill Park, Enfield, Middlesex EN1 2HP
e-mail: helen.stafford@blueyonder.co.uk
Fax: 020-8482 0371   Tel: 020-8360 6329

STAGE CENTRE MANAGEMENT Ltd
PM Co-operative
41 North Road, London N7 9DP
e-mail: stagecentre@aol.com
Fax: 020-7609 0213   Tel: 020-7607 0872

STARLINGS THEATRICAL AGENCY
45 Viola Close
South Ockendon, Essex RM15 6JF
Website: www.webspawner.com/users/starlings
e-mail: julieecarter@aol.com
Mobile: 07941 653463   Tel: 01708 859109

STEVENSON Natasha MANAGEMENT
(See NSM)

STIVEN CHRISTIE MANAGEMENT
(Incorporating The Actors Agency of Edinburgh)
1 Glen Street, Tollcross, Edinburgh EH3 9JD
Fax: 0131-228 4645   Tel: 0131-228 4040

ST. JAMES'S MANAGEMENT
PM Write SAE
19 Lodge Close,
Stoke D'Abernon, Cobham, Surrey KT11 2SG
Fax: 01932 860444   Tel: 01932 860666

STONE Annette ASSOCIATES*
(See ALTARAS Jonathan ASSOCIATES Ltd/JAA)

STONE Ian ASSOCIATES
4 Masons Avenue, Croydon, Surrey CR0 9XS
Fax: 020-8680 9912   Tel: 020-8667 1627

STONE Richard PARTNERSHIP The*
PM
2 Henrietta Street, London WC2E 8PS
e-mail: all@richstonepart.co.uk
Fax: 020-7497 0869   Tel: 020-7497 0849

STORM ARTISTS MANAGEMENT
4th Floor
6-10 Lexington Street, London W1F 0LB
Website: www.stormartists.com
e-mail: info@stormartists.co.uk
Fax: 020-7437 4314   Tel: 020-7437 4313

STORM FORCE COMMUNICATIONS Ltd
(Ian Richardson)
Dudswell Lane, Berkhamsted, Herts HP4 3TQ
e-mail: ian.storm@btinternet.com
Fax: 01442 879954   Tel: 01442 879082

STRALLEN MANAGEMENT
Flat 4, 145 West End Lane, London NW6 2PH
e-mail: sandy@showpeopleuk.com
Fax: 020-7372 7435   Tel: 020-7372 6964

STREETJAM
(Dancers, Choreographers
Singers, Stylists, Make-up Artists)
The Media House
13 Juno Way, London SE14 5RW
Website: www.streetjamagency.com
e-mail: stjamltd@aol.com
Fax: 020-8671 4330   Tel: 020-8671 4618

STUNTMAN AND SHOWMANS PROMOTIONS Ltd
BSA House
249 Barking Road, East Ham
London E6 1LB   Tel: 020-8472 8301

SUCCESS
Suite 73-74
Kent House, 87 Regent Street, London W1B 4EH
Website: www.successagency.co.uk
e-mail: ee@successagency.co.uk
Fax: 020-7494 3787   Tel: 020-7734 3356

SUCCESSFUL CHOICE
13 Cambridge Drive, Lee Green
London SE12 8AG   Tel: 020-8852 4955

SUMMERS Mark MANAGEMENT
14 Russell Garden Mews, London W14 8EU
Website: www.marksummers.com
e-mail: mark@marksummers.com
Fax: 0870 4435621   Tel: 0870 4435623

SUMMERTON Michael MANAGEMENT Ltd
PM M C
Mimosa House, Mimosa Street, London SW6 4DS
Fax: 020-7731 0103   Tel: 020-7731 6969

T.A. MANAGEMENT
18 Kingsdale Gardens, Notting Hill, London W11 4TZ
e-mail: tamanagement@hotmail.com
          Tel/Fax: 020-7603 3471

TALENT ARTISTS Ltd*
59 Sydner Road, London N16 7UF
Fax: 020-7923 2009   Tel: 020-7923 1119

TALENT PARTNERSHIP Ltd The*
Riverside Studios, Crisp Road
Hammersmith, London W6 9RL
e-mail: info@thetalentpartnership.co.uk
Fax: 020-8237 1041   Fax: 020-8237 1040

TALKBACK MANAGEMENT*
20-21 Newman Street, London W1T 1PG
Fax: 020-7861 8061   Tel: 020-7861 8060

TAM MANAGEMENT
192 Derby Lane, Stoneycroft, Liverpool L13 6QQ
Mobile: 07870 807723   Tel/Fax: 0151-259 6017

Kim Medcalf

Gerald Kyd

TAYLOR Brian - QUICK Nina ASSOCIATES*
50 Pembroke Road, Kensington, London W8 6NX
e-mail: briantaylor@nqassoc.freeserve.co.uk
Fax: 020-7602 6301   Tel: 020-7602 6141

TCG ARTIST MANAGEMENT
(Rachel Cranmer-Gordon, Kristin Tarry)
Garden Studios
11-15 Betterton Street, London WC2H 9BP
Website: www.tcgam.co.uk
e-mail: kristin@tcgam.co.uk
Fax: 020-7470 8857   Tel: 020-7470 8856

TELFORD Paul MANAGEMENT
PM
23 Noel Street, London W1F 8GT
e-mail: paul@telford-mgt.com
Fax: 020-7434 1200   Tel: 020-7434 1100

TERRY Sue MANAGEMENT
18 Broadwick Street, London W1V 8HS
Fax: 020-7434 2042   Tel: 020-7287 8040

THEATRE EXPRESS PERFORMING ARTS AGENCY
PO Box 97
Cleveleys FY5 5XA   Tel/Fax: 01253 868757

THOMAS & BENDA ASSOCIATES Ltd
Top Floor, 15-16 Ivor Place
London NW1 6HS   Tel/Fax: 020-7723 5509

THOMPSON Jim
Herricks, School Lane
Arundel, West Sussex BN18 9DR
e-mail: jim@thompson42.freeserve.co.uk
Fax: 01903 885887   Tel: 01903 885757

THOMPSON Peggy OFFICE The
PM
1st and 2nd Floor Offices, 296 Sandycombe Road,
Kew, Richmond, Surrey TW9 3NG
Fax: 020-8332 1127   Tel: 020-8332 1003

THORNTON AGENCY
(Specialist Agency for Small People)
72 Purley Downs Road, Croydon CR2 0RB
Website: www.dwarfs4hire.com
e-mail: thorntons.leslie@tinyworld.co.uk
Fax: 020-7385 6647   Tel: 020-8660 5588

THRESH Melody MANAGEMENT ASSOCIATES Ltd (MTM)
MTM House, 29 Ardwick Green North
Ardwick, Manchester M12 6DL
Website: www.melody-thresh-management.co.uk
e-mail: melody.thresh@melody-thresh-management.co.uk
Fax: 0161-273 5455   Tel: 0161-273 5445

THURSTONS PERSONAL MANAGEMENT
4 Park Gate, Mount Avenue, London W5 1PX
e-mail: jtashton@yahoo.com
Fax: 020-8930 8162   Tel: 020-8248 6574

TINKER Victoria MANAGEMENT
(Technical, Non-Acting)
Birchenbridge House, Brighton Road
Mannings Heath, Horsham
West Sussex RH13 6HY   Tel/Fax: 01403 210653

TINSELTOWN ARTS AGENCY
44-46 St John Street, London EC1M 4DF
e-mail: info@tinseltown.online.co.uk
Tel: 020-7689 7860

TONER CASTING Ltd
Unit E6 Brunswick Business Centre
Brunswick Dock, Brunswick Way, Liverpool L3 4BD
Website: www.tonercasting.com
e-mail: tonercasting@toner.fsnet.co.uk
Tel: 0151-708 6400

TOP CATS PROMOTIONS & MODELS
Llantrisant Road, Capel Llanilltern, Cardiff CF5 6JR
Website: www.topcatsmodels.co.uk
e-mail: topcatspromotions@btinternet.com
Tel: 029-2089 0800

TOP MODELS Ltd
57 Holland Park, London W11 3RS
Fax: 020-7243 6046   Tel: 020-7243 6042

TOTS-TWENTIES
Suite 3, Ground Floor, Clements Court
Clements Lane, Ilford, Essex IG1 2QY
Website: www.tots-twenties.co.uk
e-mail: sara@tots-twenties.co.uk
Fax: 020-8553 1880   Tel: 020-8478 1848

TRAIN HOUSE The
27 Prospect Road, Long Ditton, Surrey KT6 5PY
e-mail: agents@trainhouse.demon.co.uk
Fax: 020-8873 2782   Tel: 020-8873 7932

TRENDS AGENCY & MANAGEMENT
54 Lisson Street, London NW1 5DF
e-mail: info@trendsgroup.co.uk
Fax: 020-7258 3591   Tel: 020-7723 8001

TROLAN Gary MANAGEMENT
PM Write
30 Burrard Road, London NW6 1DB
e-mail: garytrolanmgmt@aol.com
Tel/Fax: 020-7794 4429   Tel: 020-7431 4367

TROUPERS.COM
Unit 62, Maltings Yard, Walton Road
Wavendon, Milton Keynes MK17 8LW
Website: www.troupers.com
e-mail: info@troupers.com
Fax: 01908 586979   Tel: 01908 282925

TUCKER Tommy AGENCY
Suite 66
235 Earls Court Road, London SW5 9FE
e-mail: tttommytucker@aol.com
Fax: 020-7370 4784   Tel: 020-7370 3911

TV MANAGEMENTS
Brink House
Avon Castle, Ringwood, Hants BH24 2BL
Fax: 01425 480123   Tel: 01425 475544

TWINS
(See PC THEATRICAL & MODEL AGENCY)

TWINS & TRIPLETS
(Identical Babies, Children
Teenagers & Adults for Film/Television)
Holmhurst Road, Upper Belvedere DA17 6HW
Website: www.twins.triplets.freeuk.com
e-mail: twinsontv@aol.com
Fax: 01322 447250   Tel: 01322 440184

TWIST & FLIC SPORTS AGENCY
1A Calton Avenue
Dulwich Village
London SE21 7ED
Website: www.sportsmodels.com
e-mail: info@sportsmodels.com
Fax: 020-8299 8600   Tel: 020-8299 8800

TWO'S COMPANY
244 Upland Road
London SE22 0DN
e-mail: 2scompany@britishlibrary.net
Fax: 020-8299 3714   Tel: 020-8299 4593

UGLY MODELS
Tigris House
256 Edgware Road
London W2 1DS
Website: www.ugly.org
e-mail: info@ugly.org
Fax: 020-7402 0507   Tel: 020-7402 5564

UNIQUE MANAGEMENT GROUP
Beaumont House
Kensington Village
Avonmore Road
London W14 8TS
e-mail: celebrities@uniquegroup.co.uk
Fax: 020-7605 1101   Tel: 020-7605 1100

UNITED COLOURS OF LONDON Ltd
4th Floor (FBI)
20-24 Kirby Street
London EC1N 8TS
Fax: 020-7242 8125   Tel: 020-7242 5542

UNITED PRODUCTIONS
(Stylists, Dancers, Choreographers)
Southbank House
Black Prince Road
London SE1 7SJ
Website: www.united-productions.co.uk
                              Tel/Fax: 020-7793 4112

UPBEAT MANAGEMENT
(Theatre Touring & Events - No Actors)
PO Box 63
Wallington
Surrey SM6 9YP
Website: www.upbeat.co.uk
e-mail: info@upbeat.co.uk
Fax: 020-8669 6752   Tel: 020-8773 1223

URBAN-BABE CHOREOGRAPHERS AGENCY
(Choreographic Specialists for
Commercials, Film & Music Industry)
4 Glyn Road
London E5 0JD
Website: www.urban-babe.com
e-mail: admin.babe@virgin.net
                              Tel/Fax: 020-7682 0865

URBAN TALENT
54 Princess Street
Manchester M1 6HS
Fax: 0161-236 7557   Tel: 0161-228 6444

VACCA Roxane MANAGEMENT*
73 Beak Street
London W1R 9SR
Fax: 020 7734 8086   Tel: 020-7734 8085

VALLÉ ACADEMY THEATRICAL AGENCY The
The Rosedale Old Cestrians Club
Andrews Lane
Cheshunt
Herts EN7 6TB
Website: www.valleacademy.co.uk
e-mail: agency@valleacademy.co.uk
Fax: 01992 622868   Tel: 01992 622861

DENIKA FAIRMAN

DAVID BECKFORD

ABACUS PHOTOGRAPHY
creative portfolios
M4 corridor - studio or location
www.abacus-photography.co.uk

01793 537257

VIDAL-HALL Clare*
(Directors, Designers
Choreographers, Lighting Designers, Composers)
28 Perrers Road
London W6 0EZ
e-mail: clarevidalhall@email.com
Fax: 020-8741 9459   Tel: 020-8741 7647

VINE Michael ASSOCIATES
(Light Entertainment)
29 Mount View Road
London N4 4SS
e-mail: mpvine@aol.com
Fax: 020-8348 3277   Tel: 020-8348 5899

W6 AGENCY The
Riverside Studios
Crisp Road, Hammersmith
London W6 9RL
e-mail: info@thew6agency.co.uk
Fax: 020-8237 1041   Tel: 020-8237 1046

WADE Thelma PERSONAL MANAGEMENT*
54 Harley Street
London W1G 5PZ
e-mail: tandtwade@hotmail.com
Fax: 020-7580 2337   Tel: 020-7580 9860

WALMSLEY Peter ASSOCIATES
(Agent's Locum/Assistant. No Representation)
37A Crimsworth Road
London SW8 4RJ
e-mail: pwalmsley1@supanet.com
Mobile: 07778 347312   Tel: 020-7787 6419

WARING & McKENNA*
22 Grafton Street
London W1S 4EX
e-mail: dj@waringandmckenna.demon.co.uk
Fax: 020-7409 7932   Tel: 020-7491 2666

WEEKS Kimberley MANAGEMENT
116 Earlham Grove
Forest Gate
London E7 9AS   Tel: 020-8519 4473

WELCH Janet PERSONAL MANAGEMENT
11 Sunbury Court Island
Lower Hampton Road
Sunbury-on-Thames
Middlesex TW16 5PP
Fax: 01932 766191   Tel: 01932 766190

WEST CENTRAL MANAGEMENT
Co-operative
Room 4, East Block
38 Mount Pleasant
London WC1X 0AP
Website: www.westcentralmanagement.co.uk
e-mail: mail@westcentralmanagement.co.uk
          Tel/Fax: 020-7833 8134

WEST END MANAGEMENT
Dalziel House
Garden Flat
7 Claremont Terrace
Glasgow G3 7XR
e-mail: info@westendmanagement.fsbusiness.co.uk
Fax: 0141-353 6385   Tel: 0141-331 2519

WHATEVER ARTISTS MANAGEMENT Ltd
1 York Street
London W1U 6PA
Website: www.wamshow.biz
e-mail: wam@agents-uk.com
Fax: 020-7487 3311   Tel: 020-7487 3111

WILD THEATRICAL MANAGEMENT
PO Box 222
 Rainham
Essex RM13 7WQ
e-mail: wildtm@lineone.net   Tel: 01708 505543

WILDE Vivien Ltd*
193 Wardour Street
London W1F 8ZF
e-mail: vivien.wilde@virgin.net
Fax: 020-7439 1941   Tel: 020-7439 1940

WILKINSON David ASSOCIATES*
115 Hazlebury Road
London SW6 2LX
Fax: 020-7371 5161   Tel: 020-7371 5188

WILLOW PERSONAL MANAGEMENT
(Specialist Agency for Short Actors)
151 Main Street
Yaxley
Peterborough
Cambs PE7 3LD
e-mail: info@willowmanagement.co.uk
          Tel/Fax: 01733 240392

WILLS Newton MANAGEMENT
The Studio
 29 Springvale Avenue
Brentford, Middlesex TW8 9QT
e-mail: newtonwills@aol.com
Fax: 00 33 241 823108   Mobile: 07989 398381

WINSLETT Dave ASSOCIATES
6 Kenwood Ridge
Kenley
Surrey CR8 5JW
Website: www.davewinslett.com
e-mail: info@davewinslett.com
Fax: 020-8668 9216   Tel: 020-8668 0531

WIZARD MANAGEMENT
5 Clare Lawn
London SW14 8BH
e-mail: attwiz@aol.com
Fax: 020-8878 3821   Tel: 020-8876 0406

WYMAN Edward AGENCY
F TV (English & Welsh Language)
67 Llanon Road
Llanishen, Cardiff CF14 5AH
e-mail: edwardwymanagency@ukonline.co.uk
Fax: 029-2075 2444   Tel: 029-2075 2351

WYPER Carolynne MANAGEMENT
2 Kimberley Road
London NW6 7SG
e-mail: info@soundtrackcwm.co.uk
Fax: 020-7328 1444   Tel: 020-7328 8211

X-FACTOR MANAGEMENT
Suite 306
100 New Kings Road
London SW6 4LX
Website: www.x-factormanagement.com
e-mail: natalie@xfactor.com
Fax: 020-7371 9953   Tel: 020-7736 1602

YELLOW BALLOON PRODUCTIONS Ltd
Freshwater House
Outdowns, Effingham
Surrey KT24 5QR
e-mail: yellowbal@aol.com
Fax: 01483 281502   Tel: 01483 281500

YEOH Eddie MANAGEMENT
37 Falmouth Gardens
Redbridge
Essex IG4 5JU
Fax: 020-8550 0348   Tel: 020-8550 9994

YOUNG April Ltd
11 Woodlands Road
Barnes, London SW13 0JZ
Fax: 020-8878 7017   Tel: 020-8876 7030

YOUNG ACTORS FILE The
91 Holmesdale Road
South Norwood
London SE25 6JH
e-mail: actorstile@aol.com
Fax: 020-8771 2262   Tel: 020-8771 7047

ZAHL Ann PERSONAL MANAGEMENT
57 Great Cumberland Place
London W1H 7LJ
Fax: 020-7262 4143   Tel: 020-7724 3684

ZAHRA & REMICK
F TV Theatre
186 Albert Road
London N22 7AH   Tel/Fax: 020-8889 6225

ZWICKLER Marlene & ASSOCIATES
2 Belgrave Place
Edinburgh EH4 3AN   Tel/Fax: 0131-343 3030

A & J MANAGEMENT
551 Green Lanes, London N13 4DR
Website: www.ajmanagement.co.uk
e-mail: ajmanagement@bigfoot.com
Fax: 020-8882 5983   Tel: 020-8882 7716

ABACUS AGENCY
The Studio, 4 Bailey Road
Westcott, Dorking, Surrey RH4 3QS
Website: www.abacusagency.co.uk
e-mail: admin@abacusagency.co.uk
Fax: 01306 877813   Tel: 01306 877144

ACADEMY MANAGEMENT
41 Worcestershire Lea
Warfield, Berks RG42 3TQ
Fax: 01344 426410   Tel: 01344 426313

ACT ONE DRAMA STUDIO & AGENCY
31 Dobbin Hill, Sheffield S11 7JA
Website: www.actonedrama.co.uk
e-mail: casting@actonedrama.co.uk
Fax: 07971 112153   Tel: 0114-266 7209

ACT OUT AGENCY
22 Greek Street, Stockport, Cheshire SK3 8AB
e-mail: ab22@supanet.com Tel/Fax: 0161-429 7413

ACTIVATE DRAMA SCHOOL
(Drama School and Agency)
Priestman Cottage
Sea View Road, Sunderland SR2 7UP
Website: website.lineone.net/~lesley.mcdonough
e-mail: activate_agcy@hotmail.com
Fax: 0191-551 2051   Tel: 0191-565 2345

AFFINITY MODELLING & CASTING
(Babies, Children & Teenagers)
16 Paddock Gardens
East Grinstead, Sussex RH19 4AE
Website: www.affinity-management.com
e-mail: affinityartist@aol.com
Fax: 01342 326655   Tel: 01342 311425

AGENCY K-BIS
Clermont Hall, Cumberland Road
Brighton BN1 6SL
e-mail: k-bis@zoom.co.uk   Tel/Fax: 01273 564366

ALEXANDER Suzanne MANAGEMENT
170 Town Lane, Higher Bebington, Wirral CH63 8LG
e-mail: suzyalex@hotmail.com
                                  Tel/Fax: 0151-608 9655

ALLSORTS (DRAMA FOR CHILDREN)
(Sasha Leslie, Melissa Healy)
2 Pember Road, London NW10 5LP
e-mail: enquiries@allsorts.ltd.uk
                                  Tel/Fax: 020-8969 3249

ANDREWS Amanda AGENCY
30 Caverswall Road, Blythe Bridge
Stoke-on-Trent
Staffordshire ST11 9BG   Tel/Fax: 01782 393889

ANNA'S MANAGEMENT
(Formerly of ALADDIN'S CAVE)
25 Tintagel Drive, Stanmore, Middlesex HA7 4SR
Fax: 020-8238 2899   Tel: 020-8958 7636

ARAENA/COLLECTIVE
10 Bramshaw Gardens
South Oxhey
Herts WD1 6XP   Tel/Fax: 020-8428 0037

ARRAN KIDZ
6 Greenland Quay, Surrey Quays, London SE16 7RN
e-mail: info@tk1management.com
Fax: 020-7740 3119   Tel: 020-7252 3402

DMS
Agency

In association with
Dorothy Marshall School of Dance & Drama

The Children & Young Adult Theatrical Agency

T/F **020 8317 6622**   M **07740 288869**

LONDON BASED

Professionally trained
dancers, singers & actors
Available for work in all areas of the
entertainment industry

ARTS ACADEMY The (T.A.A.)
15 Lexham Mews
London W8 6JW
Fax: 020-7376 2416   Tel: 020-7376 0267

ASHCROFT ACADEMY OF DRAMATIC ART
Bellenden Old School
Bellenden Road
London SE15 4DG
Website: www.ashcroftacademy.co.uk
                              Tel/Fax: 020-8693 8088

AWA - ANDREA WILDER AGENCY
23 Cambrian Drive
Colwyn Bay
Conwy LL28 4SL
Website: www.awagency.co.uk
e-mail: casting@awagency.co.uk
Fax: 07092 249314   Tel: 01492 547542

KIDS PLUS / A PLUS
Acting & Modelling Agency

Kids Plus - children birth - 16 yrs
A Plus - young adults 16-26 yrs
Films, TV, Commercials, Photographic, Theatre

We have close links with local drama
schools and most of our children attend
regular acting classes.
Casting Directory is available on request
Tel/Fax: 020 7737 3901
web: www.kidsplusuk.com
email: janekidsplus@aol.com
54 Grove Park, London SE5 8LG

BARDSLEY'S Pamela UNIQUE AGENCY
1 Birkdale Mews, 15A Liverpool Road
Birkdale, Southport
Merseyside PR8 4AS   Tel/Fax: 01704 566771

BELCANTO LONDON ACADEMY Ltd
(Stage School & Agency)
Performance House
20 Passey Place, London SE9 5DQ
e-mail: enquiries@theatretraining.com
Fax: 020-8850 9944   Tel: 020-8850 9888

BODEN AGENCY
99 East Barnet Road
New Barnet, Herts EN4 8RF
Website: www.bodenstudios.com
e-mail: bodens2692@aol.com
Fax: 020-8449 5212   Tel: 020-8447 0909

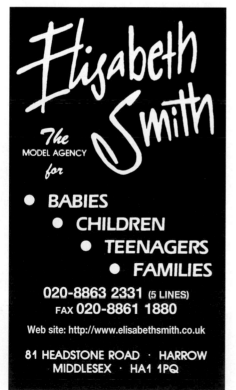

Elisabeth Smith
The MODEL AGENCY *for*

● **BABIES**
    ● **CHILDREN**
        ● **TEENAGERS**
            ● **FAMILIES**

020-8863 2331 (5 LINES)
FAX **020-8861 1880**

Web site: http://www.elisabethsmith.co.uk

**81 HEADSTONE ROAD · HARROW
MIDDLESEX · HA1 1PQ**

JACKIE PALMER
AGENCY

**30 Daws Hill Lane
High Wycombe, Bucks
Office 01494 520978
Fax 01494 510479**
E-mail jackie.palmer@btinternet.com

Well behaved, natural children,
teenagers and young adults.
All nationalities, many bi-lingual.
Acrobatics are a speciality.
Pupils regularly appear in
West End Theatre, including
RSC, Royal National Theatre and
in Film and Television.

We are just off the M40
within easy reach of London, Oxford,
Birmingham and the South West.

Licensed tutors and chaperones

BONNIE KIDS
8 Church Road, Teddington, Middlesex TW11 8PB
e-mail: bonniekids@touchdownpromotions.co.uk
Fax: 020-8943 1024   Tel: 020-8977 5471

BOURNEMOUTH YOUTH THEATRE The (BYT)
14 Cooper Dean Drive, Bournemouth BH8 9LN
Website: www.thebyt.com
e-mail: klair@thebyt.com
Fax: 01202 393290   Tel: 01202 255826

BRIGHT SPARKS PERFORMERS & AGENCY
1A South Parade, Stafford Road
Wallington
Surrey SM6 9AJ   Tel/Fax: 020-8769 3500

BRUCE & BROWN
203 Canalot Studios
222 Kensal Road, London W10 5BN
Fax: 020-8964 0457   Tel: 020-8968 5585

BUBBLEGUM
Ardreigh, Beaconsfield Road
Farnham Royal, Bucks SL2 3BP
Website: www.bubblegummodels.com
e-mail: kids@bubblegummodels.com
Fax: 01753 669255   Tel: 01753 646348

BYRON'S CASTING
(Children, Babies & Young Adults)
North London Performing Arts Centre
76 St James Lane, Muswell Hill, London N10 3DF
Website: www.byronscasting.co.uk
e-mail: byronscasting@aol.com
Fax: 020-8444 4040   Tel: 020-8444 4445

C.A.L.S. CASTING
(Children & Teenagers)
Unit E2, Bellevale Shopping Centre, Liverpool L25 2RG
Mobile: 07904 551914   Tel/Fax: 0151-487 8500

CAPITAL ARTS
Wyllyotts Centre
Darkes Lane, Potters Bar, Herts EN6 2HN
e-mail: capitalartstheatre@genie.co.uk
Mobile: 07885 232414   Tel/Fax: 020-8449 2342

CARR Norrie MODEL AGENCY
Holborn Studios
49-50 Eagle Wharf Road, London N1 7ED
Website: www.norriecarr.com
e-mail: info@norriecarr.com
Fax: 020-7253 1772   Tel: 020-7253 1771

CARTEURS THEATRICAL AGENCY
170A Church Road, Hove, East Sussex BN3 2DJ
Website: www.stonelandschool.co.uk
e-mail: www@stonelandsschool.co.uk
Fax: 01273 770444   Tel: 01273 770445

C D G AGENCY
11 Princes Park Parade, Hayes, Middlesex UB3 1LA
e-mail: peterwareham@blueyonder.co.uk
          Tel/Fax: 020-8581 4545

CENTRE STAGE MANAGEMENT
(Children & Young Adults)
The Croft, 7 Cannon Road, Southgate, London N14 7HE
e-mail: carole@centrestageuk.com
Fax: 020-8886 7555   Tel: 020-8886 4264

CHARACTERS MANAGEMENT Ltd
110 Stoke Newington Church Street
London N10 0JX   Tel: 020-7923 0606

CHILDREN OF LONDON ACTING & MODEL AGENCY
The Playhouse, 273 Malden Road, Surrey KT3 6AH
e-mail: childrenoflondon@aol.com
Fax: 020-8949 0522   Tel: 020-8949 0450

CHILDSPLAY THE CHILDREN'S AGENCY
1 Cathedral Street, London SE1 9DE
Website: www.childsplaylondon.co.uk
e-mail: childsplaylondon@aol.com
Fax: 020-7403 1656   Tel: 020-7403 4834

CHRYSTEL ARTS AGENCY
15 Churchill Road, Edgware
Middlesex HA8 6NX
e-mail: chrystelarts@talk21.com   Tel: 020-8952 1281

CIRCUS MANIACS
(Circus, Theatre, Dance, Extreme Sports)
Office 8A, The Kingswood Foundation
Britannia Road, Kingswood, Bristol BS15 8DB
e-mail: agency@circusmaniacs.com
Mobile: 07977 247287   Tel/Fax: 0117-947 7042

CITY LITES
PO Box 29673
London E8 3FH
e-mail: gulcan@freeuk.com
Mobile: 07773 353645   Tel/Fax: 020-7683 9016

CLAPPERBOARD CASTING
(Main Agents for Stagecoach Schools)
PO Box 153
Manchester M7 4YU
Fax: 0161-792 4285   Tel: 0161-792 2277

CLARKE Rose MANAGEMENT & THEATRE SCHOOL
51 Shooters Hill
Blackheath, London SE18 3RL
e-mail: roseclarkemanagement@hotmail.com
Tel/Fax: 020-8856 2536

GP ASSOCIATES AGENCY

In association with Greasepaint Anonymous
Youth Theatre Company
Representing Children & Teenagers
Tel: 020 8886 2263 Fax: 020 8882 9189
E-mail: clients@gpassociates.co.uk
Gallus Close, Winchmore Hill, N21 1JR

ACT ONE Drama Studio & Agency

Children & adults up to 35 yrs. available for tv, theatre,
radio, films, commercials, voice overs, corporate videos etc.

31 Dobbin Hill, Sheffield, S11 7JA.
tel 0114 2667209   mobile 07971 850617
fax 07971 112153
email casting@actonedrama.co.uk
web www.actonedrama.co.uk

COLIN'S PERFORMING ARTS AGENCY
(Colin's Performing Arts Ltd)
The Studios, 219B North Street, Romford, Essex RM1 4QA
Website: www.colinsperformingarts.co.uk
e-mail: agency@colinsperformingarts.co.uk
Fax: 01708 766077   Tel: 01708 766444

COLLINS STUDENT MANAGEMENT
St Dunstan's Hall, East Acton Lane
East Acton, London W3 7EG
e-mail: collinsstudents@aol.com
Fax: 020-8740 6542   Tel: 020-8743 9514

CONTI Italia AGENCY Ltd
23 Goswell Road, London EC1M 7AJ
e-mail: sca@italiaconti36.freeserve.co.uk
Fax: 020-7253 1430   Tel: 020-7608 7500

D & B MANAGEMENT & THEATRE SCHOOL
470 Bromley Road, Bromley, Kent BR1 4PN
Fax: 020-8697 8100   Tel: 020-8698 8880

DIMPLES MODEL & CASTING ACADEMY
(Adults & Children)
Suite 2, 2nd Floor, Magnum House
33 Lord Street, Leigh, Lancs WN7 1BY
e-mail: dimples_m_c_a@btinternet.com
Fax: 01942 262232   Tel: 01942 262012

DMS AGENCY
30 Lakedale Road, Plumstead, London SE18 1PP
Mobile: 07740 288869   Tel/Fax: 020-8317 6622

DRAGON DRAMA
(Drama for Children)
1B Station Road, Hampton Wick, Kingston KT1 4HG
Website: www.dragondrama.co.uk
e-mail: dragondrama@hotmail.com
                                   Tel/Fax: 020-8943 1504

EARNSHAW Susi MANAGEMENT
5 Brook Place, Barnet, Herts EN5 2DL
Website: www.susiearnshaw.co.uk
e-mail: casting@susiearnshaw.co.uk
Fax: 020-8364 9618   Tel: 020-8441 5010

ENGLISH Doreen '95
(Gerry Kinner)
4 Selsey Avenue, Aldwick
Bognor Regis
West Sussex PO21 2QZ   Tel: 01243 825968

**EUROKIDS & ADULTS INTERNATIONAL CASTING
& MODELLING AGENCY**
The Warehouse Studio, Glaziers Lane
Culcheth, Warrington, Cheshire WA3 4AQ
Website: www.eurokidsandadults.co.uk
e-mail: info@eurokidsandadults.co.uk
Fax: 01925 767563   Tel: 0870 7572002

EXTRAS UNLIMITED
14 Russell Garden Mews, London W14 8EU
Website: www.marksummers.com
e-mail: mark@marksummers.com
Fax: 0870 4435621   Tel: 0870 4435622

FBI AGENCY Ltd The
PO Box 250, Leeds LS1 2AZ
e-mail: j.spencer@fbi-agency.ltd.uk
                                   Tel/Fax: 07050 222747

**FIORENTINI Anna THEATRE & FILM SCHOOL
& AGENCY**
87 Glyn Road, Hackney, London E5 0JA
Website: www.annafiorentini.co.uk
e-mail: info@annafiorentini.co.uk
                                   Tel/Fax: 020-7682 1403

TOTS-TWENTIES AGENCY

3 CLEMENTS COURT
CLEMENTS LANE
ILFORD ESSEX
IG1 2QY

Representing Babies to Young Adults

Telephone:
020-8478 1848/8382
Fax:
020-8553 1880
Mobile:
07702 031519
Email:
sara@tots-twenties.co.uk

PUPILS OF ALL NATIONALITIES INCLUDING IDENTICAL TWINS - ALL AGES, BABY TO ADULT
Professionally Trained in:
DRAMA, SPEECH, TAP, BALLET, MODERN DANCE & SINGING.
Licensed Chaperones Supplied. Complimentary Audition Facilities Available at our offices,
near Ilford main line station. 10 Minutes travelling form Liverpool Station

FOOTSTEPS THEATRE SCHOOL CASTING
55 Pullan Avenue
Eccleshill, Bradford BD2 3RP
e-mail: helen@footsteps.fslife.co.uk
Tel/Fax: 01274 637429

FOX Betty AGENCY
The Friends Institute
220 Moseley Road, Birmingham B12 0DG
e-mail: bettyfox.school@virgin.net
Tel/Fax: 0121-440 1635

GAPA MANAGEMENT
2A Bellevue Mews
Bellevue Road
Friern Barnet, London N11 3ET
e-mail: gapakids@lycos.co.uk   Tel: 020-8368 6444

GLYNNE Frances MANAGEMENT
11 High Ash Avenue, Leeds LS17 8RS
e-mail: franandmo@cwctv.net
Fax: 0113-295 9408   Tel: 0113-266 4286

GO FOR IT CHILDREN'S AGENCY
(Children & Teenagers)
47 North Lane, Teddington, Middlesex TW11 0HU
e-mail: info@goforittheatreschool.co.uk
Fax: 020-8287 9405   Tel: 020-8943 1120

GOBSTOPPERS MANAGEMENT
50 Bencroft Road, Hemel Hempstead, Herts HP2 5UY
e-mail: chrisgobstoppers@hotmail.com
Mobile: 07961 372319   Tel: 01442 269543

G. P. ASSOCIATES
4 Gallus Close, Winchmore Hill, London N21 1JR
e-mail: clients@gpassociates.co.uk
Fax: 020-8882 9189   Tel: 020-8886 2263

GRAYSTONS
843-845 Green Lanes,
Winchmore Hill, London N21 2RX
e-mail: graystons@btinternet.com
Fax: 020-8364 2009   Tel: 020-8360 5700

GREVILLE Jeannine THEATRICAL AGENCY
Melody House, Gillotts Corner
Henley-on-Thames
Oxon RG9 1QU
Fax: 01491 411533   Tel: 01491 572000

HARLEQUIN CASTING AGENCY
Lee Chapel Centre, Kibcaps
The Knares, Basildon
Essex SS16 5RX
e-mail: harlequincasting@aol.com
Mobile: 07799 761089   Tel: 01268 440184

HARLEQUIN STUDIOS AGENCY FOR CHILDREN
223 Southcoast Road
Peacehaven
East Sussex BN10 8LB   Tel: 01273 581742

HARRIS AGENCY Ltd The
52 Forty Avenue
Wembley Park, Middlesex HA9 8LQ
e-mail: sharrisltd@aol.com
Fax: 020-8908 4455   Tel: 020-8908 4451

HEWITT PERFORMING ARTS
160 London Road
Romford
Essex RM7 9QL
e-mail: hewittcontrol@aol.com   Tel: 01708 727784

HINDIN ASSOCIATES Dee
(Affiliated with Drama-Dance-Song)
67 York Street
London W1H 1QA
Fax: 020-7724 0822   Tel: 020-7724 0022

HOBSON'S KIDS
62 Chiswick High Road, London W4 1SY
e-mail: gaynor@hobsons-international.com
Fax: 020-8996 5350   Tel: 020-8995 3638

HORNIMANS MANAGEMENT
31 Stafford Street, Gillingham, Kent ME7 5EN
Mobile: 07866 689865   Tel/Fax: 01634 576191

**HOWE Janet CHILDREN'S CASTING &
MODELLING AGENCY**
Studio 1, Whitebridge Estate
Whitebridge Lane, Stone, Staffs ST15 8LQ
Tel/Fax: 01785 816888   Tel/Fax: 01785 818480

40 Princess Street, Manchester M1 6DE
Website: www.janethowe.co.uk
e-mail: janet@jhowecasting.fsbusiness.co.uk
Mobile: 07801 942178   Tel/Fax: 0161-233 0700

INTER-CITY KIDS
Portland Tower
Portland Street, Manchester M1 3LF
Website: www.iccast.co.uk
e-mail: intercity@bigfoot.com
                               Tel/Fax: 0161-226 0103

JABBERWOCKY AGENCY
(Representing Pineapple Performing Arts School
and Woolborough Academy of Performing Arts)
(Children & Teenagers 6 Months-18 Years)
Wood Pecker Barn
Wickhurst Farm, Lamberhurst, Kent TN3 8BH
Website: www.jabberwockyagency.com
e-mail: janella00@aol.com
Mobile: 07884 431724   Tel/Fax: 01892 890499

JB ASSOCIATES
3 Stevenson Square
Manchester M1 1DN
e-mail: united_cities@compuserve.com
Fax: 0161-237 1809   Tel: 0161-237 1808

JIGSAW ARTS MANAGEMENT
(Representing Children and Young People
from Jigsaw Performing Arts Schools)
64-66 High Street, Barnet, Hertfordshire EN5 5SJ
Website: www.jigsaw-arts.co.uk/agency
                               Tel: 020-8447 4530

JOHNSTON & MATHERS ASSOCIATES Ltd
PO Box 3167, Barnet, Hertfordshire EN5 2WA
e-mail: johnstonmathers@aol.com
                               Tel/Fax: 020-8449 4968

JUNO CASTING AGENCY
(in association with Drama Studio Edinburgh)
19 Belmont Road, Edinburgh EH14 5DZ
Website: www.thedramastudio.co.uk
e-mail: thedra@thedramastudio.co.uk
Fax: 0131-453 3108   Tel: 0131-453 3284

KIDS LONDON
67 Dulwich Road, London SE24 0NJ
e-mail: kids.london@virgin.net
Fax: 020-7924 9766   Tel: 020-7924 9595

KIDS PLUS
54 Grove Park, London SE5 8LG
Website: www.kidsplusuk.com
e-mail: janekidsplus@aol.com
Mobile: 07759 944215   Tel/Fax: 020-7737 3901

KIDZ-2000 MODEL MANAGEMENT
Riverside House
High Street, Crayford, Kent DA1 4HG
Website: www.kidz-2000.co.uk
e-mail: info@kidz-2000.co.uk
Fax: 01322 359435   Tel: 01322 350635

KIDZ IN THE BIZ
The Lime House
Leaves Green Road, Keston, Kent BR2 6DQ
Website: www.kidzinthebiz.co.uk
e-mail: agency@kidzinthebiz.co.uk
Fax: 01959 576632   Tel: 01959 542552

KIDZ NATIONAL MODEL & CASTING AGENCY
21 Bolton Road, Manchester M28 3AX
Website: www.kidzltd.com
e-mail: info@kidzltd.com
Tel/Fax: 0870 2414418   Tel/Fax: 0870 2416260

K M C AGENCIES AND THEATRE SCHOOL
PO Box 122, 48 Great Ancoats Street
Manchester M4 5AB
e-mail: kids@kmcagencies.co.uk
Fax: 0161-237 9812   Tel: 0161-237 3009

KRACKERS KIDS THEATRICAL AGENCY
6/7 Electric Parade
Seven Kings Road, Ilford, Essex IG3 8BY
Website: sites.netscape.net/krackerskids/homepage
e-mail: krackerskids@hotmail.com
                              Tel/Fax: 01708 502046

LAINE BETTY MANAGEMENT
The Studios, East Street, Epsom, Surrey KT17 1HH
e-mail: enquiries@betty-laine-management.co.uk
                              Tel/Fax: 01372 721815

LAMONT CASTING AGENCY
94 Harington Road, Formby, Liverpool L37 7PZ
Website: www.lamontcasting.co.uk
e-mail: diane@lamontcasting.co.uk
Fax: 01704 872422   Tel: 01704 877024

LINTON MANAGEMENT
3 The Rock, Bury BL9 0JP
Fax: 0161-761 1999   Tel: 0161-761 2020

LITTLE ACORNS
London House
271-273 King Street, London W6 9LZ
e-mail: acorns@dircon.co.uk
Fax: 020-8408 3077   Tel: 020-8563 0773

LITTLE ADULTS ACADEMY & MODELLING AGENCY Ltd
Studio 11, Suite 13, Essex House
375-377 High Street, Stratford, London E15 4QZ
Website: www.littleadults.co.uk
e-mail: donna@littleadults.demon.co.uk
Fax: 020-8519 9797   Tel: 020-8519 9755

LITTLE GEMS
11 Thorn Road
Farnham, Surrey GU10 4TU
e-mail: littlegems@hotmail.com
Mobile: 07960 978439   Tel/Fax: 01252 792078

LIVE & LOUD
Dalziel House
7 Claremont Terrace, Glasgow G3 7XR
e-mail: info@liveandloud.fsbusiness.co.uk
Fax: 0141-535 6385   Tel: 0141-331 2519

LIVEWIRES CASTING AGENCY
PO Box 23199, Edinburgh EH7 5AH
e-mail: livewiresscotland@genie.co.uk
Fax: 0131-557 2437   Tel: 0131-557 2647

MOVIEMITES AGENCY
30 Spedan Close, Branch Hill
Hampstead, London NW3 7XF
Website: www.moviemitesagency.com
e-mail: kids@moviemitesagency.com
Fax: 020-7794 0771   Tel: 020-7431 5698

MOXEY CASTING
34 Davenport Road
Felpham, West Sussex PO22 7JS
e-mail: amanda@moxey.ssnet.co.uk
Mobile: 07860 717713   Tel: 01243 869566

MRS WORTHINGTON'S
(Under 18's Only)
16 Ouseley Road
London SW12 8EF   Tel/Fax: 020-8767 6944

NEXT GENERATION
26 Devonshire Way
Shirley, Croydon CRO 8BR
e-mail: nextgeneration27@aol.com
          Tel/Fax: 020-8406 9805

NOEL CASTING
(Specialising in Character Actors
and Ethnic and Asian Actors)
Suite 501, International House
223 Regent Street, London W1B 2QD
e-mail: noelcasting@yahoo.com
Fax: 020-7544 1090   Tel: 020-7544 1010

NORTHERN FILM & DRAMA
PO Box 27, Tadcaster, North Yorks LS24 9XS
Website: www.connew.com/nfd
e-mail: alyson@connew.com
Mobile: 07932 653466   Tel: 01977 681949

NUTOPIA PERSONAL MANAGEMENT
Number 8
132 Charing Cross Road, London WC2H 0LA
Website: www.nutopia.co.uk
          Tel/Fax: 020-8882 6299

O'FARRELL STAGE & THEATRE SCHOOL
36 Shirley Street, Canning Town
London E16 1HU   Tel: 020-7511 9444

ORR THEATRE DANCE CENTRE & AGENCY
20 Bembridge Drive, Bolton BL3 1RJ
Website: www.orrdance.co.uk
e-mail: barbara@orrdance.co.uk
          Tel/Fax: 01204 579842

PALMER Jackie AGENCY
30 Daws Hill Lane, High Wycombe, Bucks HP11 1PW
Website: www.jackiepalmer.co.uk
e-mail: jackie.palmer@btinternet.com
Fax: 01494 510479   Tel: 01494 520978

PATMORE Sandra SCHOOL AND AGENCY
(Dancing, Drama & Acrobatic)
173 Uxbridge Road, Rickmansworth
Herts WD3 2DW   Tel/Fax: 01923 772542

PC THEATRICAL & MODEL AGENCY
10 Strathmore Gardens
Edgware, Middlesex HA8 5HJ
Website: www.twinagency.com
e-mail: twinagy@aol.com
Fax: 020-8933 3418   Tel: 020-8381 2229

PHA YOUTH
Tanzaro House
Ardwick Green North, Manchester M12 6FZ
Website: www.pha-agency.co.uk
e-mail: youth@pha-agency.co.uk
Fax: 0161-273 4567   Tel: 0161-273 4444

POLLYANNA MANAGEMENT
PO Box 30661, London E1W 3GG
Website: www.eada.demon.co.uk/pollyanna
e-mail: pollyanna-mgmt@yahoo.co.uk
Fax: 020-7480 6761   Tel: 020-7702 1937

POWER CHILDREN MODEL MANAGEMENT CASTING AGENCY
The Royal, 25 Bank Plain, Norwich NR2 4SF
Website: www.powerchildmodels.co.uk
e-mail: powermodelmanagement@btinternet.com
Fax: 01603 621101   Tel: 01603 621100

PRIDE ARTIST MANAGEMENT
The Burnside Centre, Burnside Crescent
Middleton, Manchester M24 5NN
Website: www.pride-artist-management.co.uk
e-mail: artistes@pride-artist-management.co.uk
    Tel/Fax: 0161-643 6266

RASCALS MODEL AGENCY
13 Jubilee Parade, Snakes Lane East
Woodford Green, Essex IG8 7QG
Website: www.rascals.co.uk
e-mail: kids@rascals.co.uk
Fax: 020-8559 1035   Tel: 020-8504 1111

RAVENSCOURT MANAGEMENT
Tandy House
30-40 Dalling Road, London W6 0JB
e-mail: ravenscourt@hotmail.com
Fax: 020-8741 1786   Tel: 020-8741 0707

REDROOFS THEATRE SCHOOL AGENCY
Pinewood Studios, Iver Heath
Bucks
Fax: 01753 785443   Tel: 01753 785444

REEL KIDS
(Children 0 -16 years)
99 Vellum Drive
Carshalton, Surrey SM5 2TU
e-mail: dmm@blueyonder.co.uk
Fax: 020-8286 3243   Tel: 020-8286 2906

REYNOLDS THEATRICAL AGENCY
Westgate House
Spital Street, Dartford, Kent DA1 2EH
Website: www.reynoldsgroup.co.uk
e-mail: info@reynoldsgroup.co.uk
Fax: 01634 329079   Tel: 01322 277200

RIDGEWAY STUDIOS SCHOOL OF PERFORMING ARTS
Fairley House, Andrews Lane
Cheshunt, Herts EN7 6LB
Website: www.ridgewaystudios.co.uk
e-mail: info@ridgewaystudios.co.uk
Fax: 01992 633844   Tel: 01992 633775

S.A.M. YOUTH AGENCY
170 Town Lane, Higher Bebington
Wirral CH63 8LG   Tel/Fax: 0151-608 9655

SBZ AGENCY
PO Box 350
Ashford, Kent TN24 9ZE
e-mail: enquiries@sbzagency.co.uk
    Tel/Fax: 01233 650045

SCALLYWAGS AGENCY
1 Cranbrook Rise
Ilford, Essex IG1 3QW
Website: www.scallywags.co.uk
e-mail: kids@scallywags.co.uk
Fax: 020-8924 0262   Tel: 020-8518 1133

SCHER Anna THEATRE The
70-72 Barnsbury Road, London N1 0ES
e-mail: abby@astm.co.uk
Fax: 020-7833 9467   Tel: 020-7278 2101

SCREAM MANAGEMENT
3 Mersey Road
Blackpool
Lancashire FY4 1EN
Website: www.screammanagement.com
e-mail: info@screammanagement.com
                          Tel/Fax: 01253 298602

SHARONA STAGE SCHOOL AGENCY
& MANAGEMENT
82 Grennell Road
Sutton, Surrey SM1 3DN
Fax: 020-8395 0009   Tel: 020-8642 9396

SINGER Sandra ASSOCIATES
21 Cotswold Road
Westcliff on Sea, Essex SS0 8AA
Website: www.sandrasinger.com
e-mail: sandrasingeruk@aol.com
Fax: 01702 339393   Tel: 01702 331616

SMITH Elisabeth Ltd
81 Headstone Road
Harrow, Middlesex HA1 1PQ
Website: www.elisabethsmith.com
e-mail: models@elisabethsmith.com
Fax: 020-8861 1880   Tel: 020-8863 2331

SOLE FILE AGENCY The
(Children & Young Adults)
151A Field End Road
Eastcote, Middlesex HA5 1QL
e-mail: sole.file@virgin.net
Fax: 020-8429 7279   Tel: 020-8868 7960

SOUTH WEST CASTINGS Ltd
The Courtyard, Whitchurch
Ross-on-Wye HR9 6DA
Website: www.southwestcasting.co.uk
e-mail: agent@southwestcasting.co.uk
Fax: 01600 891099   Tel: 01600 891160

SPEAKE Barbara AGENCY
East Acton Lane, London W3 7EG
e-mail: speakekids1@aol.com
Fax: 020-8740 6542   Tel: 020-8743 6096

SPORT ENTERTAINMENT & MEDIA GROUP
98 Cockfosters Road, Barnet, Herts EN4 0DP
Fax: 020-8447 4251   Tel: 020-8447 4250

STAGE 84 YORKSHIRE SCHOOL
OF PERFORMING ARTS
Old Bell Chapel, Town Lane
Bradford, West Yorks BD10 8PR
Mobile: 07785 244984   Tel: 01274 569197

STAGE ONE THEATRE SCHOOL & AGENCY
32 Westbury Lane, Buckhurst Hill, Essex IG9 5PL
e-mail: stage01@lineone.net
Mobile: 07939 121154   Tel/Fax: 020-8506 0949

STAGE PLUS AGENCY
Park Meadow House, Wycombe Road
Princes Risborough
Bucks HP27 0DH   Tel: 01844 344114

STAGECOACH AGENCY
The Courthouse, Elm Grove
Walton-on-Thames, Surrey KT12 1LZ
Website: www.stagecoach.co.uk
e-mail: vmoore@stagecoach.co.uk
Fax: 01932 222894   Tel: 01932 254333

Representing children and teenagers for Film, Television, Theatre, Commercials and Modelling

TOTS 2 TEENS

Suite 306,
100 New Kings Road,
London, SW6 4LX

Tel: 020 7610 9529
Fax: 020 7371 9953
www.tots2teens.com

STARLINGS THEATRICAL AGENCY
45 Viola Close
South Ockendon, Essex RM15 6JF
Website: www.webspawner.com/users/starlings
e-mail: julieecarter@aol.com
Mobile: 07941 653463   Tel: 01708 859109

**STARSHINE CHILDREN'S THEATRE WORKSHOP
& AGENCY**
St Helier Congregational Church
Green Lane, Morden, Surrey SM4
e-mail: starshinectw@aol.com
                                       Mobile: 07939 398630

STEVENS Dacia
Glenavon Lodge, Lansdowne Road
South Woodford
London E18 2BE   Tel: 020-8989 0166

Alex Wilson (Andrex Commercial 2001)

JANET HOWE AGENCY
Children's Casting/Modelling Agency

Children <u>Open</u> Licensed For Television
Experience in
TV : Film : Commercials : Theatre : Modelling
Available for work in a wide range of areas
including London, Midlands and the North
Licensed Chaperones : Tutors
Workshops arranged for Casting Directors
Manchester Office 0161 233 0700
Staffordshire Office 01785 818480/816888
E-mail: janet@jhowecasting.fsbusiness.co.uk

STONELANDS SCHOOL OF BALLET & THEATRE ARTS
170A Church Road
Hove
East Sussex BN3 2DJ
Website: www.stonelandsschool.co.uk
e-mail: www@stonelandsschool.co.uk
Fax: 01273 770444   Tel: 01273 770445

SUMMERS Mark MANAGEMENT & AGENCY
14 Russell Garden Mews
London W14 8EU
Website: www.marksummers.com
e-mail: mark@marksummers.com
Fax: 0870 4435623   Tel: 0870 4435621

SUPERARTS AGENCY
26-28 Ambergate Street
London SE17 3RX   Tel/Fax: 020-7735 4975

T.A.A.
(See ARTS ACADEMY The)

TANWOOD
46 Bath Road
Swindon, Wilts SN1 4AY
Fax: 01793 643219   Tel: 01793 523895

THEATRE ARTS (WEST LONDON)
18 Kingsdale Gardens
Notting Hill
London W11 4TZ
e-mail: theatreartswestlondon@hotmail.com
                                       Tel/Fax: 020-7603 3471

THEATRE EXPRESS
PO Box 97
Cleveleys FY5 5XA   Tel/Fax: 01608 676024

THOMPSON Jim CHILDREN'S SECTION
(Jenny Donnison)
Herricks, School Lane
Arundel
West Sussex BN18 9DR
Fax: 01903 885887   Tel: 01903 885757

TOP-SPOTS AGENCY
(Commercials, Films, Babies to Adults)
314 Haydons Road
Wimbledon
London SW19 8JZ
Website: www.topspots.co.uk   Tel: 020-8543 7766

TOTS 2 TEENS Ltd
Suite 306
100 New Kings Road, London SW6 4LX
Website: www.tots2teens.com
e-mail: tots2teens@onetel.net.uk
Fax: 020-7371 9953   Tel: 020-7610 9529

TOTS-TWENTIES AGENCY
Suite 3 Ground Floor
Clements Court
Clements Lane
Ilford, Essex IG1 2QY
Website: www.tots-twenties.co.uk
e-mail: sara@tots-twenties.co.uk
Fax: 020-8553 1880   Tel: 020-8478 1848

TROUPERS.COM
Unit 62, Maltings Yard, Walton Road
Wavendon, Milton Keynes MK17 8LW
Website: www.troupers.com
e-mail: info@troupers.com
Fax: 01908 586979   Tel: 01908 282925

TRULY SCRUMPTIOUS Ltd
The Worx
16-24 Underwood Street
London N1 7JQ
e-mail: bookings@trulyscrumptious.co.uk
Fax: 020-7251 5767   Tel: 020-7608 3806

TUESDAYS CHILD
Gateway House, Watersgreen
Macclesfield, Cheshire SK11 6LH
Website: www.tuesdayschildagency.co.uk
e-mail: bookings@tuesdayschildagency.co.uk
Tel/Fax: 01625 501765   Tel: 01625 612244

TWINS
(see PC THEATRICAL & MODEL AGENCY)

TWINS & TRIPLETS
(Identical Babies, Children,
Teenagers & Adults for Film/Television)
Holmhurst Road
Upper Belvedere, Kent DA17 6HW
Website: www.twins.triplets.freeuk.com
e-mail: twinsontv@aol.com
Fax: 01322 447250   Tel: 01322 440184

VALLÉ ACADEMY THEATRICAL AGENCY The
The Rosedale Old Cestrians Club
Andrews Lane, Cheshunt
Herts EN7 6TB
Website: www.valleacademy.co.uk
e-mail: agency@valleacademy.co.uk
Fax: 01992 622868   Tel: 01992 622861

VISIONS AGENCY
Foxbury Studios
39A Foxbury Road
Bromley, Kent BR1 4DG
e-mail: frances.cooper@talk21.com
Tel/Fax: 020-8466 7782

WHITEHALL PERFORMING ARTS CENTRE
Rayleigh Road, Leigh-on-Sea
Essex SS9 5UU   Tel/Fax: 01702 529290

WHIZZ KIDS STAGE & SCREEN AGENCY
3 Marshall Road, Cambridge CB1 7TY
Website: www.whizzkidsdrama.co.uk
e-mail: goforit@whizzkidzdrama.co.uk
Fax: 01223 512431   Tel: 01223 512423

WYSE AGENCY
1 Hill Farm Road
Whittlesford, Cambs CB2 4NB
e-mail: frances.wyse@btinternet.com
Fax: 01223 839414   Tel: 01223 832288

YOUNG ACTORS FILE The
91 Holmesdale Road
South Norwood, London SE25 6JH
e-mail: actorsfile@aol.com
Fax: 020-8771 2262   Tel: 020-8771 7047

YOUNG BLOOD
The Talent Partnership, Riverside Studios
Crisp Road, Hammersmith, London W6 9RL
e-mail: info@thetalentpartnership.co.uk
Fax: 020-8237 1041   Tel: 020-8237 1040

YOUNG STARGAZERS
Stonesthrow, 18 Thornham Close
Clayton, Newcastle, Staffs ST5 4LR
e-mail: info@young-stargazers.freeserve.co.uk
Fax: 01782 610363   Tel: 01782 751900

YOUNG 'UNS AGENCY
Sylvia Young Theatre School
Rossmore Road, Marylebone, London NW1 6NJ
e-mail: enquiries@youngunsagency.co.uk
Fax: 020-7723 1040   Tel: 020-7723 0037

2 CASTING AGENCY & MANAGEMENT
Tiptoes House, 2 Collingwood Place
Layton, Blackpool FY3 8HU
Fax: 01253 302610   Tel: 01253 302614

2020 CASTING Ltd
2020 Hopgood Street, London W12 7JU
Website: www.2020casting.com
e-mail: info@2020casting.com
Fax: 020-8735 2727   Tel: 020-8746 2020

ADF MANAGEMENT
& MODEL CASTING AGENCY
17 Thorley Lane
Timperley, Altrincham WA15
Website: www.adfmanagement.co.uk
e-mail: adfmanagement@hotmail.com
Fax: 0161-282 5083   Tel: 0161-980 2536

A LITTLE EXTRA
7 Tregoze Way
The Prinnels, Swindon, Wiltshire SN5 6NW
Website: www.a-little-extra.co.uk
e-mail: tracy@a-little-extra.co.uk
Fax: 020-8771 2262   Tel: 020-8771 7047

ALLSORTS THE AGENCY Ltd
1 Cathedral Street, London SE1 9DE
Website: www.allsortstheagency.co.uk
e-mail: joannaallsorts@aol.com
Fax: 020-7403 1656   Tel: 020-7403 4834

AVENUE ARTISTES Ltd
8 Winn Road, Southampton SO17 1EN
Fax: 023-8090 5703   Tel: 023-8055 1000

AWA - ANDREA WILDER AGENCY
23 Cambrian Drive
Colwyn Bay, Conwy LL28 4SL
Website: www.awagency.co.uk
e-mail: casting@awagency.co.uk
Fax: 07092 249314   Tel: 01492 547542

BALDIES CASTING AGENCY
(The only agency purely for bald people)
6 Marlott Road, Poole, Dorset BH15 3DX
Mobile: 07860 290437   Tel: 01202 666001

BRISTOL EXTRA SERVICE TEAM (B.E.S.T.)
(Ernest Jones)
(Film & TV Actors, Extras, Speciality Artists)
21 Ellesmere
Thornbury, Near Bristol BS35 2ER
e-mail: ernestjones.best@virgin.net
Mobile: 07951 955759   Tel/Fax: 01454 411628

BROADCASTING
Unit 23 Canalot Studios
222 Kensal Road, London W10 5BN
Fax: 020-7460 5223   Tel: 020-7460 5222

BROMLEY CASTING
(Film & TV)
77 Widmore Road, Bromley BR1 3AA
Website: www.bromleycasting.tv
e-mail: admin@bromleycasting.tv
                    Tel/Fax: 020-8466 8239

BROOK Dolly CASTING AGENCY
PO Box 5436, Dunmow CM6 1WW
Fax: 01371 875996   Tel: 01371 875767

CAIRNS AGENCY The
Dalziel House
7 Claremont Terrace, Glasgow G3 7XR
e-mail: info@thecairnsagency.fsbusiness.co.uk
Fax: 0141-353 6385   Tel: 0141-331 2519

CAMCAST
Laragain, Upper Banavie
Fort William, Inverness-shire PH33 7PB
Website: www.camcast.co.uk
e-mail: anne@camcast.co.uk
Fax: 01397 772456   Tel: 01397 772523

CASTING NETWORK Ltd The
122A The Broadway
Tolworth, Surbiton, Surrey KT6 7HT
Website: www.thecastingnetwork.co.uk
e-mail: casting-network@talk21.com
Fax: 020-8390 0605   Tel: 020-8339 9090

CELEX CASTING & MANAGEMENT
(Children available)
11 Glencroft Drive
Stenson Fields, Derby DE24 3LS
Website: www.celex.co.uk
e mail: anne@celex.co.uk
Fax: 01332 232115   Tel: 01332 232445

COAST 2 COAST PERSONALITIES
Suite 306
100 New Kings Road, London SW6 4LX
Website: www.coast2coastpersonalities.com
e-mail: nataliec2c@aol.com
Fax: 020-7371 9953   Tel: 020-7736 1602

CORNWALL FILM AGENCY
East Trevelmond Farm
Trevelmond, Liskeard, Cornwall PL14 4LY
e-mail: frances@cornwall-film-agency.fsnet.co.uk
Tel/Fax: 01579 321858

CYBER 2000/IN THE CAN Ltd
20 Old Steine, Brighton BN1 1EL
Website: www.cyberartists.co.uk
e-mail: cyber.1@btclick.com
Fax: 01273 571085   Tel: 01273 671234

DAVID AGENCY The
153 Battersea Rise, London SW11 1HP
Website: www.davidagency.net
e-mail: casting@davidagency.net
Fax: 020-7924 2334   Tel: 020-7223 7720

DRAG QUEEN AGENCY The
(David Gordon)
691 Seven Sisters Road, London N15 5LA
Mobile: 07941 226430   Tel: 020-8211 0828

ELLIOTT AGENCY The
PO Box 2772, Lewes, Sussex BN8 4DW
Website: www.elliottagency.co.uk
e-mail: info@elliottagency.co.uk
Fax: 01273 400814   Tel: 01273 401264

**EUROKIDS AND ADULTS INTERNATIONAL
CASTING AND MODEL AGENCY**
The Warehouse Studio, Glaziers Lane, Culcheth,
Warrington, Cheshire WA3 4AQ
Website: www.eurokidsandadults.co.uk
e-mail: info@eurokidsandadults.co.uk
Fax: 01925 767563   Tel: 0870 7572002

EXTRAS UNLIMITED
14 Russell Garden Mews, London W14 8EU
Website: www.marksummers.com
e-mail: mark@marksummers.com
Fax: 0870 4435623   Tel: 0870 4435622

EXTRASPECIAL Ltd
38 Commercial Street, London E1 6LP
Website: www.extraspecial2000.com
e-mail: info@skyblue-extraspecial.com
Fax: 020-7375 1466   Tel: 020-7375 1400

FACES CASTING AGENCY
95 Ditchling Road
Brighton
East Sussex BN1 4ST
Fax: 01273 689021   Tel: 01273 571989

FBI AGENCY Ltd The
PO Box 250, Leeds LS1 2AZ
e-mail: j.spencer@fbi-agency.ltd.uk
                    Tel/Fax: 07050 222747

FBI Ltd
4th Floor
21-24 Kirby Street, London EC1N 8TS
Website: www.fullybooked-inc.com
e-mail: fbi@dircon.co.uk
Fax: 020-7242 8125   Tel: 020-7242 5542

FLOSS EXTRAS
14 Ritz Buildings, Church Road
Tunbridge Wells
Kent TN1 1HP
Website: www.newmangroup.co.uk
e-mail: floss.extras@newmangroup.co.uk
Fax: 01892 514173   Tel: 01892 524122

FRESH AGENTS
82 Queens Road, Brighton BN1 3XE
Website: www.freshagents.com
e-mail: info@freshagents.com
Fax: 01273 711778   Tel: 01273 711777

G2
15 Lexham Mews, London W8 6JW
e-mail: g2@galloways.ltd.uk
Fax: 020-7376 2416   Tel: 020-7376 2133

GUYS & DOLLS CASTING
Trafalgar House
Grenville Place, Mill Hill, London NW7 3SA
Fax: 020-8381 0080   Tel: 020-8906 4144

HOWE Janet CASTING AGENCY
Studio 1, Whitebridge Estate
Whitebridge Lane
Stone, Staffs ST15 8LQ
e-mail: janet@jhowecasting.fsbusiness.co.uk
Tel/Fax: 01785 818480   Tel/Fax: 01785 816888

40 Princess Street, Manchester M1 6DE
Mobile: 07801 942178   Tel/Fax: 0161-233 0700

ISLAND TV & FILM EXTRAS
Unit 7 Central Market
Scarrots Lane, Newport
Isle of Wight PO30 1JP
Fax: 01983 525128   Tel: 01923 522039

JACLYN 2000
52 Bessemer Road
Norwich, Norfok NR4 6DQ
Website: www.jaclyn2000.co.uk
Fax: 01603 612532   Tel: 01603 622027

J B AGENCY Ltd
7 Stonehill Mansions
8 Streatham High Road, London SW16 1DD
Fax: 020-8769 9567   Tel: 020-8769 0123

KNIGHT Ray CASTING
21A Lambolle Place
Belsize Park, London NW3 4PG
Website: www.rayknight.co.uk
e-mail: casting@rayknight.co.uk
Fax: 020-7722 2322   Tel: 020-7722 4111

KREATE Ltd
Unit 201
30 Great Guildford Street, London SE1 0HS
e-mail: kreate@btconnect.com
Fax: 020-7401 3003   Tel: 020-7401 9007

LEE'S PEOPLE
60 Poland Street, London W1F 7NT
e-mail: lee@lees-people.co.uk
Fax: 020-7734 3033   Tel: 020-7734 5775

LEMON CASTING & MANAGEMENT
23 Lucas Road
Farnworth, Bolton BL4 9RP
e-mail: andreaking@lemoncastings6.fsnet.co.uk
Mobile: 07890 701544   Tel/Fax: 01204 456253

MAC-10 Ltd
Unit 69, 2 Hellidon Close
Ardwick, Manchester M12 4AH
Website: www.mac-10.co.uk
e-mail: info@mac-10.co.uk
Fax: 0161-275 9610   Tel: 0161-275 9510

MAD DOG CASTING Ltd
Camden House
156 Camden High Street
London NW1 0NE
e-mail: info@maddogcasting.com
Fax: 020-7916 1512   Tel: 020-7916 1511

NEMESIS AGENCY
54 Princess Street
Manchester M1 6HS
Website: www.nemesisagency.co.uk
Fax: 0161-236 1771   Tel: 0161-237 1515

NIDGES CASTING AGENCY
Half Moon Chambers
Chapel Walks, Manchester M2 1HN
e-mail: moneypenny@nidgescasting.co.uk
Fax: 0161-832 5219   Tel: 0161-832 8259

**NORTHERN PROFESSIONALS CASTING
COMPANY**
21 Cresswell Avenue
North Shields, Tyne & Wear NE29 9BQ
e-mail: bill.gerard@northpro83.freeserve.co.uk
Fax: 0191-296 3243   Tel: 0191-257 8635

ORIENTAL AFRO ASIAN ARTISTS
(FBI Ltd) 4th floor
20-24 Kirby Street, London EC1N 8TS
Website: fullybooked-inc.com
e-mail: fbi@dircon.co.uk
Fax: 020-7242 8125   Tel: 020-7242 5542

ORIENTAL CASTING AGENCY Ltd (Peggy Sirr)
(Afro/Asian Artists)
1 Wyatt Park Road
Streatham Hill, London SW2 3TN
Website: www.orientalcasting.com
e-mail: peggy.sirr@btconnect.com
Fax: 020-8674 9303   Tel: 020-8671 8538

ORION CASTING AGENCY
DBH House
Boundary Street
Liverpool L5 9YJ   Tel/Fax: 0151-482 5565

PC THEATRICAL & MODEL AGENCY
10 Strathmore Gardens
Edgware, Middlesex HA8 5HJ
Website: www.twinagency.com
e-mail: twinagy@aol.com
Fax: 020-8933 3418   Tel: 020-8381 2229

PHA CASTING
Tanzaro House
Ardwick Green North, Manchester M12 6FZ
Website: www.pha-agency.co.uk
e-mail: info@pha-agency.co.uk
Fax: 0161-273 4567   Tel: 0161-273 4444

PHOENIX AGENCY
PO Box 387, Bristol BS99 3JZ
Fax: 0117-973 4160   Tel: 0117-973 1100

POWER CASTING AGENCY
The Royal, 25 Bank Plain, Norwich NR2 4SF
Website: www.powermodelmanagement.co.uk
e-mail: powermodelmanagement@btinternet.com
Fax: 01603 621101   Tel: 01603 621100

PRAETORIAN ASSOCIATES
(Specialist Extras)
Pierie Lodge, 61 Spruce Hills, London E17 4LB
Website: www.praetorianasc.com
e-mail: e17one@aol.com
Fax: 020-8923 7177   Tel: 020-8923 9075

PRIDE ARTIST MANAGEMENT
The Burnside Centre, Burnside Crescent
Middleton, Manchester M24 5NN
Website: www.pride-artist-management.co.uk
e-mail: extras@pride-artist-management.co.uk
                          Tel/Fax: 0161-643 6266

REYNOLDS Sandra CASTING
50 Fitzroy Street, London W1T 5BT
Website: www.sandrareynolds.co.uk
e-mail: tessa@sandrareynolds.co.uk
Fax: 020-7387 5848   Tel: 020-7387 5858

35 St Georges Street, Norwich NR3 1DA
Fax: 01603 219825   Tel: 01603 623842

celex

Comprehensive register of experienced actors, supporting artists and walk- ons, on open licence, children also available

Contact: Anne Sweeting, Celex Casting
11 Glencroft Drive, Stenson Fields, Derby DE24 3LS
Tel: 01332 232445   Fax: 01332 232115
http://www.celex.co.uk e-mail: anne@celex.co.uk

RHINO MANAGEMENT
Kobe House, Halstead Hill
Goffs Oak, Waltham Cross, Herts EN7 5NA
Website: www.rhino-management.co.uk
e-mail: rhino.management@virgin.net
Mobile: 07901 528988   Tel/Fax: 01992 638852

RUBICON ARTISTS AGENCY
27 Inderwick Road, Crouch End
London N8 9LB   Tel/Fax: 020-8374 1836

SKYBLUE CASTING Ltd
38 Commercial Street, London E1 6LP
e-mail: info@skyblue-extraspecial.com
Fax: 020-7375 1466   Tel: 020-7375 1400

SO DAM TUFF Ltd
The Coach House, Battersea Square
136 West Bridge Road, London SW11 3PF
Website: www.sodamtuff.com
e-mail: tiger@sodamtuff.com
Fax: 020-7352 0001   Tel: 020-7223 7377

SOUTH WEST CASTING Ltd
The Courtyard
Whitchurch, Ross-on-Wye HR9 6DA
Website: www.southwestcasting.co.uk
e-mail: agent@southwestcasting.co.uk
Fax: 01600 891099   Tel: 01600 891160

TONER CASTING Ltd
Unit E6, Brunswick Small Business Centre
Brunswick Dock, Liverpool L3 4BD
Website: www.tonercasting.com
e-mail: tonercasting@toner.fsnet.co.uk
Fax: 0151-707 8414   Tel: 0151-708 6400

TOP-SPOTS AGENCY
(Commercials, Films, Babies to Adults)
314 Haydons Road, Wimbledon, London SW19 8JZ
Fax: 020-8543 5511   Tel: 020-8543 7766

TROUPERS.COM
Unit 62 Mallings Yard, Walton Road
Wavendon, Milton Keynes MK17 8LW
Website: www.troupers.com
e-mail: info@troupers.com
Fax: 01908 586979   Tel: 01908 282925

UGLY ENTERPRISES Ltd
Tigris House
256 Edgware Road, London W2 1DS
Website: www.ugly.org
e-mail: info@ugly.org
Fax: 020-7402 0507   Tel: 020-7402 5564

UNITED COLOURS OF LONDON Ltd
(FBI) 4th Floor, 20-24 Kirby Street, London EC1N 8TS
Website: www.fullybooked-inc.com
e-mail: fbi@dircon.co.uk
Fax: 020-7242 8125   Tel: 020-7242 5542

YOUNG ACTORS FILE The
91 Holmesdale Road
South Norwood, London SE25 6JH
e-mail: actorsfile@aol.com
Fax: 020-8771 2262   Tel: 020-8771 7047

YOUNG STARGAZERS
Stonesthrow, 18 Thornham Close
Clayton, Newcastle, Staffs ST5 4LR
e-mail: info@young-stargazers.freeserve.co.uk
Fax: 01782 610363   Tel: 01782 751900

SAMUEL FRENCH LTD

Publishers of Plays • Agents for the Collection of Royalties
Specialist Booksellers
52 Fitzroy Street London W1T 5JR
Tel 020 7255 4300 (Bookshop) 020 7387 9373 (Enquiries)
Fax 020 7387 2161 www.samuelfrench-london.co.uk
e-mail: theatre@samuelfrench-london.co.uk

For information regarding membership of the
Personal Managers' Association please contact:
Personal Managers' Association Ltd
Rivercroft, 1 Summer Road, East Molesey, Surrey KT8 9LX
Tel: 020-8398 9796
* Denotes PMA Membership

A & B PERSONAL MANAGEMENT Ltd*
Paurelle House, 91 Regent Street, London W1B 4EL
e-mail: billellis@aandb.co.uk
Fax: 020-7734 6318   Tel: 020-7734 6047

ABNER STEIN
10 Roland Gardens, London SW7 3PH
e-mail: abner@abnerstein.co.uk
Fax: 020-7370 6316   Tel: 020-7373 0456

ACTAC
7 Isles Court, Ramsbury, Wiltshire SN8 2QW
Fax: 01672 520166   Tel: 01672 520274

AGENCY (LONDON) Ltd The*
24 Pottery Lane, Holland Park, London W11 4LZ
e-mail: info@theagency.co.uk
Fax: 020-7727 9037   Tel: 020-7727 1346

A.J. ASSOCIATES
Scripts Department, Rough Lee Barn
Higherhouse Lane, White Coppice, Chorley PR6 9BU
e-mail: ajassociates@tinyworld.co.uk
Tel/Fax: 01257 273148   Tel: 01257 269788

A M HEATH & CO Ltd
(Fiction & Non-Fiction only)
79 St Martin's Lane, London WC2N 4RE
Fax: 020-7497 2561   Tel: 020-7836 4271

ASPER Pauline MANAGEMENT
Jacobs Cottage, Reservoir Lane
Seddlescombe, East Sussex TN33 0PJ
e-mail: pauline.asper@virgin.net
                    Tel/Fax: 01424 870412

BLAKE FRIEDMANN
(Novels, TV/Film Scripts)
122 Arlington Road, London NW1 7HP
e-mail: julian@blakefriedmann.co.uk
Fax: 020-7284 0442   Tel: 020-7284 0408

BRITTEN Nigel MANAGEMENT*
Suite 508, Riverbank House
1 Putney Bridge Approach, London SW6 3JD
e-mail: nbm.office@virgin.net
Fax: 020-7384 3862   Tel: 020-7384 3842

BRODIE Alan REPRESENTATION Ltd*
(Incorporating Michael Imison Playwrights)
211 Piccadilly, London W1J 9HF
Website: www.alanbrodie.com
e-mail: info@alanbrodie.com
Fax: 020-7917 2872   Tel: 020-7917 2871

BRYANT Peter (WRITERS)
3 Jasper Road, London SE19 1SJ
Fax: 020-8670 7310   Tel: 020-8670 7820

BURKEMAN Brie*
14 Neville Court, Abbey Road, London NW8 9DD
e-mail: brie.burkeman@mail.com
Fax: 0709 2239111   Tel: 0709 2239113

CANN Alexandra REPRESENTATION*
12 Abingdon Road, London W8 6AF
e-mail: enquiries@alexandracann.com
Fax: 020-7938 4228   Tel: 020-7938 4002

CASAROTTO RAMSAY & ASSOCIATES Ltd*
National House
60-66 Wardour Street
London W1V 4ND
Website: www.casarotto.uk.com
e-mail: agents@casarotto.uk.com
Fax: 020-7287 9128   Tel: 020-7287 4450

CLOWES Jonathan Ltd*
10 Iron Bridge House
Bridge Approach, London NW1 8BD
Fax: 020-7722 7677   Tel: 020-7722 7674

COCHRANE Elspeth PERSONAL MANAGEMENT*
14/2, 2nd Floor
South Bank Commercial Centre
140 Battersea Park Road, London SW11 4NB
e-mail: elspethc@dircon.co.uk
Fax: 020-7622 5815   Tel: 020-7622 0314

CREATIVE MEDIA INTERNATIONAL
(No unsolicited scripts, first instance sypnopsis only)
22 Kingsbury Avenue
Dunstable
Bedfordshire LU5 4PU   Tel/Fax: 01582 510869

CURTIS BROWN GROUP Ltd*
Haymarket House
28-29 Haymarket
London SW1Y 4SP
e-mail: cb@curtisbrown.co.uk
Fax: 020-7396 0110   Tel: 020-7396 6600

DAISH Judy ASSOCIATES Ltd*
2 St Charles Place, London W10 6EG
Fax: 020-8964 8966   Tel: 020-8964 8811

DE WOLFE Felix*
Garden Offices
51 Maida Vale, London W9 1SD
e-mail: felixdewolfe@aol.com
Fax: 020-7289 5731   Tel: 020-7289 5770

DREW Bryan Ltd
Mezzanine, Quadrant House
80-82 Regent Street
London W1B 5AU
e-mail: bryan@bryandrewltd.com
Fax: 020-7437 0561   Tel: 020-7437 2293

FARNES Norma MANAGEMENT
9 Orme Court
London W2 4RL
Fax: 020-7792 2110   Tel: 020-7727 1544

FILLINGHAM Janet ASSOCIATES
52 Lowther Road
London SW13 9NU
e-mail: jfillassoc@aol.com
Fax: 020-8748 7374   Tel: 020-8748 5594

FILM RIGHTS Ltd
Mezzanine, Quadrant House
80-82 Regent Street, London W1B 5AU
Website: www.filmrights.ltd.uk
e-mail: information@filmrights.ltd.uk
Fax: 020-7734 0044   Tel: 020-7734 9911

FITCH Laurence Ltd
Mezzanine, Quadrant House
80-82 Regent Street, London W1B 5AU
Fax: 020-7734 0044   Tel: 020-7734 9911

FOSTER Jill Ltd*
9 Barb Mews, London W6 7PA
Fax: 020-7602 9336   Tel: 020-7602 1263

FRENCH Samuel Ltd*
52 Fitzroy Street, Fitzrovia, London W1T 5JR
Website: www.samuelfrench-london.co.uk
e-mail: theatre@samuelfrench-london.co.uk
Fax: 020-7387 2161   Tel: 020-7387 9373

FUTERMAN, ROSE & ASSOCIATES
(TV/Film/Stage Play Scripts)
Heston Court Business Park
Camp Road, Wimbledon, London SW19 4UW
Website: www.futermanrose.co.uk
e-mail: guy@futermanrose.co.uk
Fax: 020-8605 2162   Tel: 020-8947 0188

GILLIS Pamela MANAGEMENT
46 Sheldon Avenue, London N6 4JR
Fax: 020-8341 5564   Tel: 020-8340 7868

GLASS Eric Ltd
25 Ladbroke Grove, London W11 1PS
e-mail: eglassltd@aol.com
Fax: 020-7229 6220   Tel: 020-7229 9500

HALL Rod AGENCY Ltd The*
3 Charlotte Mews, London W1T 4DZ
Website: www.rodhallagency.com
e-mail: office@rodhallagency.com
Fax: 020-7637 0807   Tel: 020-7637 0706

HANCOCK Roger Ltd*
4 Water Lane, London NW1 8NZ
e-mail: hancockltd@aol.com
Fax: 020-7267 0705   Tel: 020-7267 4418

HATTON Richard Ltd*
29 Roehampton Gate, London SW15 5JR
Fax: 020-8876 8278   Tel: 020-8876 6699

HIGHAM David ASSOCIATES Ltd*
5-8 Lower John Street
Golden Square, London W1F 9HA
Fax: 020-7437 1072   Tel: 020-7434 5900

HOSKINS Valerie ASSOCIATES
20 Charlotte Street, London W1T 2NA
e-mail: vha@vhassociates.co.uk
Fax: 020-7637 4493   Tel: 020-7637 4490

HOWARD Amanda ASSOCIATES Ltd*
21 Berwick Street, London W1F 0PZ
Fax: 020-7287 7785   Tel: 020-7287 9277

HURLEY LOWE MANAGEMENT*
36 Redcliffe Road, London SW10 9NJ
Fax: 020-7351 1033   Tel: 020-7352 6878

I C M (International Creative Management)*
Oxford House, 76 Oxford Street, London W1D 1BS
Fax: 020-7323 0101   Tel: 020-7636 6565

IMISON Michael PLAYWRIGHTS Ltd
(See BRODIE Alan REPRESENTATION Ltd)

KANAL Roberta
82 Constance Road
Twickenham, Middlesex TW2 7JA
Fax: 020-8894 7952   Tel: 020-8894 2277

KASS Michelle ASSOCIATES*
36-38 Glasshouse Street, London W1B 5DL
Fax: 020-7734 3394   Tel: 020-7439 1624

LE BARS Tessa MANAGEMENT*
(Existing Clients Only)
54 Birchwood Road, Petts Wood, Kent BR5 1NZ
e-mail: tessa.lebars@ntlworld.com
Mobile: 07860 287255   Tel/Fax: 01689 837084

LONDON MANAGEMENT*
2-4 Noel Street, London W1F 8GB
Fax: 020-7287 3036   Tel: 020-7287 9000

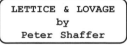

LOWE Ian
Glan Dulas, Cusop
Hay-on-Wye, Hereford HR3 5RQ
e-mail: ianlowe@scripts-uk.demon.co.uk
Tel/Fax: 01497 821780

MACNAUGHTON LORD 2000 Ltd*
Douglas House
16-18 Douglas Street
London SW1P 4PB
e-mail: info@ml2000.org.uk
Fax: 020-7834 4949   Tel: 020-7834 4646

MANN Andrew Ltd*
1 Old Compton Street
London W1D 5JA
e-mail: manscript@onetel.net.uk
Fax: 020-7287 9264   Tel: 020-7734 4751

MANS Johnny PRODUCTIONS Ltd
PO Box 196, Hoddesdon, Herts EN10 7WQ
Fax: 01992 470516   Tel: 01992 470907

MARJACQ SCRIPTS Ltd
34 Devonshire Place, London W1G 6JW
Website: www.marjacq.com
e-mail: enquiries@marjacq.com
Fax: 020-7935 9115   Tel: 020-7935 9499

MARVIN Blanche*
21A St Johns Wood High Street, London NW8 7NG
e-mail: blanchemarvin@madasafish.com
Tel/Fax: 020-7722 2313

M.B.A. LITERARY AGENTS Ltd*
62 Grafton Way
London W1T 5DW
e-mail: agent@mbalit.co.uk
Fax: 020-7387 2042   Tel: 020-7387 2076

McLEAN BILL PERSONAL MANAGEMENT Ltd
23B Deodar Road
London SW15 2NP   Tel: 020-8789 8191

ML 2000 Ltd
(See MACNAUGHTON LORD 2000 Ltd)

MORRIS William AGENCY (UK) Ltd*
52-53 Poland Street, London W1F 7LX
Fax: 020-7534 6900   Tel: 020-7534 6800

NARROW ROAD COMPANY*
(Richard Ireson)
182 Brighton Road, Coulsdon, Surrey CR5 2NF
e-mail: coulsdon@narrowroad.co.uk
Fax: 020-8763 9329   Tel: 020-8763 9895

P F D*
Drury House, 34-43 Russell Street, London WC2B 5HA
Fax: 020-7836 9539   Tel: 020-7344 1000

POLLINGER Laurence Ltd
Goldsmiths House
137-141 Regent Street, London W1B 4HZ
e-mail: laurencepollinger@compuserve.com
Fax: 020-7025 78297   Tel: 020-7205 7820

RADALA & ASSOCIATES
17 Avenue Mansions
Finchley Road, London NW3 7AX
Fax: 020-7431 7636   Tel: 020-7794 4495

ROSICA COLIN Ltd
1 Clareville Grove Mews, London SW7 5AH
Fax: 020-7244 6441   Tel: 020-7370 1080

RUPERT CREW Ltd
(No Plays, Films or TV scripts)
1A King's Mews, London WC1N 2JA
e-mail: rupertcrew@compuserve.com
Fax: 020-7831 7914   Tel: 020-7242 8586

SAYLE SCREEN Ltd*
(Wrires and Directors for Film & TV)
11 Jubilee Place, London SW3 3TD
Fax: 020-7823 3363   Tel: 020-7823 3883

SEIFERT DENCH ASSOCIATES*
24 D'Arblay Street, London W1F 8EH
Fax: 020-7439 1355   Tel: 020-7437 4551

SHARLAND ORGANISATION Ltd*
The Manor House, Manor Street
Raunds, Northants NN9 6JW
e-mail: tsoshar@aol.com
Fax: 01933 624860   Tel: 01933 626600

SHAW Vincent ASSOCIATES Ltd
51 Byron Road, London E17 4SN
Website: www.vincentshaw.com
e-mail: info@vincentshaw.com
Fax: 020-8521 1588   Tel: 020-8509 2211

SHEIL LAND ASSOCIATES Ltd*
(Literary, Theatre & Film)
43 Doughty Street, London WC1N 2LH
e-mail: info@sheilland.co.uk
Fax: 020-7831 2127   Tel: 020-7405 9351

SOMMERFIELD Ltd
35 Old Queen Street, London SW1H 9JD
Fax: 020-7654 5226   Tel: 020-7222 9070

STEEL Elaine*
(Writers' Agent)
110 Gloucester Avenue, London NW1 8HX
e-mail: ecmsteel@aol.com
Fax: 020-8341 9807   Tel: 020-8348 0918

STEINBERG Micheline PLAYWRIGHTS*
4th Floor
104 Great Portland Street
London W1W 6PE
e-mail: steinplays@aol.com   Tel: 020-7287 4383

STEVENS Rochelle & CO*
2 Terretts Place
Upper Street, London N1 1QZ
Fax: 020-7354 5729   Tel: 020-7359 3900

TENNYSON AGENCY The
10 Cleveland Avenue
Merton Park, London SW20 9EW
e-mail: enquiries@tenagy.co.uk
Tel/Fax: 020-8543 5939

THEATRE OF LITERATURE
(c/o Calder Publications)
51 The Cut, London SE1 8LF
Fax: 020-7928 5930   Tel: 020-7633 0599

THURLEY J M MANAGEMENT
30 Cambridge Road
Teddington, Middlesex TW11 8DR
e-mail: jmthurley@aol.com
Fax: 020-8943 2678   Tel: 020-8977 3176

TYRELL Julia MANAGEMENT
55 Fairbridge Road, London N19 3EW
e-mail: jtmanagement.co.uk
Fax: 020-7272 2400   Tel: 020-7272 4000

WARE Cecily LITERARY AGENTS*
19C John Spencer Square, London N1 2LZ
e-mail: cware@dial.pipex.com
Fax: 020-7226 9828   Tel: 020-7359 3787

WEINBERGER Josef Ltd*
12-14 Mortimer Street, London W1T 3JJ
Website: www.josef-weinberger.com
e-mail: general.info@jwmail.co.uk
Fax: 020-7436 9616   Tel: 020-7580 2827

ALEXANDER PERSONAL MANAGEMENT Ltd
16 Roughdown Avenue
Hemel Hempstead, Hertfordshire HP3 9BH
e-mail: apm@onetel.net.uk
Fax: 01442 241099   Tel: 01442 252907

A.P.M. (LINDA FRENCH)
(See ALEXANDER PERSONAL MANAGEMENT Ltd)

ARLINGTON ENTERPRISES Ltd
1-3 Charlotte Street, London W1T 1RD
Website: www.arlingtonenterprises.co.uk
e-mail: info@arlington.enterprises.co.uk
Fax: 020-7580 4994   Tel: 020-7580 0702

BLACKBURN SACHS ASSOCIATES
88-90 Crawford Street
London W1H 2BS
Website: www.blackburnsachsassociates.com
e-mail: presenters@blackburnsachsassociates.com
Fax: 020-7258 6162   Tel: 020-7258 6158

BURNETT GRANGER ASSOCIATES Ltd
Prince of Wales Theatre
31 Coventry Street, London W1D 6AS
Fax: 020-7839 0438   Tel: 020-7839 0434

CAMERON Sara MANAGEMENT
At Take Three Management
110 Gloucester Avenue,
Primrose Hill, London NW1 8HX
e-mail: sara@take3management.com
Fax: 020-7209 3770   Tel: 020-7209 3777

CANTOR WISE REPRESENTATION
At Take Three Management
110 Gloucester Avenue
Primrose Hill, London NW1 8HX
e-mail: melanie@take3management.com
Fax: 020-7209 3770   Tel: 020-7209 3777

CHASE PERSONAL MANAGEMENT
The Barn, Hulseheath Lane
Mere, Cheshire WA16 6PR
e-mail: sue@sammon.fsnet.co.uk
Mobile: 07775 683955   Tel: 01565 830052

COMEDY CLUB
165 Peckham Rye, London SE15 3HZ
Website: www.comedyclub.org.uk
e-mail: comedyclub@cwcom.net
Fax: 020-7732 9292   Tel: 020-7732 3434

CRAWFORDS
6 Brook Street, London W1S 1BB
Website: www.crawfords.tv
e-mail: cr@wfords.com
Fax: 020-7355 1084   Tel: 020-7629 6464

CURTIS BROWN GROUP Ltd
(Sue Freathy, Julian Beynon)
Haymarket House, 28-29 Haymarket, London SW1Y 4SP
e-mail: presenters@curtisbrown.co.uk
Fax: 020-7396 0110   Tel: 020-7396 6600

CYBER 2000/IN THE CAN Ltd
20 Old Steine, Brighton BN1 1EL
Website: www.cyberartists.co.uk
e-mail: cyber.1@btclick.com
Fax: 01273 571085   Tel: 01273 671234

DAVID ANTHONY PROMOTIONS
PO Box 286, Warrington, Cheshire WA2 8GA
Website: www.davewarwick.co.uk
e-mail: dave@davewarwick.co.uk
Fax: 01925 416589   Tel: 01925 632496

DOWNES PRESENTERS AGENCY
96 Broadway, Bexleyheath, Kent DA6 7DE
e-mail: downes@presentersagency.com
Fax: 020-8301 5591   Tel: 020-8304 0541

DYNAMIC FX Ltd
(Magical Effect Designers & Performers)
Regent House, 291 Kirkdale, London SE26 4QD
e-mail: mail@dynamicfx.co.uk
Fax: 020-8659 8118   Tel: 020-8659 8130

EARNSHAW Susi MANAGEMENT
5 Brook Place, Barnet, Herts EN5 2DL
Website: www.susiearnshaw.co.uk
e-mail: casting@susiearnshaw.co.uk
Fax: 020-8364 9618   Tel: 020-8441 5010

EVANS Jacque MANAGEMENT Ltd
Top Floor Suite, 14 Holmesley Road, London SE23 1PJ
e-mail: jacque@jemltd.demon.co.uk
Fax: 020-8699 5192   Tel: 020-8699 1202

EXCELLENT TALENT COMPANY The
53 Goodge Street, London W1T 1TG
Website: www.excellentvoice.co.uk
e-mail: ruth@excellentvoice.co.uk
Fax: 020-7636 1631   Tel: 020-7636 1636

FBI AGENCY Ltd The
PO Box 250, Leeds LS1 2AZ
e-mail: j.spencer@fbi-agency.ltd.uk
                              Tel/Fax: 07050 222747

FLETCHER ASSOCIATES
(Broadcast & Media)
25 Parkway, London N20 0XN
Fax: 020-8361 8866   Tel: 020-8361 8061

FOX ARTIST MANAGEMENT Ltd
Concorde House
101 Shepherds Bush Road, London W6 7LP
e-mail: fox.artist@btinternet.com
Fax: 020-7603 2352   Tel: 020-7602 8822

GAY Noel ARTISTS
19 Denmark Street, London WC2H 8NA
Website: www.noelgay.com
Fax: 020-7287 1816   Tel: 020-7836 3941

GLASS Eric Ltd
25 Ladbroke Crescent
Notting Hill, London W11 1PS
e-mail: eglassltd@aol.com
Fax: 020-7229 6220   Tel: 020-7229 9500

GRANT James MANAGEMENT
Syon Lodge, 201 London Road
Isleworth, Middlesex TW7 5BH
Website: www.jamesgrant.co.uk
e-mail: enquiries@jamesgrant.co.uk
Fax: 020-8232 4101   Tel: 020-8232 4100

GURNETT J. PERSONAL MANAGEMENT Ltd
2 New Kings Road, London SW6 4SA
Website: www.jgpm.co.uk
e-mail: mail@jgpm.co.uk
Fax: 020-7736 5455   Tel: 020-7736 7828

HICKS Jeremy ASSOCIATES
11-12 Tottenham Mews, London W1T 4AG
Website: www.jeremyhicks.com
e-mail: hicksworld@aol.com
Fax: 020-7636 8880   Tel: 020-7636 8008

HOBBS Liz GROUP Ltd
68 Castlegate, Newark, Notts NG24 1BG
Website: www.lizhobbsgroup.com
e-mail: info@lizhobbsgroup.com
Fax: 0870 3337009   Tel: 08700 702702

HUGHES Jane MANAGEMENT
The Coach House
PO Box 123, Knutsford, Cheshire WA16 9HX
Fax: 01565 722211   Tel: 01565 723000

INTERNATIONAL ARTISTES Ltd
Mezzanine Floor
235 Regent Street, London W1B 2AX
e-mail: (name)@intart.co.uk
Fax: 020-7409 2070   Tel: 020-7439 8401

IVELAW-CHAPMAN Julie
The Chase, Chaseside Close
Cheddington, Beds LU7 0SA
e-mail: jic@collectorsworldwide.co.uk
Fax: 01296 662451   Tel: 01296 662441

JAYMEDIA
(Nigel Jay)
10A Crewe Road, Alsager, Cheshire ST7 2ES
e-mail: media@jaymedia.co.uk
Fax: 0870 1209079   Tel: 01270 884453

JLA (Jeremy Lee Associates Ltd)
4 Stratford Place, London W1C 1AT
e-mail: talk@jla.co.uk
Fax: 020-7907 2801   Tel: 020-7907 2800

KBJ MANAGEMENT Ltd
(TV Presenters)
7 Soho Street, London W1D 3DQ
e-mail: candida@kbjmgt.co.uk
Fax: 020-7287 1191   Tel: 020-7434 6767

KNIGHT AYTON MANAGEMENT
114 St Martin's Lane, London WC2N 4BE
Website: www.knightayton.co.uk
e-mail: info@knightayton.co.uk
Fax: 020-7836 8333   Tel: 020-7836 5333

LADKIN Michael PERSONAL MANAGEMENT
Suite 1, Ground Floor
1 Duchess Street, London W1W 6AN
Fax: 020-7436 4627   Tel: 020-7436 4626

MARKS PRODUCTIONS Ltd
2 Gloucester Gate Mews, London NW1 4AD
Fax: 020-7486 2165   Tel: 020-7486 2001

MARSH Billy ASSOCIATES Ltd
174-178 North Gower Street, London NW1 2NB
e-mail: bmarsh@bmarsh.demon.co.uk
Fax: 020-7388 6848   Tel: 020-7388 6858

McLEAN-WILLIAMS MANAGEMENT
212 Piccadilly, London W1J 9HG
e-mail: alex@mclean-williams.com
Fax: 020-7917 2805   Tel: 020-7917 2806

MEDIA PEOPLE
12 Nottingham Place
London W1M 3FA
Website: www.media-people.org
e-mail: info@celebrity.co.uk
Fax: 020-7224 6060   Tel: 020-7224 5050

MILES John ORGANISATION
Cadbury Camp Lane
Clapton-in-Gordano
Bristol BS20 7SB
e-mail: john@johnmiles.org.uk
Fax: 01275 810186   Tel: 012/5 854675

MPC ENTERTAINMENT
MPC House
15-16 Maple Mews, London NW6 5UZ
e-mail: mpc@mpce.com
Fax: 020-7624 4220   Tel: 020-7624 1184

NCI MANAGEMENT Ltd
51 Queen Anne Street, London W1G 9HS
e-mail: nicola@nci-management.com
Fax: 020-7935 1258   Tel: 020-7224 3960

NOEL John MANAGEMENT
2nd Floor, 10A Belmont Street, London NW1 8HH
e-mail: john@johnnoel.com
Fax: 020-7428 8401   Tel: 020-7428 8400

OFF THE KERB PRODUCTIONS
3rd Floor, Hammer House
113-117 Wardour Street, London W1F 0UN
Website: www.offthekerb.co.uk
e-mail: offthekerb@aol.com
Fax: 020-7437 0647   Tel: 020-7437 0607

22 Thornhill Crescent, London N1 1BJ
e-mail: info@offthekerb.co.uk
Fax: 020-7700 4646   Tel: 020-7700 4477

PHA CASTING
Tanzaro House
Ardwick Green North, Manchester M12 6FZ
Website: www.pha-agency.co.uk
e-mail: info@pha-agency.co.uk
Fax: 0161-273 4567   Tel: 0161-273 4444

PRINCESS TALENT MANAGEMENT
Newcombe House
45 Notting Hill Gate, London W11 3LQ
Website: www.princess.uk.com
e-mail: talent@princess.uk.com
Fax: 020-7908 1934   Tel: 020-7243 5100

PVA MANAGEMENT Ltd
Hallow Park, Hallow, Worcester WR2 6PG
e-mail: clients@pva.co.uk
Fax: 01905 641842   Tel: 01905 640663

QDOS Ltd
8 King Street, Covent Garden, London WC2E 8HN
e-mail: info@qdosentertainment.plc.uk
Fax: 020-7240 4956   Tel: 020-7240 5052

QUADRAPHOLD MANAGEMENT
Queens Chambers
Queen Street, Blackpool, Lancashire FY1 1PD
Website: www.quadraphold.com
e-mail: info@quadraphold.com
Fax: 01253 290019   Tel: 01253 311112

RAZZAMATAZZ MANAGEMENT
Crofters, East Park Lane
New Chapel, Surrey RH7 6HS
e-mail: mcgrogan@tinyworld.co.uk
Fax: 01342 835433   Tel: 01342 835359

RDF MANAGEMENT
48 Princes Place, Holland Place, London W11 4QA
e-mail: debi.allen@rdfmanagement.com
Fax: 020-7908 1363   Tel: 020-7908 1238

RHINO MANAGEMENT
Kobe House, Halstead Hill
Goffs Oak, Waltham Cross, Herts EN7 5NA
Website: www.rhino-management.co.uk
e-mail: rhino.management@virgin.net
Mobile: 07901 528988   Tel/Fax: 01992 638852

RK COMMERCIALS
205 Chudleigh Road, London SE4 1EG
Website: www.rkcommercials.com
e-mail: mail@rkcommercials.com
Fax: 020-8690 7999   Tel: 020-8690 6542

ROSEMAN ORGANISATION The
11 Grove Park Gardens, Chiswick, London W4 3RY
Website: www.theromanorganisation.co.uk
e-mail: info@theromanorganisation.co.uk
Fax: 020-8742 0554   Tel: 020-8742 0552

RUBY TALENT
Apartment 9, Goldcrest Building
1 Lexington Street, London W1F 9TA
e-mail: tara@ruby-talent.co.uk
Fax: 020-7439 1649   Tel: 020-7439 4554

SEVERN MANAGEMENT SERVICES
16 Graham Crescent, Rubery, Birmingham B45 9DD
Fax: 0121-693 0180   Tel: 0121-693 0190

SHAW Vincent ASSOCIATES Ltd
51 Byron Road, London E17 4SN
e-mail: info@vincentshaw.com
Fax: 020-8521 1588   Tel: 020-8509 2211

SILVER FOX ARTIST MANAGEMENT
8-18 Rampart Street, London E1 2LA
Website: www.silverfoxartist.co.uk
e-mail: enquiries@silverfoxartist.co.uk
Fax: 020-7791 2842   Tel: 020-7791 2952

SINGER Sandra ASSOCIATES
21 Cotswold Road, Westcliff on Sea, Essex SS0 8AA
Website: www.sandrasinger.com
e-mail: sandrasingeruk@aol.com
Fax: 01702 339393   Tel: 01702 331616

SOUTHWEST MANAGEMENT AND CASTING Ltd
The Courtyard, Whitchurch, Ross-on-Wye HR9 6DA
Website: www.southwestcasting.co.uk
e-mail: agent@southwestcasting.co.uk
Fax: 01600 891099   Tel: 01600 892005

SPEAK-EASY Ltd
1 Dairy Yard, High Street
Market Harborough, Leics LE16 7NL
Website: www.speak-easy.co.uk
e-mail: enquiries@speak-easy.co.uk
Fax: 01858 461994   Tel: 0870 0135126

STORM ARTISTS MANAGEMENT
4th Floor, 6-10 Lexington Street, London W1F 0LB
e-mail: info@stormartists.co.uk
Fax: 020-7437 4314   Tel: 020-7437 4313

SWEENEY MANAGEMENT
Ramilles House, 1-2 Ramilles Street, London W1F 7LN
e-mail: info@sweeneymanagement.co.uk
Fax: 020-7731 0103   Tel: 020-7731 6969

TAKE THREE MANAGEMENT
110 Gloucester Avenue, Primrose Hill, London NW1 8HX
e-mail: info@take3management.com
Fax: 020-7209 3770   Tel: 020-7209 3777

TALKBACK MANAGEMENT
20-21 Newman Street, London W1T 1PG
Fax: 020-7861 8061   Tel: 020-7861 8060

UNIQUE MANAGEMENT GROUP
Beaumont House, Kensington Village
Avonmore Road, London W14 8TS
e-mail: celebrities@uniquegroup.co.uk
Fax: 020-7605 1101   Tel: 020-7605 1100

VAGABOND HEART
2 Grassmere Road, Hornchurch, Essex RM11 3DP
e-mail: vagabond@virgin.net   Tel: 01708 781994

VENTURE ARTISTES
PO Box 299, Oxford OX2 6LN
e-mail: venture-artistes@msn.com
Fax: 07000 402002   Tel: 07000 402001

V R M
PO Box 82, Altrincham, Cheshire WA15 0QD
Fax: 0161-928 7849   Tel: 0161-928 3222

WHATEVER ARTISTS MANAGEMENT
1 York Street, London W1U 6PA
e-mail: wam@agents-uk.com
Fax: 020-7487 3311   Tel: 020-7487 3111

WILLCOCKS John MEDIA AGENCY Ltd
34 Carisbrook Close, Enfield, Middlesex EN1 3NB
Fax: 020-8292 5060   Tel: 020-8364 4556

WYPER Carolynne MANAGEMENT
2 Kimberley Road, London NW6 7SG
e-mail: info@soundtrck.cwm.co.uk
Fax: 020-7328 1444   Tel: 020-7328 8211

AD VOICE
Oxford House
76 Oxford Street, London W1D 1BS
Fax: 020-7323 0101   Tel: 020-7323 2345

ANOTHER TONGUE VOICES Ltd
48 Dean Street
London W1V 5HL
e-mail: info@anothertongue.com
Fax: 020-7494 3300   Tel: 020-7494 0300

ASQUITH & HORNER
Write with SAE
The Studio
14 College Road, Bromley, Kent BR1 3NS
Fax: 020-8313 0443   Tel: 020-8466 5580

BURNETT GRANGER ASSOCIATES Ltd
Prince of Wales Theatre
31 Coventry Street, London W1D 6AS
e-mail: bgavo@waitrose.com
Fax: 020-7839 0438   Tel: 020-7839 0434

CALYPSO VOICES
25-26 Poland Street, London W1F 8QN
e-mail: calypso@calypsovoices.com
Fax: 020-7437 0410   Tel: 020-7734 6415

CASTAWAY
3 Kingly Street, London W1B 5PD
Website: www.castaway.org.uk
e-mail: sheila@castaway.org.uk
Fax: 020-7287 2202   Tel: 020-7439 7414

CONWAY VAN GELDER Ltd
(Kate Plumpton)
3rd Floor, 18-21 Jermyn Street, London SW1Y 6HP
e-mail: kate@conwayvg.co.uk
Fax: 020-7494 3324   Tel: 020-7287 1070

CREATIVE CASTING
65 Hazelbank Terrace, Edinburgh EH11 1SL
e-mail: creativecasting@hotmail.com
                              Tel: 0131-478 5455

CYBER 2000/IN THE CAN Ltd
20 Old Steine, Brighton BN1 1EL
Website: www.cyberartists.co.uk
e-mail: cyber.1@btclick.com
Fax: 01273 571085   Tel: 01273 671234

DOUBLEFVOICES
(Singers Agency)
2 Pendrill Place
Cockmount Lane, Wadhurst, East Sussex TN5 6UE
e-mail: rob@doublefvoices.com
Mobile: 07976 927764   Tel: 01892 927764

DREW Bryan Ltd
Mezzanine, Quadrant House
80-82 Regent Street, London W1B 5AU
e-mail: bryan@bryandrewltd.com
Fax: 020-7437 0561   Tel: 020-7437 2293

EVANS O'BRIEN
115 Humber Road, London SE3 7LW
Website: www.evansobrien.co.uk
e-mail: eobvoice@dircon.co.uk
Fax: 020-8293 7066   Tel: 020-8293 7077

EXCELLENT VOICE COMPANY
53 Goodge Street, London W1T 1TG
Website: www.excellentvoice.co.uk
e-mail: info@excellentvoice.co.uk
Fax: 020-7636 1631   Tel: 020-7636 1636

FOREIGN VERSIONS Ltd
(Translation)
Bakerloo Chambers
304 Edgware Road, London W2 1DY
Website: www.foreignversions.com
e-mail: info@foreignversions.co.uk
Fax: 020-7723 5018   Tel: 020-7723 5744

GAY Noel VOICES
19 Denmark Street
London WC2H 8NA
Website: www.noelgay.com
Fax: 020-7287 1816   Tel: 020-7836 3941

GORDON & FRENCH
12-13 Poland Street, London W1F 8QB
e-mail: mail@gordonandfrench.net
Fax: 020-7734 4832   Tel: 020-7734 4818

HOBSON'S SINGERS
62 Chiswick High Road, London W4 1SY
e-mail: singers@hobsons-international.com
Fax: 020-8996 5350   Tel: 020-8995 3628

HOBSON'S VOICES
62 Chiswick High Road, London W4 1SY
e-mail: voices@hobsons-international.com
Fax: 020-8996 5330   Tel: 020-8995 3628

HOPE Sally ASSOCIATES
108 Leonard Street, London EC2A 4XS
e-mail: casting@sallyhope.biz
Fax: 020-7613 4848   Tel: 020-7613 5353

HOWARD Amanda ASSOCIATES
21 Berwick Street, London W1F 0PZ
Website: www.amandahowardassociates.co.uk
e-mail: mail@amandahowardassociates.co.uk
Fax: 020-7287 7785   Tel: 020-7287 9277

INTERNATIONAL ARTISTES VOICE OVERS
(Nicola Sandon)
Mezzanine Floor
235 Regent Street, London W1B 2AX
Website: www.intart.co.uk
e-mail: nikki@intart.co.uk
Fax: 020-7409 2665   Tel: 020-7434 7820

LIP SERVICE
4 Kingly Street
London W1B 5PE
Website: www.lipservice.co.uk
e-mail: bookings@lipservice.co.uk
Fax: 020-7734 3373   Tel: 020-7734 3393

LONDON MANAGEMENT
2-4 Noel Street, London W1F 8GB
Fax: 020-7287 3036   Tel: 020-7287 9000

MANSON Andrew
(Genuine Americans only)
288 Munster Road, London SW6 6BQ
Website: www.talentroom.com
e-mail: amanson@aol.com
Fax: 020-7381 8874   Tel: 020-7386 9158

MARKHAM & FROGGATT Ltd
4 Windmill Street
London W1P 1HF
e-mail: fiona@markhamfroggatt.co.uk
Fax: 020-7637 5233   Tel: 020-7636 4412

do you know how to judge a quality voice-over showreel?

Consistently produce Showreels of the highest Standard.
David Hodge - Hobson's Voices

Definitely the best Showreels
Penny Warnes - Earache Voice Agency

Very high quality. I've always been impressed
Sheila Britten - Castaway Voice Agency

A professional and high quality Showreel
Penny Brown - Voicecall

the voice agencies do.

Call for your FREE one Hour consultation worth £80

Your FREE consultation is designed to find your vocal qualities in order to successfully plan your showreel so that it is effective in selling your voice to the correct audience.
These qualities determine the type of work you'll be booked for and hence drive which scripts you record on your Showreel. We spend time selecting the right material for your voice because there is no point recording material you will never be booked for. The consultation is FREE and you are not committed in anyway to book a Showreel.

We produce your showreel in exactly the same way as the industry would produce commercial work.
We don't produce demos we produce the real thing, real commercials, real documentaries and real talking books. We place your voice with the right script and the right music to create a totally authentic package. The listener believes they are hearing your voice doing real work because in essence they are.

We never re-cycle a script.
Because your Voice Showreel is the first thing an agent or client hears it is essential that they hear a fresh script and not one they have heard before. For this reason we never re-cycle a script ensuring the Showreel is as individual as you are.

Choose the Showreel package to suite you and your budget.
All of our Showreel packages can be customised. Choose from a selection of voice training, recording sessions and high quality duplication services. This gives you the flexibility to tailor your Showreel package to your needs.

Choose from a selection of Voice-over, Singing and Character showreels.
If you're a voice artist, singer or actor you can choose the Showreel to fit your talents. We provide the same high quality service to voice artists, singers and actors with the same high quality results.

We master, duplicate and print our CD's in full colour with 'on-body' printing.
This means that we never put a sticky label on your duplicated CD's and lower the quality of the final Showreel. Best of all we include duplicated CD's in each of our Showreel packages for FREE.

Your duplicated Showreel in your hand at the end of the session.
Not only is the CD quality superior but because we produce our CD's in house you can have your Showreel duplications in your hand at the end of the session. So you don't have to wait for a delivery to move your career forward.

Comfortable, soundproofed, air-conditioned Studios
Our two studios and vocal booths are fully soundproofed and air-conditioned with ample room to relax and focus on your Showreel.

Top of the line 64 track Pro Tools Digital recording environment .
The audio quality of the Showreel is essential in professionally presenting your voice to agencies and clients. Because of this we have invested heavily in the best equipment creating a totally silent Digital environment where the only thing on the Showreel is what we put there.

Industry Contacts provided FREE.
Our website provides instant access to industry contacts along with a wealth of related information to help you succeed.

Learn everything you need to know from the UK's online Voice Community at theshowreel.co.uk
Our website hosts the UK's only online Voice Community where you can share your knowledge and experience with other professionals.

Call **(020) 8995 3232** to claim your free consultation or visit the web site at **www.theshowreel.co.uk**

the**Showreel**
trust us to get it right

Knightsbridge House, 229 Acton Lane, Chiswick, London W4 5DD   tel (020) 8995 3232   email info@theshowreel.co.uk

MBA
3rd Floor Suite
10-11 Lower John Street
London W1F 9EB
e-mail: info@braidman.com
Fax: 020-7439 3600   Tel: 020-7437 0817

McREDDIE Ken Ltd
91 Regent Street, London W1B 4EL
Fax: 020-7734 6530   Tel: 020-7439 1456

NATURAL VOICE
2 Meard Street
London W1 5AR
Fax: 020-7439 0582   Tel: 020-7439 0581

NOEL John MANAGEMENT
2nd Floor
10A Belmont Street, London NW1 8HH
e-mail: john@johnnoel.com
Fax: 020-7428 8401   Tel: 020-7428 8400

NUTOPIA VOICES
Number 8
132 Charing Cross Road, London WC2H 0LA
Website: www.nutopia.co.uk
                           Tel/Fax: 020-8882 6299

P F D
Drury House
34-43 Russell Street, London WC2B 5HA
Fax: 020-7836 9539   Tel: 020-7344 1000

QVOICE
8 King street
Covent Garden, London WC2E 8HN
Website: www.qvoice.co.uk
e-mail: info@qvoice.co.uk
Fax: 020-7240 4956   Tel: 020-7420 6825

RABBIT VOCAL MANAGEMENT
2nd Floor
18 Broadwick Street, London W1F 8HS
Website: www.rabbit.uk.net
e-mail: info@rabbit.uk.net
Fax: 020-7287 6566   Tel: 020-7287 6466

RHUBARB
Bakerloo Chambers
304 Edgware Road, London W2 1DY
Website: www.rhubarb.co.uk
e-mail: enquiries@rhubarb.co.uk
Fax: 020-7724 1030   Tel: 020-7724 1300

SHINING MANAGEMENT Ltd
82C Shirland Road, London W9 2EQ
Website: www.shiningvoices.com
e-mail: info@shiningvoices.com
Fax: 020-7286 6123   Tel: 020-7286 6092

SOMMERFIELD Ltd
35 Old Queen Street, London SW1H 9JD
Fax: 020-7654 5226   Tel: 020-7222 9070

SOUTHWEST MANAGEMENT AND CASTING Ltd
The Courtyard
Whitchurch, Ross-on-Wye HR9 6DA
Website: www.southwestcasting.co.uk
e-mail: agent@southwestcasting.co.uk
Fax: 01600 891099   Tel: 01600 892005

SPEAK Ltd
140 Devonshire Road
Chiswick, London W4 2AW
Website: www.speak-voices.com
e-mail: speak@dircon.co.uk
Fax: 020-8742 1333   Tel: 020-8742 1001

SPEAK-EASY Ltd
1 Dairy Yard, High Street
Market Harborough, Leicestershire LE16 7NL
Website: www.speak-easy.co.uk
e-mail: enquiries@speak-easy.co.uk
Fax: 01858 461994   Tel: 0870 0135126

SPEAKERS CORNER AT CRAWFORDS
6 Brook Street, London W1S 1BB
e-mail: vo@crawfords.tv
Fax: 020-7355 1084   Tel: 020-7629 6464

STONE Richard PARTNERSHIP The
2 Henrietta Street, London WC2E 8PS
e-mail: all@richstonepart.co.uk
Fax: 020-7497 0869   Tel: 020-7497 0849

SUMMERS Mark MANAGEMENT & AGENCY
14 Russell Garden Mews
London W14 8EU
e-mail: info@marksummers.com
Fax: 0870 4435623　　　Tel: 0870 4435621

TALKING HEADS
88-90 Crawford Street
London W1H 2BS
Website: www.talkingheadsvoices.com
e-mail: voices@talkingheadsvoices.com
Fax: 020-7258 6162　　　Tel: 020-7258 6161

TERRY Sue VOICES Ltd
18 Broadwick Street
London W1F 8HS
Website: www.sueterryvoices.co.uk
Fax: 020-7434 2042　　　Tel: 020-7434 2040

TONGUE & GROOVE
3 Stevenson Square
Manchester M1 1DN
Website: www.tongueandgroove.co.uk
e-mail: info@tongueandgroove.co.uk
Fax: 0161-237 1809　　　Tel: 0161-228 2469

VACCA Roxane VOICES
73 Beak Street, London W1F 9SR
Website: www.voiceover.org.uk
e-mail: mail@roxanevaccavoices.com
Fax: 020-7734 8086　　　Tel: 020-7734 8085

VOCAL POINT
25 Denmark Street, London WC2H 8NJ
Website: www.vocalpoint.net
e-mail: enquiries@vocalpoint.net
Fax: 020-7419 0699　　　Tel: 020-7419 0700

VOICE & SCRIPT INTERNATIONAL
Aradco Hse, 132 Cleveland St, London W1T 6AB
Website: www.vsi.tv　　　e-mail: info@vsi.tv
Fax: 020-7692 7711　　　Tel: 020-7692 7700

VOICE BOX
PO Box 82, Altrincham, Cheshire WA15 0QD
Website: www.thevoicebox.co.uk
Fax: 0161-928 7849　　　Tel: 0161-928 3222

VOICE SHOP
Bakerloo Chambers, 304 Edgware Rd, London W2 1DY
Website: www.voice-shop.co.uk
e-mail: info@voice-shop.co.uk
Fax: 020-7706 1002　　　Tel: 020-7402 3966

VOICE SQUAD
62 Blenheim Gardens, London NW2 4NT
Website: www.voicesquad.com
e-mail: bookem@voicesquad.com
Fax: 020-8452 7944   Tel: 020-8450 4451

VOICEBANK, THE IRISH VOICE OVER AGENCY
The Barracks
76 Irishtown Road, Dublin 4, Ireland
Website: www.voicebank.ie
e-mail: voicebank@voicebank.ie
Fax: 00 353 1 6607850   Tel: 00 353 1 6687234

VOICECALL
67A Gondar Gardens, London NW6 1EP
e-mail: voicecall@blueyonder.co.uk
                                Tel: 020-7209 1064

VOICES Ltd
2 Kirkgate Lane
Wighton
Wells-next-the-Sea, Norfolk NR23 1PL
Fax: 01328 820951   Tel: 01328 820950

WOOTTON Suzy VOICES
75 Shelley Street
Kingsley, Northampton NN2 7HZ
e-mail: suzy@suzywoottonvoices
Fax: 0870 7659668   Tel: 0870 7659660

YAKETY YAK
8 Bloomsbury Square, London WC1A 2NE
Website: www.yaketyyak.co.uk
e-mail: yakyak@netcomuk.co.uk
Fax: 020-7404 6109   Tel: 020-7430 2600

Animals

A1 ANIMALS
(Farm, Domestic & Exotic Animals)
Folly Farm, Folly Lane, Bramley, Hants RG26 5BD
Website: www.a1animals.co.uk
e-mail: info@a1animals.freeserve.co.uk
Fax: 01256 880653   Tel: 01256 880993

ABNALLS HORSES
Abnalls Farm
Cross in Hand Lane, Lichfield, Staffs WS13 8DZ
e-mail: wofford@iname.com
Fax: 01543 417226   Tel: 01543 417075

ALTERNATIVE ANIMALS
(Animatronics/Taxidermy)
28 Greaves Road, High Wycombe, Bucks HP13 7JU
Website: www.animalworld.org.uk
e-mail: animalworld@bushinternet.com
Fax: 01494 441385   Tel: 01494 448710

AMAZING STUNT DOGS
18 Rosewood Avenue
Kingsway, Rugby, Warwickshire CV22 5PJ
Website: www.amazingstuntdogs.co.uk
Mobile: 07759 804813   Tel: 01788 812703

ANIMAL ACTING
(Stunts, Prop, Horse-Drawn Vehicles)
15 Wolstenvale Close
Middleton, Manchester M24 2HP
Website: www.animalacting.com
e-mail: information@animalacting.com
Fax: 0161-655 3700   Tel: 0800 387755

ANIMAL ACTORS
95 Ditching Road, Brighton
Sussex BN1 4ST   Tel: 020-8654 0450

ANIMAL AMBASSADORS
Old Forest, Hampstead Norreys Road
Hermitage, Berks RG18 9SA
e-mail: kayweston@tiscali.co.uk
Mobile: 07831 558594   Tel/Fax: 01635 200900

ANIMAL ARK
(Animals & Animal Prop Shop)
Studio, 29 Somerset Road
Brentford, Middlesex TW8 8BT
Website: www.animal-ark.co.uk
e-mail: info@animal-ark.co.uk
Fax: 020-8560 5762   Tel: 020-8560 3029

ANIMAL ARRANGERS
(Animal Suppliers & Co-ordinators)
19 Greaves Road, High Wycombe, Bucks HP13 7JU
e-mail: 07956564715@one2one.net
Fax: 01494 441385   Tel: 01494 442750

ANIMAL CASTING
11 Tudor Avenue, Worcester Park, Surrey KT4 8TY
e-mail: silcresta@aol.com
Mobile: 07956 246450   Tel: 020-8330 6710

ANIMAL EXTRAS
(Donkeys, Ponies, Farm Animals etc)
Ground Floor Offices, 3 Polmorla Road,
Wadebridge, Cornwall PL27 7ND
Fax: 01208 816645   Tel: 01208 816640

ANIMAL WELFARE FILMING FEDERATION
28 Greaves Road, High Wycombe
Bucks HP13 7JU   Mobile: 07798 831768

ANIMAL WELFARE INSPECTION SERVICES
(Independent Consultancy of All Aspects of Use of
Animals in Media Productions)
15B St Annes Road, Eastbourne BN21 2AJ
e-mail: animal.insp.svcs@amserve.net
    Tel/Fax: 01323 726105

ANIMAL WORLD
19 Greaves Road, High Wycombe, Bucks HP13 7JU
Website: www.animalworld.org.uk
e-mail: animalworld@bushinternet.com
Fax: 01494 441385   Tel: 01494 442750

ANIMALATION
16 Wiltshire Avenue, Crowthorne, Berks RG45 6NG
Fax: 01344 779437   Tel: 01344 775244

ANIMALS GALORE
208 Smallfield Road, Horley, Surrey RH6 9LS
Fax: 01342 841546   Tel: 01342 842400

ANIMALS O KAY
3 Queen Street, Chipperfield
Kings Langley, Herts WD4 9BT
Website: www.animalsokay.com
e-mail: kay@animalsokay.com
Fax: 01923 269076   Tel: 01923 291277

ANTHEA'S EQUINES
(BHS Approved, Large Schooled Quality Horses,
Ponies, Cobs for Film)
Wildwoods Riding Centre
Ebbisham Lane, Walton-on-the-Hill, Surrey KT20 5BH
e-mail: info@wildwoodsriding.co.uk
Tel/Fax: 01737 814872   Tel: 01737 812146

A-Z ANIMALS Ltd
The Bell House, Bell Lane, Fetcham, Surrey KT22 9ND
e-mail: xlence@a-zanimals.com
Fax: 01372 377666   Tel: 01372 377111

A-Z DOGS
The Bell House, Bell Lane, Fetcham, Surrey KT22 9ND
e-mail: dogs@a-zanimals.com
Fax: 01372 377666   Tel: 020-7248 6222

BOORMAN-WOODS Sue
(Specialising in Domestic Cats, Rodents,
Poultry & Farm Stock)
White Rocks Farm
Underriver, Sevenoaks, Kent TN15 0SL
Website: www.animalspromotions.co.uk
Fax: 01732 763767   Tel: 01732 762913

BUGS & THINGS
28 Greaves Road, High Wycombe, Bucks HP13 7JU
Website: www.animalworld.org.uk
e-mail: 07956564715@one2one.net
Fax: 01494 441385   Tel: 01494 448710

CANINE FILM ACADEMY The
57C Cheapside Road, Ascot, Berks SL5 7QR
Website: www.thecaninefilmacademy.com
e-mail: katie.cfa@virgin.net
Mobile: 07767 341424   Tel: 01344 291465

CAVALRY & OTHER HORSES
(James Mackie)
Cownham Farm, Broadwell
Moreton in Marsh, Gloucestershire GL56 0TT
e-mail: jamesmackie@cownham.fsnet.co.uk
Fax: 01451 832442   Tel: 01451 830294

CHEESEMAN Virginia
3 Sutton Road, Heston
Hounslow, Middlesex TW5 0PG
Website: www.virginiacheeseman.co.uk
e-mail: virginia@virginiacheeseman.co.uk
    Tel/Fax: 020-8572 0414

CLIFT Pauline
15 Gwendale, Pinkneys Green
Maidenhead, Berks SL6 6SH
e-mail: paulineclift@btclick.com
    Tel/Fax: 01628 788564

COTSWOLD FARM PARK
(Rare Breeds Survival Centre)
Guiting Power
Cheltenham, Gloucestershire GL54 5UG
Fax: 01451 850423   Tel: 01451 850307

CREATURE FEATURE
(Animal Agent)
Gubhill Farm, Ae, Dumfries, Scotland DG1 1RL
Website: www.creaturefeature.co.uk
e-mail: david@creaturefeature.co.uk
Mobile: 07770 774866   Tel/Fax: 01387 860648

DUDLEY YVONNE
(Glamour Dog)
55 Cambridge Park, Wanstead
London E11 2PU   Tel: 020-8989 1528

EAST NOLTON RIDING STABLES
Nolton, Nr Newgale
Haverfordwest, Pembrokeshire SA62 3NW
Fax: 01437 710967   Tel: 01437 710360

FILM HORSES
(Horses, Saddlery, Equestrian Centre)
The Shire Horse Centre, Bath Road
Littlewick Green, Maidenhead, Berks SL6 3QA
Mobile: 07831 629662   Tel/Fax: 01628 822770

A

FREE ANIMAL CONSULTANT SERVICES
28 Greaves Road, High Wycombe, Bucks HP13 7JU
Fax: 01494 441385   Tel: 08000 749383

GET STUFFED
(Taxidermy)
105 Essex Road, London N1 2SL
Website: www.thegetstuffed.co.uk
e-mail: taxidermy@thegetstuffed.co.uk
Fax: 020-7359 8253   Tel: 020-7226 1364

GRAY Robin COMMENTARIES
(Equestrian Equipment)
Comptons, Isington
Alton, Hants GU34 4PL   Tel: 01420 23347

HEATHER'S HEAVY HORSES
Botany Bay Farm
The Ridgeway, Enfield
Middlesex EN2 8AP   Tel/Fax: 020-8364 5979

HORSEPOWER
(Hilary Parren)
Bekesbourne Stables
Aerodrome Road, Bekesbourne
Kent CT4 5EX   Tel: 01227 830910

KNIGHTS OF ARKLEY The
Glyn Sylen Farm, Five Roads, Llanelli SA15 5BJ
Website: www.knightsofarkley.com
e-mail: penny@knightsofarkley.fsnet.co.uk
                                      Tel/Fax: 01269 861001

McLEOD Janis
(Dogs, Trick Performing, Shaggy Cross-Breed for TV
Appearances & Commercials)
10 Edinburgh Road, Wallasey, Merseyside CH45 4LR
e-mail: janswonderdogs@aol.com
Mobile: 07818 263147   Tel/Fax: 0151-200 7174

MILLENNIUM BUGS
(Live Insects)
28 Greaves Road, High Wycombe, Bucks HP13 7JU
e-mail: animalworld@bushinternet.com
Fax: 01494 441385   Tel: 01494 448710

MORTON Geoff
(Shire Horse & Equipment)
Hasholme Carr Farm
Holme on Spalding Moor
York YO43 4BD   Tel: 01430 860393

OTTERS
(Tame Otters, Daphne & Martin Neville)
Baker's Mill, Frampton Mansell, Stroud, Glos GL6 8JH
e-mail: martin.neville@ukgateway.net
                                      Tel: 01285 760234

PATCHETTS EQUESTRIAN CENTRE
Hillfield Lane, Aldenham, Watford, Herts WD25 8PE
Website: www.patchetts.co.uk
Fax: 01923 859289   Tel: 01923 855776

PROP FARM Ltd
(Pat Ward)
Grange Farm, Elmton
Nr Creswell, North Derbyshire S80 4LX
e-mail: pat/les@propfarm.free-online.co.uk
Fax: 01909 721465   Tel: 01909 723100

RATS!
(Trained Fancy Rats and Handler)
e-mail: esbat@blueyonder.co.uk   Tel: 020-8683 2173

ROCKWOOD ANIMALS ON FILM
Lewis Terrace, Llanbradach, Caerphilly CF83 3JZ
Website: www.rockwoodanimals.com
e-mail: rockwood@globalnet.co.uk
Mobile: 07973 930983   Tel: 029-2088 5420

SCHOOL OF NATIONAL EQUITATION Ltd
(Sam Humphrey)
Bunny Hill Top, Costock, Loughborough LE12 6XE
Website: www.bunny-hill.co.uk
e-mail: sam@bunny-hill.co.uk
Fax: 01509 856067   Tel: 01509 852366

STUDIO & TV HIRE
(Stuffed Animal Specialists)
3 Ariel Way, Wood Lane, White City, London W12 7SL
Website: www.stvhire.com
e-mail: enquiries@stvhire.com
Fax: 020-8740 9662   Tel: 020-8749 3445

STUNT DOGS
3 The Chestnuts, Clifton, Deddington, Oxon OX15 0PE
e-mail: gill@euro-stuntdogs.co.uk
                                      Tel/Fax: 01869 338546

SUZANNE'S RIDING SCHOOL
(Rural Surroundings)
Copse & Brookshill Farms, Brookshill Drive
Harrow Weald, Middlesex HA3 6SB
Fax: 020-8420 6461   Tel: 020-8954 3618

TATE Olive
(Trained Dogs & Cats)
49 Upton Road, Bexleyheath, Kent DA6 8LW
Mobile: 07710 933163   Tel/Fax: 020-8303 0683

TATE'S Nigel DOGSTARS
17 Papion Grove
Walderslade Woods, Chatham, Kent ME5 9BS
Website: www.dogstars.co.uk
e-mail: animals@dogstars.co.uk
Fax: 01634 327447   Tel: 01634 869634

THORNE'S OF WINDSOR
(Beekeeping and Other Insect Suppliers)
Oakley Green Farm
Oakley Green, Windsor, Berks SL4 4PZ
e-mail: mattallan@aol.com
Fax: 01753 830605   Tel: 01753 830256

WELLINGTON RIDING
Basingstoke Road, Heckfield RG27 0LJ
Fax: 0118-932 6661   Tel: 0118-932 6308

WHITE DOVE COMPANY Ltd The
(Provision of up to 100 Doves for Release)
The Dovecote
9-11 High Beech Road, Loughton, Essex IG10 4BN
Website: www.thewhitedovecompany.co.uk
e-mail: thewhitedovecompany@llneone.net
Fax: 020-8502 2461   Tel: 020-8508 1414

WOLF AND HOUND SPECIALISTS The
Butler's Farm, Beenham, Reading, Berks RG7 5NT
Website: www.ukwolf.org
e-mail: ukwct@ukwolf.org   Tel: 0118-971 3330

ARTS COUNCIL OF WALES - MID & WEST WALES OFFICE
Ceredigion, Camarthenshire, Pembrokeshire, Powys,
Swansea, Neath, Port Talbot
6 Gardd Llydaw
Jackson's Lane, Carmarthen SA31 1QD
Fax: 01267 233084   Tel: 01267 234248

ARTS COUNCIL OF WALES - NORTH WALES
Anglesey, Gwynedd, Conwy
Denbighshire, Flintshire, Wrexham
36 Prince's Drive, Colwyn Bay, Conwy LL29 8LA
e-mail: information@ccc-acw.org.uk
Fax: 01492 533677   Tel: 01492 533440

EAST ENGLAND ARTS
Norfolk, Suffolk, Bedfordshire, Cambridgeshire, Essex,
Hertfordshire and the unitary authorities of Luton,
Peterborough, Southend-on-Sea and Thurrock
Eden House
48-49 Bateman Street, Cambridge CB2 1LR
Website: www.eastenglandarts.co.uk
e-mail: info@eearts.co.uk
Fax: 0870 242271   Tel: 01223 454400

EAST MIDLANDS ARTS
Derbyshire (excluding High Peak District),
Leicestershire, Lincolnshire, Rutland, Northamptonshire,
Nottinghamshire
Mountfields House
Epinal Way, Loughborough, Leics LE11 0QE
Fax: 01509 262214   Tel: 01509 218292

LONDON ARTS
The arts funding and development agency for the
32 London boroughs and the Corporation of London.
Joined with the Arts Council of England on 1 April 2002
2 Pear Tree Court, London EC1R 0DS
Website: www.arts.org.uk/londonarts
e-mail: info@lonab.co.uk
Fax: 020-7608 4100   Tel: 020-7608 6100

NORTH WEST ARTS BOARD
Greater Manchester, Merseyside
Lancashire, Cheshire & Cumbria
Manchester House
22 Bridge Street, Manchester M3 3AB
Website: www.arts.org.uk/nwab
e-mail: info@nwarts.co.uk
Fax: 0161-834 6969   Tel: 0161-834 6644

NORTHERN ARTS
Teeside, Durham, Northumberland, Tyne and Wear
Central Square, Forth Street
Newcastle-upon-Tyne NE1 3PJ
Website: www.northernarts.org
e-mail: info@northernarts.org.uk
Fax: 0191-230 1020   Tel: 0191-255 8500

SOUTH WEST ARTS
The unitary authorities of Bristol, Bath, Torbay
Plymouth and the counties of Devon, Cornwall,
Gloucestershire, Somerset and Dorset
(except Bournemouth, Christchurch & Poole)
Bradninch Place, Gandy Street, Exeter, Devon EX4 3LS
Website: www.swa.co.uk
e-mail: info@swa.co.uk   Tel: 01392 218188

SOUTHERN ARTS
Buckinghamshire, Hampshire, Isle of Wight, Oxfordshire,
Wiltshire, County areas of Berkshire and SE Dorset.
13 St Clement Street, Winchester, Hants SO23 9DQ
Website: www.arts.org.uk
e-mail: info@southernarts.co.uk
Fax: 01962 861186   Tel: 01962 855099

SOUTHERN & SOUTH EAST ARTS (WINCHESTER OFFICE)
Slough, Southampton, West Berkshire, Windsor,
Wokingham and Maidenhead.
13 St. Clement Street
Winchester, Hampshire SO23 9DQ
Fax: 0870 2421257   Tel: 01962 855099

SOUTHERN & SOUTH EAST ARTS (TUNBRIDGE WELLS OFFICE)
Kent, Surrey, East & West Sussex, and the unitary
authorities of Brighton & Hove, Medway, Bucks,
Hampshire, Isle of Wight, Oxfordshire, Bracknell Forest,
Milton Keynes, Portsmouth and Reading.
Union House, Eridge Road
Tunbridge Wells, Kent TN4 8HF
Fax: 0870 2421259   Tel: 01892 507200

WEST MIDLANDS ARTS
Herefordshire, Worcestershire, Staffordshire,
Warwickshire and Shropshire, Stoke on Trent,
Telford and Wrekin & districts of Birmingham, Coventry,
Dudley, Sandwell, Solihull, Walsall & Wolverhampton
82 Granville Street, Birmingham B1 2LH
Website: www.west-midlands.arts.org.uk
e-mail: info@west-midlands-arts.co.uk
Fax: 0121-643 7239   Tel: 0121-631 3121

YORKSHIRE ARTS
Yorkshire & Humberside
21 Bond Street, Dewsbury, West Yorks WF13 1AX
Website: www.arts.org.uk
e-mail: info@yarts.co.uk
Fax: 01924 466522   Tel: 01924 455555

ALDERSHOT
West End Centre (SA)
Queens Road, Aldershot, Hants GU11 3JD
Admin: 01252 408040   BO: 01252 330040

ANDOVER
Cricklade Theatre
Charlton Road, Andover, Hants SP10 1EJ
Arts Administrator: Holly Bednal
e-mail: hbednal@cricklade.ac.uk
Fax: 01264 360066   Tel: 01264 360063

BAMPTON
West Ox Arts
WOA Gallery, Market Square
Bampton, Oxfordshire OX18 2JH
Administrator: Abigail Ballinger
e-mail: www.westoxarts@yahoo.co.uk
                          Tel: 01993 850137

BANGOR
Theatr Gwynedd, Ffordd Deiniol
Bangor, Gwynedd LL57 2TL
Website: www.theatrgwynedd.com
e-mail: theatr@theatrgwynedd.co.uk
BO: 01248 351708   Admin: 01248 351707

BEDHAMPTON
(See HAVANT)

BILLERICAY
Billericay Arts Association
The Fold
72 Laindon Road, Billericay, Essex CM12 9LD
Secretary: Edmond Philpott   Tel: 01277 659286

BINGLEY
Bingley Arts Centre
Main Street, Bingley, West Yorkshire BD16 2LZ
Head of Halls: Mark Davies   Tel: 01274 751576

BIRMINGHAM
The Custard Factory
Gibb Street, Digbeth, Birmingham B9 4AA
Website: www.custardfactory.com
e-mail: custardfactory@clara.net
Fax: 0121-604 8888   Tel: 0121-693 7777

BIRMINGHAM
Midlands Arts Centre (MAC)
Cannon Hill Park, Birmingham B12 9QH
Director: Dorothy Wilson
BO: 0121-440 3838   Admin: 0121-440 4221

BOSTON
Blackfriars Arts Centre (EMA)
Spain Lane, Boston, Lincolnshire PE21 6HP
Website: www.blackfriars.uk.com
e-mail: marketing@blackfriars.uk.com
Fax: 01205 358855   Tel: 01205 363108

BRACKNELL
South Hill Park Arts Centre
Ringsmead, Bracknell RG12 7PA
Chief Executive: Ron McAllister
e-mail: southhillpark.org.uk
Fax: 01344 411427   Tel: 01344 484858

BRADFORD
Theatre in the Mill, University of Bradford,
Shearbridge Road, Bradford, West Yorkshire BD7 1DP
Artistic Director: Andrew Loretto
e-mail: theatre-manager@brad.ac.uk
                          Tel: 01274 233188

BRAINTREE
The Town Hall Centre (EEA)
Market Square, Braintree, Essex CM7 3YG
General Manager: Jean Grice   Tel: 01376 557776

BRENTFORD
Watermans (LA)
40 High Street, Brentford, Middlesex TW8 0DS
Fax: 020-8232 1030
BO: 020-8232 1010   Admin: 020-8232 1020

BRIDGWATER
Bridgwater Arts Centre (SWA)
11-13 Castle Street, Bridgwater, Somerset TA6 3DD
Website: www.bridgwaterart.org.uk
e-mail: c.dearden-bac@totalserve.co.uk
                          Tel: 01278 422700

BRIGHTON
Gardner Arts Centre
University of Sussex, Falmer, Brighton BN1 9RA
Director: Sue Webster
Fax: 01273 678551
BO: 01273 685861   Admin: 01273 685447

BRISTOL
Arnolfini, 16 Narrow Quay, Bristol BS1 4QA
Operations Manager: Polly Cole
Director: Caroline Collier
e-mail: arnolfini@arnolfini.demon.co.uk
Fax: 0117-925 3876   Tel: 0117-929 9191

BUILTH WELLS
Wyeside Arts Centre (ACW)
Castle Street, Builth Wells, Powys LD2 3BN
Fax: 01982 553995   Tel: 01982 553668

BURTON UPON TRENT
The Brewhouse
Union Street, Burton upon Trent, Staffs DE14 1EB
Director: Clive Lyttle
General Manager: Mike Mear
Website: www.brewhouse.co.uk
e-mail: info@brewhouse.co.uk
Fax: 01283 515106
BO: 01283 516030   Admin: 01283 567720

BURY
The Met Arts Centre
Market Street, Bury, Lancs BL9 0BW
Director: Ged Kelly
e-mail: mail@metarts.demon.co.uk
Fax: 0161-763 5056
BO: 0161-761 2216   Admin: 0161-761 7107

CANNOCK
Prince of Wales Centre
Church Sreet, Cannock, Staffs WS11 1DE
General Manager: Richard Kay   Tel: 01543 466453

CARDIFF
Chapter Arts Centre
Market Road, Canton, Cardiff CF5 1QE
Theatre Programmer: James Tyson
BO: 029-2030 4400   Admin: 029-2031 1050

CHESTERFIELD
The Arts Centre (EMA)
Chesterfield College
Sheffield Road, Chesterfield
Derbyshire S41 7LL
Co-ordinator: Joe Littlewood Tel/Fax: 01246 500578

CHIPPING NORTON
The Theatre (SA)
2 Spring Street
Chipping Norton, Oxon OX7 5NL
Director: Simon Stallworthy
General Manager: Chris Durham
Website: www.chippingnortontheatre.co.uk
e-mail: admin@chippingnortontheatre.co.uk
Fax: 01608 642324
BO: 01608 642350   Admin: 01608 642349

CHRISTCHURCH
The Regent Centre (SA)
51 High Street, Christchurch, Dorset BH23 1AS
General Manager: David Hopkins
Website: www.regentcentre.co.uk
e-mail: info@regentcentre.co.uk
Fax: 01202 479952
BO: 01202 499148   Admin: 01202 479819

CIRENCESTER
Brewery Arts
Brewery Court, Cirencester, Glos GL7 1JH
Artistic Director: Dan Scrivener
e-mail: admin@breweryarts.freeserve.co.uk
Fax: 01285 644060
BO: 01285 655522   Admin: 01285 657181

COLCHESTER
Colchester Arts Centre (EEA), Church Street,
Colchester, Essex CO1 1NF
Director: Anthony Roberts
Website: www.colchesterartscentre.com
e-mail: colchester.artscentre@virgin.net
                              Tel: 01206 500900

CORNWALL
Sterts Theatre & Arts Centre, Upton Cross, Liskeard,
Cornwall PL14 5AZ
Tel/Fax: 01579 362962   Tel/Fax: 01579 362382

COVENTRY
Warwick Arts Centre
University of Warwick, Coventry CV4 7AL
Director: Alan Rivett
Website: www.warwickcentre.co.uk
e-mail: arts.centre@warwick.ac.uk
BO: 024-7652 4524   Admin: 024-7652 3734

CUMBERNAULD
Cumbernauld Theatre
Kildrum, Cumbernauld G67 2BN
Administrator: Debbie Murdoch
Artistic Director: Simon Sharkey
Fax: 01236 738408
BO: 01236 732887   Admin: 01236 737235

DARLINGTON
Darlington Arts Centre
Vane Terrace, Darlington
County Durham DL3 7AX
BO: 01325 486555   Admin: 01325 483271

DORSET
Bryanston Arts Centre
Blandford Forum, Dorset DT11 0PX
Administrator: Sarah Moore
e-mail: bac@bryanston.co.uk
Fax: 01258 484506   Tel: 01258 456533

EDINBURGH
Netherbow
Scottish Storytelling Centre
The Netherbow
43-45 High Street, Edinburgh EH1 1SR
Director: Dr Donald Smith
Website: www.storytellingcentre.org.uk
e-mail: netherbow-storytelling@dial.pipex.com
                              Tel: 0131-556 9579

EDINBURGH
Theatre Workshop
34 Hamilton Place
Edinburgh EH3 5AX
Director: Robert Rae
Fax: 0131-220 0112   Tel: 0131-225 7942

EPSOM
Playhouse (SEA)
Ashley Avenue
Epsom, Surrey KT18 5AL
Venues Manager: Trevor Mitchell
Website: www.epsomplayhouse.co.uk
e-mail: tmitchell@epsom-ewell.gov.uk
Fax: 01372 726228
BO: 01372 742555   Admin: 01372 742226

EVESHAM
Evesham Arts Centre (WMA)
Victoria Avenue
Evesham, Worcestershire WR11 4QH
Director: Lauri Griffith-Jones
BO: 01386 45567
Theatre: 01386 48883   Director: 01386 446067

EXETER
Exeter Phoenix
Bradninch Place
Gandy Street, Exeter, Devon EX4 3LS
Business Manager: Anthony Doherty
e-mail: admin@exeterphoenix.org.uk
Fax: 01392 667599
BO: 01392 667080   Admin: 01392 667060

FAREHAM
Ashcroft Arts Centre (SA)
Osborn Road
Fareham, Hants PO16 7DX
Director: Steve Rowley
Website: www.theashcroft.co.uk
e-mail: admin@theashcroft.co.uk
Fax: 01329 825661
BO: 01329 310600   Tel: 01329 235161

FROME
Merlin Theatre (SWA)
Bath Road, Frome
Somerset BA11 2HG
e-mail: info@merlintheatre.fsnet.co.uk
BO: 01373 465949   Admin: 01373 461360

GAINSBOROUGH
Trinity Arts Centre
Trinity Street, Gainsborough
Lincolnshire DN21 2AL
e-mail: info@trinityarts.demon.co.uk
Fax: 01427 811198
BO: 01427 810710   Admin: 01427 810298

GREAT TORRINGTON
The Plough Arts Centre (SWA)
9-11 Fore Street, Great Torrington, Devon EX38 8HQ
Website: www.plough-arts.org
BO: 01805 624624   Admin: 01805 622552

HARLECH
Theatr Ardudwy (ACW)
Harlech, Gwynedd LL46 2PU
Theatre Director: Mickey Plum   BO: 01766 780667

HAVANT
Havant Arts Centre
East Street, Havant, Hants PO9 1BS
Director: Paul Sadler
Website: www.havantartsactive.org
e-mail: info@havanartsacrchive.org
Fax: 023-9249 8577
BO: 023-9247 2700   Admin: 023-9248 0113

HEMEL HEMPSTEAD
Old Town Hall Arts Centre (EEA)
High Street, Hemel Hempstead, Herts HP1 3AE
General Manager: Alison Young
Website: www.oldtownhall.co.uk
e-mail: othadmin@dacorum.gov.uk
BO: 01442 228091   Admin: 01442 228095

HEXHAM
Queens Hall Arts (NA), Beaumont Street
Hexham, Northumberland NE46 3LS
Artistic Director: Geof Keys
Website: www.queenshall.co.uk
e-mail: boxoffice@queenshall.co.uk
Fax: 01434 652478   Tel: 01434 652476

HORSHAM
Horsham Arts Centre (SEA)
North Street, Horsham, West Sussex RH12 1RL
General Manager: Mick Gattrell
Fax: 01403 215268   Tel: 01403 215100

HUDDERSFIELD
Kirklees (various venues)
Kirklees Cultural Services
Red Doles Lane, Huddersfield HD2 1YF
Head of Performing Arts: Glenis Burgess
BO: 01484 223200   Admin: 01484 226300

INVERNESS
Eden Court Theatre
Bishop's Road, Inverness IV3 5SA
Director: Colin Marr
e-mail: pscott@eden-court.co.uk
BO: 01463 234234   Admin: 01463 239841

JERSEY
Jersey Arts Centre
Phillips Street, St Helier, Jersey JE2 4SW
Director: Daniel Austin
Deputy Director: Sarah Johnson
Fax: 01534 726788
BO: 01534 700444   Admin: 01534 700400

KENDAL
Brewery Arts Centre (NA)
Highgate, Kendal, Cumbria LA9 4HE
Chief Executive: Sam Mason
BO: 01539 725133   Admin: 01539 722833

KING'S LYNN
Corn Exchange
Tuesday Market Place
King's Lynn, Norfolk PE30 1JW
Marketing Manager: Suzanne Hopp
e-mail: suzanne.hopp@west-norfolk.gov.uk
Fax: 01553 762141
BO: 01553 764864   Tel: 01553 765565

KING'S LYNN
Kings' Lynn Arts Centre (EEA)
27-29 King's Street, King's Lynn, Norfolk PE30 1HA
Fax: 01553 762141
BO: 01553 764864   Tel: 01553 765565

LEICESTER
Phoenix Arts Centre
21 Upper Brown Street, Leicester LE1 5TE
e-mail: jeane@phoenix.org.uk
BO: 0116-255 4854   Admin: 0116-224 7700

LICHFIELD
Lichfield District Arts Association
Donegal House, Bore Street, Lichfield WS13 6NE
Administrator: Brian Pretty
Website: www.lichfieldarts.org.uk
Fax: 01543 308211   Tel: 01543 262223

LIVERPOOL
Bluecoat Arts Centre (NWA)
School Lane, Liverpool L1 3BX
Director: Bryan Biggs
e-mail: admin@bluecoatartscentre.com
                             Tel: 0151-709 5297

LONDON
BAC
Lavender Hill, Battersea, London SW11 5TN
Website: www.bac.org.uk
e-mail: mailbox@bac.org.uk
Fax: 020-7978 5207
BO: 020-7223 2223   Admin: 020-7223 6557

LONDON
The Bull
(Theatre, Gallery & Studios)
68 High Street, Barnet, London EN5 5SJ
e-mail: admin@thebull.org.uk
Fax: 020-8364 9037
BO: 020-8449 0048   Admin: 020-8449 5189

LONDON
Chats Palace
42-44 Brooksby's Walk, Hackney, London E9 6DF
Administrator: Lisa Bittlestone
BO: 020-8986 6714   Admin: 020-8533 0227

LONDON
Cockpit Theatre
Gateforth Street, London NW8 8EH
e-mail: dave.wybrow@cwc.ac.uk
Fax: 020-7258 2921
BO: 020-7258 2925   Admin: 020-7258 2920

LONDON
The Drill Hall
16 Chenies Street, London WC1E 7EX
Website: www.drillhall.co.uk
e-mail: admin@drillhall.co.uk
Fax: 020-7307 5062   Tel: 020-7307 5061

LONDON
Hoxton Hall Arts Centre (LA)
130 Hoxton Street, London N1 6SH
Venue Manager: Jonathan Salisbury
Website: www.hoxtonhall.co.uk
e-mail: office@hoxtonhall.co.uk
Fax: 020-7729 3815
BO: 020-7739 5431   Admin: 020-7684 0060

LONDON
Institute of Contemporary Arts
The Mall, London SW1Y 5AH
Head of Live Arts: Andrew Missingham
Website: www.ica.org.uk
e-mail: performingarts@ica.org.uk
Fax: 020-7306 0122
Admin: 020-7930 0493   BO: 020-7930 3647

Arts Centres

LONDON
Islington Arts Factory
2 Parkhurst Road, London N7 0SF
e-mail: islington@artsfactory.fsnet.co.uk
Fax: 020-7700 7229   Tel: 020-7607 0561

LONDON
Jacksons Lane
269A Archway Road, London N6 5AA
Fax: 020-8348 2424
BO: 020-8341 4421   Admin: 020-8340 5226

LONDON
The Nettlefold
West Norwood Library Centre
1 Norwood High Street, London SE27 9JX
Centre Development Officers: Jean Johnson,
Mark Sheehan
Fax: 020-7926 8071   Tel/BO: 020-7926 8070

LONDON
October Gallery
24 Old Gloucester Street, London WC1N 3AL
Contact: Chili Hawes
Website: www.theoctobergallery.com
e-mail: octobergallery@compuserve.com
Fax: 020-7405 1851   Tel: 020-7242 7367

LONDON
Oval House (LA)
52-54 Kennington Oval, London SE11 5SW
Director: Deborah Bestwick
Website: www.ovalhouse.com
e-mail: info@ovalhouse.com   Tel: 020-7582 0080

LONDON
Polish Social & Cultural Association (LA)
238-246 King Street
London W6 0RF   Tel: 020-8741 1940

LONDON
Riverside Studios (LA)
Crisp Road, Hammersmith, London W6 9RL
Website: www.riversidestudios.co.uk
e-mail: online@riversidestudios.co.uk
Fax: 020-8237 1001
BO: 020-8237 1111   Tel: 020-8237 1000

LOWESTOFT
Seagull Theatre (EA)
Morton Road, Lowestoft, Suffolk NR33 0JH
Advisory Drama Teacher: Sandra Redsell
Fax: 01502 515338   Tel: 01502 562863

MAIDENHEAD
Norden Farm Centre For The Arts
Altwood Road, Maidenhead SL6 4PF
Director: Simon Daykin
Website: www.nordenfarm.org
e-mail: admin@nordenfarm.org
Fax: 01628 682525
BO: 01628 788997   Admin: 01628 682555

MAIDSTONE
Corn Exchange Complex
Earl Street, Maidstone, Kent ME14 1PL
Commercial Manager: Mandy Hare
Fax: 01622 602194
BO: 01622 758611   Admin: 01622 753922

MANCHESTER
The Forum (NWA), Civic Centre Complex,
Wythenshawe, Manchester M22 5RX
BO: 0161-437 9663   Admin: 0161-935 4073

MANCHESTER
Green Room (NWA)
54-56 Whitworth Street West, Manchester M1 5WW
Artistic Director: Garfield Allen
Website: www.greenroomarts.org
e-mail: greenroom@easynet.co.uk
Fax: 0161-615 0516
BO: 0161-615 0500   Admin: 0161-615 0515

MANCHESTER
The Lowry
Pier 8, Salford Quays M50 3AZ
Theatre Production Bookings: Vicky Turner
Website: www.thelowry.com
e-mail: info@thelowry.com
Fax: 0161-876 2021
BO: 0161-876 2000   Admin: 0161-876 2020

MANSFIELD
New Perspectives Theatre Company
The Old Library, Leeming Street
Mansfield, Notts NG18 1NG
Website: www.newperspectives.co.uk
e-mail: info@newperspectives.co.uk
                          Tel: 01623 635225

MILFORD HAVEN
Torch Theatre, St Peter's Road
Milford Haven, Pembrokeshire SA73 2BU
Artistic Director: Peter Doran
Website: www.torchtheatre.org
e-mail: info@torchtheatre.co.uk
Fax: 01646 698919
BO: 01646 695267   Admin: 01646 694192

NEWPORT (ISLE OF WIGHT)
Quay Arts
Sea Street, Newport Harbour
Isle of Wight PO30 5BD
Fax: 01983 526606
BO: 01983 528825   Tel: 01983 822490

NORWICH
Norwich Arts Centre
Reeves Yard, St Benedicts Street
Norwich, Norfolk NR2 4PG
Director: Pam Reekie
Website: www.norwichartscentre.co.uk
e-mail: pamreekie@norwichartscentre.co.uk
BO: 01603 660352   Admin: 01603 660387

NUNEATON
Abbey Theatre & Arts Centre
Pool Bank Street, Nuneaton, Warks CV11 5DB
Chairman: Tony Deeming
Website: www.abbeytheatre.co.uk
e-mail: admin@abbeytheatre.co.uk
BO: 024-7635 4090   Tel: 024-7632 7359

PLYMOUTH
Plymouth Arts Centre
38 Looe Street, Plymouth, Devon PL4 0EB
Director: Ian Hutchinson
Website: www.plymouthac.org.uk
e-mail: arts@plymouthac.org.uk
Fax: 01752 206118   Tel: 01752 206114

POOLE
Poole Arts Centre (SA)
Kingland Road, Poole, Dorset BH15 1UG
Website: www.pooleartscentre.co.uk
BO: 01202 685222   Admin: 01202 665334

RADLETT
The Radlett Centre
1 Aldenham Avenue, Radlett, Herts WD7 8HL
Website: www.radlettcentre.co.uk
Fax: 01923 857592   Tel: 01923 857546

ROTHERHAM
Rotherham Theatres
Walker Place, Rotherham, South Yorkshire S65 1JH
Strategic Leader Culture/Leisure/Lifelong Learning :
Phil Rodgers
Website: www.rotherham.gov.uk
BO: 01709 823621   Admin: 01709 823641

Arts Centres

SALISBURY
Salisbury Arts Centre (SA)
Bedwin Street, Salisbury, Wiltshire SP1 3UT
e-mail: info@salisburyarts.co.uk
Fax: 01722 331742
BO: 01722 321744   Admin: 01722 430700

SHREWSBURY
Shrewsbury & District Arts Association (WMA)
The Gateway
Chester Street
Shrewsbury, Shropshire SY1 1NB
e-mail: gate_ed@hotmail.com   Tel: 01743 355159

SOUTHPORT
Southport Arts Centre (NWA)
Lord Street, Southport, Merseyside PR8 1DB
Website: www.seftonarts.co.uk
e-mail: artsops@seftonarts.co.uk
BO: 01704 540011   Admin: 01704 540004

STAMFORD
Stamford Arts Centre (EEA)
27 St Mary's Street
Stamford, Lincolnshire PE9 2DL
General Manager: David Popple
Fax: 01780 766690
BO: 01780 763203   Admin: 01780 480846

STIRLING
MacRobert
University of Stirling
Stirling FK9 4LA
Director: Liz Moran
Website: www.macrobert.org   Tel: 01786 467155

SWANSEA
Taliesin Arts Centre (ACW)
University of Wales Swansea
Singleton Park, Swansea SA2 8PZ
General Manager: Sybil Crouch
Website: www.taliesinartscentre.co.uk
e-mail: s.e.crouch@swansea.ac.uk
                          Tel: 01792 295438

SWINDON
Wyvern Theatre, Theatre Square
Swindon, Wiltshire SN1 1QN
BO: 01793 524481   Admin: 01793 535534

TAUNTON
Brewhouse (SWA)
Coal Orchard, Taunton, Somerset TA1 1JL
Artistic Director: Glenys Gill
Website: www.brewhouse-theatre.co.uk
e-mail: brewhouse@btconnect.co.uk
Fax: 01823 323116
BO: 01823 283244   Admin: 01823 274608

TOTNES
Dartington Arts (SWA)
The Barn, Dartington Hull
Totnes, Devon TQ9 6DE
e-mail: admin@dartingtonarts.co.uk
BO: 01803 847070   Admin: 01803 847074

TUNBRIDGE WELLS
Trinity Theatre & Arts Centre
Church Road, Tunbridge Wells, Kent TN1 1JP
Director: Helen Winning
BO: 01892 678678   Admin: 01892 678670

ULEY
Prema
South Street, Uley, Nr Dursley, Glos GL11 5SS
Director: Gordon Scott
Website: www.prema.demon.co.uk
e-mail: info@prema.demon.co.uk
Fax: 01453 860123   Tel: 01453 860703

VALE OF GLAMORGAN
St Donats Arts Centre (ACW)
St Donats Castle, The Vale of Glamorgan CF61 1WF
Artistic Director: David Ambrose
Fax: 01446 799101   Tel: 01446 799099

WAKEFIELD
Wakefield Arts Centre (YA)
Wakefield College, Thornes Park Centre
Thornes Park, Horbury Road, Wakefield WF2 8QZ
Facilities Officer: Carole Clark   Tel: 01924 789824

WALLSEND
Buddle Arts Centre (NA)
258B Station Road
Wallsend, Tyne & Wear NE28 8RG
Contact: Geoffrey A Perkins
Fax: 0191-200 7142   Tel: 0191-200 7132

WASHINGTON
The Arts Centre Washington (NA)
Biddick Lane, Fatfield, District 7
Washington, Tyne & Wear NE38 8AB
Fax: 0191-219 3466   Tel: 0191-219 3455

WELLINGBOROUGH
The Castle, Castle Way
Wellingborough, Northants NN8 1XA
Executive Director: Graham Brown
Artistic Director: David Bown
Website: www.thecastle.org.uk
e-mail: info@thecastle.org.uk
Fax: 01933 229888   Tel: 01933 229022

WIMBORNE
Layard Theatre
Canford School, Canford Magna
Wimborne, Dorset BH21 3AD
Director of Drama: Stephen Hattersley
Administrator: Christine Haynes
e-mail: layardtheatre@canford.com
Fax: 01202 849134
BO: 01202 849134   Admin: 01202 841254

WINCHESTER
Tower Arts Centre
Romsey Road, Winchester, Hampshire SO22 5PW
Director: John Tellett   Tel: 01962 867986

WINDSOR
Windsor Arts Centre (SA)
St Leonard's Road, Windsor, Berks SL4 3BL
Director: Debbie Stubbs
Website: www.windsorartscentre.org
e-mail: admin@windsorartscentre.org
Fax: 01753 621527
BO: 01753 859336   Admin: 01753 859421

WOLVERHAMPTON
Afro-Caribbean Cultural Centre (WMA)
2 Clarence Street, Wolverhampton WV1 4JH
Arts Co-ordinator: CJ Antonio   Tel: 01902 420109

WREXHAM
Wrexham Arts Centre (ACW)
Rhosddu Road, Wrexham LL11 1AU
e-mail: arts.centre@wrexham.gov.uk
Fax: 01978 292611   Tel: 01978 292093

CHARLES FRENCH

PHOTOGRAPHY

MOBILE: 07946 565510

TEL/FAX: 020-8878 2784

ADAMSON Joanne CASTING
4 Hillthorpe Square, Leeds LS28 8NQ
e-mail: watts07@hotmail.com
Mobile: 07787 311270

AILION PipFpa
3 Towton Road, London SE27 9EE
Tel/Fax: 020-8670 4816   Tel: 020-8761 7095

ALEXANDER Pam
Granada Television
Quay Street
Manchester M60 9EA   Tel: 0161-832 7211

**ALL DIRECTIONS OF LONDON
PERSONAL MANAGEMENT & CASTINGS**
7 Rupert Court
Off Wardour Street
London W1D 6EB   Tel: 020-7437 5879

ANDREW Dorothy CASTING
Campus Manor
Childwall Abbey Road, Childwall, Liverpool L16 0JP
Fax: 0151-722 9079   Tel: 0151-722 9122

ARNELL Jane
Flat 2, 39 St Peter's Square, London W6 9NN

BAIG Shaheen
c/o Southwood Studios, 14 Southwood Hall
Muswell Hill Road, London N6 5UF
Fax: 020-8374 6548   Tel: 020-8374 6546

BAIN James
Granada Television
Quay Street
Manchester M60 9EA   Tel: 0161-827 2129

BALDIES CASTING AGENCY
(The only agency purely for bald people)
6 Marlott Road, Poole, Dorset BH15 3DX
Mobile: 07860 290437   Tel: 01202 666001

BARBOUR Penny
Rosemary Cottage
Fontridge Lane, Etchingham, East Sussex TN19 7DD

BARNES Michael CDG
25 Old Oak Road, London W3 7HN
Fax: 020-8742 9385   Tel: 020-8749 1354

BARTLETT Carolyn CDG
22 Barton Road, London W14 9HD

BBC DRAMA SERIES CASTING
BBC Centre House
Room DG03
56 Wood Lane, White City, London W12 7SB
Fax: 020-8576 4947   Tel: 020-8225 6475

BBC DRAMA SERIES CASTING
BBC Elstree Centre
Neptune House, Room N412
Clarendon Road
Borehamwood, Herts WD6 1JF
Fax: 020-8228 8311   Tel: 020-8228 8620

BEARDSALL Sarah CDG
73 Wells Street, London W1T 3QG
e-mail: casting@beardsall.com
Fax: 020-7436 8859   Tel: 020-7323 4040

BERTRAND Leila CASTING
53 Hormead Road, London W9 3NQ
e-mail: surfchow@aol.com   Tel: 020-8964 0683

BEWICK Maureen CASTING
104A Dartmouth Road
London NW2 4HB   Tel: 020-8450 1604

BIG FISH CASTING
(Des Hamilton & Kahleen Crawford)
2nd Floor
95-107 Lancefield Street, Glasgow G3 8JD
Fax: 0141-221 1356   Tel: 0141-204 5207

BILL The - THAMES TELEVISION Ltd
Bosun House
1 Deer Park Road, Merton
London SW19 3TL   Tel: 020-8540 0600

BIRD Sarah CDG
PO Box 32658, London W14 0XA
Fax: 020-7602 8601   Tel: 020-73/1 3248

BOOTH Stephanie
52 Bates Road
Brighton BN1 6PG   Tel/Fax: 01273 500202

BOULTING Lucy CDG
Riverbank House
1 Putney Bridge Approach, London SW6 3JD
Fax: 020-7371 0066   Tel: 020-7751 0606

BRACKE Siobhan CDG
Basement Flat
22A The Barons
St Margaret's TW1 2AP   Tel: 020-8891 5686

BROADCASTING
(Lesley Beastall, Sophie North & Jon Levene)
23 Canalot Studios
222 Kensal Road, London W10 5BN
Fax: 020-8968 6462   Tel: 020-7460 5220

Advanced casting information. Breakdowns covering theatre, television, films and commercials. Early leads and unique free telephone information service for subscribers. Who's Where indices including casting directors. Over 34 years PCR has built up an unbeatable network of leads and information. Subscribing costs only £27.50 for 5 weekly issues. Every Monday direct to you by post.

Editorial Office:
PCR P.O. Box 11, London N1 7JZ
020-7566 8282
Subscription Office:
PCR P.O. Box 100, Broadstairs, Kent CT10 1UJ
01843 860885
www.pcrnewsletter.com

BRUFFIN Susie CDG
133 Hartswood Road
London W12 9NG   Tel: 020-8740 9895

BRUSCHELLE Barbara
(See CASTING UNLIMITED UK & LOS ANGELES)

BRYDEN Kate
Unit 7, 93 Paul Street
London EC2A 4NY
e-mail: katebrydencasting@hotmail.com
Fax: 020-7251 9255   Tel: 020-7684 0465

CAIRD LITTLEWOOD CASTING
(Angela Caird)
PO Box MT 86
Leeds LS17 8YQ
e-mail: cairdlitt@aol.com
Fax: 0113-266 6068   Tel: 0113-288 8014

C.A.L.S. CASTING
(Children & Teenagers)
Unit E2
Bellevale Shopping Centre
Liverpool L25 2RG
Mobile: 07930 889057   Tel/Fax: 0151-487 8500

CANDID CASTING
2nd Floor
111-113 Great Titchfield Street
London W1W 6RY
e-mail: mail@candidcasting.co.uk
Fax: 020-7636 5522   Tel: 020-7636 6644

CANNON John CDG
(See ROYAL SHAKESPEARE COMPANY)

CANNON DUDLEY & ASSOCIATES
43A Belsize Square
London NW3 4HN
e-mail: casting@dudley.dircon.co.uk
Fax: 020-7433 3599   Tel: 020-7433 3393

CARLING Di CASTING CDG
1st Floor
49 Frith Street, London W1D 4SG
Fax: 020-7287 6844   Tel: 020-7287 6446

CARLTON TELEVISION
35-38 Portman Square, London W1H 0NU
Fax: 020-7612 7528   Tel: 020-7486 6688

CARROLL Anji CDG
109 Ritherdon Road, London SW17 8QH
e-mail: anjicarrollcdg@yahoo.co.uk
Fax: 020-8772 6408   Tel: 020-8772 9806

CASTING ANGELS The
(London & Paris)
Suite 4, 14 College Road
Bromley, Kent BR1 3NS   Tel/Fax: 020-8313 0443

CASTING COMPANY (UK) The
(Michelle Guish CDG, Associate Gaby Kester CDG)
3rd Floor Rear
112-114 Wardour Street, London W1F 0TS
Fax: 020-7434 2346   Tel: 020-7734 4954

CASTING COMPANY The (SPAIN)
Pasaje Ramos Puente no 4, Edificio Sol bajo b
29620 Torremolinos, Malaga, Spain
Website: www.thecastingcompanyspain.com
e-mail: theteam@thecastingcompanyspain.com
Tel/Fax: +34 952 382 106

CASTING CONNECTION The
(Michael Syers)
Dalrossie House
16 Victoria Grove, Stockport, Cheshire SK4 5BU
Fax: 0161-442 7280   Tel: 0161-432 4122

CASTING COUCH PRODUCTIONS Ltd
(Moira Townsend)
Canalot Production Studios
222 Kensal Road, London W10 5BN
e-mail: moiratownsend@yahoo.co.uk
Fax: 020-8208 2373   Tel: 020-8438 9679

CASTING DIRECTORS The
(Gillian Hawser & Caroline Hutchings)
24 Cloncurry Street, London SW6 6DS
e-mail: carohutchings@hotmail.com
e-mail: gillian.hawser@virgin.net
Fax: Gillian: 020-7731 0738
Fax: Caroline: 020-8336 1067   Tel: 020-7731 5988

CASTING UK
(Andrew Mann)
88-90 Grays Inn Road, London WC1X 8AA
Website: www.castinguk.com
e-mail: info@castinguk.com
Fax: 020-7430 1155   Tel: 020-7430 1122

C

CASTING UNLIMITED (LONDON)
14 Russell Garden Mews, London W14 8EU
e-mail: info@castingdirector.co.uk
Fax: 0870 4435623   Tel: 0870 4435621

CASTING UNLIMITED (LOS ANGELES)
e-mail: info@castingdirector.co.uk

CATLIFF Suzy CDG
PO Box 32658, London W14 0XA
e-mail: suzy.catliff@ukgateway.net
Fax: 020-7602 8601   Tel: 020-7371 3248

CELEBRITY MANAGEMENT Ltd
12 Nottingham Place, London W1U 5NE
Website: www.celebrity.co.uk
e-mail: info@celebrity.co.uk
Fax: 020-7224 6060   Tel: 020-7224 5050

CHARD Alison CDG
23 Groveside Court
Lombard Road, Battersea, London SW11 3RQ
e-mail: alisonchard@castingdirector.freeserve.co.uk
                         Tel/Fax: 020-7223 9125

CHARKHAM CASTING
(Beth Charkham)
Suite 5.1, Moray House
23-31 Great Titchfield Street, London W1W 7PA
Fax: 020-7436 4943   Tel: 020-7436 4842

CLARK Andrea
(See ZIMMERMANN Jeremy CASTING)

COGAN Ben
(See BBC DRAMA SERIES CASTING - CENTRE HOUSE)

COHEN Abi CASTING
c/o Southwood Studios, 14 Southwood Hall
Muswell Hill Road, London N6 5UF
Fax: 020-8374 6548   Tel: 020-8374 6550

COLLINS Jayne CASTING
38 Commercial Street, London E1 6LP
Website: www.jaynecollinscasting.com
e-mail: info@jaynecollinscasting.com
Fax: 020-7422 0015   Tel: 020-7422 0014

COLLINS Katrina
(See BBC DRAMA SERIES CASTING - CENTRE HOUSE)

CORDORAY Lin
66 Cardross Street, London W6 0DR

COTTON Irene CDG
25 Druce Road, London SE21 7DW
e-mail: oliver36@btopenworld.com
Tel/Fax: 020-8299 2787   Tel: 020-8299 1595

CRAMPSIE Julia
(See BBC DRAMA SERIES CASTING - CENTRE HOUSE)

CRAWFORD Margaret
92 Castelnau
London SW13 9EU   Tel/Fax: 020-8748 8929

CROCODILE CASTING COMPANY The
(C. Gibbs & T. Saban)
9 Ashley Close, Hendon, London NW4 1PH
Website: www.crocodilecasting.com
e-mail: croccast@aol.com
Fax: 020-8203 7711   Tel: 020 8203 7009

CROWE Sarah CASTING
24 Poland Street, London W1F 8QL
e-mail: sarah@crowecasting.demon.co.uk
Fax: 020-7287 2147   Tel: 020-7734 5464

CROWLEY POOLE CASTING
11 Goodwins Court, London WC2N 4LL
Fax: 020-7379 5971   Tel: 020-7379 5965

MICHELLE LIVINGSTONE

KEVIN WHATELY

JOHN FLETCHER

PHOTOGRAPHER

020-8203-4816

CROWLEY Suzanne CDG
(See CROWLEY POOLE CASTING)

CYBER 2000/IN THE CAN Ltd
20 Old Steine, Brighton BN1 1EL
Website: www.cyberartists.co.uk
e-mail: cyber.1@btclick.com
Fax: 01273 571085   Tel/Fax: 01273 671234

DAVIES Jane CASTING Ltd
(Jane Davies CDG & John Connor CDG)
PO Box 680, Sutton, Surrey SM1 3ZG
e-mail: janedaviescasting@blueyonder.co.uk
Fax: 020-8644 9746   Tel: 020-8715 1036

DAVIS Leo (Miss)
(JUST CASTING)
128 Talbot Road, London W11 1JA
Fax: 020-7792 3043   Tel: 020-7229 3471

DAVY Gary CDG
33 Fitzroy Street, London W1T 6DU
Fax: 020-7636 0881   Tel: 020-7636 0880

DAY Kate CDG
Pound Cottage
27 The Green South, Warborough
Oxon OX10 7DR   Tel/Fax: 01865 858709

DE FREITAS Paul CDG
6 Brook Street, Mayfair, London W1S 1BB

DEITCH Jane
(See BBC DRAMA SERIES CASTING - CENTRE HOUSE)

DENMAN Jack CASTING
Burgess House
Main Street, Farnsfield
Notts NG22 8EF   Tel/Fax: 01623 882272

DENNISON Lee ASSOCIATES
Fushion
27 Old Gloucester Street
London WC1N 3XX
e-mail: castings@fushion-uk.com
Fax: 08700 111020   Tel: 08700 111100

DICKENS Laura CASTING CDG
11 Egerton Court
Paradise Road, Richmond, Surrey TW9 1LN

DOWD Kate
Chelsea Chambers
262A Fulham Road, London SW10 9EL
Fax: 020-7352 6997   Tel: 020-7352 1086

DRURY Malcolm CDG
34 Tabor Road
London W6 0BW   Tel: 020-8748 9232

DUDLEY Carol CDG
(See CANNON DUDLEY & ASSOCIATES)

DUFF Julia CDG
73 Wells Street
London W1T 3QG
Fax: 020-7436 8859   Tel: 020-7436 8860

DUFF Maureen CDG
(See STEVENS Gail CASTING)

DUFFY Jennifer CDG
42 Old Compton Street, London W1D 4TX
Fax: 020-7287 7752   Tel: 020-7287 7751

EAST Irene CASTING CDG
40 Brookwood Avenue, Barnes, London SW13 0LR
e-mail: irneast@aol.com   Tel: 020-8876 5686

EASTON Andrew
51 Links Road
London SW17 9EE   Tel: 020-8767 1623

EJ CASTING
Lower Ground Floor
86 Vassall Road
London SW9 6JA
e-mail: info@ejcasting.com
Mobile: 07976 726869   Tel: 020-7564 2688

EMMERSON Chloe
110 Goldhawk Road
London W12 8HD   Tel/Fax: 020-8749 0439

ENGLAND Liz CASTING CDG
34 Connaught Street
London W2 2AF

**ET-NIK-A
PRIME MANAGEMENT AND CASTINGS Ltd**
Unit 4
1A Hollybush Place, London E2 9QX
Website: www.et-nik-a.co.uk
e-mail: info@et-nik-a.co.uk
Fax: 020-7739 6718   Tel: 020-7739 6738

EVANS Karen CDG
Carlton Television
35-38 Portman Square, London W1H 0NU

EVANS Kate
(See KATE & ALI CASTING)

EVANS Richard CDG
10 Shirley Road
London W4 1DD
Website: www.evanscasting.co.uk
e-mail: contact@evanscasting.co.uk
Fax: 020-8742 1010   Tel: 020-8994 6304

Pip Torrens   Kerry Condon   Kenneth Branagh

Charlie Carter

P H O T O G R A P H E R

0 2 0 7 7 5 1 0 5 7 5

casting rooms

- 5 Spacious, bright, air-conditioned rooms.
- Soundproofed.
- Free receptionist service.
- Video Camera, TV and VCR.
- Free online access to Spotlight Interactive facilites.

UK's Premier Casting Facilities in the heart of theatreland - the best rates in London

To book, please phone
020 7437 7631 or
email **info@spotlightcd.com**
or book online at
www.spotlightcd.com/rooms

FALLON & POLENTARUTTI CDG
(Elaine Fallon & Tania Polentarutti CDG)
Top Floor, 37 Berwick Street, London W1F 8RS
Fax: 020-7734 3549   Tel: 020-7734 1819

FEARNLEY Ali
(See KATE & ALI CASTING)

FIELDEN Ann CDG
5 Rectory Lane, London SW17 9PZ
Fax: 020-8672 4803   Tel: 020-8767 3939

FIELDEN Cornelia
Waterside, 99 Rotherhithe Street, London SE16 4NF
Fax: 020-7394 0016   Tel: 020-7394 1444

FIGGIS Susie
19 Spencer Rise
London NW5 1AR   Tel: 020-7482 2200

FILDES Bunny CASTING CDG
56 Wigmore Street
London W1   Tel: 020-7935 1254

FINCHER Sally CDG
Carlton Television
35-38 Portman Square, London W1H 6NU

FOTHERGILL Janey CASTING
18-21 Jermyn Street
London SW1Y 6HP   Tel: 01225 774211

FOX Celestia
5 Clapham Common Northside, London SW4 0QW
e-mail: celestia.fox@virgin.net

FRAZER Janie CDG
London Weekend TV
Television Centre, South Bank, London SE1 9LT
e-mail: janie.frazer@granadamedia.com
          Tel: 020-7261 3848

FRECK Rachel
e-mail: rachelfreck@btopenworld.com
          Tel: 020-8673 2455

FRISBY Jane CASTING CDG
51 Ridge Road, London N8 9LJ
e-mail: j.frisbycast@amserve.net

FUNNELL Caroline CDG
25 Rattray Road, London SW2 1AZ
Fax: 020-7326 1713   Tel: 020-7326 4417

GALLIE Joyce
37 Westcroft Square, London W6 0TA

GANE CASTING
(Natasha Gane)
1 The Willows, 1025 High Road, London N20 0QE
e-mail: natasha@ganecasting.com
Fax: 020-8446 2508   Tel: 020-8446 2551

GB CASTING UK Ltd (Karin Grainger)
1 Charlotte Street, London W1P 1DH
e-mail: kggbuk@lineone.net
Fax: 020-7255 1899   Tel: 020-7636 2437

GILLHAM Tracey
(Entertainment - Comedy)
BBC Television Centre, Wood Lane, London W12 7RJ
e-mail: tracey.gillham@bbc.co.uk
Fax: 020-8576 4414   Tel: 020-8225 7585

GOLD Nina CDG
10 Kempe Road, London NW6 6SJ
e-mail: nina@ninagold.co.uk
Fax: 020-8968 6777   Tel: 020-8960 6099

GOOCH Miranda CASTING
102 Leighton Gardens, London NW10 3PR
e-mail: mirandagooch@hotmail.com
Fax: 020-8962 9579   Tel: 020-8962 9578

GRAYBURN Lesley
74 Leigh Gardens, London NW10 5HP
Fax: 020-8969 2846   Tel: 020-8969 6112

GREEN Jill
Fax: 020-7580 6048   Tel: 020-7580 6037

GREENE Francesca CASTING
79 Ashworth Mansions, London W9 1LN
Fax: 020-7266 9001   Tel: 020-7286 5957

GRESHAM Marcia CDG
3 Langthorne Street
London SW6 6JT   Tel: 020-7381 2876

GROSVENOR CASTING
(Angela Grosvenor CDG)
27 Rowena Crescent, London SW11 2PT
Fax: 020-7652 6256   Tel: 020-7738 0449

GUISH Michelle CDG
(See CASTING COMPANY UK The)

HALL Janet
1 Shore Avenue, Shaw, Oldham OL2 8DA
e-mail: hallcastings@netscapeonline.co.uk
Mobile: 07780 783489   Tel: 01706 291459

HALL Pippa
(Children & Teenagers only)
128 Talbot Road, London W11 1JA
e-mail: pippahall.casting@virgin.net
                    Tel/Fax: 020-8785 7184

HAMMOND Louis
39 Queensmill Road, London SW6 6JP

HANCOCK Gemma CDG
(See ROYAL SHAKESPEARE COMPANY)

HAUSSMAN Ashley CASTING
c/o Serious Pictures, 1A Rede Place, London W2 4TU
e-mail: haussman-casting@hotmail.com
                    Tel: 020-7792 4477

HAWSER Gillian CASTING
24 Cloncurry Street, London SW6 6DS
e-mail: gillian.hawser@virgin.net
Fax: 020-7731 0738   Tel: 020-7731 5988

HAYFIELD Judi CDG
Granada Television
Quay Street
Manchester M60 9EA   Tel: 0161-832 7211

HENDERSON Anne CASTING Ltd CDG
93 Kelvin Road, Highbury, London N5 2PL
Fax: 020-7354 5880   Tel: 020-7354 3786

HICKLING Matthew
(See BBC DRAMA SERIES CASTING - ELSTREE)

HILL Serena CDG
Royal National Theatre
Upper Ground, South Bank, London SE1 9PX
Website: www.nt-online.org
Fax: 020-7452 3340   Tel: 020-7452 3333

HILTON Carrie
HG4, Aberdeen Centre
22-24 Highbury Grove, London N5 2EA
Fax: 020-7359 5070   Tel: 020-7226 0097

HOOTKINS Polly CDG
PO Box 25191, London SW1V 2WN
e-mail: polly@clara.net
Fax: 020-7828 5051   Tel: 020-7233 8724

HORAN Julia
26 Falkland Road
London NW5 2PX   Tel: 020-7267 5261

BRENDA
FRICKER

NICOLE
FARADAY

DAMIEN
MATTHEWS

Shari Hughes

Stuart | ALLEN

PHOTOGRAPHER
07776 258829

www.stuartallenphotos.com

STUDENT DISCOUNTS

Al Gregg

HOWE Gary
34 Orbit Street, Roath, Cardiff CF24 0JX
Tel/Fax: 029-2025 0181   Tel: 029-2033 1341

HUBBARD CASTING
(Ros Hubbard, John Hubbard, Dan Hubbard CDG)
2nd Floor, 19 Charlotte Street, London W1T 1RL
e-mail: email@hubbardcasting.com
Fax: 020-7636 7117   Tel: 020-7636 9991

HUBBARD CASTING (DUBLIN)
c/o Irish Film Centre
6 Eustace Street, Temple Bar, Dublin 2

HUDSON Mark CASTING
Ground Floor
29 Ardwick Green North, Manchester M12 6DL
e-mail: markcasting@aol.com
Fax: 0161-275 9523   Tel: 0161-275 9522

HUGHES Sarah
Stephen Joseph Theatre, Westborough,
Scarborough
North Yorkshire YO11 1JW   Tel: 01723 370540

HUGHES Sylvia
Casting Suite, The Deanwater
Wilmslow Road, Woodford, Cheshire SK7 1RJ
Fax: 01565 723707   Tel: 01565 722707

HUTCHINGS Caroline
PO Box 1119, Kingston & Surbiton KT2 7WY
e-mail: carohutchings@hotmail.com
Fax: 020-8336 1067   Mobile: 07768 615343

JACKSON Sue
Yorkshire Television, The TV Centre, Leeds LS3 1JS

JAFFA SILLS CASTING
67 Starfield Road, London W12 9SN
e-mail: jaffasills@supaworld.com
Fax: 020-8743 9561   Tel: 020-7565 2877

JAFFREY Jennifer
136 Hicks Avenue, Greenford, Middlesex UB6 8HB
e-mail: jaffreymag@aol.com
Fax: 020-8575 0369   Tel: 020-8578 2899

JAMES Julie CASTING
Mobile: 07931 219054   Tel/Fax: 020-7834 0967

JAY Jina CASTING CDG
1st & 2nd Floor
50 Chiswick High Road, London W4 1SZ
Fax: 020-8994 1113   Tel: 020-8995 9090

JENKINS Lucy CDG
74 High Street, Hampton Wick
Kingston-upon-Thames KT1 4DQ
e-mail: lucy@littlejenkins.freeserve.co.uk
Fax: 020-8977 0466   Tel: 020-8943 5328

JN CASTING & PRODUCTION
The Worx, 16-24 Underwood Street, London N1 7JQ
e-mail: james@jncasting.com
Fax: 020-7684 8587   Tel: 020-7684 8586

JOHN Priscilla CDG
PO Box 22477, London W6 0GT
Fax: 020-8741 4005   Tel: 020-8741 4212

JOHNSON Alex CASTING
15 McGregor Road, London W11 1DE
Fax: 020-7229 1665   Tel: 020-7229 8779

JOHNSON Marilyn CDG
1st Floor, 11 Goodwins Court, London WC2N 4LL
e-mail: marilynjohnson@lineone.net
Fax: 020-7497 5530   Tel: 020-7497 5552

www.castweb.co.uk

To send your casting requirements FREE OF CHARGE to all,
or your choice, of the UK's leading agents please e-mail
castweb@netcomuk.co.uk or telephone **020 7720 9002**

CastWeb, the leading casting information service in the UK.

Fiona Kay-Mitchell   2001   Rachel Hollyhead   2001   Perry Douglin   2001

JONES Doreen CDG
PO Box 22478, London W6 0WJ
Fax: 020-8748 8533   Tel: 020-8746 3782

JONES Sam CDG
6th Floor, International House
223 Regent Street, London W1R 7DB
e-mail: get@samjones.fsnet.co.uk
Fax: 020-7493 7890   Tel: 020-7493 5456

JONES Sue CDG
24 Nicoll Road
London NW10 9AB
Fax: 020-8838 1130   Tel: 020-8838 5153

KATE & ALI CASTING
1st Floor
26 Goodge Street, London W1P 1FG
e-mail: katealicasting@btclick.com
Fax: 020-7636 8080   Tel: 020-7636 4040

KELLY Sam
(See BBC DRAMA SERIES CASTING - CENTRE HOUSE)

KEOGH Beverley
Brunel House, 4th Floor
54 Princess Street, Manchester M1 6HS
e-mail: beverley@beverleykeogh.com
Fax: 0161-236 1960   Tel: 0161-236 1900

KESTER Gaby
(See CASTING COMPANY UK The)

KESTON Sam
(Children, Young People, Families)
Fax: 01628 822461   Tel: 01628 822982 Ext 4

KNIGHT-SMITH Jerry
c/o Royal Exchange Theatre
St. Ann's Square, Manchester M2 7DH
Fax: 0161-832 0881   Tel: 0161-615 6761

KOREL Suzy CDG
20 Blenheim Road
London NW8 0LX
e-mail: suzy.korel@btopenworld.com
Fax: 020-7372 3964   Tel: 020-7624 6435

KYLE CASTING
The Summerhouse, Thames House
54 Thames Street
Hampton TW12 2DX
Fax: 020-8274 8423   Tel: 020-8274 8096

LAUREN GOLDWYN CASTING Inc
14 Dean Street
London W1D 3RS
e-mail: realcreate@aol.com
Fax: 020-7437 4221   Tel: 020-7437 4188

LAYTON & NORCLIFFE CASTING
(Belinda Norcliffe, Claudie Layton & Alix
Charpentier)
Unit 232, Canalot Studios
222 Kensal Road
London W10 5BN
e-mail: casting@laytonnorcliffe.com
Fax: 020-8968 1330   Tel: 020-8964 2055

LESSALL Matthew
Unit 5, Gun Wharf
241 Old Ford Road, London E3 5QB
e-mail: lessallcasting@hotmail.com
Fax: 020-8980 2211   Tel: 020-8980 0117

LEVINSON Sharon
30 Stratford Villas
London NW1 9SG
e-mail: sharonlev@aol.com
Fax: 020-7916 5872   Tel: 020-7485 2057

LINDSAY-STEWART Karen CDG
PO Box 2301, London W1A 1PT
Fax: 020-7439 0548   Tel: 020-7439 0544

LIP SERVICE CASTING
(Voice-Overs only)
4 Kingly Street, London W1B 5PE
Website: www.lipservice.co.uk
e-mail: castings@lipservice.co.uk
Fax: 020-7734 3373   Tel: 020-7734 3393

LISNEY Julia CDG
501A Battersea Park Road, London SW11 4LW

LONDON CASTING
114 Station Road
Alexandra Palace, London N22 7SX
e-mail: londoncasting@btconnect.com

MacGABHANN Dorothy
15 Sandycove Avenue East, Sandycove, Co. Dublin
Fax: 00 353 1 2846865   Tel: 00 353 1 2807242

MAD DOG CASTING Ltd
(Ilenka Jelowicki)
Camden House
156 Camden High Street, London NW1 0NE
e-mail: ilenka@maddogcasting.com
Fax: 020-7916 1512   Tel: 020-7916 1511

MARCH Heather
Mugshots Casting Studio
20 Greek Street, London W1D 4DU
Fax: 020-7437 0308   Tel: 020-7437 9245

MARSHALL Sophie
Royal Exchange Theatre Company
St. Ann's Square, Manchester M2 7DH
Website: www.royalexchange.co.uk
Fax: 0161-832 0881   Tel: 0161-833 9333

McCANN Joan CDG
11 Oldfield Road
London N16 0RR   Tel: 020-7923 0648

McLEOD Carolyn
PO Box 25602, London N15 3AS
e-mail: carolynmcleodcasting@hotmail.com
                        Tel/Fax: 0704 4001720

McMURRICH Chrissie
16 Spring Vale Avenue
Brentford
Middlesex TW8 9QH   Tel: 020-8568 0137

McSHANE Sooki CDG
8A Piermont Road, East Dulwich
London SE22 0LN   Tel/Fax: 020-8693 7411

McWILLIAMS Debbie
e-mail: debbiemcwilliams@hotmail.com
                        Mobile: 07785 575805

MOISELLE Frank
7 Corrig Avenue, Dun Laoghaire, Co. Dublin
Fax: 00 353 1 2803277   Tel: 00 353 1 2802857

MOISELLE Nuala
7 Corrig Avenue, Dun Laoghaire, Co. Dublin
Fax: 00 353 1 2803277   Tel: 00 353 1 2802857

MORRISON Melika
12A Rosebank, Holyport Road
London SW6 6LG   Tel/Fax: 020-7381 1571

MUGSHOTS CASTING STUDIO
(Studio Manager, Becky Kidd)
20 Greek Street, London W1D 4DU
Fax: 020-7437 1241   Tel: 020-7440 3000

NEEDLEMAN Sue
19 Stanhope Gardens, London NW7 2JD
Fax: 020-8959 0225   Tel: 020-8959 1550

NOEL CASTING
(Specialising in Character Actors and Ethnic and
Asian Actors)
Suite 501, International House
223 Regent Street, London W1B 2QD
e-mail: noelcasting@yahoo.com
Fax: 020-7544 1090   Tel: 020-7544 1010

O'BRIEN Debbie
72 High Street, Ashwell, Nr Baldock, Herts SG7 5NS
Fax: 01462 743110   Tel: 01462 742919

OCEAN CASTING (Sherrie Mead)
8 Bovingdon Road
Fulham, London SW6 2AP
e-mail: oceancasting@hotmail.com
                        Tel: 020-7384 1736

PAGE Jamie CASTING CDG
PO Box 2944, London W1A 6ET

PAIN David
(See BBC DRAMA SERIES CASTING - ELSTREE)

PALMER Helena
(See CANNON DUDLEY & ASSOCIATES)

PARRISS Susie CASTING CDG
PO Box 25796, London SW19 8WS
Fax: 020-8944 9553   Tel: 020-8944 9552

PEARCE WOOLGAR CASTING
(Formerly Jill Pearce Casting)
(Prop. Francesca Woolgar CDG)
6 Langley Street, London WC2H 9JA
Website: www.pearcewoolgar.com
Fax: 020-7379 8250   Tel: 020-7240 0316

PETTS & CLAY CASTING
125 Hendon Way
London NW2 2NA
e-mail: pettsandclay@orange.net
Fax: 020-8905 5968   Tel: 020-8458 8898

PLANTIN Kate
37 Albany Mews
Kingston-upon-Thames, Surrey KT2 5SL
e-mail: kateplantin@hotmail.com
Fax: 020-8549 7299   Tel: 020-8546 4577

POOLE Gilly CDG
(See CROWLEY POOLE CASTING)

PROCTOR Carl
15B Bury Place, London WC1A 2JB
e-mail: carlproctor@blueyonder.co.uk
Fax: 020-7916 2533   Tel: 020-7681 0034

PRYOR Andy CDG
7 Garrick Street, London WC2E 9AR
Fax: 020-7836 8299   Tel: 020-7836 8298

REICH Liora
25 Manor Park Road
London N2 0SN   Tel: 020-8444 1686

REYNOLDS Simone CDG
60 Hebdon Road, London SW17 7NN

RHODES JAMES Kate CDG
HG04, The Aberdeen Centre
22-24 Highbury Grove, London N5 2EA
e-mail: katekrj@aol.com
Fax: 020-7359 5378   Tel: 020-7704 8186

ROBERTSON CASTING
(Sasha Robertson CDG and Anna Robertson)
19 Wendell Road, London W12 9RS
e-mail: sasha.robertson@virgin.net
Fax: 020-8740 1396   Tel: 020-8740 0817

RODRIGUEZ Corinne
11 Lytton Avenue
London N13 4EH   Fax: 020-8886 5564

**ROYAL NATIONAL THEATRE
CASTING DEPARTMENT**
(Casting Director: Serena Hill CDG
Senior Casting Assistant: Gabrielle Dawes
Casting Assistant: Hannah Miller)
Upper Ground, South Bank, London SE1 9PX
Fax: 020-7452 3340   Tel: 020-7452 3336

ROYAL SHAKESPEARE COMPANY
(Casting Director: John Cannon CDG
Deputy Casting Director: Gemma Hancock CDG)
1 Earlham Street, London WC2H 9LL
e-mail: john.cannon@rsc.org.uk
Tel: 020-7845 0505   Tel: 020-7845 0500

SBS Ltd
(The Casting Information Service)
Suite 1, 16 Sidmouth Road, London NW2 5JX
e-mail: casting@sbsltd.demon.co.uk
Fax: 020-8459 7442   Tel: 020-8451 2852

SCHILLER Ginny CDG
180A Graham Road, London E8 1BS
e-mail: ginny.schiller@virgin.net
Fax: 020-8525 1049   Tel: 020-8525 1637

SCOTT Laura CDG
56 Rowena Crescent, London SW11 2PT
Website: www.castingdirectorsguild.co.uk
e-mail: laurascottcasting@mac.com
Fax: 020-7924 1907   Tel: 020-7978 6336

SEECOOMAR Nadira
PO Box 167, Twickenham TW1 2UP
Fax: 020-8744 1274   Tel: 020-8892 8478

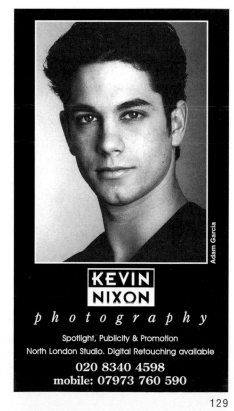

Adam Garcia

SELWAY Mary CDG
c/o Twickenham Studios
St Margaret's
Twickenham TW1 2AW   Tel: 020-8607 8888

SHAW Philip
Suite 476, 2 Old Brompton Road
South Kensington, London SW7 3DQ
e-mail: shawcastlond@aol.com
Fax: 020-8408 1193   Tel: 020-8715 8943

SHEPHERD Debbie CASTING
Suite 16, 63 St Martin's Lane, London WC2N 4JS
e-mail: dshepherd.casting@virgin.net
Fax: 020-7240 4640   Tel: 020-7240 0400

SINGER Sandra ASSOCIATES
21 Cotswold Road, Westcliff on Sea, Essex SS0 8AA
Website: www.sandrasinger.com
e-mail: sandrasingeruk@aol.com
Fax: 01702 339393   Tel: 01702 331616

SMITH Michelle CDG
220 Church Lane, Woodford, Stockport SK7 1PQ
Fax: 0161-439 0622   Tel: 0161-439 6825

SMITH Suzanne CDG
33 Fitzroy Street, London W1T 6DU
e-mail: zan@dircon.co.uk
Fax: 020-7436 9690   Tel: 020-7436 9255

SPON Wendy CDG
c/o ACT Productions
20-22 Stukeley Street
London WC2B 5LR   Tel: 020-7438 9599

STAFFORD Emma
33 Stopes Road, Radcliffe
Manchester M25 6TL   Tel: 0161-748 7940

STARK CASTING
e-mail: stark.casting@virgin.net
Mobile: 07956 150689   Tel: 020-8800 0060

STEVENS Gail CASTING CDG
54A Clerkenwell Road, London EC1M 5PS
Fax: 020-7253 6574   Tel: 020-7253 6532

STEVENSON Sam CDG
103 Whitecross Street, London EC1Y 8JD
e-mail: samstevenson@blueyonder.co.uk

STEWART Amanda CASTING
Apartment 1, 35 Fortess Road
London NW5 1AD   Tel: 020-7485 7973

STOLL Liz
(See BBC DRAMA SERIES CASTING - CENTRE HOUSE)

STREETCAST
(Jo Curtis)
14 Scott Ellis Gardens, London NW8 9HD
e-mail: jo@streetcast.co.uk
Fax: 020-7242 6200   Mobile: 07870 661682

STYLE Emma CDG
97 Third Avenue, London W10 4HS
Fax: 020-8960 8323   Tel: 020-8969 5099

SUMMERS Mark (LONDON)
(See CASTING UNLIMITED LONDON)

SUMMERS Mark (LOS ANGELES)
(See CASTING UNLIMITED LOS ANGELES)

SYERS Michael
(See CASTING CONNECTION The)

SYSON Lucinda CDG
11 Goodwins Court, London WC2N 4LL
e-mail: lscasting@yahoo.co.uk
Fax: 020-7240 7710   Tel: 020-7379 4868

TABAK Amanda CDG
(See CANDID CASTING)

TEECE Shirley
106 North View Road
London N8 7LP   Tel: 020-8347 9241

TOBIAS SHAW Rose
219 Liverpool Road
London N1 1LX   Fax: 020-7609 9028

TOPOLSKI Tessa
25 Clifton Hill, London NW8 8JY

C

TOPPS CASTING
(Nicola Topping)
The Media Centre
7 Northumberland Street, Huddersfield HD1 1RL
e-mail: topps.casting@btopenworld.com
Fax: 01484 361001   Tel: 01484 511988

TREVELLICK Jill CDG
123 Rathcoole Gardens, London N8 9PH
e-mail: jilltrevellick@lineone.net
Fax: 020-8348 7400   Tel: 020-8340 2734

TREVIS Sarah CDG
c/o Twickenham Studios
St Margaret's
Twickenham TW1 2AW   Tel: 020-8607 8888

VAN OST & MILLINGTON CASTING
(Valerie Van Ost & Andrew Millington)
PO Box 115, Petersfield GU31 5BB
Fax: 020-7436 9858   Tel: 020-7436 9838

VAUGHAN Sally
2 Kennington Park Place
London SE11 4AS   Tel: 020-7735 6539

VITAL PRODUCTIONS
PO Box 26441, London SE10 9GZ
e-mail: mail@vital-productions.co.uk
     Tel/Fax: 020-8316 4497

VOSSER Anne CASTING
PO Box 203, Aldershot GU12 4YB
e-mail: vossercasting@ntlworld.com
Fax: 01252 404716   Tel: 01252 404715

WEST June
Granada Television
Quay Street, Manchester M60 9EA
Fax: 0161-827 2004   Tel: 0161-832 7211

WESTERN Matt CASTING CDG
4th Floor, 193 Wardour Street, London W1V 3FA
e-mail: multwestern@lineone.net
Fax: 020-7439 1941   Tel: 020-7434 1230

WHALE Toby CDG
80 Shakespeare Road, London W3 6SN
Website: www.whalecasting.com
e-mail: toby@whalecasting.com
Fax: 020-8993 8096   Tel: 020-8993 2821

WHITALL Keith
(Theatre Only)
10 Woodlands Avenue
West Byfleet
Surrey KT14 6AT   Tel: 01932 343655

WILLIS Catherine
(See BBC DRAMA SERIES CASTING - CENTRE HOUSE)

WOODHAMS Keith CASTING
20 Lowther Hill, London SE23 1PY
e-mail: kwoodhams@mcmail.com
Fax: 020-8314 1950   Tel: 020-8314 1677

WOOLGAR Francesca CDG
(See PEARCE WOOLGAR CASTING)

ZIMMERMANN Jeremy CASTING
Clareville House
26-27 Oxendon Street, London SW1Y 4EL
Fax: 020-7925 0708   Tel: 020-7925 0707

C

Concert & Exhibition Halls

AMADEUS CENTRE The
50 Shirland Road, London W9 2JA
e-mail: amadeus@amadeuscentre.co.uk
Fax: 020-7266 1225   Tel: 020-7286 1686

B A C
Battersea Arts Centre
Lavender Hill, Battersea
London SW11 5TFN   Tel: 020-7326 8211

BARBICAN EXHIBITION CENTRE
Barbican, Silk Street, London EC2Y 8DS
Fax: 020-7382 7263   Tel: 020-7382 70531

BIRMINGHAM SYMPHONY HALL
Broad Street, Birmingham B1 2EA
Website: www.symphonyhall.co.uk/symphony
e-mail: symphonyhall@necgroup.co.uk
BO: 0121-780 3333   Tel: 0121-200 2000

BLACKHEATH HALLS
23 Lee Road, Blackheath, London SE3 9RQ
Website: www.blackheathhalls.com
e-mail: mail@blackheathhalls.com
Fax: 020-8852 5154   BO: 020-8463 0100

CENTRAL HALL - WESTMINSTER
Storey's Gate, Westminster, London SW1H 9NH
e-mail: events@wch.co.uk   Tel: 020-7222 8010

EARL'S COURT & OLYMPIA EXHIBITION CENTRES
Warwick Road, London SW5 9TA
Website: www.eco.co.uk
e-mail: marketing@eco.co.uk   Tel: 020-7385 1200

FAIRFIELD HALLS
Park Lane, Croydon CR9 1DG
BO: 020-8688 9291   Tel: 020-8681 0821

FERNEHAM HALL
Osborn Road, Fareham, Hants PO16 7DB
e-mail: boxoffice@fareham.gov.uk Tel: 01329 824864

GORDON CRAIG THEATRE
Stevenage Arts & Leisure Centre
Lytton Way, Stevenage, Herts SG1 1LZ
Website: www.stevenage-leisure.co.uk
e-mail: gordoncraig@stevenage-leisure.co.uk
BO: 08700 131030   Tel: 01438 242642

HEXAGON The
Queen's Walk, Reading RG1 7UA
Website: www.readingarts.com
e-mail: boxoffice@readingarts.com
Fax: 0118-939 0028   Admin: 0118-939 0390

LONDON ARENA EXHIBITION CENTRE
Limeharbour, London E14 9TH
Fax: 020-7538 5572   Tel: 020-7538 8880

MARMALADE
Studio B5R, Metropolitan Wharf, London E1W 3SS
Website: www.marmalade.online.co.uk
e-mail: info@marmalade.online.co.uk   Tel: 020-7702 2193

MINERVA STUDIO THEATRE
Oaklands Park, Chichester, West Sussex PO19 6AP
Website: www.cft.org.uk
Fax: 01243 787288   Tel: 01243 784437

NATIONAL CONCERT HALL OF WALES The
St David's Hall, The Hayes, Cardiff CF10 1SH
Website: www.stdavidshallcardiff.co.uk
Fax: 029-2087 8599   Tel: 029-2087 8500

OLYMPIA EXHIBITION CENTRES
Hammersmith Road, Kensington, London W14 8UX
Fax: 020-7598 2500   Tel: 020-7385 1200

RIVERSIDE STUDIOS
Crisp Road, London W6 9RL
Website: www.riversidestudios.co.uk
e-mail: online@riversidestudios.co.uk
Fax: 020-8237 1001   Tel: 020-8237 1000

ROYAL ALBERT HALL
Kensington Gore, London SW7 2AP
Website: www.royalalberthall.com
e-mail: admin@royalalberthall.com
Fax: 020-7823 7725   Tel: 020-7589 3203

SOUTH BANK CENTRE
(Including The Royal Festival Hall, Queen Elizabeth Hall,
Purcell, Room & Hayward Gallery).
Royal Festival Hall, London SE1 8XX
Website: www.rfh.org.uk
BO: 020-7960 4242   Tel: 020-7921 0601

ST JOHN'S
Smith Square, London SW1P 3HA
Website: www.sjss.org.uk
Fax: 020-7233 1618   Tel: 020-7222 1061

**WEMBLEY CONFERENCE
& EXHIBITION CENTRE & WEMBLEY ARENA**
Wembley HA9 0DW
Website: www.whatsonwembley.com
BO: 0870 7390739   Admin: 020-8902 8833

WIGMORE HALL
36 Wigmore Street, London W1U 2BP
e-mail: info@wigmore-hall.org.uk BO: 020-7935 2141

Concert Promoters & Agents

AMP ARTISTE MANAGEMENT PRODUCTIONS
Level 2, 65 Newman Street, London W1T 3EG
Fax: 020-7224 0111   Tel: 020-7224 1992

ARTISTE MANAGEMENT PRODUCTIONS Ltd
2nd Floor, 32-38 Osnaburgh Street, London NW1 3ND
Website: www.harveygoldsmith.com
e-mail: mail@harveygoldsmith.com
Fax: 020-7224 0111   Tel: 020-7224 1992

ASKONAS HOLT Ltd (Classical Music)
Lonsdale Chambers, 27 Chancery Lane WC2A 1PF
Website: www.askonasholt.co.uk
e-mail: info@askonasholt.co.uk
Fax: 020-7400 1799   Tel: 020-7400 1700

AVALON PROMOTIONS Ltd
4A Exmoor Street, London W10 6BD
Fax: 020-7598 7334   Tel: 020-7598 7333

BARRUCCI LEISURE ENTERPRISES Ltd (Promoters)
45-47 Cheval Place, London SW7 1EW
e-mail: barrucci@barrucci.com
Fax: 020-7581 2509   Tel: 020-7225 2255

BLOCK Derek ARTISTES AGENCY
Douglas House, 3 Richmond Buildings, London W1D 3HE
e-mail: dbaa@derekblock.demon.co.uk
Fax: 020-7434 0200   Tel: 020-7434 2100

HOBBS Liz EVENTS
68 Castlegate, Newark NG24 1BG
Website: www.lizhobbsgroup.com
e-mail: events@lizhobbsgroup.com
Fax: 0870 3337009   Tel: 08700 702702

HOCHHAUSER Victor
4 Oak Hill Way, London NW3 7LR
Fax: 020-7431 2531   Tel: 020-7794 0987

IMG ARTS & ENTERTAINMENT
Pier House, Strand on the Green, Chiswick W4 3NN
Fax: 020-8233 5001   Tel: 020-8233 5000

LEWIS Tony ENTERTAINMENTS
PO Box 11268, London SW5 0ZL
Fax: 020-7373 6427   Tel: 020-7370 0416

McINTYRE Phil PROMOTIONS Ltd
2nd Floor, 35 Soho Square, London W1D 3QX
e-mail: reception@pmcintyre.co.uk
Fax: 020-7439 2280   Tel: 020-7439 2270

MILLENNIUM ARTISTES MANAGEMENT Ltd
(Personal Management & Event Co-ordinators)
PO Box 2001, Caterham, Surrey CR3 6UA
e-mail: mamltd@ntlworld.com   Tel/Fax: 01883 347790

RBM (Comedy)
3rd Floor, 18 Broadwick Street, London W1V 1FG
Fax: 020-7287 5020   Tel: 020-7287 5010

REA Tano PERSONAL MANAGEMENT
58 Alexandra Road, London NW4 2RY
Fax: 020-8203 1064   Tel: 020-8203 1747

RIGOLETTO Ltd
4 Wigton Court, Wigton Lane
Leeds LS17 8SB   Tel: 0113-269 3720

S.F.X.
35-36 Grosvenor Street, London W1K 4QX
Fax: 0870 7490517   Tel: 020-7529 4300

ZANDER Peter CONCERT MANAGEMENT
22 Romilly Street, London W1D 5AG
Website: www.freespace.virgin.net/peterzan.berlin
e-mail: peterzan.berlin@virgin.net   Tel: 020-7437 4767

ABLE SECURITY
117 Waverley Road, Plumstead
London SE18 7TH   Tel/Fax: 020-8317 6899

ACE-UK•BIZ
(Entertainment providers, parties/corporate events)
7 Berghem Mews
Blythe Road, London W14 0HN
e-mail: sally.allen@ace-uk.biz
Fax: 020-7751 1275   Tel: 020-7603 3444

ACTORS' CONSULTANCY SERVICE
(MOMI ACTS. Andrew Ashmore.
Live Interpretation in Museums & Historic Sites)
Museum of the Moving Image
South Bank, Waterloo, London SE1 8XT
Website: www.bfi.org.uk
e-mail: andrew.ashmore@bfi.org.uk
                    Tel: 020-7815 1336

ACTOR'S 'ONE-STOP' SHOP The
(Showreels, Photographs, CV's & Actors' Websites)
54 Belsize Avenue, London N13 4TJ
Website: www.actorsone-stopshop.com
e-mail: info@actorsone-stopshop.com
Fax: 020-8482 7723   Tel: 020-8888 7006

AGENT FILE
(Software for Agents)
Website: www.agentfile.com
e-mail: info@agentfile.com
Mobile: 07956 544764   Tel: 07050 683662

AON Ltd (Trading as AON/ALBERT G. RUBEN)
(Insurance Brokers)
Pinewood Studios, Pinewood Road, Iver, Bucks SL0 0NH
Website: www.aon.co.uk
Fax: 01753 653152   Tel: 01753 658200

ARTON Michael Ph.D
(Historical Research, Technical Advisor)
122 Sunningfields Road
London NW4 4RE
e-mail: michael@arton.freeserve.co.uk
                    Tel/Fax: 020-8203 2733

ARTS CLINIC The
(Psychological Counselling,
Personal & Professional Development)
14 Devonshire Place, London W1G 6HX
e-mail: mail@artsclinic.co.uk
Fax: 020-7224 6256   Tel: 020-7935 1242

ASPEY ASSOCIATES
(Management & Team Training,
Counselling, Human Resources)
8 Bloomsbury Square, London WC1A 2LQ
Website: www.aspey.com
e-mail: hr@aspey.com
Fax: 020-7405 5541   Tel: 020-7405 0500

ATKINS Chris & COMPANY
(Accountants & Business Consultants)
Astra House, Arklow Road, London SE14 6EB
e-mail: chris.atkins@virgin.net   Tel: 020-8691 4100

BERGER Harvey FCA
(Chartered Accountant)
18 Chalk Lane
Cockfosters, Barnet, Herts EN4 9HJ
e-mail: harvey.berger@tesco.net
                    Tel/Fax: 020-8449 9328

BIG PICTURE
(Part-time Work in Computer Retail Industry)
13 Netherwood Road, London W14 0BL
e-mail: inch@ebigpicture.co.uk   Tel: 020-7371 4455

BLACKMORE Lawrence
(Production Accountant)
Suite 5, 26 Charing Cross Road, London WC2H 0DG
Fax: 020-7836 3156   Tel: 020-7240 1817

BOWKER ORFORD
(Chartered Accountants)
15-19 Cavendish Place, London W1G 0DD
Fax: 020-7580 3909   Tel: 020-7636 6391

BREBNER ALLEN TRAPP
(Chartered Accountants)
180 Wardour Street
London W1F 8LB
Website: www.brebner.co.uk
e-mail: partners@brebner.co.uk
Fax: 020-7287 5315   Tel: 020-7734 2244

BRECKMAN & COMPANY
(Chartered Accountants)
49 South Molton Street
London W1K 5LH   Tel: 020-7499 2292

BRITISH ASSOCIATION FOR DRAMA THERAPISTS The
41 Broomhouse Lane
London SW6 3DP
e-mail: gillian@badth.demon.co.uk
                    Tel/Fax: 020-7731 0160

BROOK-REYNOLDS Natalie
(Freelance Stage Manager. Member of Stage
Management Association, Equity & BECTU)
Website: www.nataliebrookreynoldsuk.pwp.blueyonder.co.uk
e-mail: nataliebrookreynoldsuk@blueyonder.co.uk
Mobile: 07976 234840   Tel: 020-8350 0877

BURGESS Chris
(Counselling for Performing Artists)
81 Arne House, Tyers Street
London SE11 5EZ   Tel: 020-7582 8229

BYFORD Simon
(Production Management Services)
22 Freshfield Place, Brighton, East Sussex BN2 2BN
e-mail: byford@compuserve.com
Fax: 01273 606402   Tel: 01273 623972

CASTLE MAGICAL SERVICES
(Magical Consultants, Michael Shepherd)
Broompark
131 Tadcaster Road, Dringhouses, York YO24 1QJ
e-mail: michael@castle.evesham.net
                    Tel/Fax: 01904 709500

CAULKETT Robin DIP.S.M., M.I.I.R.S.M.
(Abseiling, Rope Work)
3 Churchill Way, Mitchell Dean, Glos GL17 0AZ
Mobile: 07970 442003   Tel: 01594 825865

CELEBRATE
(Creative Events Development)
22 Brownhill Lane
Holmfirth, West Yorkshire HD9 2QW
e-mail: info@celebrateprojects.co.uk
                    Tel: 01484 688219

CELEBRITY CHEFS
c/o Sandra Singer Associates
21 Cotswold Road
Westcliff-on-Sea, Essex SS0 8AA
e-mail: sandrasingeruk@aol.com
Fax: 01702 339393   Tel: 01702 331616

COMPAGNIE LIAN
(Artist Promotion, Image Consultancy
Copy Writing, Full Translation Services)
2 Ravenscourt Park, London W6 0TH
e-mail: armaninora@aol.com   Tel: 020-8563 0220

COURTENAY Julian
(NLP Master Practitioner MANLP Mental Fitness UK)
42 Langdon Park Road, London N6 5QG
e-mail: info@mentalfitness.uk.com
                    Tel: 020-8348 9033

CREATINGPLENTY COACHING
(Building Self-Esteem, Enhancing Confidence)
                    Tel: 0870 7580318

DREAM
(Reflexology, Head, Neck
& Shoulder Massage in the Workplace)
117B Gaisford Street, London NW5 2EG
Website: www.dreamtherapies.co.uk
e-mail: dreamtherapies@hotmail.com
                    Mobile: 07973 731026

DZEYEN
(Web Services)
Unit 4B, The Coda Centre
189 Munster Road, Fulham, London SW6 6AW
Website: www.dzeyen.com
e-mail: email@dzeyen.com
Fax: 020-7386 0356   Tel: 020-7381 5283

EAGLES Steve
(International Sharpshooter & Firearms Lecturer)
Wivenhoe, 46 Hartwood Road
Southport, Merseyside PR9 9AW
e-mail: sn03@dial.pipex.com
Mobile: 07721 464611   Tel/Fax: 01704 547884

EARLE Kenneth PERSONAL MANAGEMENT
214 Brixton Road, London SW9 6AP
Fax: 020-7274 9529   Tel: 020-7274 1219

EDWARDS Simon (PEOPLE FOR BUSINESS Ltd)
(Hypnotherapy for
Professionals in Film, TV and Theatre)
15 Station Road
Quainton, Nr Aylesbury, Bucks HP22 4BW
e-mail: simongedwards@genie.co.uk
Mobile: 07889 333680   Tel: 01296 651259

ENTERTRAIN UK Ltd
(Entertainment Consultants)
14 Hawthorne Court
Rickmansworth Road, Pinner, Middlesex HA5 3UN
Website: www.entertrainltd.com
Mobile: 07740 802602   Tel: 020-8429 2171

EQUITY INSURANCE SERVICES
131-133 New London Road
Chelmsford, Essex CM2 0QZ
Website: www.equity-ins-services.com
e-mail: enquiries@equity-ins-services.com
Fax: 01245 491641   Tel: 01245 357854

EXECUTIVE AUDIO VISUAL
(Showreels for Actors & Presenters)
80 York Street
London W1H 1QW   Tel/Fax: 020-7723 4488

FACADE
(Creation and Production of Musicals)
43A Garthorne Road
London SE23 1EP   Tel: 020-8699 8655

FAITH Gordon BA DHC MCHC (UK)
(Hypnotherapy, Obstacles to Performing
Positive Affirmation, Focusing)
1 Wavel Mews, Priory Road
London NW6 3AB   Tel: 020-7328 0446

FILMANGEL
(Film Finance & Script Services)
110 Trafalgar Road, Portslade, East Sussex BN41 1GS
Website: www.filmangel.co.uk
e-mail: filmangels@freenetname.co.uk
Fax: 01277 05451   Tel: 01273 27733

FITNESS COACH The
(Jamie Baird)
6 Mysore Road, London SW11 5SB
e-mail: jamie@thefitnesscoach.co.uk
                    Tel: 07970 782476

FORD Jonathan & Co
(Chartered Accountants)
9 Victoria Street, Rainhill, Merseyside L35 0LB
Website: www.jonathanford.co.uk
e-mail: jford@jonathanford.co.uk
                    Tel: 0151-426 4512

FREE ELECTRON
(Website Design)
45 Alpha Street, Slough, Berks SL1 1RA
Website: www.free-electron.co.uk
e-mail: mikelynn@globalnet.co.uk
                    Tel/Fax: 01753 693074

GILMOUR (HEALING) CENTRE INTERNATIONAL The
(Spiritual Healing,
Counselling, Paranormal Investigator)
Website: www.sandrasinger.com
                    Tel: 01702 331616

GLOBAL DEVELOPMENT RESOURCES
(Training, Recruitment & Development)
2nd Floor, Hanover House, Coombe Road
Kingston-upon-Thames, Surrey KT2 7AZ
Website: www.gdrl.co.uk
e-mail: info@gdrl.co.uk
Fax: 020-8546 0184   Tel: 020-8549 4477

tarlo lyons

For all your legal requirements, contact Simon Meadon at:

Tarlo Lyons, Watchmaker Court,
33 St. John's Lane,
LONDON EC1M 4DB

Telephone: 020 7405 2000
email: simon.meadon@tarlolyons.com

Visit our website at www.tarlolyons.com

Daniel Hussey
International Paranormal Occult Investigator & Consultant

PO Box 24250, London SE9 3ZH

Tel: 020 83786844
Mobile: 07764428318

E-mail: enquiries@paranormaloccultinvestigator.com
www.paranormaloccultinvestigator.com
www.lifeafterdeath.net

Psychic Research - Paranormal Phenomena

Practical Ritual Workings - Physical Mediumship

Materialisation's - Haunting's - Exorcisms

Criminal   Paranormal   Investigation's

Spiritualism - Transcendental Magic

Witchcraft & Occult Esoteric Problems

GORDON LEIGHTON
(Chartered Accountants, Business Advisors)
50 Queen Anne Street, London W1G 9HQ
Website: www.gordonl.co.uk
e-mail: gl@gordonl.com
Fax: 020-7487 2566   Tel: 020-7935 5737

HALL Francesca Cert. Dip. IATE. UKCP reg
(Creative Arts Counsellor & Psychotherapist)
68 Tavistock Crescent
Notting Hill
London W11 1AL   Tel: 020-7243 8355

HAMMOND John B. Ed (Hons) ICHFST
(Fitness Consultancy, Sports & Relaxation Massage)
4 Glencree, Billericay, Essex CM11 1EB
Mobile: 07703 185198   Tel/Fax: 01277 632830

HARDSELL Ltd
(Advertising, Marketing, Design)
Lafone House, The Leathermarket (11-3-1)
Weston Street, London SE1 3HN
e-mail: bigideas@hardsell.co.uk
Fax: 020-7403 5381   Tel: 020-7403 4037

HARVEY MONTGOMERY Ltd
(Chartered Accountants)
3 The Fairfield, Farnham, Surrey GU9 8AH
Website: www.harveymontgomery.co.uk
e-mail: harveyca@btconnect.com
Fax: 01252 734394   Tel: 01252 734388

HASLAM Dominic
(Arranger & Composer)
c/o Sandra Singer Associates
21 Cotswold Road
Westcliff-on-Sea, Essex SS0 8AA
Website: www.sandrasinger.com
e-mail: sandrasingeruk@aol.com
Fax: 01702 339393   Tel: 01702 331616

HERITAGE RAILWAY ASSOCIATION
7 Robert Close, Potters Bar
Herts EN6 2DH
Website: www.ukhrail.uel.ac.uk   Tel: 01707 643568

HOMEMATCH PROPERTY FINANCE
(Mortgages for Entertainers)
6 Shaw Street, Worcester WR1 3QQ
e-mail: chrisjcatchpole@aol.com
Fax: 01905 22121   Tel: 01905 22007

HONRI Peter
(Music Hall Consultant)
1 Evingar Road, Whitchurch
Hants RG28 7EY   Tel: 01256 892161

HUSSEY Daniel
(International Paranormal Occult Investigator
& Consultant)
PO Box 24250, London SE9 3ZH
Website: www.lifeafterdeath.net
e-mail: enquiries@paranormaloccultinvestigator.com
Mobile: 07764 428318   Tel: 020-8378 6844

HYPNOTHERAPY & PSYCHOTHERAPY
(Including Performance Improvement
Karen Mann DCH DHP)
1A Wedderburn House
Wedderburn Road, Hampstead, London NW3 5QR
Website: www.karenmann.co.uk
Tel: 020-7794 5843

IMAGE DIGGERS
(Slide/Stills/Audio/Video Library & Theme Research)
618B Finchley Road, London NW11 7RR
e-mail: ziph@macunlimited.net
Tel/Fax: 020-8455 4564

IMAGE MAKERS
(Image Consultants to the Entertainment Business)
150 Regents Park Road, London NW1 8XN
Website: www.imagemakersuk.com
e-mail: info@imagemakersuk.com
Fax: 020-7916 7470   Tel: 020-7209 1213

IMPACT AGENCY
(Public Relations)
3 Bloomsbury Place, London WC1A 2QL
Fax: 020-7580 7200   Tel: 020-7580 1770

I R A - INDEPENDENT REVIEWS ARTS SERVICES
(Stories from World of Film/Art/Showbiz))
12 Hemingford Close, London N12 9HF
e-mail: e.lovatt@btinternet.com
Mobile: 07956 212916   Tel/Fax: 020-8343 7437

JACKSON Kim
(Arts Education Consultancy)
1 Mellor Road, Leicester LE3 6HN
e-mail: jacksongillespie@hotmail.com
Tel: 0116-233 8432

JFL
(Recruitment Consultants)
47 New Bond Street, London W1S 1DJ
Fax: 020-7493 7161   Tel: 020-7493 8824

JOSHI CLINIC The
57 Wimpole Street, London W1G 8YP
Fax: 020-7487 3130   Tel: 020-7487 5456

KELLER Don
(Marketing Consultancy & Project Management)
65 Glenwood Road, Harringay, London N15 3JS
e-mail: donkeller@waitrose.com
Fax: 020-8809 6825   Tel: 020-8800 4882

KERR John CHARTERED ACCOUNTANTS
369-375 Eaton Road, West Derby, Liverpool L12 2AH
e-mail: advice@fkca.co.uk
Fax: 0151-228 3792   Tel: 0151-228 8977

KIEVE Paul
(Magical Effects for Theatre & Film)
23 Terrace Road, South Hackney, London E9 7ES
Website: www.stageillusion.com
e-mail: mail@stageillusion.com
                              Tel/Fax: 020-8985 6188

LAMBOLLE Robert
(Script Evaluation/Editing)
618B Finchley Road, London NW11 7RR
e-mail: ziph@macunlimited.net
                              Tel/Fax: 020-8455 4564

LARK INSURANCE BROKING GROUP
(Insurance Brokers)
Wigham House, Wakering Road, Barking, Essex IG11 8PJ
Fax: 020-8557 2430   Tel: 020-8557 2300

LEE Philip
(Marketing, Press and Publicity)
Top Floor, 21 Denmark Street, London WC2H 8NA
e-mail: philip@leep.biz
Fax: 020-7916 0031   Tel: 020-7916 0030

LINGUA FRANCA
(French Dialogue & Script Translators/Subtitlers)
12 Ack Lane West, Cheadle Hulme
Cheshire SK8 7EL   Tel: 0161-485 3357

LOCATION TUTORS NATIONWIDE
(Fully Qualified/ Experienced Support Teachers,
Covering all Key Stages in National Curriculum)
16 Poplar Walk, Herne Hill, London SE24 0BU
Fax: 020-7207 8794   Tel: 020-7978 8898

LOVE Billie HISTORICAL PHOTOGRAPHS
(Picture Research.
Formerly 'Amanda' Theatrical Portraiture)
3 Winton Street, Ryde
Isle of Wight PO33 2BX   Tel: 01983 812572

MAGIC KEY PARTNERSHIP The
(Life Coaching)
1 Ellerton Close, Theale
Berks RG7 5QN   Tel: 0845 1297401

MATRIX ENERGY FIELD THERAPY
121 Church Road, Wimbledon, London SW19 5AH
e-mail: dannie@lovingorganization.org
Mobile: 07762 821828   Tel: 020-8946 8534

McKENNA Deborah Ltd
(Celebrity Chefs & Television Writers)
Claridge House
29 Barnes High Street, London SW13 9LW
e-mail: info@deborahmckenna.com
Fax: 020-8392 2462   Tel: 020-8876 7566

MEDIA LEGAL
(Education Services)
83 Clarendon Road, Sevenoaks
Kent TN13 1ET   Tel: 01732 460592

MESURE Steve
(Science Theatre Practitioners)
10 Warren Drive
Chelsfield, Kent BR6 6EX
e-mail: stevemesure@ic24.net   Tel: 01689 812200

MILDENBERG Vanessa
(Choreographer of Theatre)
30 Mount Ephraim Road, London SW16 1LW
e-mail: cassandraprod@hotmail.com
Mobile: 07796 264828   Tel: 020-7372 0733

MILITARY ADVISORY & INSTRUCTION SPECIALISTS
(John Sessions) (Advice on Weapons, Drill,
Period to Present. Ex-Army Instructors)
e-mail: mais@ntlworld.com   Tel: 01904 491198

MILLER ALLAN Ann
(Private Lessons, Consultancy, Choreography)
The Belly Dance Centre, Mayfield
5 Rother Road, Seaford
East Sussex BN25 4HT
e-mail: annrustyallan@hotmail.com
                                   Tel: 01323 899083

MORGAN Jane ASSOCIATES
(Marketing, Publicity & Press)
8 Heathville Road, London N19 3AJ
e-mail: morgans@dircon.co.uk
Fax: 020-7263 9877   Tel: 020-7263 9867

MULLEN Julie
(Improvisors/Comedy Consultancy)
The Impro Lab
34 Watts Lane
Teddington Lock TW11 8HQ   Mobile: 07956 877839

NEATE Rodger PRODUCTION MANAGEMENT
15 Southcote Road, London N19 5BJ
e-mail: rneate@dircon.co.uk
Fax: 020-7697 8237   Tel: 020-7609 9538

NEOVISION
(Location & Production Services)
46 rue de Berne, 1201 Geneva, Switzerland
e-mail: lmouchet@worldcom.ch
Fax: (41 22) 741 1208   Tel: (41 79) 357 5417

NETWORK The
(Security & Investigation Services.
Contact: Ross Barker-Chesterton)
29 Queensdown Road, London E5 8NN
e-mail: network.sis@btinternet.com
                                   Tel: 07951 147268

NORTON Michael R
(Implant/Reconstructive Dentistry)
98 Harley Street, London W1G 7HZ
Website: www.nortonimplants.com
e-mail: drnorton@nortonimplants.com
Fax: 020-7486 9119   Tel: 020-7486 9229

NUMBERCRUNCHERS ACCOUNTING SERVICES
29 Dudley Road, Tunbridge Wells, Kent TN1 1LE
e-mail: numbercrunchers@lineone.net
                            Tel/Fax: 01892 511035

NWA-UK HAMMERLOCK
(Advice on Wrestling Events & Promotion)
PO Box 282, Ashford, Kent TN23 7ZZ
e-mail: nwauk@hammerlockwrestling.com
Fax: 0709 1131004   Tel: 0709 1131002

NYMAN LIBSON PAUL
(Chartered Accountants)
Regina House, 124 Finchley Road, London NW3 5JS
Website: www.nymanlibsonpaul.co.uk
e-mail: entertainment@nymanlibsonpaul.co.uk
Fax: 020-7431 1109   Tel: 020-7794 5611

ORANGE TREE STUDIO & MUSIC SERVICES
(Personal Sound Design for Music/Media Industry)
Po Box 99, Kings Langley WD4 8FB
Website: www. orangetreestudio.com
e-mail: richard@orangetreestudio.com
Mobile: 07768 146200   Tel: 01923 440550

PEAK PERFORMANCE TRAINING
(Tina Reibl, Hypnotherapy, NLP, Success Strategies)
42 The Broadway, Maidenhead
Berks SL6 1LU
e-mail: tina.reibl@tesco.net   Tel: 01628 633509

PERSONAL EVOLUTION
49 Babbacombe Gardens
Redbridge, Ilford, Essex IG4 5LZ
Website: www.personal-evolution.com
e-mail: infoevolution@aol.com
Mobile: 07762 577520   Tel/Fax: 020-8550 6348

POLAND DENTAL STUDIOS
(Film/Stage Dentistry)
1 Devonshire Place, London W1N 1PA
e-mail: polandslab@aol.com
Fax: 020-7486 3952   Tel: 020-7935 6919

PRESTIGE INSURANCE
Garrick House, 161 High Street
Hampton Hill, Middlesex TW12 1NG
Fax: 020-8939 3060   Tel: 020-8393 3969

PRIDE MEDIA ASSOCIATION Ltd
(Alternative Therapies
Psychic & Paranormal Phenomena)
The Burnside Centre, 38 Burnside Crescent
Middleton, Manchester M24 5NN
Website: www.prideradio.co.uk
e-mail: pma@prideradio.co.uk
                            Tel/Fax: 0161-643 6266

PRYCE Jacqui-Lee
(Personal Trainer, Boxing, Muay-Thai & Kick-Boxing)
                            Mobile: 07930 304809

REDD EVENTS
(Events/PR)
Studio One
7 Chalcot Road, Primrose Hill, London NW1 8LH
Website: www.showbizshow.co.uk
e-mail: reddevents@hotmail.com
                            Mobile: 07957 218885

RETROGRAPH NOSTALGIA ARCHIVE Ltd
(Nostalgia Picture Consultants 1880-1970)
164 Kensington Park Road
Notting Hill, London W11 2ER
Website: www.retrograph.com
e-mail: retropix1@aol.com
Fax: 020-7229 3395   Tel: 020-7727 9378

RIPLEY-DUGGAN PARTNERSHIP The
(Tour Booking)
52 Tottenham Street
London W1T 4RN
e-mail: ripleyduggan@aol.com   Tel: 020-7436 1392

DZEYEN
www.dzeyen.com

The Actor's web solution

Providing custom website design for individual actors and actresses as well as agencies and companies.

Tel: 020 7381 5283   Email: email@dzeyen.com   Mobile: 07979 955 250

ROBERT CARTER
(Solicitor)
8 West Street, London WC2H 9NG
Fax: 020-7836 2786   Tel: 020-7836 2785

SEAGER Martin
(Composer/Lyricist for Film/TV/Theatre)
14 Neal's Yard, Covent Garden, London WC2H 9DP
e-mail: martinseager@onetel.net.uk
                                  Tel: 020-8943 4145

SHAW Bernard
(Specialist in Recording and Directing Voice Tapes)
Horton Manor, Canterbury CT4 7LG
Website: www.bernardshaw.co.uk
e-mail: bernard@bernardshaw.co.uk
                              Tel/Fax: 01227 730843

SINGER Sandra PUBLIC RELATIONS
(Entertainers, Promotions Staff & Events)
21 Cotswold Road, Westcliff-on-Sea, Essex SS0 8AA
e-mail: sandrasingeruk@aol.com
Fax: 01702 339393   Tel: 01702 331616

SPEAKERPOWER.CO.UK
48 Fellows Road, London NW3 3LH
Website: www.speakerpower.co.uk
e-mail: barbara@speakerpower.co.uk
Fax: 020-7722 5255   Tel: 020-7586 4361

SPENCER Ivor
(Professional Toastmaster
Events Organiser & Head Butler)
12 Little Bornes, Dulwich, London SE21 8SE
Website: www.ivorspencer.com
e-mail: ivor@ivorspencer.com
Fax: 020-8670 0055   Tel: 020-8670 8424

SPORTS WORKSHOP PROMOTIONS Ltd
(Production Advisors, Sport, Stunts, Safety)
PO Box 878
Crystal Palace National Sports Centre, London SE19 2BH
e-mail: info@sportspromotions.co.uk
Fax: 020-8776 7772   Tel: 020-8659 4561

STAGE CRICKET CLUB
(Cricketers & Cricket Club)
39-41 Hanover Steps
St George's Fields, Albion Street, London W2 2YG
e-mail: brianjfilm@aol.com
Fax: 020-7262 5736   Tel: 020-7402 7543

STUNT ACTION SPECIALISTS
110A Trafalgar Road
Portslade, East Sussex BN41 1GS
Website: www.stuntactionspecialists.com
e-mail: wayne@stuntactionspecialists.co.uk
Fax: 01273 708699   Tel: 01273 230214

SUMMERS David & COMPANY
(Chartered Accountants)
Argo House, Kilburn Park Road, London NW6 5LF
e-mail: dsummersfca@hotmail.com
Fax: 020-7644 0678   Tel: 020-7644 0478

TAKE FIVE CASTING STUDIO
(Showreels)
25 Ganton Street
London W1F 9BP
Website: www.takefivestudio.co.uk
Fax: 020-7287 3035   Tel: 020-7287 2120

TANI MORENA,
SPANISH CHOREOGRAPHY FOR PROFESSIONALS
(Theatre, Opera, Ballet)   Tel: 020-8452 0407

TARLO LYONS
(Solicitors)
Watchmaker Court
33 St John's Lane, London EC1M 4DB
Website: www.tarlolyons.com
e-mail: info@tarlolyons.com
Fax: 020-7814 9421   Tel: 020-7405 2000

TARRY Angela
(Clairvoyant & Aura Photography)
c/o Sandra Singer Associates
21 Cotswold Road, Westcliff-on-Sea, Essex SS0 8AA
Website: www.sandrasinger.com
e-mail: sandrasingeruk@aol.com
Fax: 01702 339393   Tel: 01702 331616

TAX FILES (UK)
(Tax Consultants)
Suite 123-124, Salisbury House
163-164 London Wall, London EC2M 5ST
Fax: 020-7628 2577   Tel: 020-7628 1464

TAYLOR Charlotte
(Stylist/Props Buyer)
18 Eleanor Grove
Barnes, London SW13 0JN
Mobile: 07836 708904   Tel/Fax: 020-8876 9085

TAYLOR Chris
(Arts Administration)
1 Chichester Terrace, Brighton BN2 1FG
e-mail: chris.taylor@clara.co.uk
Fax: 01273 675922   Tel: 01273 625132

TELESCRIPT Ltd
The Barn, Handpost Farmhouse
Maidens Green, Berkshire RG42 6LD
Fax: 01344 890655   Tel: 01344 890470

THEATRE PROJECTS CONSULTANTS
4 Apollo Studios
Charlton Kings Road, London NW5 2SW
Website: www.tpcworld.com
Fax: 020-7284 0636   Tel: 020-7482 4224

THEATRICAL DENTISTRY
(Richard D Casson)
6 Milford House
7 Queen Anne Street, London W1G 9HN
Website: www.richardcasson.com
                              Tel/Fax: 020-7935 8854

Consultants

C

THORNTON W. M.
(Military Adviser & Researcher)
37 Wolsey Close
Southall, Middlesex UB2 4NQ
e-mail: maitland@thornton44.fsnet.co.uk
Tel: 020-8574 4425

TODS MURRAY WS
(Richard Findlay Entertainment Lawyer)
66 Queen Street, Edinburgh EH2 4NE
e-mail: richard.findlay@todsmurray.com
Fax: 0131-225 3676   Tel: 0131-226 4771

TOUCHWOOD PRODUCTION STUDIO
(Voice-Over Showreels, Digital Editing etc)
Knightsbridge House
229 Acton Lane, Chiswick, London W4 5DD
Fax: 020-8995 2144   Tel: 020-8995 3232

TRUEWAYS
(Tasha Sangster, Holistic Practitioner in Indian Head
Massage, Facelift Massage & Feng Shui)
Tel: 020-7403 6564

TURNER Jeff
(Psychotherapy, Counselling & Coaching)
Life Management Systems
14 Randell's Road, London N1 0DH
Website: www.lifemanagement.co.uk
e-mail: info@lifemanagement.co.uk
Tel: 020-7837 9871

TV UK Ltd/LATITUDE MEDIA COURSES
(Voice-Over Courses, Alan Meyer)
PO Box 2183
London W1A 1UB
Website: www.tvuk.net
e-mail: alanmeyer@tvuk.net   Tel: 020-7727 7447

UPFRONT TELEVISION Ltd
(Celebrity)
39-41 New Oxford Street, London WC1A 1BN
e-mail: upfront@btinternet.com
Fax: 020-7836 7701   Tel: 020-7836 7702

VANTIS MORTON THORNTON
(Accountants/Business Advisers)
Torrington House
47 Holywell Hill
St Albans, Hertfordshire AL1 1HD
e-mail: ian.skelton@vantisplc.com
Fax: 01727 861052   Tel: 01727 838255

VENTURINO Antonio
(Commedia dell' Arte
& Mask Specialist & Movement Director)
Coup de Masque
97 Moore Road, Mapperley, Nottingham NG3 6EJ
e-mail: a-and-t@coup-de-masque.fsnet.co.uk
Tel/Fax: 0115-985 8409

VITAL TOUCH The
(On-Site Massage Company)
11 Evering Road, London N16 7PX
Website: www.thevitaltouch.com
e-mail: nunu@thevitaltouch.com
Tel: 020-8451 5500

VSI
132 Cleveland Street, London W1T 6AB
Website: www.vsi.tv
e-mail: info@vsi.tv
Fax: 020-7692 7711   Tel: 020-7692 7700

WELBOURNE Jacqueline
(Circus Trainer, Choreographer, Consultant)
43 Kingsway Avenue
Kingswood, Bristol BS15 8DB
e-mail: jackie@welbourne.co.uk
Mobile: 07977 247287   Tel/Fax: 0117-947 7042

WHITE Leonard
(Production & Script Consultant)
Highlands, 40 Hill Crest Road
Newhaven, Brighton
East Sussex BN9 9EG   Tel/Fax: 01273 514473

WILD DREAM CONSULTANCY
(Achievement Training
Confidence Class, Personal Development)
Tel: 020-8374 3924

WITCH FINDER GENERAL
(Occult Consultants)
BCM AKADEMIA, London WC1N 3XX
e-mail: esbat@blueyonder.co.uk
Tel: 020-8683 2173

WWW.PUPPETSPRESENT.COM
c/o Peter Charlesworth & Associates
68 Old Brompton Road, London SW7 3LD
Website: www.puppetspresent.com
e-mail: puppetspresent@btinternet.com
Tel: 020-7581 2478

WYKEHAMS RELOCATION
(Relocation Services)
6 Kendrick Place
Reece Mews, London SW7 3HF
Fax: 020-7589 8886   Tel: 020-7581 1935

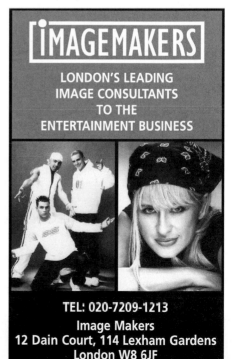

IMAGEMAKERS

**LONDON'S LEADING
IMAGE CONSULTANTS
TO THE
ENTERTAINMENT BUSINESS**

TEL: 020-7209-1213
**Image Makers
12 Dain Court, 114 Lexham Gardens
London W8 6JF**
www.imagemakersUK.com

ACADEMY COSTUMES Ltd
50 Rushworth Street, London SE1 0RB
Website: www.academycostumes.com
e-mail: academyco@aol.com
Fax: 020-7928 6287   Tel: 020-7620 0771

ANELLO & DAVIDE Ltd
Shop: 47 Beauchamp Place, Chelsea
London SW3 1NX
Fax: 020-7225 3375   Tel: 020-7225 2468

ANELLO & DAVIDE Ltd
(Bespoke, Bridal, Dance & Theatrical Footwear)
28C Standard Road
Park Royal, London NW10 6EU
Fax: 020-8965 4111   Tel: 020-8963 1220

ANGELS
(Fancy Dress & Revue)
119 Shaftesbury Avenue, London WC2H 8AE
Website: www.fancydress.com
e-mail: party@fancydress.com
Fax: 020-7240 9527   Tel: 020-7836 5678

ANGELS THE COSTUMIERS
1 Garrick Road, London NW9 6AA
Website: www.angels.uk.com
e-mail: angels@angels.uk.com
Fax: 020-8202 1820   Tel: 020-8202 2244

ANGELS PARIS
(Costume and Uniform Hire)
Cap 18, 189 Rue d'Aubervilles
75018 Paris, France
Website: www.angels.fr
e-mail: angels@angels.fr
Fax: 00 33 1 44 729060   Tel: 00 33 1 44 728282

ANGELS WIGS
(Wig Hire/Makers, Facial Hair Suppliers)
1 Garrick Road, London NW9 6AA
Website: www.angels.uk.com
e-mail: wigs@angels.uk.com
Fax: 020-8202 1820   Tel: 020-8202 2244

ANICHINI Carlo
(Hairdresser)
14 Piccadilly Arcade
London SW1Y 6NH   Tel: 020-7493 5692

ARMS & ARCHERY
(Armour, Weaponry, Chainmail, Period Costumes)
The Coach House
London Road, Ware, Herts SG12 9QU
e-mail: tgou104885@aol.com
Fax: 01920 461044   Tel: 01920 460335

BABOO William
(Theatrical Tailor)
46 Berwick Street
London W1F 8SG   Tel: 020-7434 1680

BAHADLY R
(Hair & Make-Up Specialist, Cheshire Area)
48 Ivy Meade Road, Macclesfield, Cheshire
Mobile: 07973 553073   Tel/Fax: 01625 869712

BBC COSTUME & WIGS
172-178 Victoria Road, North Acton, London W3 6UL
Fax: 020-8993 7040   Tel: 020-8576 7885

BERTRAND Henry
(London Stockhouse for Silk)
52 Holmes Road, London NW5 3AB
Fax: 020-7424 7001   Tel: 020-7424 7000

BIRMINGHAM COSTUME HIRE
Suites 209-210, Jubilee Centre
130 Pershore Street, Birmingham B5 6ND
e-mail: info@birminghamcostumehire.co.uk
Fax: 0121-622 2758   Tel: 0121-622 3158

BOSANQUET Pamela COSTUME SERVICES
2 Lebanon Park, Twickenham TW1 3DG
e-mail: lily.jones@virgin.net
Fax: 020-8891 6259   Tel: 020-8891 4346

BROE Bert
(Make-Up Artist, Consultant, Lecturer)
38A The Avenue, Hatch End
Middlesex HA5 4EY   Tel: 020-8428 5706

BRYAN PHILIP DAVIES ENTERPRISES
(Lavish Pantomime Costumes/Revue Costumes)
68 Court Road, Lewes, East Sussex BN7 2SA
Website: www.bpdcostumes.co.uk
e-mail: bryan.davies4@btinternet.com
Mobile: 07931 249097   Tel/Fax: 01273 481004

BUTTERFIELD 8
(Formerly Jo Dalby, Vintage Costume 1910-1980's)
Top Floor, Herbert House, Bristol Temple Meads Station
Bristol   Tel: 01432 840765

CALICO
(Suppliers of Unbleached Calico
for Stage Costumes, Backdrops etc)
3 Ram Passage
High Street, Kingston-upon-Thames KT1 1HH
Website: www.calicofabrics.co.uk
e-mail: sales@calicofabrics.co.uk
Fax: 020-8546 7755   Tel: 020-8541 5274

CATCO MILLINERY
134 Mercers Road
London N19 4PV   Tel: 020-7272 4833

CAVALCADE COSTUMES
(Period & Light Entertainment Costumes
Single Outfits to Full Productions)
57 Pelham Road, London SW19 1NW
Fax: 020-8540 2243   Tel: 020-8540 3513

CHRISANNE Ltd
(Specialist Fabrics & Accessories)
Chrisanne Hous
14 Locks Lane, Mitcham, Surrey CR4 2JX
Website: www.chrisanne.co.uk
e-mail: sales@chrisanne.co.uk
Fax: 020-8640 2106   Tel: 020-8640 5921

COLTMAN Mike
(See COSTUME CONSTRUCTION)

COOK Sheila
(Period Jewellery, Textiles
Costumes and Accessories for Hire/Sale)
283 Westbourne Grove, London W11 2QA
e-mail: sheilacook@sheilacook.co.uk
Fax: 020-7229 3855   Tel: 020-7792 8001

COSPROP Ltd
(Costumes & Accessories)
26-28 Rochester Place, London NW1 9JR
e-mail: enquiries@cosprop.com
Fax: 020-7485 5942   Tel: 020-7485 6731

COSTUME CONSTRUCTION
(Costumes, Masks, Props, Puppets)
21A Silchester Road
London W10 6SF   Tel/Fax: 020-8968 9136

COSTUME REPRODUCTIONS
(Costumiers)
200 Main Road, Goostrey, Cheshire CW4 8PD
Website: www.replicawarehouse.co.uk
e-mail: lesleyedwards@replicawarehouse.co.uk
                          Tel/Fax: 01477 534075

COSTUME STUDIO Ltd
(Costumes & Wigs)
Montgomery House
159-161 Balls Pond Road, London N1 4BG
e-mail: costume.studio@easynet.co.uk
Tel/Fax: 020-7837 6576   Tel: 020-7275 9614

COUNTY DRAMA WARDROBE
(Costume Hire)
25 Gwydir Street
Cambridge CB1 2LG   Tel: 01223 313423

CRAZY CLOTHES CONNECTION
(1920's-1970's for Sale or Hire)
134 Lancaster Road
Ladbroke Grove
London W11 1QU   Tel: 020-7221 3989

DARBY Kevin COSTUMES
(Costumes, Hats, Headdresses
& Feathers Designed, Supplied & Hired)
Unit 10, Douglas Buildings
Royal Stuart Lane, Cardiff CF10 5EL
Fax: 029-2045 1628   Tel: 029-2045 1646

DELANEY Catherine
(Hats/Millinery)
Coombe Villa
6 Coombe Lane, Tenterden, Kent TN30 6HD
Website: www.catherinedelaney.co.uk
e-mail: cat@seaina.force9.co.uk
Fax: 020-7231 9051   Tel: 020-7231 7173

DESIGNER ALTERATIONS
(Restyling & Remodelling of Clothes & Costumes)
York House
347 York Road, Battersea, London SW11 3QU
Website: www.designeralterations.com
Fax: 020-8877 0880   Tel: 020-7498 4360

D'OYLY CARTE OPERA COMPANY
(Wardrobe Services)
The Powerhouse, 6 Sancroft Street, London SE11 5UD
Website: www.doylycarte.org.uk
Fax: 020-7793 7300   Tel: 020-7793 7100

EASTON Derek
(Wigs For Theatre, Film & TV)
1 Dorothy Avenue, Kingsway Court
Second Avenue, Peacehaven, East Sussex BN10 8LP
Website: www.derekeastonwigs.co.uk
Mobile: 07768 166733   Tel/Fax: 01273 770069

EDA ROSE MILLINERY
(Ladies' Model Hat Design & Manufacture)
Lalique, Mongewell, Wallingford
Oxon OX10 8BP   Tel/Fax: 01491 837174

FOSTER Pam ASSOCIATES
(Wig Makers)
Unit 009, The Chandlery
50 Westminster Bridge Road, London SE1 7QY
e-mail: pam@pfosterassoc.demon.co.uk
Fax: 020-7721 7409   Tel: 020-7721 7641

FOX Charles H. Ltd
(Professional Make-Up & Wigs)
22 Tavistock Street, London WC2E 7PY
Website: www.charlesfox.co.uk
Fax: 0870 2001369   Tel: 0870 2000369

FREED OF LONDON
(Dancewear & Danceshoes)
94 St Martin's Lane, London WC2N 4AT
Website: www.freedoflondon.com
e-mail: shop@freed.co.uk
Fax: 020-7240 3061   Tel: 020-7240 0432

FROCKS
(Dina Hall) (Costume Supervisor & Maker)
Lower Wrescombe Farm Cottage
Yealmpton
Nr Plymouth PL8 2NL   Tel: 01752 881443

FUNN Ltd
(Silk, Cotton Wool Stockings
Opaque Opera Tights & 40's Rayon Stockings)
PO Box 102 Steyning
West Sussex BN44 3DS
e-mail: funnltd@bigfoot.com   Tel/Fax: 01903 892841

GAMBA THEATRICAL
(Theatrical Footwear Company Ltd)
Unit 14, Chingford Industrial Centre
Hall Lane, Chingford, London E4 8DJ
e-mail: gambatheatrical@yahoo.com
Fax: 020-8529 7995   Tel: 020-8259 9195

GAV NICOLA THEATRICAL SHOES
1A Suttons Lane, Hornchurch, Essex RM12 6RD
e-mail: sales@gavnicola.freeserve.co.uk
Mobile: 07961 974278   Tel/Fax: 01708 438584

GIAMPIERI Eleonora
(Freelance Make-Up Artist for Cinema and Fashion)
88 Mill Lane
West Hampstead, London NW6 1NL
Website: www.move.to/make-up
e-mail: make-up@move.to   Mobile: 07950 368293

GILLHAM Felicite
(Wigs)
15 Newland
Sherborne, Dorset DT9 3JG
e-mail: f.gillham.wigs@gmx.net   Tel: 01935 814328

HAIRAISERS
(Wigs)
9-11 Sunbeam Road, Park Royal, London NW10 6JP
Fax: 020-8963 1600   Tel: 020-8965 2500

HARVEYS OF HOVE
(Theatrical Costumes & Military Specialists)
110 Trafalgar Road, Portslade, Sussex BN41 1GS
e-mail: wayne@stuntactionspecialists.co.uk
Fax: 01273 708699   Tel: 01273 430323

HERALD & HEART HATTERS
(Men's & Women's Hats
& Headdresses - Period & Modern)
20 Half Moon Lane, London SE24 9HV
Website: www.heraldandheart.com
                              Tel: 020-7627 2414

HIREARCHY
(Classic & Contemporary Costume)
45-47 Palmerston Road
Boscombe
Bournemouth, Dorset BH1 4HW
Website: www.hirearchy.co.uk
e-mail: hirearchy1@aol.com   Tel: 01202 394465

HIYA COSTUME
(Hire of Theatre Costumes for Adults & Children)
1-2 Ham Road, Shoreham-by-Sea
Sussex BN43 6PA   Tel: 01273 453421

HODIN Annabel
(Costume Designer/Stylist)
12 Eton Avenue, London NW3 3EH
e-mail: annabelhodin@aol.com
Mobile: 07836 754079   Tel: 020-7431 8761

JULIETTE DESIGNS
(Diamante Jewellery Manufacturers)
90 Yerbury Road, London N19 4RS
Website: stagejewellery.com
Fax: 020-7281 7326   Tel: 020-7263 7878

K & D Ltd
(Footwear)
Unit 7A, Thames Road Industrial Estate
Thames Road, Silvertown, London E16 2EZ
Website: www.shoemaking.co.uk
e-mail: k&d@shoemaking.co.uk
Fax: 020-7476 5220   Tel: 020-7474 0500

KING Shelley J
(Make-up Artist/Wigdresser)
Vine Bank Cottage
High Street, Limpsfield, Surrey RH8 0DR
Mobile: 07973 249998   Tel: 01883 715095

LANDSFIELD Warren
(Period Legal Wigs)
47 Glenmore Road
London NW3 4DA   Tel: 020-7722 4581

LAURENCE CORNER THEATRICALS
(Theatrical Costumiers - Militaria,
Uniforms - Hire & Sale)
62-64 Hampstead Road, London NW1 2NU
Website: www.laurencecorner.com
Fax: 020-7813 1413   Tel: 020-7813 1010

LEWIS HENRY Ltd
(Dress Makers)
3rd Floor
42 Great Titchfield Street
London W1P 7AE   Tel: 020-7636 6683

LONDON HAT HOUSE The
(Hatmakers, Masks, Headdresses & Specialist Dyers)
Unit 006, The Chandlery
50 Westminster Bridge Road
London SE1 7QY   Tel: 020-7721 8771

MADDERMARKET THEATRE
(Period Clothing, Costume Hire & Wig Hire)
St John's Alley, Norwich NR2 1DR
Website: www.maddermarket.freeserve.co.uk
e-mail: theatre@maddermarket.freeserve.co.uk
Fax: 01603 661357   Tel: 01603 626292

MAKEUP CENTRE The
(Make-Up Lessons & Supplies)
52A Walham Grove, London SW6 1QR
Website: www.themake-upcentre.co.uk
e-mail: info@themake-upcentre.co.uk
Tel: 020-7381 0213

MANNEE Nichola
(Make-Up Artist)
e-mail: nicki_makeup@hotmail.com
Mobile: 07946 850385

MASTER CLEANERS The
(Theatrical Costumes & Antique Garments)
189 Haverstock Hill
London NW3 4QG   Tel: 020-7431 3725

MBA COSTUMES
Goodyear House
52-56 Osnaburgh Street, London NW1 3ND
e-mail: nhowarduk@aol.com
Fax: 020-7383 2038   Tel: 020-7388 4994

McKAY Glynn MASKS
(Specialists in Special Effect Make-Up)
11 Mount Pleasant, Framlingham, Suffolk IP13 9HQ
Mobile: 07780 865073   Tel/Fax: 01728 723865

MIDNIGHT
Costume Design & Wardrobe (Film, Music, Theatre)
e-mail: midnight_wardrobe@hotmail.com
Mobile: 07941 313223

MUMFORD Jean
(Costume Maker)
92B Fortess Road
London NW5 2HJ   Tel: 020-7267 5829

NICOLERENEE
(Wedding & Evening Dresses/Ball Gowns)
4 Puma Court, Spitalfields, City, London E1 6QG
e-mail: info@nicolerenee.co.uk
Fax: 020-7247 9276   Mobile: 07961 180949

ORIGINAL KNITWEAR
(Inc. Fake Fur)
Waterside, 99 Rotherhithe Street, London SE16 4NF
Fax: 020-7231 9051   Tel: 020-7231 9020

PATEY (LONDON) Ltd
Unit 1, 9 Gowlett Road, London SE15 4HX
Website: www.pateyhats.com
e-mail: pateyhats@aol.com
Fax: 020-7732 9538   Tel: 020-7635 0030

PERMODE
(Costume)
46 Berwick Street
London W1F 8SG   Tel: 020-7434 1680

PINK POINTES DANCEWEAR
1A Suttons Lane, Hornchurch, Essex RM12 6RD
e-mail: sales@gavnicola.freeserve.co.uk
Tel/Fax: 01708 438584

POLAND DENTAL STUDIO
(Film/Stage Dentistry)
1 Devonshire Place, London W1N 1PA
e-mail: polandslab@aol.com
Fax: 020-7486 3952   Tel: 020-7935 6919

PROBLOOD
11 Mount Pleasant, Framlingham
Suffolk IP13 9HQ   Tel/Fax: 01728 723865

PULLON PRODUCTIONS
(Costumiers)
St George's Studio
Wood End Lane, Fillongley, Coventry CV7 8DF
Website: www.pm-productions.co.uk
e-mail: junepullon@faxvia.net
Tel/Fax: 01676 541390

RAINBOW PRODUCTIONS Ltd
(Manufacture and
Handling of Costume Characters)
Rainbow House
56 Windsor Avenue, London SW19 2RR
Website: www.rainbowproductions.co.uk
e-mail: info@rainbowproductions.co.uk
Fax: 020-8545 0777   Tel: 020-8545 0700

ROBBINS Sheila
(Costumes & Wigs)
60 Hurst Street, Oxford OX4 1HA
Fax: 01865 735524   Tel: 01865 240268

ROYAL EXCHANGE THEATRE COSTUME HIRE
(Period Costumes, Wigs & Accessories)
47-53 Swan Street, Manchester M4 4JY
e-mail: costume.hire@royalexchange.co.uk
Tel/Fax: 0161-615 6800

ROYAL LYCEUM THEATRE COMPANY
(Theatrical Costume Hire)
29 Roseburn Street, Edinburgh EH12 5PE
Fax: 0131-346 8072   Tel: 0131-337 1997

ROYAL NATIONAL THEATRE
(Costume & Furniture Hire)
Chichester House, Kennington Park Estate
1-3 Brixton Road, London SW9 6DE
e-mail: costume_hire@nationaltheatre.org.uk
Tel: 020-7735 4774 (Costume)   Tel: 020-7820 1358 (Props)

RUMBLE Jane
(Masks, Millinery, Helmets Made to Order)
121 Elmstead Avenue, Wembley
Middlesex HA9 8NT   Tel: 020-8904 6462

RUSSELL HOWARTH Ltd
35 Hoxton Square, London N1 6MM
Fax: 020-7729 0107   Tel: 020-7739 6960

SCOTT Allan COSTUMES
(Costume Hire, Stage, Film & TV)
Offley Works, Unit F, Prima Road
London SW9 0NA   Tel: 020-7793 1197

SEXTON Sally Ann
(Hair & Make-Up Stylist)
31 Sylvester Road, East Finchley, London N2 8HN
Mobile: 07973 802842   Tel: 020-8346 2745

SHOWBIZ WIGMASTERS
(Theatrical Wigmakers & Hire)
7 Tumulus Close, Southampton SO19 6RL
Website: www.website.lineone.net/~showbizwigs
Tel/Fax: 023-8040 6699

SIDE EFFECTS
(Custom-made Character/FX Costumes)
Unit 4, Camberwell Trading Estate
117 Denmark Road, London SE5 9LB
e-mail: sfx@lineone.net
Fax: 020-7738 5198   Tel: 020-7738 5199

SINGER Sandra ASSOCIATES
21 Cotswold Road, Westcliff on Sea, Essex SS0 8AA
Website: www.sandrasinger.com
e-mail: sandrasingeruk@aol.com
Fax: 01702 339393   Tel: 01702 331616

SKINNER Rachel MILLINERY
13 Princess Road, London NW1 8JR
Website: www.rachelskinner.co.uk
e-mail: rachel@rachelskinner.co.uk
Tel/Fax: 020-7209 0066

SLEIMAN Hilary
(Specialist & Period Knitwear)
72 Godwin Road, London E7 0LG
e-mail: hilarysl@aol.com
Mobile: 07940 555663   Tel: 020-8555 6176

SOFT PROPS
(Costume & Modelmakers)
Unit 4, Camberwell Trading Estate
117-119 Denmark Road, London SE5 9LB
e-mail: jackie@softprops.co.uk
Fax: 020-7738 5198   Tel: 020-7738 6324

STEP BACK IN TIME
(Decade by Decade Collection of Costume,
Props etc 1890's to Present, 1940's Specialist)
Walkers Industrial Park
Ollerton Road, Tuxford, Notts NG22 0PQ
Fax: 01777 870033   Tel: 01777 870044

STUDIO FOUR COSTUMES
(Childrenswear for Hire to Film & TV)
4 Warple Mews, Warple Way
Acton, London W3 0RF   Tel/Fax: 020-8749 6569

SWINFIELD Rosemarie
(Make-Up Design & Training)
Rosie's Make-Up Box
6 Brewer Street, Soho, London W1R 3FS
Website: www.rosiesmake-up.co.uk
e-mail: rosemarie@rosiesmake-up.co.uk
Fax: 020-8390 7773   Mobile: 07976 965520

THEATRICAL FOOTWEAR CO The Ltd
(See GAMBA THEATRICAL)

TRENDS PRODUCTIONS Ltd
(Theatrical Costume Hire, Design & Making)
54 Lisson Street
London NW1 5DF
e-mail: info@trendsgroup.co.uk
Fax: 020-7258 3591   Tel: 020-7723 8001

TRYFONOS Mary
(Mask Maker)
59 Shaftesbury Road
London N19 4QW
e-mail: marytryfonos@aol.com
Mobile: 07764 587433   Tel: 020-7561 9880

VICKERS Jean
(Costumes made for Stage, TV & Film)
40 Abingdon Road
London W8 6AR   Tel: 020-7937 2870

VIVAS INTERNATIONAL
(Dance & Costume Hire)
L'Apache
Woodgate, Chichester
West Sussex PO20 6SS
e-mail: vivas@vivas.demon.co.uk
Fax: 01243 543844   Tel: 01243 542020

WAIN SHIELL & SON Ltd
(High Quality Cloth Merchants)
12 Savile Row, London W15 3PQ
e-mail: wainshiell@compuserve.com
Fax: 020-7437 0093   Tel: 020-7734 1464

7 Sheffield Road, New Mill, Huddersfield HD9 7BW
Fax: 01484 688796   Tel: 01484 688848

WEST YORKSHIRE FABRICS Ltd
(Melton, Crepe, Suiting, Barathea, Cut Lengths)
20 High Ash Drive
Leeds HD9 7BW
e-mail: info@stroud-brothers.demon.co.uk
          Tel/Fax: 0870 4439842

WIG ROOM The
22 Coronation Road
Basingstoke, Hants RG21 4HA
e-mail: wigroom@fsbdial.co.uk
          Tel/Fax: 01256 415737

WIG SPECIALITIES Ltd
(Wigs and Facial Hair, Hair Extensions etc)
173 Seymour Place
London W1H 4PW
e-mail: wigspecialities@btconnect.com
Fax: 020-7723 1566   Tel: 020-7262 6565

WILLIAMS Emma
(Costume Designer & Stylist - Film, TV & Theatre)
e-mail: emmaw@costume.fsnet.co.uk
Mobile: 07710 130345   Tel/Fax: 01225 447169

WILSON Marian WIGS
(Theatrical & Film Wigmaker)
59 Gloucester Street, Faringdon, Oxon SN7 7JA
e-mail: wigmaker@wigmaker.screaming.net
Fax: 01367 242438   Tel: 01367 241696

WORLD OF FANTASY
(Costumes & Props)
Swansnest, Rear of 2 Windmill Road
Hampton Hill, Middlesex TW12 1RH
Fax: 020-8783 1366   Tel: 020-8941 1595

Critics (London Papers)

DAILY EXPRESS   Tel: 020-7928 8000
Theatre: Robert Gore-Langton
Films: Ryan Gilbey, Alan Hunter
Television: Tim Hulse
    Jeremy Novick
Saturday Magazine/
Programmes: Pat Stoddart

DAILY MAIL   Tel: 020-7938 6000
Theatre: Michael Coveney
Films: Chris Tookey
Television: Peter Paterson
    Christopher Matthew

DAILY STAR   Tel: 020-7928 8000
Show Business & Television: Laura Benjamin
    Julia Etherington
    Sean Hamilton
    Nigel Pauley
    Debbie Pogue
    Gareth Morgan
    Ben Todd
    Amy Watts
Films & Video: Rachel Dobson
    Alan Frank

DAILY TELEGRAPH   Tel: 020-7538 5000
Theatre: Charles Spencer
Films: Sukhdev Sandhu
Radio: Gillian Reynolds
Art: Richard Dorment
Dance: Ismene Brown
Music: Geoffrey Norris

FINANCIAL TIMES   Tel: 020-7873 3000
Theatre: Alastair MacAulay
Films: Nigel Andrews
Television: Graham McCann

GUARDIAN   Tel: 020-7278 2332
Theatre: Michael Billington
Films: Peter Bradshaw
Television: Nancy Banks-Smith
Radio: Elisabeth Mahoney

INDEPENDENT   Tel: 020-7005 2000
Television: Tom Sutcliffe

LONDON EVENING STANDARD
    Tel: 020-7938 6000
Theatre: Nicholas de Jongh
    Rachel Halliburton
    Fiona Mountford
Films: Alexander Walker
Television: Victor Lewis-Smith
    Terry Ramsay
Radio: Terry Ramsay
Classical Music: Brian Hunt
Opera: Fiona Maddocks

MAIL ON SUNDAY   Tel: 020-7938 6000
(Review Section)
Theatre: Georgina Brown
Films: Jason Solomons
Television: Jaci Stephen
Radio: Simon Garfield

MIRROR   Tel: 020-7510 3000
Films: Jonathan Ross
Television: Nicola Methuen

MORNING STAR   Tel: 020-7538 5181
Theatre & Films: Bunmi Daramola
Television: Kevin Russell
    Alex Reid

NEWS OF THE WORLD   Tel: 020-7782 4000
Show Business/Films: Rav Singh
    Paul Ross
    Shebah Ronayh

OBSERVER   Tel: 020-7278 2332
Theatre: Susanna Clapp
Films: Philip French
    Akin Ofumu
Radio: Sue Arnold
    Stephanie Billu

SPORT   Tel: 0161-238 8151
Show Business/Features: Sarah Stephens

SUN   Tel: 020-7782 4000
Television: Gary Bushell

SUNDAY EXPRESS   Tel: 020-7928 8000
Theatre: Robert Gore-Langton
    Zoe Hall
Films: Henry Fitzherbert
Television: Tim Hulse
    Jeremy Norick
    Glyn George
Radio: Ken Garner

SUNDAY MIRROR   Tel: 020-7510 3000
Theatre & Television: Ian Hyland
Films: Quentin Falk

SUNDAY PEOPLE   Tel: 020-7510 3000
Television & Radio: Olivia Buxton
Films: Jane Simon
Show Business   Sean O'Brien
Features: Dawn Alford

SUNDAY TELEGRAPH   Tel: 020-7538 5000
Theatre: John Gross
Films: Jenny McCartney
Television: John Preston
Radio: David Sexton

SUNDAY TIMES   Tel: 020-7782 5000
Theatre: John Peter
Films: Cosmo Landesman
Television: A.A. Gill
Radio: Paul Donovan

TIMES   Tel: 020-7782 5000
Theatre: Benedict Nightingale
Film: Barbara Ellen
Television: Joe Joseph
Radio: Vanora Benett
Video: Geoff Brown

D

ADVENTURES IN MOTION PICTURES
(Managed by KDM)
Horseshoe Wharf, 6A Clink Street, London SE1 9FD
Website: www.kdmanagement.co.uk
e-mail: info@kdmanagement.co.uk
Fax: 020-7357 8002   Tel: 020-7357 6633

ADZIDO
Canonbury Business Centre
202 New North Road, London N1 7BL
e-mail: info@adzido.co.uk
Fax: 020-7704 0300   Tel: 020-7359 7453

AKADEMI
(South Asian Dance in the UK)
Hampstead Town Hall
Haverstock Hill, London NW3 4QP
Website: www.akademi.co.uk
e-mail: admin@akademi.co.uk
Fax: 020-7691 3211   Tel: 020-7691 3210

ALSTON Richard DANCE COMPANY
The Place, 17 Duke's Road, London WC1H 9PY
e-mail: radc@theplace.org.uk
Fax: 020-7383 5700   Tel: 020-7387 0324

BALLET CREATIONS
3 Blackbird Way, Bransgore
Nr Christchurch, Hants BH23 8LG
Website: www.ballet-creations.co.uk
e-mail: info@ballet-creations.co.uk
                    Tel/Fax: 01425 674163

BALLROOM - LONDON THEATRE OF
(Artistic Director - Paul Harris)
24 Ovett Close, Upper Norwood, London SE19 3RX
e-mail: paulharrisdance@hotmail.com
Mobile: 07958 784462   Tel/Fax: 020-8771 4274

BIRMINGHAM ROYAL BALLET
Thorp Street, Birmingham B5 4AU
Website: www.brb.org.uk
e-mail: administrator@brb.org.uk
Fax: 0121-245 3570   Tel: 0121-245 3500

B.O.P. PRODUCTIONS Ltd
(Jazz Theatre Company)
10 Stayton Road
Sutton, Surrey SM1 1RB
e-mail: info@bop.demon.co.uk   Tel: 020-8641 6959

CAPITAL ARTS THEATRE SCHOOL
(Kathleen Shanks)
Wyllyotts Centre
Darkes Lane, Potters Bar, Herts EN6 2HN
e-mail: capitalartstheatre@genie.co.uk
Mobile: 07885 232414   Tel/Fax: 020-8449 2342

CHOLMONDELEYS The
LFI .1
Lafone House, The Leathermarket
11-13 Leathermarket Street, London SE1 3HN
e-mail: admin@cholmondeleys.freeserve.co.uk
                    Tel: 020-7378 8800

COMPANY OF CRANKS
1st Floor, 62 Northfield House
Frensham Street
London SE15 6TN   Tel: 020-7358 0571

CREATIVE DANCE ARTISTS TRUST
15B Lauriston Road
London SW19 4TJ   Tel: 020-8946 3444

DANCE FOR EVERYONE Ltd
30 Sevington Road
London NW4 3RX
e-mail: orders@dfe.org.uk   Tel: 020-8202 7863

DANCE UK
(Including the Healthier Dancer Programme)
Battersea Arts Centre
Lavender Hill, London SW11 5TN
Website: www.danceuk.org
e-mail: info@danceuk.org
Fax: 020-7223 0074   Tel: 020-7228 4990

DANCE UMBRELLA
20 Chancellors Street, London W6 9RN
Website: www.danceumbrella.co.uk
e-mail: mail@danceumbrella.co.uk
Fax: 020-8741 7902   Tel: 020-8741 4040

ENGLISH NATIONAL BALLET Ltd
Markova House
39 Jay Mews, London SW7 2ES
Website: www.ballet.org.uk
e-mail: info@ballet.org.uk
Fax: 020-7225 0827   Tel: 020-7581 1245

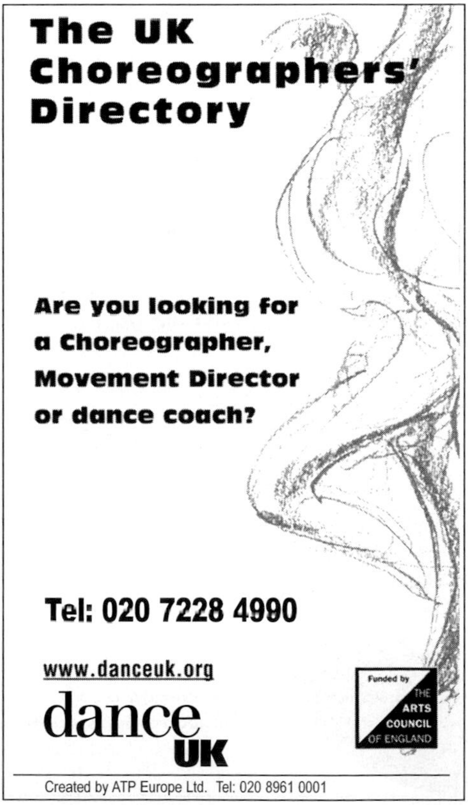

FEATHERSTONEHAUGHS The
LFI .1
Lafone House
The Leathermarket
11-13 Leathermarket
London SE1 3HN
e-mail: admin@cholmondeleys.freeserve.co.uk
Tel: 020-7378 8800

FREEDANZ.COM
23 Haymarket
London SW1Y 4DG
Website: www.freedanz.com
Fax: 020-7839 4555   Tel: 020-7839 2684

GIELGUD BALLET The
Wimbledon Theatre
The Broadway
London SW19 1QG
Website: www.gielgud.com
e-mail: ballet@gielgud.com
Fax: 020-8542 8081   Tel: 020-8542 9712

IDTA (INTERNATIONAL DANCE TEACHERS' ASSOCIATION)
International House
76 Bennett Road, Brighton, East Sussex BN2 5JL
Website: www.idta.co.uk
e-mail: info@idta.co.uk
Fax: 01273 674388   Tel: 01273 685652

KOSH The
(Physical Theatre)
59 Stapleton Hall Road
London N4 3QF
e-mail: the-kosh@dircon.co.uk
Fax: 020-8374 5661   Tel: 020-8374 0407

LONDON CONTEMPORARY DANCE SCHOOL
The Place
17 Duke's Road, London WC1H 9PY
e-mail: lcds@theplace.org.uk
Fax: 020-7387 3976   Tel: 020-7387 0152

LUDUS DANCE AGENCY
Assembly Rooms
King Street, Lancaster LA1 1RE
e-mail: info@ludus.org
Fax: 01524 847744   Tel: 01524 35936

MUDRALAYA DANCE THEATRE
Formerly Pushkala Gopal Unnikrishnan & Co
(Classical Indian Dance-Theatre)
20 Brisbane Road, Ilford
Essex IG1 4SR   Tel/Fax: 020-8554 4054

NATIONAL RESOURCE CENTRE FOR DANCE
University of Surrey
Guildford GU2 7XH
e-mail: nrcd@surrey.ac.uk   Tel: 01483 689316

NORTHERN BALLET THEATRE
West Park Centre, Spen Lane, Leeds LS16 5BE
e-mail: directors@nbtdance.demon.co.uk
Fax: 0113-274 5381   Tel: 0113-274 5355

PHOENIX DANCE COMPANY
3 St Peter's Building, St Peter's Square, Leeds LS9 8AH
Website: www.phoenixdance.org.uk
e-mail: info@phoenixdance.org.uk
Fax: 0113-244 4736   Tel: 0113-242 3486

RAMBERT DANCE COMPANY
94 Chiswick High Road, London W4 1SH
Website: www.rambert.org.uk
e-mail: rdc@rambert.org.uk
Fax: 020-8747 8323   Tel: 020-8630 0600

ROYAL BALLET THE
Royal Opera House
Covent Garden, London WC2E 9DD
Fax: 020-7212 9502   Tel: 020-7240 1200

SCOTTISH BALLET
261 West Princes Street, Glasgow G4 9EE
Website: www.scottishballet.co.uk
e-mail: sb@scottishballet.co.uk
Fax: 0141-331 2629   Tel: 0141-331 2931

SCOTTISH DANCE THEATRE
Dundee Repertory Theatre
Tay Square, Dundee DD1 1PB
Website: www.sdt.dircon.co.uk
e-mail: achinn@dundeereptheatre.co.uk
Fax: 01382 228609   Tel: 01382 342600

SOUTH EAST DANCE - NATIONAL DANCE AGENCY
5 Palace Place
Castle Square, Brighton, East Sussex BN1 1EF
e-mail: southeast.dance@virgin.net
Fax: 01273 205540   Tel: 01273 202032

UNION DANCE COMPANY
c/o Marylebone Dance Studio
12 Lisson Grove, London NW1 6TS
e-mail: union.danceco@virgin.net
Fax: 020-7224 8911   Tel: 020-7724 5765

YORKSHIRE DANCE CENTRE NATIONAL DANCE AGENCY
3 St Peter's Buildings
St Peter's Square, Leeds LS9 8AH
Website: www.yorkshiredance.org.uk
e-mail: admin@yorkshiredance.org.uk
Tel: 0113-243 9867

ASH SCHOOL OF DANCE AND DRAMA The
50 Craneford Way, Twickenham, Middlesex TW2 7SE
e-mail: ashschool@hotmail.com   Tel: 020-8892 6554

BALLROOM - LONDON THEATRE OF
(Artistic Director - Paul Harris)
24 Ovett Close, Upper Norwood, London SE19 3RX
e-mail: paulharrisdance@hotmail.com
Mobile: 07958 784462   Tel/Fax: 020-8771 4274

BELLYDANCE CENTRE The
(Private Lessons, Consultancy, Choreography)
Mayfield
5 Rother Road, Seaford
East Sussex BN25 4HT
e-mail: annrusty@hotmail.com   Tel: 01323 899083

BIRD COLLEGE OF PERFORMING ARTS
(Dance & Theatre Performance Diploma/BA (Hons)
Degree Course)
Birkbeck Centre
Birkbeck Road, Sidcup, Kent DA14 4DE
Fax: 020-8308 1370   Tel: 020-8300 6004

BODEN STUDIOS
(Part-time Performing Arts Classes)
99 East Barnet Road, New Barnet, Herts EN4 8RF
e-mail: bodens2692@aol.com
Fax: 020-8449 5212   Tel: 020-8449 0982

BRITISH BALLET ORGANIZATION The
(Dance Examining Society & Teacher Training)
Woolborough House
39 Lonsdale Road
Barnes, London SW13 9JP
Website: www.bbo.org.uk
e-mail: info@bbo.org.uk   Tel: 020-8748 1241

CAPITAL ARTS THEATRE SCHOOL
Wyllyotts Centre
Darkes Lane, Potters Bar, Herts EN6 2HN
e-mail: capitalartstheatre@genie.co.uk
Mobile: 07885 232414   Tel/Fax: 020-8449 2342

CENTRAL SCHOOL OF BALLET
(Dance Classes & Professional Training)
10 Herbal Hill, Clerkenwell Road, London EC1R 5EG
Website: www.centralschoolofballet.co.uk
e-mail: info@csbschool.co.uk
Fax: 020-7833 5571   Tel: 020-7837 6332

CENTRE PERFORMING ARTS COLLEGE The
c/o 152 Earshall Road
Eltham Park, London SE9 1PN
e-mail: dance@thecentrese9.freeserve.co.uk
Tel/Fax: 020-8859 6918

COLIN'S PERFORMING ARTS Ltd
The Studios, 219B North Street, Romford RM1 4QA
Website: www.colinsperformingarts.co.uk
e-mail: admin@colinsperformingarts.co.uk
Fax: 01708 766077   Tel: 01708 766007

COLLECTIVE DANCE & DRAMA
The Studio, Rectory Lane
Rickmansworth
Herts WD3 2AD   Tel/Fax: 020-8428 0037

CONTI Italia ACADEMY
(Full time 3 year Musical Theatre Course)
Italia Conti House
23 Goswell Road, London EC1M 7AJ
e-mail: sca@italiaconti36.freeserve.co.uk
Fax: 020-7253 1430   Tel: 020-7608 0047

CUSTARD FACTORY
(Professional Dance Classes and Dance Studio Hire)
Gibb Street, Digbeth, Birmingham B9 4AA
e-mail: custardfactory@clara.net
Fax: 0121-604 8888   Tel: 0121-693 7777

DANCEWORKS
(Also Fitness, Yoga & Martial Arts Classes,
Studio/Rehearsal Rooms for Hire)
16 Balderton Street
London W1   Tel: 020-7629 6183

D & B
(Three Year Musical Theatre Course)
Central Studios
470 Bromley Road, Bromley
Kent BR1 4PN   Tel: 020-8698 8880

DUFFILL Drusilla THEATRE SCHOOL
Grove Lodge
Oakwood Road, Burgess Hill, West Sussex RH15 0HZ
e-mail: drusillaschool@btclick.com
Tel/Fax: 01444 232672

ELMHURST - SCHOOL FOR DANCE & PERFORMING ARTS
Heathcote Road
Camberley, Surrey GU15 2EU
Website: www.elmhurstdance.co.uk
e-mail: elmhurst@cableol.co.uk
Fax: 01276 670320   Tel: 01276 65301

GREASEPAINT ANONYMOUS
4 Gallus Close
Winchmore Hill, London N21 1JR
e-mail: info@greasepaintanonymous.co.uk
Fax: 020-8882 9189   Tel: 020-8886 2263

HAMPSTEAD DANCE THEATRE GROUP
(Creative Dance Part-Time 4-25 year olds)
6 Brampton Grove, Wembley Park
Middlesex HA9 9QU   Tel: 020-8908 4375

HARRIS Paul
(Movement for Actors, Choreography, Coaching in
Traditional & Contemporary Social Dance)
24 Ovett Close
Upper Norwood, London SE19 3RX
e-mail: paulharrisdance@hotmail.com
Mobile: 07958 784462   Tel: 020-8771 4274

ISLINGTON ARTS FACTORY
2 Parkhurst Road, London N7 0SF
e-mail: islington@artsfactory.fsnet.co.uk
Fax: 020-7700 7229   Tel: 020-7607 0561

KIDZ IN THE BIZ
The Lime House
Leaves Green Road
Keston, Kent BR2 6DQ
Website: www.kidzinthebiz.co.uk
e-mail: nicky@kidzinthebiz.co.uk
Fax: 01959 576632   Tel: 01959 542552

LEE STAGE SCHOOL The
(Office)
38 The Chase
Rayleigh, Essex SS6 8QN
e-mail: lynn@leetheatre.fsnet.co.uk
                         Tel: 01268 773204

LONDON CONTEMPORARY DANCE SCHOOL
(Full-time Contemporary Training at Degree,
Certificate & Postgraduate Level)
The Place
17 Duke's Road, London WC1H 9PY
Website: www.theplace.org.uk
e-mail: lcds@theplace.org.uk
Fax: 020-7387 3976   Tel: 020-7387 0152

LONDON STUDIO CENTRE
42-50 York Way, London N1 9AB
Website: www.london-studio-centre.co.uk
e-mail: enquire@london-studio-centre.co.uk
Fax: 020-7837 3248   Tel: 020-7837 7741

MANN Stella COLLEGE
(Professional Dance Course for
Performers & Teachers)
343A Finchley Road, Hampstead, London NW3 6ET
Fax: 020-7435 3782   Tel: 020-7435 9317

NORTH LONDON PERFORMING ARTS CENTRE
(Performing Arts Classes 3-19 yrs/All Dance Forms)
76 St James Lane, Muswell Hill, London N10 3DF
e-mail: nlpac@compuserve.com
Fax: 020-8444 4040   Tel: 020-8444 4544

PAUL'S THEATRE SCHOOL
Fairkytes Arts Centre
51 Billet Lane, Hornchurch, Essex RM11 1AX
e-mail: paul@the-theatreschool.fsnet.co.uk
Fax: 01708 475286   Tel: 01708 447123

PERFORMERS COLLEGE
2-4 Chase Road, Corringham, Essex SS17 7QH
Website: www.performerscollege.co.uk
e-mail: pdc@dircon.co.uk
Fax: 01375 672353   Tel: 01375 672053

PINEAPPLE DANCE STUDIOS
7 Langley Street
London WC2H 9JA   Tel: 020-7836 4004

PULLEY Rosina SCHOOL OF STAGE DANCING
5 Lancaster Road
London E11 3EH   Tel: 020-8539 7740

RIDGEWAY STUDIOS
PERFORMING ARTS COLLEGE
Fairley House
Andrews Lane, Cheshunt, Herts EN7 6LB
Website: www.ridgewaystudios.co.uk
e-mail: info@ridgewaystudios.co.uk
Fax: 01992 633844   Tel: 01992 633775

ROEBUCK Gavin
(Classical Ballet)
51 Earls Court Square, London SW5 9DG
e-mail: grads@fsmail.net
Fax: 020-7370 5456   Tel: 020-7370 7324

RUSS Claire
(Choreography,
Private Movement Tuition for Actors)
74A Queens Road, Twickenham TW1 4ET
Mobile: 07932 680224   Tel/Fax: 020-8892 9281

SOLE THEATRE SCHOOL
151A Field End Road, Eastcote, Middlesex HA5 1QL
e-mail: sole.file@virgin.net
Fax: 020-8429 7279   Tel: 020-8868 7960

STEP ONE DANCE AND DRAMA SCHOOL
Rear of 24 Penrhyn Road
Colwyn Bay, Conwy LL29 8LG   Tel: 01492 534424

URDANG ACADEMY The
20-22 Shelton Street
Covent Garden, London WC2H 9JJ
Website: www.urdang-academy.co.uk
e-mail: info@theurdangacademy.com
Fax: 020-7836 7010   Tel: 020-7836 5709

VALLÉ ACADEMY OF PERFORMING ARTS Ltd The
The Rosedale Old Cestrians Club
Andrews Lane, Cheshunt, Herts EN7 6TB
Website: www.valleacademy.co.uk
e-mail: enquiries@valleacademy.co.uk
Fax: 01992 622868   Tel: 01992 622862

WHITEHALL PERFORMING ARTS CENTRE
Rayleigh Road, Leigh-on-Sea
Essex SS9 5UU   Tel/Fax: 01702 529290

YOUNG Sylvia THEATRE SCHOOL
Rossmore Road, London NW1 6NJ
Fax: 020-7723 1040   Tel: 020-7402 0673

Stretch Yourself to the Max

Photo by Peter Teigen

ALRA (ACADEMY OF LIVE AND RECORDED ARTS)
The Royal Victoria Building
Fitzhugh Grove, Trinity Road
London SW18 3SX
Website: www.alra.demon.co.uk
e-mail: acting@alra.demon.co.uk
Fax: 020-8875 0789   Tel: 020-8870 6475

ARTS EDUCATIONAL SCHOOLS LONDON
14 Bath Road, London W4 1LY
Website: www.artsed.co.uk
e-mail: drama@artsed.co.uk
Fax: 020-8987 6699   Tel: 020-8987 6666

BIRMINGHAM SCHOOL OF SPEECH & DRAMA
The Link Building
Paradise Place, Birmingham B3 3HJ
Website: www.bssd.ac.uk
e-mail: bssd@bssd.ac.uk
Fax: 0121-262 6801   Tel: 0121-262 6800

BRISTOL OLD VIC THEATRE SCHOOL
2 Downside Road
Clifton, Bristol BS8 2XF
Website: www.oldvic.drama.ac.uk
e-mail: enquiries@oldvic.drama.ac.uk
Fax: 0117-923 9371   Tel: 0117-973 3535

CENTRAL SCHOOL OF SPEECH & DRAMA
Embassy Theatre
64 Eton Avenue
Swiss Cottage, London NW3 3HY
Tel: 020-7722 8183

CONTI Italia ACADEMY OF THEATRE ARTS
Avondale Road
72 Landor Road, London SW9 9PH
e-mail: baacting.italiaconti@btinternet.com
Fax: 020-7737 2728   Tel: 020-7733 3210

CYGNET TRAINING THEATRE
New Theatre, Friars Gate
Exeter, Devon EX2 4AZ
e-mail: cygnetarts@btinternet.com
                              Tel/Fax: 01392 277189

DRAMA CENTRE LONDON
176 Prince of Wales Road, London NW5 3PT
Website: http://dcl.drama.ac.uk
e-mail: drama@linst.ac.uk
Fax: 020-7485 7129   Tel: 020-7267 1177

EAST 15 ACTING SCHOOL
The University of Essex
Hatfields & Corbett Theatre
Rectory Lane, Loughton, Essex IG10 3RY
Website: www.east15.ac.uk
e-mail: east15.acting@ukonline.co.uk
Fax: 020-8508 7521   Tel: 020-8508 5983

GSA GUILDFORD SCHOOL OF ACTING
Millmead Terrace, Guildford, Surrey GU2 4YT
Website: http://gsa.drama.ac.uk
e-mail: enquiries@gsa.drama.ac.uk
                              Tel: 01483 560701

GUILDHALL SCHOOL OF MUSIC & DRAMA
Silk Street, Barbican, London EC2Y 8DT
Website: www.gsmd.ac.uk
e-mail: info@gsmd.ac.uk
Fax: 020-7256 9438   Tel: 020-7382 7149

LAMDA
Tower House
226 Cromwell Road, London SW5 0SR
Website: www.lamda.org.uk
e-mail: enquiries@lamda.org.uk
Fax: 020-7370 4739   Tel: 020-7373 9883

**MANCHESTER METROPOLITAN UNIVERSITY
SCHOOL OF THEATRE**
The Mabel Tylecote Building
Cavendish Street, Manchester M15 6BG
Website: www.capitoltheatre.co.uk
                              Tel: 0161-247 1305

MOUNTVIEW
Academy of Theatre Arts
Ralph Richardson Memorial Studios, Kingfisher Place
Wood Green, London N22 6XF
Website: www.mountview.ac.uk
e-mail: enquiries@mountview.ac.uk
Fax: 020-8829 0034   Tel: 020-8881 2201

OXFORD SCHOOL OF DRAMA The
Sansomes Farm Studios
Woodstock, Oxford OX20 1ER
e-mail: info@oxford.drama.ac.uk
Fax: 01993 811220   Tel: 01993 812883

QUEEN MARGARET UNIVERSITY COLLEGE
The Gateway Theatre
Elm Row, Edinburgh EH7 4AH
Website: www.qmuc.ac.uk
e-mail: admissions@qmuc.ac.uk
Fax: 0131-317 3902   Tel: 0131-317 3900

ROSE BRUFORD COLLEGE
Lamorbey Park
Burnt Oak Lane
Sidcup, Kent DA15 9DF
Website: www.bruford.ac.uk
e-mail: admiss@bruford.ac.uk
Fax: 020-8308 0542   Tel: 020-8300 3024

ROYAL ACADEMY OF DRAMATIC ART
62-64 Gower Street, London WC1E 6ED
Website: www.rada.org.uk
e-mail: enquiries@rada.ac.uk
Fax: 020-7323 3865   Tel: 020-7636 7076

**ROYAL SCOTTISH ACADEMY
OF MUSIC AND DRAMA**
100 Renfrew Street
Glasgow G2 3DB
Website: www.rsamd.ac.uk
e-mail: registry@rsamd.ac.uk   Tel: 0141-332 4101

ROYAL WELSH COLLEGE OF MUSIC AND DRAMA
Drama Department
Castle Grounds
Cathays Park, Cardiff CF10 3ER
Website: www.rwcmd.ac.uk
e-mail: drama.admissions@rwcmd.ac.uk
Fax: 029-2039 1302   Tel: 029-2039 1327

WEBBER DOUGLAS ACADEMY OF DRAMATIC ART
30 Clareville Street, London SW7 5AP
e-mail: webberdouglas@btclick.com
Fax: 020-7373 5639   Tel: 020-7370 4154

CONFERENCE OF DRAMA SCHOOLS

The Conference of Drama Schools was founded in 1969. The member schools of the CDS offer courses in Acting, Musical Theatre, Stage Management and Technical Courses. The CDS exists to:

- Contribute to maintaining and developing standards of vocational drama training and education within its member institutions.
- Encourage good practice with its member institutions
- Represent the interests of its member institutions at regional, national, European and International levels.
- Advise on matters relating to the interest of students and staff within its member institutions
- Encourage diversity of provision and/or qualifications within the vocational drama training sector as a whole.

CDS Member Schools

ALRA Academy of Live and Recorded Arts

The Arts Educational Schools London

Birmingham School of Speech and Drama

The Bristol Old Vic Theatre School

The Central School of Speech and Drama

Cygnet Training Theatre

Drama Centre London

East 15 Acting School

GSA Guildford School of Acting

Guildhall School of Music and Drama

The Italia Conti Academy of Theatre Arts

LAMDA The London Academy of Music and Dramatic Art

Manchester Metropolitan University School of Theatre

Mountview Academy of Theatre Arts

The Oxford School of Drama

Queen Margaret University College - Department of Drama

Rose Bruford College

RADA The Royal Academy of Dramatic Art

The Royal Scottish Academy of Music and Drama

Royal Welsh College of Music and Drama

The Webber Douglas Academy of Dramatic Art

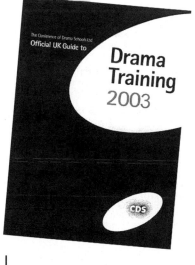

The Conference of Drama Schools Ltd
Official UK Guide to

Drama Training 2003

CDS

Further information on careers and the courses offered by our member schools can be found in the **CDS Official UK Guide to Drama Training.** For a free copy, please write (including a C5 SAE for 44p postage per Guide) to:

The Executive Secretary
Conference of Drama Schools
PO Box 34252
London NW5 1XJ

For information on the CDS:

The Executive Secretary
Conference of Drama Schools
PO Box 34252
London NW5 1XJ

Tel/Fax: 020-7692 0032
e-mail: enquiries@cds.drama.ac.uk
or see our website on:
http://www.drama.ac.uk

Abbreviations: SS Stage School for Children **D** Dramatic Art (incl Coaching. Audition Technique etc) **DS** Full time Drama Training **E** Elocution Coaching (incl Correction of Accents. Speech Therapy, Dialects etc) **S** Singing **Md** Modelling **Sp** Specialised Training

A1 VOX Ltd
(Specialising in Voices, Audio Editing, Voice-Over Training and Demo CDs)
20 Old Crompton Street, London W1D 4TW
Website: www.voxtraining.com
e-mail: info@voxtraining.com
Fax: 020-7434 4414   Tel: 020-7434 4404

A B CENTRE OF PERFORMING ARTS
22 Greek Street, Stockport, Cheshire SK3 8AB
e-mail: ab22@supanet.com   Tel/Fax: 0161-429 7413

ACADEMY DRAMA SCHOOL The
DS (2 year F/T Evening Course & Day Time Preparatory)
189 Whitechapel Road, London E1 1DN
Website: www.eada.demon.co.uk
e-mail: academy@eada.demon.co.uk
                                Tel: 020-7377 8735

ACADEMY OF CHILDREN'S THEATRE
(Part-time Children's Theatre School)
373 Lower Addiscombe Road
Croydon CR0 6RJ   Tel: 020-8655 3438

ACE ACCOMPANIST
S (Accompanist and Bands for Rehearsal & Recordings)
165 Gunnersbury Lane
London W3 8LJ   Tel: 020-8993 2111

ACKERLEY STUDIOS OF SPEECH, DRAMA & PUBLIC SPEAKING
SP D Margaret Christina Parsons (Principal)
5th Floor, Hanover House
Hanover Street
Liverpool L1 3DZ   Tel: 0151-709 5995

ACT @ SCHOOL
(Drama for Children 5-18 years)
Part of APM Training Group
PO Box 834, Hemel Hempstead HP3 9ZP
Website: www.apmtraining.co.uk
e-mail: info@apmtraining.co.uk
Fax: 01442 241099   Tel: 01442 252989

ACT ONE DRAMA STUDIO & AGENCY
31 Dobbin Hill, Sheffield S11 7JA
Website: www.actonedrama.co.uk
e-mail: casting@actonedrama.co.uk
Fax: 07971 112153   Tel: 0114-266 7209

ACT UP
(Acting Classes for Everyone)
Unit 88, Battersea Business Centre
99-109 Lavender Hill, London SW11 5QL
Website: www.act-up.co.uk
e-mail: info@act-up.co.uk
Fax: 020-7924 6606   Tel: 020-7924 7701

ACTING & AUDITION SUCCESS
(Philip Rosch LALAM, FVCM, ANEA, B.A. Adv. Dip. Acting) (Associate Guildhall Teacher)
26C Rotherwick Road, London NW11 7DA
e-mail: phil.rosch@virgin.net   Tel: 020-8455 5126

ACTORCLUB
17 Inkerman Road, London NW5 3BT
Website: www.actorclub.co.uk
e-mail: johncunningham@actorclub.fsnet.co.uk
                           Mobile: 07956 940453

ACTORS SPACE The
D E Sp (Auditions, Improvisation, Voice and Text)
83 Palmerston Road
Bounds Green
London N22 8QS
Website: www.actorspace.co.uk
e-mail: drama@london.com   Tel: 020-8881 1455

SCHOOL OF MUSICAL THEATRE
Director: Ian Watt-Smith
T: 020 8987 6677 **F:** 020 8987 6680
E: mts@artsed.co.uk **W:** www.artsed.co.uk

SCHOOL OF ACTING
Director: Jane Harrison
Associate Director: Adrian James

Tel: 020 8987 6655 **Fax:** 020 8987 6656
e-mail: drama@artsed.co.uk **web:** www.artsed.co.uk

BA (Hons) Acting
3 Year Acting Course
An NCDT Accredited Course
Validated by City University

A 3-year course offering the full range of acting skills to Adult students aged 18 or over. The emphasis is on the actor in performance and the relationship with an audience. Classes and tutorial work include: a range of textual, psychological and physical acting techniques, screen acting and broadcasting, voice and speech, movement and dance, mask and theatre history.

MA Acting
The Acting Company - 1 Year Course
An NCDT Accredited Course
Validated by City University

An intensive one year post-graduate acting course offering a fully integrated ensemble training for mature students with a degree or equivalent professional experience. Emphasis is on the pro-active contemporary performer.

Post Diploma BA (Hons) Acting
Validated by City University

1 Year part time degree conversion course for anyone who has graduated since 1995 from a NCDT accredited 3 year acting course: or for those who can offer appropriate professional experience

3 Year Musical Theatre Course
National Diploma in Professional Dance (Musical Theatre)
A CDET Accredited Course

A full time course (18+). A flexible approach providing outstanding training in dance, acting and singing by leading professionals. Training the Complete Performer with excellent employment opportunities for graduates.

Latest Government Inspection praised the high standard of student achievement, quality of teaching, well balanced training, effective links with the industry, good graduate employment record.

The Arts Educational Schools
14 Bath Road, Chiswick, London W4 1LY

DIALECT COACH

LINDA JAMES R.A.M. Dip. Ed., I.P.D. (Lon Univ), L.R.A.M.

FILMS, TV., STAGE & PRIVATE COACHING, ERADICATION OF ACCENT

020 8568 2390

ACTORS' THEATRE SCHOOL
DS
32 Exeter Road, London NW2 4SB
Website: www.mywebaddress.net
e-mail: ats@mywebaddress.net
Fax: 020-8450 1057   Tel: 020-8450 0371

ACTS Ayres-Clark Theatre School
12 Gatward Close, Winchmore Hill
London N21   Tel: 020-8884 4749

A & J THEATRE WORKSHOP
The Open Door Community Centre
Beaumont Road, London SW19
Website: www.ajmanagement.co.uk
Fax: 020-8882 5983   Tel: 020-8882 7716

ALEXANDER ALLIANCE
(Alexander Technique, Voice and Audition Coaching)
3 Hazelwood Drive
St Albans, Herts   Tel: 01727 843633

ALEXANDER CENTRE The Bloomsbury
(Alexander Technique)
Bristol House
80A Southampton Row
London WC1B 4BB
Website: www.alexcentre.com
e-mail: bloomsbury.alexandercentre@btinternet.com
          Tel: 020-7404 5348

ALEXANDER Helen
(Audition Technique/Drama School Entry)
14 Chestnut Road
Raynes Park
London SW20 8EB   Tel: 020-8543 4085

ALEXANDER TECHNIQUE
(Jackie Coote MSTAT)
27 Britannia Road
London SW6 2HJ   Tel: 020-7731 1061

PAUL GREGORY ACTOR / DRAMA COACH

Ex RSC & R.N.T., Films including Henry V with Kenneth Branagh.

Acted with & Directed by Sir Laurence Olivier, Anthony Hopkins, Leonard Rossiter.

Current Students in the following: CHITTY, CHITTY, BANG, BANG - London Palladium.

Feature Films including HARRY POTTER, ALI G THE MOVIE, THE LADS, PROPHECY.

BBC TV Comedy Series: FIFTEEN STOREYS HIGH and more to come.

TV Commercials include: AUDI QUATTRO, VOLKSWAGEN PASSATT.

Gives private classes for Theatre, Film, TV& Radio to Adults and Children.

Very recent successful applicants including Scholarships to ALRA, DRAMA CENTRE, LAMDA, CENTRAL, GUILDHALL, BOV, EAST 15, GSA, CYGNET, DSL, MOUNTVIEW, THE ACTORS COMPANY, POOR SCHOOL THE ACADEMY & NW5.

Many of my students also now represented by Top Agents.

Call me on: **020 8789 5726** *Putney Bridge Underground*

Bodens
Studio & Agency

99 East Barnet Road, New Barnet, Herts EN4 8RF

PERFORMING ARTS CLASSES

Evenings & Weekends

FULLY EQUIPPED

Studios & Theatre Available for Rehearsals & Auditions

(Close to main bus and train routes)

EXAMINATIONS

Acting, Speech & Drama: GUILDHALL, Dance: ISTD

Singing: ASSOCIATED BOARD of THE ROYAL SCHOOLS OF MUSIC

PROFESSIONAL REPRESENTATION

For Children, Teenagers & Adults

A Copy Of The Current 'Boden Agency Casting Book' Of Children
& Young Adults, Is Available On Request.

HOLIDAY COURSES

We Offer A Variety Of Courses And Workshops Throughout The
School Holiday Periods For Children Aged 4 - 17 Years

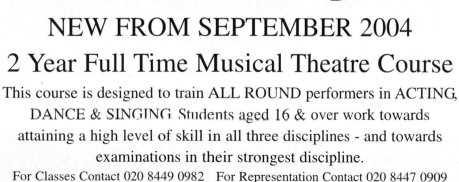

NEW FROM SEPTEMBER 2004

2 Year Full Time Musical Theatre Course

This course is designed to train ALL ROUND performers in ACTING,
DANCE & SINGING. Students aged 16 & over work towards
attaining a high level of skill in all three disciplines - and towards
examinations in their strongest discipline.

For Classes Contact 020 8449 0982   For Representation Contact 020 8447 0909

www.bodenstudios.com

ALEXANDER TECHNIQUE AND VOICE
(Robert Macdonald)
Flat 5, 17 Hatton Street
London NW8 8PL   Mobile: 07956 852303

ALL EXPRESSIONS
(Children & Teenagers)
5 Osterley Avenue, Osterley, Middlesex TW7 4QF
Fax: 020-8560 3562   Tel: 020-8560 8857

ALLSORTS - DRAMA FOR CHILDREN
2 Pember Road, London NW10 5LP
e-mail: enquiries@allsorts.ltd.uk
          Tel/Fax: 020-8969 3249

ALRA, ACADEMY OF LIVE & RECORDED ARTS
See DRAMA SCHOOLS (Conference of)

AND ALL THAT JAZZ
(Eileen Hughes - Accompanist and Vocal Coaching)
165 Gunnersbury Lane
Acton Town, London W3 8LJ   Tel: 020-8993 2111

ARDEN SCHOOL OF THEATRE The
Sale Road, Northenden
Manchester M23 0DD
e-mail: ast@ccm.ac.uk   Tel/Fax: 0161-957 1715

ARTEMIS FOUNDATION The
25 Athelstan Road, Tuckton, Bournemouth BH6 5LY
Website: www.doorways2power.co.uk
e-mail: artemis@doorways2power.co.uk
          Tel: 01202 418880

ARTS EDUCATIONAL LONDON SCHOOLS
See DRAMA SCHOOLS (Conference of)

ARTS EDUCATIONAL SCHOOL
(Performing Arts School)
Tring Park, Tring, Herts HP23 5LX
Website: www.aestring.com
e-mail: info@aestring.com   Tel: 01442 824255

Outstanding Training in Acting, Musical Theatre and Stage Management

Full Time and Short Courses Available
Accredited by the NCDT

Tel: **020 8870 6475**

or access on-line **www.alra.demon.co.uk**
e-mail **acting@alra.demon.co.uk**

ARTTS INTERNATIONAL
Highfield Grange, Bubwith, North Yorks YO8 6DP
Website: www.artts.co.uk
e-mail: admin@artts.co.uk
Fax: 01757 288253   Tel: 01757 288088

ASH SCHOOL OF DANCE AND DRAMA The
50 Craneford Way, Twickenham
Middlesex TW2 7SE
e-mail: ashschool@hotmail.com   Tel: 020-8892 6554

ASHCROFT ACADEMY OF DRAMATIC ART The
(Drama LAMDA, Dance ISTD, Singing, Age 4-18 yrs,
Students 19+)
Bellenden Old School
Bellenden Road, London SE15 4DG
Website: www.ashcroftacademy.co.uk
                              Tel/Fax: 020-8693 8088

BAC
(Children's Drama Classes, Age 2-25)
Lavender Hill, London SW11 5TN
e-mail: mailbox@bac.org.uk
Fax: 020-7978 5207   Tel: 020-7223 6557

BARNES Bi Bi
(Feldenkrais Practitioner & Voice Coach)
Rose Cottage, Church Road
Ashmanhaugh, Norwich NR12 8YL
e-mail: bibibarnes@aol.com
Mobile: 07770 375339   Tel: 01603 781281

BARNES Joan THEATRE SCHOOL
SS D E
20 Green Street, Hazlemere
High Wycombe
Bucks HP15 7RB   Tel: 01494 523193

BATE Richard MA (Theatre) LGSM (TD) PGCE (FE) Equity
D E
78 Greengate Lane
High Green, Sheffield S35 3GT
Mobile: 07944 982193   Tel: 0114-284 8194

BECK Eirene
D E
Flat 4, 57 Knightsbridge
London SW1X 7RA   Tel: 020-7235 4659

BECKMANN Jane MA
(Spoken Voice Coaching & Accents)
Flat 6, Primrose House
19 Adelaide Road, London NW3 3HH
e-mail: beckmann@ukgateway.net
                         Tel: 020-7483 2105

BELCANTO LONDON ACADEMY Ltd
(Stage School & Agency)
Performance House
20 Passey Place, Eltham, London SE9 5DQ
e-mail: enquiries@theatretraining.com
Fax: 020-8850 9944   Tel: 020-8850 9888

BENCH Paul MED LGSM ALAM FRSA LJBA (Hons) MASC MIFA (Reg)
D E
1 Whitehall Terrace, Shrewsbury, Shropshire SY2 5AA
e-mail: paulbench@compuserve.com
                         Tel/Fax: 01743 233164

BENSKIN Eileen
(Dialect Coach)   Tel: 020-8455 9750

BERKERY Barbara
(Dialogue/Dialect Coach for Film & Television)
ICM, Oxford House, 76 Oxford Street, London W1D 1BS
Fax: 020-7323 0101   Tel: 020-7636 6565

BEST SHOT YOUTH THEATRE COMPANY
(Weekly Drama Classes and Theatre Based Holiday Courses)
1 Queensland Avenue, Wimbledon SW19 3AD
Website: www.bestshot.org.uk
e-mail: enquiries@bestshot.org.uk
                         Tel/Fax: 020-8540 1238

BEST THEATRE ARTS
61 Marshalswick Lane, St Albans, Herts AL1 4UT
Website: www.besttheatrearts.com
e-mail: bestarts@aol.com   Tel: 01727 759634

BILLINGS Una
(Dance Training)
Methodist Church, Askew Road
London W12   Tel: 020-7603 8156

BIRD COLLEGE
(Drama/Musical Theatre College)
Birkbeck Centre
Birkbeck Road, Sidcup, Kent DA14 4DE
Website: www.birdcollege.co.uk
e-mail: admin@birdcollege.co.uk
Fax: 020-8308 1370   Tel: 020-8300 6004

BIRMINGHAM SCHOOL OF SPEECH & DRAMA
See DRAMA SCHOOLS (Conference of)

BIRMINGHAM THEATRE SCHOOL
The Old Rep Theatre
Station Street
Birmingham B5 4DY   Tel/Fax: 0121-643 3300

BODEN STUDIOS
D S E SS DS
99 East Barnet Road, New Barnet, Herts EN4 8RF
Website: www.bodenstudios.com
e-mail: bodens2692@aol.com
Fax: 020-8449 5212   Tel: 020-8449 0982

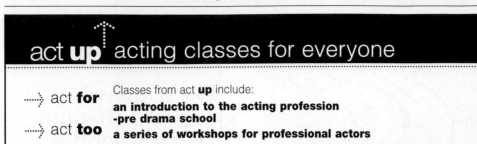

BODYWISE
(Alexander Technique)
119 Roman Road
London E2 0QN
e-mail: bodywise2@msn.com   Tel: 020-8981 6938

BORLAND Denise LRAM, PG Dip RAM,
Perf Dip **GSMD**
(Singing and Acting Coach)
25 Frogston Road West, Edinburgh EH10 7AB
e-mail: deniseborland@hotmail.com
Fax: 0131-445 7492   Tel: 0131-445 7491

BOURNEMOUTH YOUTH THEATRE The (BYT)
(Klair/Lucinda Spencer)
14 Cooper Dean Drive, Bournemouth BH8 9LN
Website: www.thebyt.com
e-mail: klair@thebyt.com
Fax: 01202 393290   Tel: 01202 255826

BOYD Beth
D S
10 Prospect Road, Long Ditton
Surbiton, Surrey KT6 5PY   Tel: 020-8398 6768

BRAITHWAITE'S ACROBATIC SCHOOL
8 Brookshill Avenue
Harrow Weald, Middlesex   Tel: 020-8954 5638

BRIDGE THEATRE TRAINING CO The
Cecil Sharp House
2 Regent's Park Road, London NW1 3AY
Website: www.thebridge-tcc.org
Fax: 020-7424 9118   Tel: 020-7424 0860

BRIGHT SPARKS PERFORMERS & AGENCY
SS
1A South Parade, Stafford Road
Wallington
Surrey SM6 9AJ   Tel/Fax: 020-8769 3500

BRIGHTON SCHOOL OF MUSIC & DRAMA
96 Claremont Road, Seaford
East Sussex BN25 2QA   Tel: 01323 492918

BRISTOL OLD VIC THEATRE SCHOOL
See DRAMA SCHOOLS (Conference of)

BRITISH AMERICAN DRAMA ACADEMY
14 Gloucester Gate
Regent's Park, London NW1 4HG
Website: www.badaonline.com
Fax: 020-7487 0731   Tel: 020-7487 0730

B.R.I.T. SCHOOL FOR PERFORMING ARTS &
TECHNOLOGY The
60 The Crescent, Croydon CR0 2HN
Fax: 020-8665 8676   Tel: 020-8665 5242

C.A.L.S. THEATRE SCHOOL
Unit E2, Bellevale Shopping Centre
Liverpool L25 2RG   Tel/Fax: 0151-487 8500

CAMERON BROWN Jo PGDVS
(Dialect and Voice)
6 The Bow Brook, Gathorne Street, London E2 0PW
Agent: Representation Joyce Edwards 020-7735 5736
e-mail: jocameronbrown@hotmail.com
Mobile: 07970 026621   Tel: 020-8981 1005

CAMPBELL Kenneth
S E D
Parkhills, 6 Clevelands Park
Northam, Bideford, North Devon EX39 3QH
e-mail: kencam@tinyworld.co.uk   Tel: 01237 425217

CAMPBELL Ross ARCM, Dip RCM (Perf)
(Singing Coach, Accompanist & Music Director)
17 Oldwood Chase, Farnborough, Hants GU14 0QS
e-mail: rosscampbell@ntlworld.com
Tel: 01252 510228

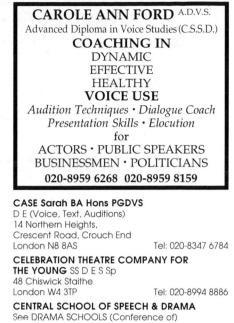
CAPITAL ARTS THEATRE SCHOOL
(Kathleen Shanks)
Wyllyotts Centre
Darkes Lane, Potters Bar, Herts EN6 2HN
e-mail: capitalartstheatre@genie.co.uk
Mobile: 07885 232414   Tel/Fax: 020-8449 2342

CARR Norrie AGENCY & DRAMA SCHOOL
(4-16 year olds) (Principal: Emma Taylor)
Holborn Studios
49 Eagle Wharf Road, London N1 7ED
e-mail: emma.rebaldi@btinternet.com
Mobile: 07961 3034491   Tel: 020-7253 1/74

CARTEURS THEATRICAL AGENCY
170A Church Road, Hove, East Sussex BN3 2DJ
Website: www.stonelandsschool.co.uk
e-mail: dianacarteur@stonelandsschool.co.uk
Fax: 01273 770444   Tel: 01273 770445

CASE Sarah BA Hons PGDVS
D E (Voice, Text, Auditions)
14 Northern Heights,
Crescent Road, Crouch End
London N8 8AS   Tel: 020-8347 6784

CELEBRATION THEATRE COMPANY FOR THE YOUNG SS D E S Sp
48 Chiswick Staithe
London W4 3TP   Tel: 020-8994 8886

CENTRAL SCHOOL OF SPEECH & DRAMA
See DRAMA SCHOOLS (Conference of)

CENTRE STAGE SCHOOL OF PERFORMING ARTS
(Students 4-18 years) (Southgate & Chelmsford)
The Croft, 7 Cannon Road, Southgate, London N14 7HJ
Website: www.centrestageuk.com
Fax: 020-8886 7555   Tel: 020-8886 4264

CENTRESTAGE SCHOOL OF PERFORMING ARTS
(All Day Saturday Classes, Summer Courses, Private
Coaching for Professionals)
33 Margaret Street, London W1G 0JD
Website: www.centrestageschool.co.uk
e-mail: centrest@dircon.co.uk
Fax: 020-7372 2728   Tel: 020-7328 0788

CHARLTON Catherine
8 Tudor Gates, Highfield Avenue, London NW9 0QE
e-mail: charlton@zoo.co.uk
Mobile: 07711 079292   Exec Mgt: 01753 646677

CHARRINGTON Tim
E D
54 Topmast Point, Strafford Street, London E14 8SN
e-mail: tim.charrington@lycos.co.uk
Mobile: 07967 418236   Tel: 020-7987 3028

CHEKHOV Michael CENTRE UK
1 St Paul's Road, London N1 2QH
Website: www.michaelchekhov.org.uk
e-mail: admin@michaelchekov.org.uk
Fax: 020-7226 2062   Tel: 020-7226 4454

CHRISKA STAGE SCHOOL
37-39 Whitby Road, Ellesmere Port
Cheshire L64 8AA   Tel: 01928 739166

CHRYSTEL ARTS AGENCY & THEATRE SCHOOL
15 Churchill Road, Edgware, Middlesex HA8 6NX
e-mail: chrystelarts@talk21.com   Tel: 020-8952 1281

CHURCHER Mel MA
(Acting & Vocal Coach)
32 Denman Road, London SE15 5NP
e-mail: melchurcher@hotmail.com
          Tel: 020-7701 4593

CIRCUS MANIACS
(Part-time Day & Evenings, Act Preparation, Private
Tuition)
Office 8A, The Kingswood Foundation
Britannia Road, Kingswood, Bristol BS15 8DB
e-mail: info@circusmaniacs.com
Mobile: 07977 247287   Tel/Fax: 0117-947 7042

CITY LIT The
(Part-time Day & Evening)
16 Stukeley Street, Off Drury Lane
London WC2B 5LJ   Tel: 020-7430 0544

CITY LITES
PO Box 29673, London E8 3FH
e-mail: gulcan_ismail@yahoo.com
Mobile: 07773 353645   Tel/Fax: 020-7683 9016

CLASS ACT THEATRE SCHOOL
(Schools in Herts, Bucks & London)
(Part-timeweekend 5-16yrs) (Principal: Alice Hyde)
(Singing, Musical Theatre & Drama Training)
47 St Margaret's Road, Twickenham, Middlesex TW1 2LL
Fax: 020-8395 2808   Tel: 020-8891 6663

CLEMENTS Anne MA LGSM
(Drama/Speech/Auditions/Coaching)
293 Shakespeare Tower, Barbican
London EC2Y 8DR   Tel: 020-7374 2748

COLDIRON M. J.
(Private Coaching, Audition Preparation &
Presentation Skills)
21 Chippendale Street, London E5 0BB
e-mail: jiggs@blueyonder.co.uk
Fax: 020-8525 0687   Tel: 020-8533 1506

COLGAN Valerie
The Green, 17 Herbert Street
London NW5 4HA   Tel: 020-7267 2153

The Actors Company is a one-year intensive, affordable and accessible full-time training, exclusively for mature students and post-graduates (21+), held on one site in superb studios in fashionable Hoxton.

Agents, Casting Directors, Producers and the theatre-going public attend The Actors Company six week Repertory Season at The Jermyn Street Theatre in London's West End at the conclusion of the fourth, final term.

Auditioning now for 2003

The first three twelve week terms comprise the highest quality training by established and highly experienced professionals. The lack of government funding for one-year courses precipitated LCTS to create this uniquely presented and very successful course run forty hours per week on Wednesday evenings, and all day Thursday, Friday and Saturday, thus enabling professional people to support themselves during training.

Excellence is achieved by offering a clear philosophy and approach to acting as a craft, creating ensemble playing in productions, where 'the play is the star'.

For a prospectus contact:
The London Centre for Theatre Studies
12–18 Hoxton Street London N1 6NG

T/F 020 7739 5866
E ldncts@aol.com
www.lcts.co.uk

THE ACTORS COMPANY

VOICE CONSULTANT & COACH

Jessica Higgs

Tel/Fax: 020-7359 7848   Mobile: 079-4019 3631

Basic vocal technique - text and acting - Consultancy in all areas of voice use.

COLIN'S PERFORMING ARTS Ltd
(Full-time 3 year Performing Arts College)
The Studios
219B North Street, Romford, Essex RM1 4QA
Website: www.colinsperformingarts.co.uk
e-mail: admin@colinsperformingarts.co.uk
Fax: 01708 766077   Tel: 01708 766007

COMPAGNIE LIAN
(Voice, Accent & Speech Coaching and Language Tuition)
2 Ravenscourt Park, London W6 0TH
Website: www.noraarmani.com
e-mail: info@noraarmani.com   Tel: 020-8563 0220

CONSTRUCTIVE TEACHING CENTRE Ltd
(Alexander Technique Teacher Training)
18 Lansdowne Road, London W11 3LL
Website: www.alexandertek.com
e-mail: info@alexandertek.com   Tel: 020-7727 7222

CONTI Dizi
D Sp E
4 Brentmead Place
London NW11 9LH   Tel: 020-8458 5535

CONTI Italia ACADEMY OF THEATRE ARTS
See DRAMA SCHOOLS (Conference of)

CONTI Italia ACADEMY OF THEATRE ARTS Ltd
SS
Italia Conti House, 23 Goswell Road, London EC1M 7AJ
e-mail: sca@italiaconti36.freeserve.co.uk
Fax: 020-7253 1430   Tel: 020-7608 0047

CORNER Clive AGSM LRAM
(Qualified Teacher, Private Coaching and Audition Training)
73 Gloucester Road, Hampton
Middlesex TW12 2UQ
e-mail: cornerclive@aol.com   Tel: 020-8287 2726

COURT THEATRE TRAINING COMPANY
The Courtyard Theatre
10 York Way, King's Cross, London N1 9AA
Website: www.thecourtyard.org.uk
e-mail: info@thecourtyard.org.uk
                              Tel/Fax: 020-7833 0870

COURTENAY Julian
(NLP Master Practitioner)
42 Langdon Park Road, London N6 5QG
e-mail: julian@mentalfitness.uk.com
                              Tel: 020-8348 9033

CREATIVE PERFORMANCE
(Circus Skills, TIE/Workshops, Children 5-11 Part-time)
20 Pembroke Road
North Wembley, Middlesex HA9 7PD
Website: www.jennymayers.co.uk
e-mail: mjennymayers@aol.com
                              Tel/Fax: 020-8908 0502

CREATIVE THEATRE SCHOOL
(& Private Coaching)
PO Box 222, Rainham, Essex RM13 7WQ
e-mail: wildtrm@lineone.net   Tel 01708 505543

CYGNET TRAINING THEATRE
See DRAMA SCHOOLS (Conference of)

DALLA VECCHIA Sara
(Italian Teacher)
549A Chiswick High Road
London W4 3AY   Mobile: 07774 703686

DAVIDSON Clare
D E
30 Highgate West Hill, London N6 6NP
Website: www.csf.edu
e-mail: cdavidson@csf.edu   Tel: 020-8348 0132

D & B SCHOOL OF PERFORMING ARTS
Central Studios, 470 Bromley Road
Bromley BR1 4PN
Fax: 020-8697 8100   Tel: 020-8698 8880

DE COURCY Bridget
S (Singing Teacher)
19 Muswell Road, London N10   Tel: 020-8883 8397

DE FLOREZ Jane LGSM
(Singing Teacher - Musical Theatre, Jazz, Classical)
70 Ipsden Buildings
Windmill Walk, Waterloo
London SE1 8LT   Tel: 020-7803 0835

DIGNAN Tess PDVS
(Audition, Text & Voice Coach)
60 Mereton Mansions, Brookmill Road
London SE8 4HS   Tel: 020-8691 4275

DONNELLY Elaine
(Children's Acting Coach)
The Talent Partnership
Riverside Studios, Crisp Road
London W6 9RL   Tel: 020-8237 1040

DRAGONDRAMA
(Drama for Children)
1B Station Road, Hampton Wick, Kingston KT1 4HG
Website: www.dragondrama.co.uk
e-mail: dragondrama@hotmail.com
                              Tel/Fax: 020-8943 1504

DRAMA ASSOCIATION OF WALES
(Summer Courses for Amateur Actors & Directors)
The Old Library
Singleton Road, Splott, Cardiff CF24 2ET
e-mail: aled.daw@virgin.net
Fax: 029-2045 2277   Tel: 029-2045 2200

DRAMA CENTRE LONDON
See DRAMA SCHOOLS (Conference of)

DRAMA STUDIO EDINBURGH The
(Children's weekly drama workshops)
19 Belmont Road
Edinburgh EH14 5DZ
Website: www.thedramastudio.co.uk
e-mail: thedra@thedramastudio.co.uk
Fax: 0131-453 3108   Tel: 0131-453 3284

DRAMA STUDIO LONDON
DS
Grange Court, Grange Road
London W5 5QN
Website: www.dramastudiolondon.co.uk
e-mail: admin@dramastudiolondon.co.uk
Fax: 020-8566 2035   Tel: 020-8579 3897

DRAMA ZONE
(Weekend Acting Classes)
14-16 Guilford Street, London WC1N 1DW
e-mail: dramazone@harrispearson.co.uk
                    Tel/Fax: 020-7430 9890

DRAMA-DANCE-SONG
(Affiliated with Dee Hindin Associates)
67 York Street, Whitefield, London W1H 1QA
Fax: 020-7724 0822   Tel: 020-7724 0022

10 Hillingdon Road, Whitefield
Manchester M45 7QN
Fax: 0161-280 7678   Tel: 0161-766 5221

DRAMASCENE
(Speech and drama classes, 6 - late teens,
Lynda Gregory LTCL)
23 High Ash Avenue, Leeds LS17 8RS
Fax: 0113-268 1162   Tel: 0113-268 4519

HOLLY WILSON

LLAM. Actor. Teacher-London Drama Schools.

Voice, Speech & Drama, Audition coaching. Private tuition.

Tel: 020-8878 0015

DUNMORE Simon
(Acting & Audition Tuition)
Website: www.simon.dunmore.btinternet.co.uk
e-mail: simon.dunmore@btinternet.com

DURRENT Peter
(Audition & Rehearsal Pianist & Vocal Coach)
Blacksmiths Cottage, Bures Road, Little Cornard,
Sudbury, Suffolk CO10 0NR   Tel: 01787 373483

EARNSHAW Susi THEATRE SCHOOL
SS
5 Brook Place, Barnet EN5 2DL
Website: www.susiearnshaw.co.uk
e-mail: casting@susiearnshaw.co.uk
Fax: 020-8364 9618   Tel: 020-8441 5010

EAST 15 ACTING SCHOOL
See DRAMA SCHOOLS (Conference of)

ECOLE INTERNATIONALE DE THEATRE JACQUES LECOQ
57 rue du Faubourg Saint-Denis, 75010 Paris
e-mail: ecole-jacques-lecoq@wanadoo.fr
Fax: 00 331 45 234014   Tel: 00 331 47 704478

ELLIOTT CLARKE SCHOOL
(Saturday & Evening Classes in Dance & Drama)
75A Bold Street
Liverpool L1 4EZ   Tel: 0151-709 3323

ENTERTRAIN UK Ltd
(TV Presenter Training)
14 Hawthorne Court
Rickmansworth Road, Pinner, Middlesex HA5 3UN
Website: www.entertrainltd.com
Mobile: 07740 802602   Tel: 020-8429 2171

FAITH Gordon BA IPA Dip REM Sp MCHC (UK)
Sp
1 Wavel Mews, Priory Road
London NW6 3AB   Tel: 020-7328 0446

FBI AGENCY Ltd
(Acting Classes for Everyone)
PO Box 250, Leeds LS1 2AZ
e-mail: j.spencer@fbi-agency.ltd.uk
                           Tel/Fax: 07050 222747

FERRIS Anna MA (VOICE STUDIES, CSSD)
DE
Gil'cup Leaze, Hilton, Blandford Forum, Dorset DT11 0DB
e-mail: atcferris@aol.com
Mobile: 07905 656661   Tel: 01258 881098

FINBURGH Nina
D Sp
1 Buckingham Mansions
West End Lane
London NW6 1LR   Tel/Fax: 020-7435 9484

FLYING DOG PRODUCTIONS
(TV Presenters Courses & Training)
29 Maiden Lane
Covent Garden
London WC2E 7JS   Tel: 020-7692 9203

FORD Carole Ann ADVS
E D Sp
The Ridge, Hendon Wood Lane, London NW7 4HR
Fax: 020-8906 4669   Tel: 020-8959 8159

FORD Robert L
(Drama, LAMDA and Audition Coaching)
58 Holyhead Road
Oakengates, Telford
Shropshire TF2 6BN   Tel: 01952 618569

FORREST Dee
(Voice/Dialects, Film & TV)
602A High Road, Leytonstone, London E11 3DA
e-mail: dee_forrest@yahoo.com
Tel: 01273 204779   Tel: 020-8556 3828

FOX Betty STAGE SCHOOL
The Friends Institute
220 Moseley Road, Birmingham B12 0DG
e-mail: bettyfox.school@virgin.net
                        Tel/Fax: 0121-440 1635

FRANKLIN Michael
(Meisner Technique)
Correspondence: c/o The Spotlight
7 Leicester Place
London WC2H 7RJ   Tel/Fax: 020-8979 9185

FRIEZE Sandra
D E Sp (English & Foreign Actors)
30 Canfield Gardens
London NW6 3LA   Mobile: 07802 865305

GAPA
2A Bellevue Mews, Bellevue Road, London N11 3ET
e-mail: goughacademy@hotmail.com
                           Tel: 020-8368 6444

GEORGESON Rosalind BA HONS
(Drama for Children)
(See DRAGONDRAMA)

GIRAUDON Olivier
(Alexander Technique Teacher)
26 Church Rise, Forest Hill
London SE23 2UD   Tel: 020-8699 9080

GLYNNE Frances THEATRE STUDENTS
SS
11 High Ash Avenue, Leeds LS17 8RS
e-mail: franandmo@cwctv.net
Fax: 0113-295 9408   Tel: 0113-266 4286

GO FOR IT THEATRE SCHOOL
47 North Lane, Teddington, Middlesex TW11 0HU
Fax: 020-8287 9405   Tel: 020-8943 1120

GRAYSON John
(Vocal Tuition)
14 Lile Crescent, Hanwell, London W7 1AH
e-mail: john@bizzybee.freeserve.co.uk
Mobile: 07702 188031   Tel: 020-8578 3384

GREASEPAINT ANONYMOUS
Youth Theatre & Training Company
4 Gallus Close, Winchmore Hill, London N21 1JR
e-mail: info@greasepaintanonymous.co.uk
Fax: 020-8882 9189   Tel: 020-8886 2263

GREGORY Paul
(Drama Coach)
133 Kenilworth Court, Lower Richmond Road,
Putney, London SW15 1HB   Tel: 020-8789 5726

GREVILLE Jeannine THEATRE SCHOOL
Melody House. Gillott's Corner
Henley-on-Thames
Oxon RG9 1QU   Tel: 01491 572000

GROUT Philip
81Clarence Road
London N22 8PG   Tel: 020-8881 1800

GSA GUILDFORD SCHOOL OF ACTING
See DRAMA SCHOOLS (Conference of)

GUILDHALL SCHOOL OF MUSIC & DRAMA
See DRAMA SCHOOLS (Conference of)

HALEY Jennifer STAGE SCHOOL
(Dance RAD, ISTD, Drama LAMDA)
Toad Hall, 67 Poppleton Road
London E11 1LP   Tel: 020-8989 8364

HALL Michael THEATRE SCHOOL
21 Broadway, Blackpool, Lancs FY4 2HF
e-mail: frances@thehalls.force9.co.uk
                           Tel: 01253 346244

HANCOCK Allison LLAM
D E (Dramatic Art, Acting, Voice, Audition
Coaching, Elocution, Speech Correction etc)
38 Eve Road, Isleworth
Middlesex TW7 7HS   Tel/Fax: 020-8891 1073

**HARLEQUIN STUDIOS PERFORMING ARTS
SCHOOL**
(Drama & Dance Training)
223 Southcoast Road, Peacehaven
East Sussex BN10 8LB   Tel: 01273 581742

HARRINGTON Alex
(Audition Coach, Voice Consultant)
42 Petherton Road, London N5 2RG
e-mail: alexhvoice@aol.com
Mobile: 07979 963410   Tel: 020-7226 2136

**HARRIS Sharon NCSD LRAM
IPA Dip DA London Univ**
Sharon Harris School of Speech & Drama
52 Forty Avenue, Wembley, Middlesex HA9 8LQ
e-mail: sharrisltd@aol.com
Fax: 020-8908 4455   Tel: 020 8908 4451

HARRISON Joy
(Coaching in Audition Technique, Confidence
Building, Text Work and Drama School Entry)
e-mail: joyh@london.com   Tel: 020-7226 8377

HEIDELBACH Sabine MSTAT
(Alexander Technique)
50 Hillside Grove
London N14 6HE   Tel: 020-8882 8562

HERTFORDSHIRE THEATRE SCHOOL
Queen Street House
40 Queen Street
Hitchin, Herts SG4 9TS
Website: www.htstheatreschool.co.uk
e-mail: info@htstheatreschool.co.uk
                           Tel: 01462 421416

HESTER John LLCM (TD)
D E (Member of The Society of Teachers
of Speech & Drama)
105 Stoneleigh Park Road
Epsom, Surrey KT19 0RF
e-mail: hester92@hotmail.com   Tel: 020-8393 5705

HEWITT PERFORMING ARTS
160 London Road,
Romford, Essex RM7 9QL
e-mail: hewittcontrol@aol.com   Tel: 01708 727784

HIGGS Jessica
(Voice)
41A Barnsbury Street
London N1 1PW   Tel/Fax: 020-7359 7848

HONEYBORNE Jack
S (Accompanist & Coach)
The Studio, 165 Gunnersbury Lane
London W3 8LJ   Tel: 020-8993 2111

HOPE STREET Ltd
DS Sp (Physical Theatre Programme, University
Certificate/Workshop Leaders Programme)
13A Hope Street, Liverpool L1 9BQ
Website: www.hope-street.org
e-mail: arts@hope.u-net.com
Fax: 0151-709 3242   Tel: 0151-708 8007

HOPNER Ernest LLAM
E D Public Speaking
Bluecoat Chambers, School Lane
Liverpool L1 3BX   Tel: 0151-709 1966

HOUSEMAN Barbara
(Ex-RSC Voice Dept,
Voice/Text/Acting/Posture/Relaxation)
e-mail: barbarahouseman@hotmail.com
                                 Tel/Fax: 020-8693 9898

HUGHES Elianne
S (Accompanist & Coach for Rehearsal & Auditions)
165 Gunnersbury Lane
London W3 8LJ   Tel: 020-8993 2111

IDEAL SOLUTIONS
(Pat O'Toole - Private Coaching, Presentation,
Audition Work, Acting, Corporate, Counselling)
e-mail: patideal@aol.com
Fax: 020-7564 3147   Tel: 020-7564 3384

IMPULSE COMPANY The
e-mail: scott@impulsecompany.co.uk
                                 Tel/Fax: 020-8892 7292

INDEPENDENT THEATRE WORKSHOP The
2 Mornington Road
Ranelagh, Dublin 6
Website: www.independent-theatre-workshop.com
e-mail: itw@esatclear.ie   Tel/Fax: 00 353 1 4968808

IVES-CAMERON Elaine
(Private Coaching, Dialect, Drama School
Entrance/Auditions)
29 King Edward Walk, London SE1 7PR
Mobile: 07980 434513   Tel: 020-7928 3814

JACK Andrew
Vrouwe Johanna
Box 412, Weybridge, Surrey KT13 8WL
Website: www.andrewjack.com
                            Mobile: 07836 615839

JAMES Linda RAM Dip. Ed. IPD LRAM
(Dialect Coach)
25 Clifden Road, Brentford
Middlesex TW8 0PB   Tel: 020-8568 2390

JIGSAW PERFORMING ARTS SCHOOL
64-66 High Street, Barnet, Herts EN5 5QR
e-mail: admin@jigsaw-arts.co.uk Tel: 020-8447 4530

**JONES Desmond SCHOOL OF MIME AND
PHYSICAL THEATRE The**
20 Thornton Avenue, London W4 1QG
Website: www.desmondjones.co.uk
e-mail: enquiries@desmondjones.co.uk
                               Tel: 020-8747 3537

JORDAN Elizabeth MANAGEMENT Ltd
(Model Grooming School, Choreographers &
Fashion Show Co-ordinators)
14 Silver Birch Gardens, London E6 3SX
Website: www.elizabethjordan.co.uk
e-mail: info@elizabethjordan.co.uk
Mobile: 07957 381070   Tel/Fax: 020-7511 6746

JUSTICE Herbert ACADEMY OF THEATRE ARTS
SS
PO Box 253, Beckenham
Kent BR3 3WH   Tel: 020-8650 8878

K-BIS THEATRE SCHOOL
Clermont Hall, Cumberland Road, Brighton BN1 6SL
e-mail: k-bis@zoom.co.uk
Mobile: 07798 610010   Tel/Fax: 01273 564366

KENT YOUTH THEATRE & AGENCY
Pinks Hill House
Briton Road, Faversham, Kent ME13 8QH
e-mail: richard@kyt.org.uk   Tel/Fax: 01795 534395

KIDS AHEAD STAGE SCHOOL OF TOTTENHAM
Johnston & Mathers Associates Ltd
PO Box 3167, Barnet EN5 2WA
e-mail: johnstonmathers@aol.com
                             Tel/Fax: 020-8449 4968

KIDZ IN THE BIZ
The Lime House
Leaves Green Road, Keston, Kent BR2 6DQ
Website: www.kidzinthebiz.co.uk
e-mail: nicky@kidzinthebiz.co.uk
Fax: 01959 576632   Tel: 01959 542552

LAINE THEATRE ARTS
(Betty Laine)
The Studios, East Street, Epsom, Surrey KT17 1HH
Fax: 01372 723775   Tel: 01372 724648

LAMDA
See DRAMA SCHOOLS (Conference of)

LAMONT DRAMA SCHOOL AND CASTING AGENCY
94 Harington Road, Formby, Liverpool L37 1PZ
Website: www.lamontcasting.co.uk
e-mail: diane@lamontcasting.co.uk
Fax: 01704 872422   Tel: 01704 877024

LANG Margaret
18 Dalkeith Court
45 Vincent Street
London SW1P 4HH   Tel: 020-7828 4297

LAURIE Rona
(Coach for Auditions and Voice & Speech Technique)
Flat 1, 21 New Quebec Street
London W1H 7SA   Tel: 020-7262 4909

LEAN David Lawson BA Hons
(Acting Tuition, LAMDA Exams, Licensed Chaperone)
72 Shaw Drive, Walton-on-Thames
Surrey KT12 2LS   Tel: 01932 230273

LEE STAGE SCHOOL The
(office)
38 The Chase, Rayleigh, Essex SS6 8QN
e-mail: lynn@leetheatre.fsnet.co.uk
          Tel: 01268 773204

LEEDS METROPOLITAN UNIVERSITY
2 Queen Square, Leeds LS2 8AF
Tel: 0113-283 1900   Fax: 0113-283 1901

LESLIE Maeve
(Singing, Voice Production, Presentation)
60 Warwick Square
London SW1V 2AL   Tel: 020-7834 4912

LEVENTON Patricia BA Hons
D E Sp
113 Broadhurst Gardens
West Hampstead, London NW6 3BJ
e-mail: patricia.leventon@lites2000.com
          Tel: 020-7624 5661

LINTON MANAGEMENT
Carol Godby Theatre Workshop
The Studios, Back Broad Street, Bury, Lancs BL9 0DA
Fax: 0161-761 1999   Tel: 0161-763 6420

LITTLE ACTORS THEATRE COMPANY
12 Hardy Close, Surrey Quays, London SE16 6RT
e-mail: samanthahgiblin@hotmail.com
Fax: 0870 1645895   Tel: 020-7231 6083

LITTLE HEATH THEATRE WORKSHOP
Little Heath Parish Hall, Thorton Road
Little Heath, Potter's Bar
Herts AL9 7QG   Tel: 01582 831020

LIVE & LOUD
(Children & Teenage Drama Coaching)
Dalziel House
7 Claremont Terrace, Glasgow G3 7XR
e-mail: info@liveandloud.fsbusiness.co.uk
Fax: 0141-353 6385   Tel: 0141-331 2519

LIVERPOOL INSTITUTE FOR PERFORMING ARTS The
Mount Street, Liverpool L1 9HF
e-mail: reception@lipa.ac.uk
Fax: 0151-330 3131   Tel: 0151-330 3000

LIVINGSTON Dione LRAM FETC
Sp E D
7 St Luke's Street
Cambridge CB4 3DA   Tel: 01223 365970

LOCATION TUTORS NATIONWIDE
(Fully Qualified/Experienced Support Teachers
Covering all Key Stages in National Curriculum)
16 Poplar Walk, Herne Hill SE24 0BU
Fax: 020-7207 8794   Tel: 020-7978 8898

**LONDON ACADEMY OF PERFORMING ARTS
(LAPA)**
St Matthews Church
St Petersburgh Place, London W2 4LA
Website: www.lapadrama.com
e-mail: admin@lapadrama.com
Fax: 020-7727 0330   Tel: 020-7727 0220

LONDON DRAMA SCHOOL
(Acting, Speech Training, Singing)
30 Brondesbury Park, London NW6 7DN
Website: www.startek-uk.com
e-mail: enquiries@startek-uk.com
Fax: 020-8830 4992   Tel: 020-8830 0074

LONDON FILMMAKERS STUDIO The
10 Brunswick Centre
off Bernard Street, London WC1N 1AE
e-mail: business@skoob.com
Mobile: 07712 880909   Tel: 020-7278 8760

LONDON SCHOOL OF MUSICAL THEATRE
83 Borough Road, London SE1 1DN
e-mail: enquiries@lsmt.co.uk Tel: 020-7407 4455

LONDON STUDIO CENTRE
42-50 York Way, London N1 9AB
Website: www.london-studio-centre.co.uk
e-mail: enquire@london-studio-centre.co.uk
Fax: 020-7837 3248   Tel: 020-7837 7741

LYTTON Gloria
E D
22 Green Road, Oakwood
Southgate, London N14 4AU   Tel: 020-8441 3118

MACKEY Beatrix LGSM
E D (Coaching For Drama, Speech & Communication)
3 The Valley, Stanmore, Winchester
Hants SO22 4DG   Tel: 01962 855533

MACKINTOSH Stewart ARCM ABSM
S
106 Boundaries Road, London SW12 8HQ
e-mail: stewartmackintosh@email.com
Mobile: 07970 448109   Tel: 020-8672 6179

MADDERMARKET THEATRE
Peter Beck (Education Officer)
Education and Training Department
St John's Alley, Norwich NR2 1DR
Website: www.maddermarket.freeserve.co.uk
e-mail: trainingandeducation@maddermarket.fsnet.co.uk
Fax: 01603 661357   Tel: 01603 626560

**MANCHESTER METROPOLITAN UNIVERSITY
SCHOOL OF THEATRE**
See DRAMA SCHOOLS (Conference of)

MANCHESTER SCHOOL OF ACTING
29 Ardwick Green North, Manchester M12 6DL
e-mail: actorclass@aol.com Tel/Fax: 0161-877 0250

MARLOW Jean LGSM
D E
32 Exeter Road
London NW2 4SB   Tel: 020-8450 0371

**MARSHALL Elizabeth Tracey LGSM GSMD
LGSMD**
(Dialects, Speech Faults, Drama for Stage, Film &
Modelling, Training for Corporates eg. Presentation
Skills)
5 Mount Street, Cromer, Norfolk NR27 9DB
e-mail: marshall@grenedan.demon.co.uk
                    Tel: 01263 515769

MARTIN Liza GRSM ARMCM (Singing) ARMCM (Piano)
(Singing Tuition, Sounds Sensational) Tel: 020-8348 0346

MASTERS PERFORMING ARTS COLLEGE
(Dance, Musical Theatre Course)
Arterial Road, Rayleigh
Essex SS6 7UQ   Tel: 01268 777351

McCALLION Anna
(Alexander Technique)
Flat 2, 11 Sinclair Gardens
London W14 0AU   Tel: 020-7602 5599

McCALLION Michael
D E
Flat 2, 11 Sinclair Gardens
London W14 0AU   Tel: 020-7602 5599

McCRACKEN Jenny
2 Stamford Court, Goldhawk Road
London W6 0XB   Tel: 020-8748 7638

McDAID Marj
1 Chesholm Road
Stoke Newington, London N16 0DP
e-mail: marjmcdaid@hotmail.com
Fax: 020-7502 0412   Tel: 020-7923 4929

METHOD STUDIO, LONDON The
Conway Hall, 25 Red Lion Square, London WC1R 4RL
Website: www.themethodstudio.com
e-mail: info@themethodstudio.com
Fax: 020-7831 8319   Tel: 020-7831 7335

MICHEL Hilary ARCM
(Singing Teacher, Vocal Coaching, Accompanist,
Auditions, Technique)
82 Greenway, Totteridge, London N20 8EJ
Mobile: 07775 780182   Tel: 020-8343 7243

MIDDLESEX UNIVERSITY
(Singing Teacher, Vocal Coaching, Accompanist,
Auditions Technique)
Bramley Road, Oakwood, London N14 4YZ
Fax: 020-8441 4672   Tel: 020-8362 5000

MILNER Jack COMEDY WORKSHOPS
88 Pearcroft Road, London E11 4DR
Website: www.jackmilner.com
e-mail: jack@jackmilner.com   Tel: 020-8556 9768

MONTAGE THEATRE
(Dance, Drama, Singing - Children & Adults)
59 Embleton Road, London SE13 7DQ
Website: www.montagetheatre.com
e-mail: info@montagetheatre.com   Tel: 020-8314 5036

MONTFORD DANCE AND STAGE ACADEMY
96 Surbiton Court
St Andrews Square, Surbiton, Surrey KT6 4EE
Fax: 020-8314 5036   Tel: 020-8399 9065

MORLEY COLLEGE THEATRE SCHOOL
(LOCN Accredited Evening Theatre School,
Day-time Performing Arts Programme)
61 Westminster Bridge Road, London SE1 7HT
e-mail: nina.anderson@morleycollege.ac.uk
Fax: 020-7928 4074   Tel: 020-7450 9232

MORRIS David SCHOOL FOR PERFORMING ARTS
6 Sussex Close, Redbridge, Essex IG4 5DP
Mobile: 07957 121772   Tel: 020-8924 0197

MOUNTVIEW
See DRAMA SCHOOLS (Conference of)

MRS WORTHINGTON'S WORKSHOPS
SS S Md
(Part-time Performing Arts for Children Under 18)
16 Ouseley Road
London SW12 8EF   Tel: 020-8767 6944

MURRAY Barbara LGSM LALAM
129 Northwood Way, Northwood
Middlesex HA6 1RF   Tel: 01923 823182

NATIONAL PERFORMING ARTS SCHOOL & AGENCY The
The Factory Rehearsal Studios
35A Barrow Street, Dublin 4
e-mail: info@npas.ie   Tel/Fax: 00 353 1 6684035

NEIL Andrew
2 Howley Place, London W2 1XA
e-mail: andrewneil@surf3.net
Tel/Fax: 020-7262 9521

NEW ERA ACADEMY (Speech & Drama)
E D Examination Board
137B Streatham High Road, London SW16 1HJ
e-mail: neweraacademy@aol.com
Tel: 01905 830915

NEWNHAM Caryll
(Singing Teacher)
35 Selwyn Crescent, Hatfield, Herts AL10 9NL
e-mail: caryll@ntlworld.com
Mobile: 07976 635745   Tel: 01707 267700

NORTH LONDON PERFORMING ARTS CENTRE
(Performing Arts Classes 3-19 yrs, GCSE Drama & LAMDA Exams)
76 St James Lane, Muswell Hill, London N10 3DF
e-mail: nlpac@compuserve.com
Fax: 020-8444 4040   Tel: 020-8444 4544

NORTHERN ACADEMY TELEVISION AND THEATRE WORKSHOPS The
24-25 Booth House
Featherstall Road, Oldham OL9 7QT
Website: www.thenorthernacademy.ca.tc
Tel/Fax: 0161-652 2651

NORTHERN FILM & DRAMA
PO Box 27, Tadcaster, North Yorks LS24 9XS
Website: www.connew.com/nfd
e-mail: alyson@connew.com Tel/Fax: 01977 681949

NORTHERN THEATRE SCHOOL OF PERFORMING ARTS
The Studios, Madeley Street
Hull, East Yorkshire HU3 2AH
e-mail: northco75@aol.com
Fax: 01482 212280   Tel: 01482 328627

NUTOPIA ACTORS STUDIO LONDON
(Camera Acting and Presenting Courses)
Number 8
132 Charing Cross Road, London WC2H 0LA
Website: www.nutopia.co.uk
Tel/Fax: 020-8882 6299

O'FARRELL STAGE & THEATRE SCHOOL
(Dance, Drama, Singing)
36 Shirley Street, Canning Town, London E16 1HU
Fax: 020-7476 0010   Tel: 020-7511 9444

THE SCHOOL OF THE
SCIENCE
of
ACTING®

A charity formed to advance standards in drama training.

FULL TIME ACTING COURSES

1-Year (4 term) Daytime Acting Course

2-Year (8 term) Daytime Acting Course

3-Year (12 term) Daytime Acting Course

3-Year Evening plus 1-Year Daytime (16 term) Acting Course

DIRECTING MODULES

(7 term) Daytime (in conjunction with the 3-Year Daytime Acting Course)

(6 term) Evening + 4 terms Daytime (in conjunction with 3-Year Evening plus 1-Year Daytime (16 term) Acting Course)

PART-TIME COURSES & WORKSHOPS

Intensive Course

Spring Workshop

Summer School

August Workshop

GUARANTEE

If, after a certain period at the School of the Science of Acting you do not believe that your course is the best way to learn to act or direct in the time given, we will return your money in full.

CONTACT

The School of the Science of Acting

Dept E, 67-83 Seven Sisters Road, London N7 6BU

Tel: 020 7272 0027 Fax: 020 7272 0026

E-mail: find@scienceofacting.org.uk

Website: www.scienceofacting.org.uk

The School of Science and Acting. Nobody teaches better. Nobody cares more.

FS45916   BS EN ISO9001:1994

Registered Charity No. 1014419

Recognised as Efficient by the British Accreditation Council for Independent Further and Higher Education

OLLERENSHAW Maggie BA (Hons) Dip Ed
D Sp (TV & Theatre Coaching, Career Guidance)
151D Shirland Road, London W9 2EP
e-mail: maggieoll@aol.com   Tel: 020-7286 1126

OLSON Lise
(American Accents, Voice & Text)
17A Park Road, West Kirby, Wirral CH48 4DN
e-mail: l.olson@lipa.ac.uk
Tel: 0151-625 5667   Tel: 0151-330 3032

OMOBONI Lino
Sp
2nd Floor, 12 Weltje Road, London W6 9TG
Website: www.bluewand.co.uk
e-mail: lino@bluewand.co.uk
Mobile: 07885 528743   Tel/Fax: 020-8741 2038

OPEN VOICE
(Consultancy, Auditions, Personal Presentation -
Catherine Owen)
9 Bellsmains, Gorebridge
Near Edinburgh EH23 4QD   Tel: 01875 820175

ORTON Leslie LRAM ALAM ANEA
E D Sp
141 Ladybrook Lane, Mansfield
Notts NG18 5JH   Tel: 01623 626082

OSBORNE HUGHES John
(Art & Craft of Acting)
Venus Productions Training Department
51 Church Road, London SE19 2TE
e-mail: johughes@amserve.net
Mobile: 07801 950916   Tel: 020-8653 7735

OVERSBY William
(Singing & Vocal Projection)
Streatham
e-mail: woversby@onetel.net.uk
Mobile: 07811 946663   Tel: 020-8769 4972

OXFORD SCHOOL OF DRAMA
See DRAMA SCHOOLS (Conference of)

OXYGENESIS
(Maurice Rowdon, Breath Initiation)
Hale Clinic, Regent's Park, London W1B 1PF
Tel: 01202 744747   Tel: 020-8874 5361

PALMER Jackie STAGE SCHOOL
30 Daws Hill Lane, High Wycombe, Bucks HP11 1PW
Website: www.jackiepalmer.co.uk
e-mail: jackie.palmer@btinternet.com
Fax: 01494 510479   Tel: 01494 510597

PALMER Marie LLAM FRSA
SS E Sp (Speechcraft Consultancy)
Church Studios, Common Road, Stafford ST16 3EQ
Website: www.speechcraft.co.uk
e-mail: enquiries@speechcraft.co.uk
Tel: 01785 226326   Fax: 01785 220460

PARKES Frances MA AGSM
(Voice & Acting Coach)
451A Kingston Road
London SW20 8JP
e-mail: frances@frances25.demon.co.uk
Agent: Joyce Edwards
Tel: 020-7735 5736   Tel/Fax: 020-8542 2777

PAUL'S THEATRE SCHOOL
Fairkytes Arts Centre
51 Billet Lane
Hornchurch, Essex RM 11 1AX
e-mail: paul@the-theatreschool.fsnet.co.uk
Fax: 01708 475286   Tel: 01708 447123

PERFORM
SS
66 Churchway, London NW1 1LT
Fax: 020-7691 4822   Tel: 020-7209 3805

PERFORMERS COLLEGE
(Brian Rogers - Susan Stephens)
2-4 Chase Road
Corringham, Essex SS17 7QH
Website: www.performerscollege.co.uk
e-mail: pdc@dircon.co.uk
Fax: 01375 672353   Tel: 01375 672053

PETHICK Fiona & Claire BA Hons ADB LRAM LGSM
D Sp (Musical Theatre, Private Coaching for
Auditions, Schools, Showbiz etc)
e-mail: ata-productions@hotmail.com
Tel: 01932 702174

PHELPS Neil
D Sp
61 Parkview Court, London SW6 3LL
e-mail: nphelps@freeuk.com   Tel: 020-7731 3419

PHILLIPS Penny AGSM Dip. Ed LLAM GODA
'Shiraz' at Willow Tree Marina
West Quay Drive
Yeading in Hayes UB4 9TA
e-mail: penny@speak.free-online.co.uk
Mobile: 07976 365134   Tel/Fax: 020-8241 9287

PILATES INTERNATIONAL Ltd
(Physical Coaching, Stage, Film & Dance)
Unit 1, Broadbent Close, 20-22 Highgate High Street
London N6 5JG   Tel/Fax: 020-8348 1442

POLLYANNA CHILDRENS TRAINING THEATRE
PO Box 30661
London E1W 3GG
Website: www.eada.demon.co.uk/pollyanna
e-mail: pollyanna-mgmt@yahoo.co.uk
Fax: 020-7480 6761   Tel: 020-7702 1937

POOR SCHOOL
242 Pentonville Road
London N1 9JY   Tel: 020-7837 6030

QUEEN MARGARET COLLEGE
See DRAMA SCHOOLS (Conference of)

QUESTORS THEATRE EALING The
12 Mattock Lane, London W5 5BQ
Website: www.questors.org.uk
e-mail: admin@questors.org.uk
Fax: 020-8567 8736   Admin: 020-8567 0011

RAVENSCOURT THEATRE SCHOOL Ltd
Tandy House, 30-40 Dalling Road, London W6 0JB
Website: www.ravenscourttheatreschool.co.uk
e-mail: ravenscourt@hotmail.com
Fax: 020-8741 1786   Tel: 020-8741 0707

RE:ACTORS
15 Montrose Walk, Weybridge, Surrey KT13 8JN
Website: www.reactors.co.uk
e-mail: michael@reactors.co.uk
Fax: 01932 830248   Tel: 01932 888885

REDROOFS THEATRE SCHOOL
DS SS D E S Sp
Littlewick Green, Maidenhead, Berks SL6 3QY
Website: www.redroofs.co.uk   Iel: 01628 822982

REP COLLEGE The
17 St Mary's Avenue, Purley on Thames, Berks RG8 8BJ
Website: www.repcollege.com
e-mail: tudor@repcollege.freeserve.co.uk
                    Tel/Fax: 0118-942 1144

REYNOLDS Sandra COLLEGE
(Model Grooming School)
35 St Georges Street, Norwich NR3 1DA
Website: www.sandrareynolds.co.uk
e-mail: tessa@sandrareynolds.co.uk
Fax: 01603 219825   Tel: 01603 623842

REYNOLDS THEATRE ARTS ACADEMY
(Children/Teenagers)
2nd Floor, Westgate House
Spital Street, Dartford, Kent DA1 2EH
Website: www.reynoldsgroup.co.uk
e-mail: info@reynoldsgroup.co.uk
Fax: 01634 329079   Tel: 01322 277200

RICHMOND DRAMA SCHOOL
DS (One Year Course)
Parkshot Centre, Parkshot, Richmond, Surrey TW9 2RE
e-mail: drwhitters@aol.com   Tel: 020-8439 8944

RIDGEWAY STUDIOS PERFORMING ARTS COLLEGE
Fairley House, Andrews Lane, Cheshunt, Herts EN7 6LB
Website: www.ridgewaystudios.co.uk
e-mail: info@ridgewaystudios.co.uk
Fax: 01992 633844   Tel: 01992 633775

ROSE BRUFORD COLLEGE
See DRAMA SCHOOLS (Conference of)

ROWE James Dip GSA STSD
(Audition Coaching & Drama Courses)
Kinfauns 11 New Road, Higher Brea
Camborne, Cornwall TR14 9DD   Tel: 01209 710672

ROYAL ACADEMY OF DRAMATIC ART
See DRAMA SCHOOLS (Conference of)

ROYAL SCOTTISH ACADEMY OF MUSIC AND DRAMA
See DRAMA SCHOOLS (Conference of)

ROYAL WELSH COLLEGE OF MUSIC AND DRAMA
See DRAMA SCHOOLS (Conference of)

SCHER Anna THEATRE The
70-72 Barnsbury Road, London N1 0ES
e-mail: abby@astm.co.uk
Fax: 020-7833 9467   Tel: 020-7278 2101

SCHOOL OF THE SCIENCE OF ACTING The
Dept E
67-83 Seven Sisters Road, London N7 6BU
Website: www.scienceofacting.org.uk
e-mail: find@scienceofacting.org.uk
Fax: 020-7272 0026   Tel: 020-7272 0027

SCREENWRITERS' WORKSHOP
Screenwriters' Centre, Suffolk House
1-8 Whitfield Place, London W1T 5JU
Website: www.lsw.org.uk
e-mail: screenoffice@tiscali.co.uk
Tel/Fax: 020-7387 5511

SETTELEN Peter
181 Jersey Road, Osterley, Middlesex TW7 4QJ
Website: www.settelen.com
e-mail: talk@settelen.net
Fax: 020-8737 2987   Tel: 020-8737 1616

SHAND Mary PGDVS
D E (Voice Coach)
16 Lark Hill Rise, Winchester SO22 4LX
e-mail: voicehelp@lineone.net
Mobile: 07802 167342   Tel: 01962 855680

SHARONA STAGE SCHOOL AGENCY & MANAGEMENT
82 Grennell Road, Sutton, Surrey SM1 3DN
Fax: 020-8395 0009   Tel: 020-8642 9396

SHAW Philip
(Actors Consultancy Service, Voice/Audition Coaching)
Suite 476, 2 Old Brompton Road
South Kensington, London SW7 3DQ
e-mail: shawcastlond@aol.com
Fax: 020-8408 1193   Tel: 020-8715 8943

SHENEL Helena
(Singing Teacher)
80 Falkirk House, 165 Maida Vale
London W9 1QX   Tel: 020-7328 2921

SHERRIFF David
(Vocal Coaching, Accompanist, Act Preparation, Video Showreels)
Musical Services
106 Mansfield Drive, Merstham, Surrey RH1 3JN
Fax: 01737 271231   Tel: 01737 642829

SINGER Sandra ASSOCIATES
21 Cotswold Road, Westcliff-on-Sea, Essex SS0 8AA
Website: www.sandrasinger.com
e-mail: sandrasingeruk@aol.com
Fax: 01702 339393   Tel: 01702 331616

SOCIETY OF TEACHERS OF SPEECH AND DRAMA The
73 Berry Hill Road, Mansfield, Notts NG18 4RU
Website: www.stsd.org.uk
e-mail: ann.p.jones@btinternet.com
Tel: 01623 627636

SPEAKE Barbara STAGE SCHOOL
East Acton Lane, London W3 7EG
e-mail: speakekids1@aol.com
Tel/Fax: 020-8743 1306

SPEED Anne-Marie Hon ARAM MA (Voice Studies) CSSD ADVS BA
(Vocal Technique, Coaching, Auditions, Accents)
61 Donaldson Road, London NW6 6NE
e-mail: anne-marie.speed@virgin.net
Mobile: 07957 272554   Tel/Fax: 020-7328 2582

SPENCER Jay
(Acting and Audition Tuition)
e-mail: j.spencer@fbi-agency.ltd.uk
Tel/Fax: 07050 321654

STAGE 01 THEATRE PRODUCTION SCHOOL
32 Westbury Lane, Buckhurst Hill, Essex IG9 5PL
e-mail: stage01@lineone.net
Mobile: 07939 121154   Tel/Fax: 020-8506 0949

STAGE 84 YORKSHIRE SCHOOL OF PERFORMING ARTS
(Evening Classes, Weekend Classes and Summer Schools)
Old Bell Chapel, Town Lane
Bradford, West Yorks BD10 8PR
Mobile: 07785 244984   Tel: 01274 569197

STAGECOACH TRAINING CENTRES FOR THE PERFORMING ARTS
The Courthouse, Elm Grove
Walton-on-Thames, Surrey KT12 1LZ
Website: www.stagecoach.co.uk
e-mail: mail@stagecoach.co.uk
Fax: 01932 222894   Tel: 01932 254333

STAT (The Society of Teachers of the Alexander Technique)
129 Camden Mews, London NW1 9AH
e-mail: enquiries@stat.org.uk
Fax: 020-7482 5435   Tel: 020-7284 3338

STEP ONE DANCE AND DRAMA SCHOOL
Rear of 24 Penrhyn Road
Colwyn Bay, Conwy LL29 8LG   Tel: 01492 534424

STEVENS Dacia STAGE SCHOOL
SS E D Md Sp
Glenavon Lodge, Lansdowne Road
South Woodford
London E18 2BE   Tel: 020-8989 0166

STOCKTON & BILLINGHAM COLLEGE OF FURTHER EDUCATION
(Education & Training)
The Causeway
Billingham TS23 2DB   Tel: 01642 865566

STONELANDS SCHOOL
(Full-time Training in Ballet & Theatre Arts)
170A Church Road, Hove BN3 2DJ
e-mail: dianacarteur@stonelandsschool.co.uk
Fax: 01273 770444   Tel: 01273 770445

STREETON Jane
(Singing Teacher - RADA)
24 Richmond Road, Leytonstone
London E11 4BA   Tel: 020-8556 9297

SUTTON THEATRES
DS
39 High Street, Carshalton, Surrey SM5 3BB
Website: www.charlescryer.org.uk
e-mail: info@charlescryer.org.uk
Fax: 020-8770 4969   Tel: 020-8770 4950

SWAIN Neil BA (Hons) PGDVS CSSD
34 Saltash Road, Welling, Kent DA16 1HB
Fax: 020-8306 2934   Tel: 020-8306 2936

SWINDON YOUNG ACTORS
65 Stafford Street
Old Town, Swindon, Wiltshire SN1 3PF
e-mail: actorsfile@aol.com   Tel: 01793 423386

SWINFIELD Rosemarie (Make-Up)
Rosie's Make-Up Box
6 Brewer Street, Soho, London W1R 3FS
Website: www.rosiesmake-up.co.uk
e-mail: rosemarie@rosiesmake-up.co.uk
Fax: 020-8390 7773   Mobile: 07976 965520

TELEVISION TRAINING ACADEMY The
Unit A, 16 Campbell Road, Caterham, Surrey CR3 5JL
Website: www.televisiontrainingacademy.co.uk
Tel: 01883 346945

THEATRE ARTS (West London)
(Agency & Part-time Classes in Drama, Dance & Singing)
18 Kingsdale Gardens, Notting Hill, London W11 4TZ
e-mail: theatreartswestlondon@hotmail.com
Tel/Fax: 020-7603 3471

THEATRETRAIN
(6 -18 years, Annual West End Productions involving all Pupils)
PO Box 117, Ilford, Essex IG3 8PN
Website: www.theatretrain.co.uk
e-mail: theatretrain@talk21.com   Tel: 01992 524607

THORN Barbara
D Sp (TV & Theatre Coaching, Career Guidance)
51 Parkside, Vanbrugh Park
Blackheath, London SE3 7QF   Tel: 020-8305 0094

TIP TOE STAGE SCHOOL
45 Viola Close, South Ockendon, Essex RM15 6JF
Website: www.tiptoestageschool.com
e-mail: julieecarter@aol.com
Mobile: 07941 653463   Tel: 01708 859109

TO BE OR NOT TO BE
(TV/Film Acting Techniques using pro 'equip'
Showreels, Theatre/Audition pieces)
(Anthony Barnett)
48 Northampton Road
Kettering, Northants NN15 7JU
Website: http://homepage.ntlworld.com/tobeornottobe
e-mail: tobeornottobe@ntlworld.com
Mobile: 07958 996227   Tel/Fax: 01536 359631

TOTAL ACTOR The
(Graded, Progressive Acting Workshop, Taught by Working Actors and Directors)
66 Shaftesbury Road
London N19 4QN   Tel/Fax: 020-7281 3686

TRAPEZE AND AERIAL SKILL COACHING
(Denise and Raven Wolf)
26 Fairfield, Arlington Road, London NW1 7LE
Website: www.londonkids.net
Mobile: 07944 835639   Tel: 020-7388 3824

TROTTER William BA MA PGDVS
D E Sp
25 Thanet Lodge
Mapesbury Road
London NW2 4JA
Website: www.ukspeech.co.uk
e-mail: william.trotter@ukspeech.co.uk
Tel/Fax: 020-8459 7594

TURNER Jeff
(Psycotherapy, Counselling & Coaching)
Life Management Systems
14 Randell's Road
London N1 0DH
Website: www.lifemanagement.co.uk
e-mail: info@lifemanagement.co.uk
Tel: 020-7837 9871

TV ACTING CLASSES
(Elisabeth Charbonneau)
9 Alderton Road, Herne Hill, London SE24 0HS
e-mail: ejcharbonneau@aol.com
Mobile: 07885 621061   Tel: 020-7326 3967

TWICKENHAM THEATRE WORKSHOP FOR CHILDREN
22 Butts Crescent, Hanworth
Middlesex TW13 6HQ   Tel: 020-8898 5882

URQUHART Moray
61 Parkview Court, London SW6 3LL
e-mail: nphelps@freeuk.com   Tel: 020-7731 3419

VALLÉ ACADEMY OF PERFORMING ARTS Ltd The
D S E SS
The Rosedale Old Cestrians Club
Andrews Lane, Cheshunt, Herts EN7 6TB
Website: www.valleacademy.co.uk
e-mail: agency@valleacademy.co.uk
Fax: 01992 622868   Tel: 01992 622861

VERRALL Charles
D
19 Matilda Street, London N1 0LA
e-mail: charles.verrall@virgin.net Tel: 020-7833 1971

VOICE AND THE ALEXANDER TECHNIQUE
(Robert Macdonald)
Flat 5, 17 Hatton Street
London NW8 8PL   Mobile: 07956 852303

VOICE BODY COMMUNICATION
(Patricia Perry)
65 Castelnau
Barnes SW13 9RT   Tel/Fax: 020-8748 9699

VOICE CASTER
(Specialised Training for Voice-Overs & TV Presenters)
Fax: 020-8455 2344   Tel: 020-8455 2211

VOICE CLINIC The
99 Cobbold Road, Willesden, London NW10
e-mail: voice-clinic@hotmail.com
                              Tel: 0800 0747405

VOICE TAPE SERVICES INTERNATIONAL Ltd
(Professional Voice Over Direction & CDs)
80 Netherlands Road, New Barnet, Herts EN5 1BS
e-mail: info@vtsint.co.uk
Fax: 020-8441 4828   Tel: 020-8440 4848

WALLACE Elaine BA
D Sp Voice
249 Goldhurst Terrace, London NW6 3EP
e-mail: elainewallace33@hotmail.com
                              Tel: 020-7625 4049

WALTZER Jack
(Professional Voice-Over Direction & CDs)
5 Minetta Street Apt 2B, New York NY 10012
Website: www.jackwaltzer.com
Tel: 001 (212) 840-1234   Tel: 020-7207 1318

WEBB Bruce
S
Abbots Manor, Kirby Cane, Bungay
Suffolk NR35 2HP   Tel: 01508 518703

**WEBBER DOUGLAS ACADEMY OF
DRAMATIC ART**
See DRAMA SCHOOLS (Conference of)

WELBOURNE Jacqueline
(Circus Trainer, Choreographer, Consultant)
43 Kingway Avenue, Kingswood, Bristol BS15 8DB
e-mail: jackie@welbourne.co.uk
Mobile: 07977 247287   Tel/Fax: 0117-947 7042

WESTMINSTER KINGSWAY COLLEGE
(Performing Arts)
Regent's Park Centre
Longford Street, London NW1 3HB
Website: www.westking.ac.uk
e-mail: courseinfo@westking.ac.uk
Fax: 020-7391 6400   Tel: 020-7306 5954

WHITEHALL PERFORMING ARTS CENTRE
Rayleigh Road, Leigh-on-Sea
Essex SS9 5UU   Tel: 01702 529290

WHITWORTH Geoffrey LRAM MA
S (Piano Accompanist)
789 Finchley Road
London NW11 8DP   Tel: 020-8458 4281

WILDER Andrea
D E
23 Cambrian Drive, Colwyn Bay, Conwy LL28 4SL
Website: www.awagency.co.uk
e-mail: andrea@awagency.co.uk
Fax: 07092 249314   Tel: 01492 547542

WILMER Elizabeth J
E D
34 Campden Street
London W8 7ET   Tel: 020-7727 6624

WILSON Holly
3 Worple Street, Mortlake
London SW14 8HE   Tel: 020-8878 0015

WIMBUSH Martin Dip GSMD
D E Sp (Audition Coaching)
Flat 4, 289 Trinity Road
Wandsworth Common
London SW18 3SN   Tel: 020-8877 0086

WINDSOR Judith MA
(American Accents/Dialects)
Woodbine, Victoria Road, Deal, Kent CT14 7AS
e-mail: joyce.edwards@virgin.net
Fax: 020-7820 1845   Tel: 020-7735 5736

WOOD Tessa Teach Cert AGSM CSSD PGVDS
(Voice Coach)
11 Chaucer Road, Poet's Corner, London W3 6DR
e-mail: tessaroswood@aol.com Tel: 020-8896 2659

WOODHOUSE Alan AGSM ADVS
(Voice & Acting Coach)
33 Burton Road, Kingston, Surrey KT2 5TG
e-mail: alanwoodhouse50@hotmail.com
                          Tel/Fax: 020-8549 1374

Centres for 6 to 16 year olds
Patron: Glen Murphy

Saturdays 10am till 1pm

Builds confidence
Develops creative abilities
Complements other activities
From beginners to those with experience

DRAMA

DANCE

Singing

Head Office:
6 Sussex Close, Redbridge, Essex IG4 5DP
Tel: 020 8924 0197 Mobile: 07973 129130 Fax: 07957 121772

WOODHOUSE Nan
(Playwright & Lamda Examiner)
LGSM (Hons medal) LLAM LLCM (TD) ALCM
(Write) 2 New Street
Morecambe, Lancashire LA4 4BW

WOOSTER Margaret LRAM BAR
D E
97 Hughenden Road, High Wycombe
Bucks HP13 5HT   Tel: 01494 530756

WRIGG Ann ALAM
E D
The Little House, 6 Frith Lane
London NW7 1JA   Tel: 020-8346 6745

WYNN Madeleine
(Director & Acting Coach)
40 Barrie House, Hawksley Court, Albion Road,
London N16 0TX   e-mail: madeleine@onetel.net.uk
Tel: 01394 450265   Tel: 020-7249 4487

YOUNG PERFORMERS THEATRE SCHOOL
SS
Unit 3, Ground Floor, Clements Court
Clements Lane, Ilford, Essex IG1 2QY
e-mail: sara@tots-twenties.co.uk
Fax: 020-8553 1880   Tel: 020-8478 1848

YOUNG Sylvia THEATRE SCHOOL
SS
Rossmore Road, London NW1 6NJ
e-mail: jackie@youngunsagency.co.uk
Fax: 020-7723 1040   Tel: 020-7402 0673

ZANDER Peter
D E SP (German)
22 Romilly Street, London W1D 5AG
Website: freespace.virgin.net/peterzan.berlin
e-mail: peterzan.berlin@virgin.net
                               Tel: 020-7437 4767

For information on the FIA please contact
International Federation of Actors
Guild House, Upper St Martin's Lane
London WC2H GEG
Fax: 020-7379 8260   Tel: 020-7379 0900
e-mail: office@fia-actors.com

■ BELGIUM
ACV - Transcom
Galerie Agora
Rue du Marche aux Herbes
105, Bte 40, B-1000 Brussels
e-mail: mhendrickx.transcom@acu-csc.be
Fax: 00 32 2 512 8591   Tel: 00 32 2 549 0769

■ BELGIUM
C.G.S.P.
Confederation Generale des Services Publics
Place Fontainas 9-11, B-1000 Brussels
Fax: 00 32 2 508 59 02   Tel: 00 32 2 508 58 11

■ DENMARK
DANSK ARTIST FORBUND
Vendersgade 24, DK-1363 Copenhagen K
Website: www.artisen.dk
e-mail: artisten@artisten.dk
Fax: 00 45 33 33 73 30   Tel: 00 45 33 32 66 77

■ DENMARK
DANSK SKUESPILLERFORBUND
Sankt Knuds Vej 26
DK-1903 Frederiksberg C
Website: www.skuespillere.dk
e-mail: dsf@skuespillere.dk
Fax: 00 45 33 24 81 59   Tel: 00 45 33 24 22 00

■ FINLAND
SUOMEN NAAYTTELIJALITTO - SNL
Temppelikatu 3-5 A 11, SF-00100 Helsinki
e-mail: suomen.nattelijalutto@co.inet.fi
Fax: 00 358 9 4372 7350   Tel: 00 353 9 4342 7311

■ FRANCE
S.F.A.
Syndicat Francais des Artistes-Interpretes
21 bis, rue Victor Masse
F-75009 Paris
Website: www.sfa-cgt.fr
e-mail: sfa75@aol.com
Fax: 00 33 1 53 25 09 01   Tel: 00 33 1 53 25 09 09

■ GERMANY
G.D.B.A.
Genossenschaft Deutscher Buhen-Angehoriger
Feldbrunnenstrasse 74
D-20148 Hamburg
Website: www.buehnengenossenschaft.de
e-mail: gdba@buehnengenossenschaft.de
Fax: 00 49 40 45 93 52   Tel: 00 49 40 44 51 85

■ GREECE
HELLENIC ACTORS' UNION - HAU
33 Kaniggos Street
GR-106 82 Athens
Website: www.sei.gr
e-mail: sei@greektour.com
Fax: 00 30 10 380 8651   Tel: 00 30 10 383 3742

■ GREECE
UNION OF GREEK SINGERS - UGS
130 Patission Street, GR-112 57 Athens
Fax: 00 30 10 823 8321   Tel: 00 30 10 823 8335/6

■ IRELAND
SIPTU-IRISH ACTORS' EQUITY GROUP
Liberty Hall, Dublin 1
Website: www.siptu.ie
e-mail: equity@siptu.ie
Fax: 00 353 1 874 3691   Tel: 00 353 1 858 6403

■ ITALY
SAI
Sindicato Atton Itaiani
Via Ofanto 18, I-00198 Rome
Website: www.cgil.it/sai-slc
e-mail: sai-slc@cgil.it
Fax: 00 39 06 854 6780   Tel: 00 39 06 841 7303/1288

■ LUXEMBOURG
OGB-L
Onofhangege Gewerkschaftsbond Letzeburg
19 rue d'Epernay, B.P. 2031, L-1020 Luxembourg
Website: www.ogb-l.lu
e-mail: joel.jung@ogb-l.lu
Fax: 00 352 486 949   Tel: 00 352 496 005 Ext 213

■ NETHERLANDS
FNV KIEM
Kunsten Informatie en Media
Postbus 9354, NL-1006 AJ Amsterdam
Website: www.fnv-kiem.nl
e-mail: fnvkiem@worldonline.nl
Fax: 00 31 20 355 3737   Tel: 00 31 20 355 3636

■ NORWAY
NSF
Norsk Skuespillerforbund
Welhavensgate 3, N-0166 Oslo
Website: www.skuespillerforbund.no
e-mail: nsf@skuespillerforbund.no
Fax: 00 47 21 02 71 91   Tel: 00 47 21 02 71 90

■ PORTUGAL
STE
Sindicato dos Trabalhadores de Espectaculos
Rue Da Fe 23, 2 do Piso, P-1050 Lisbon
e-mail: sind.trab.espect@mail.telepac.pt
Fax: 00 351 21 885 3787   Tel: 00 351 21 885 2728

■ SPAIN
CC.OO.
Plaza Cristino Martos 4, 6a Planta, E-28015, Madrid
e-mail: international.fct@fct.ccoo.es
Fax: 00 34 91 548 1613   Tel: 00 34 91 540 9295/37

■ SPAIN
FAEE
Federation de Actores del Estado Espanol
C/Montera 34, do Piso, E-28013 Madrid
e-mail: fedactors@retemail.es
Fax: 00 34 91 522 6055   Tel: 00 34 91 522 2804

■ SWEDEN
TF TEATERFORBUNDET
Box 12 710, S-112 94 Stockholm
e-mail: info@teaterforbundet.se
Fax: 00 46 8 653 9507   Tel: 00 46 8 441 1300

■ UK
EQUITY
Guild House
Upper St Martin's Lane, London WC2H 9EG
Website: www.equity.org.uk
e-mail: info@equity.org.uk
Fax: 020-7379 7001   Tel: 020-7379 6000

ALDEBURGH FESTIVAL OF MUSIC AND THE ARTS
(6 - 22 June 2003)
Aldeburgh Productions
Snape Maltings Concert Hall
Snape Bridge, Nr Saxmundham, Suffolk, IP17 1SP
Website: www.aldeburgh.co.uk
e-mail: enquiries@aldeburghfestivals.org
Fax: 01728 687120   Admin: 01728 687100
BO: 01728 687110

ALMEIDA OPERA
(July 2003)
Almeida Street, Islington, London, N1 1TA
Website: www.almeida.co.uk
e-mail: pdickie@almeida.co.uk
Fax: 020-7704 9581   Tel: 020-7226 7432

BARBICAN INTERNATIONAL THEATRE EVENT (BITE)
Barbican Theatre, Silk Street, London, EC2Y 8DS
Website: www.barbican.org.uk
e-mail: gyorke@barbican.org.uk
Fax: 020-7382 7377   Tel: 020-7382 7315

BATH INTERNATIONAL MUSIC FESTIVAL
(16 May - 1 June 2003)
Bath Festivals Trust, 5 Broad Street, Bath, BA1 5LJ
Website: www.bathfestivals.org.uk
e-mail: info@bathfestivals.org.uk
Fax: 01225 445551   Tel: 01225 462231

BATH LITERATURE FESTIVAL
(3 - 11 March 2003)
Bath Festivals Trust, 5 Broad Street, Bath, BA1 5LJ
Website: www.bathfestivals.org.uk
e-mail: info@bathfestivals.org.uk
Fax: 01225 445551   Tel: 01225 462231

BELFAST FESTIVAL AT QUEEN'S
(25 Oct - 10 Nov 2002) (31 Oct - 16 Nov 2003)
25 College Gardens, Belfast, BT9 6BS
Website: www.belfastfestival.com
e-mail: festival@qub.ac.uk
Fax: 028-9066 3733   Tel: 028-9066 7687

BRIGHTON FESTIVAL
(3 - 25 May 2003)
12A Pavilion Buildings
Castle Square, Brighton, BN1 1EE
General Manager: Jane McMorrow
BO: 01273 709709   Admin: 01273 700747

BUXTON FESTIVAL
(8 - 20 July 2003)
5 The Square, Buxton, Derbyshire, SK17 6AZ
Website: www.buxtonfestival.co.uk
e-mail: info@buxtonfestival.co.uk
BO: 08451 272190   Admin: 01298 70395

CHESTER SUMMER MUSIC FESTIVAL
(July 2003)
8 Abbey Square, Chester, CH1 2HU
Contact: Fiona England
Website: www.chesterfestivals.co.uk
BO: 01244 320700

CHICHESTER FESTIVITIES (Not Chichester Festival Theatre)
(July 2003)
Canon Gate House
South Street, Chichester, West Sussex, PO19 1PU
Fax: 01243 528356   Tel: 01243 785718

DANCE UMBRELLA
(Oct - Nov 2003)
Annual Contemporary Dance Festival
20 Chancellor's Street, London, W6 9RN
Website: www.danceumbrella.co.uk
e-mail: mail@danceumbrella.co.uk
Fax: 020-8741 7902   Tel: 020-8741 4040

DUBLIN THEATRE FESTIVAL
(30 Sept - 12 Oct 2003)
44 East Essex Street, Temple Bar, Dublin 2, Ireland,
Contact: Fergus D. Linehan
e-mail: info@dublintheatrefestival.com
Website: www.dublin/theatrefestival.com
Fax: 00 353 1 6797709   Tel: 00 353 1 6778439

EDINBURGH FESTIVAL FRINGE
(3 - 25 Aug 2003)
Festival Fringe Society Ltd
180 High Street, Edinburgh, EH1 1QS
Website: www.eif.co.uk
e-mail: admin@edfringe.com
Fax: 0131-226 0016   Tel: 0131-226 0026

EDINBURGH INTERNATIONAL FESTIVAL
(10 - 30 Aug 2003)
The Hub, Castlehill, Edinburgh, EH1 2NE
Website: www.eif.co.uk
e-mail: eif@eif.co.uk
Admin: 0131-437 2099   Tickets: 0131-473 2000

GLYNDEBOURNE FESTIVAL OPERA
(End May - End Aug 2003)
Lewes, East Sussex, BN8 5UU
Website: www.glyndebourne.com
e-mail: info@glyndebourne.com
Manager: 01273 812321   Information: 01273 815000
Fax: 01273 812783

GREENWICH - DOCKLANDS FESTIVALS
(5 - 13 July 2003)
6 College Approach, Greenwich, London, SE10 9HY
Website: www.festival.org.uk
e-mail: info@festival.org
Fax: 020-8305 1188   Tel: 020-8305 1818

HARROGATE INTERNATIONAL FESTIVAL
(17 July - 2 August 2003)
1 Victoria Avenue, Harrogate, North Yorkshire, HG1 1EQ
Website: www.harrogate-festival.org.uk
e-mail: info@harrogate-festival.org.uk
Fax: 01423 521264   Tel: 01423 562303

INTERNATIONAL FESTIVAL OF MUSICAL THEATRE IN CARDIFF The
St David's House, Wood Street, Cardiff, CF10 1ES
Website: www.cardiffmusicals.com
e-mail: enquiries@cardiffmusicals.com
Fax: 029-2040 4216   Tel: 029-2090 1111

KING'S LYNN FESTIVAL
(24 July - 2 August 2003)
5 Thoresby College
Queen Street, King's Lynn, Norfolk, PE30 1HX
Website: www.kl-festival.freeserve.co.uk
Fax: 01553 767688   Tel: 01553 767557

LIFT - LONDON INTERNATIONAL FESTIVAL OF THEATRE
(Throughout Year)
19-20 Great Sutton Street, London, EC1V 0DR
Website: www.lift-info.co.uk
e-mail: info@liftfest.org.uk
Fax: 020-7490 3976   Tel: 020-7490 3964

LLANDOVERY ARTS FESTIVAL
(July 2003)
Llandovery Theatre, Stone Street
Llandovery, Carmarthenshire, SA20 0DQ
Artistic Directors: Simon Barnes, Jaqueline Harrison
Tel: 01550 720113

LONDON NEW PLAY FESTIVAL
(April - May 2003)
45 Lakeside Road, London, W1Y 0DX
Administrator: Chris Cooke
Tel: 07973 337642

LUDLOW FESTIVAL SOCIETY Ltd
(21 June - 6 July 2003)
Festival Office, Castle Square, Ludlow, Shrops, SY8 1AY
Admin: 01584 875070
Fax: 01584 877673   BO: 01584 872150

NATIONAL STUDENT DRAMA FESTIVAL
(9 - 16 April 2003, Scarborough)
Information Office, University of Hull Campus
Filey Road, Scarborough, YO11 3AZ
Artistic Director: Nick Stimson
Website: www.nsdf.org.uk
e-mail: info@nsdf.org.uk
Fax: 01723 370815   Tel: 01723 501106

VISIONS - 2002 FESTIVAL OF VISUAL PERFORMANCE
(24 Oct 2002 - 2 Nov 2002)
(Festival is Biennial)
University of Brighton & Sallis Benney Theatre,
Grand Parade, Brighton, BN2 0JY
Director: Linda Lewis
e-mail: visions.fest@bton.ac.uk
Fax: 01273 643038   Tel: 01273 643194

Film & Television Distributors

ASIAN PICTURES INTERNATIONAL Ltd
1st Floor, 587 High Road, London E11 4QS
e-mail: asianpics@bizmane.com
Fax: 020-8558 9891   Tel: 020-8539 6529

BLUE DOLPHIN FILM AND VIDEO
(Film Production/Video Distribution)
40 Langham Street, London W1N 5RG
Fax: 020-7580 7670   Tel: 020-7255 2494

CONTEMPORARY FILMS
24 Southwood Lawn Road, London N6 5SF
Website: www.contemporaryfilms.com
e-mail: inquiries@contemporaryfilms.com
Fax: 020-8348 1238   Tel: 020-8340 5715

FRAME BAR FRAME
(Short Film Distributors and Promoters)
1st Floor, 7-11 French Place
Shoreditch, London E1 6JB
Website: www.framebarframe.com
                          Tel/Fax: 020-7729 1736

GUERILLA FILMS Ltd
35 Thornbury Road, Isleworth, Middlesex TW7 4LQ
Website: www.guerilla-films.com
e-mail: david@guerilla-films.com
Fax: 020-8758 9364   Tel: 020-8758 1716

HIGH POINT FILMS & TV
(International sales)
25 Elizabeth Mews, London NW3 4UH
Website: www.highpointfilms.co.uk
e-mail: sales@highpointfilms.co.uk
Fax: 020-7586 3117   Tel: 020-7586 3686

JACKSON Brian FILMS Ltd
39 Hanover Steps
St George's Fields, Albion Street, London W2 2YG
e-mail: brianjfilm@aol.com
Fax: 020-7262 5736   Tel: 020-7402 7543

PAN EUROPEAN FILMS
110 Trafalgar Road, Portslade, Sussex BN41 1GS
Website: www.filmangel.co.uk
e-mail: filmangels@freenetname.co.uk
Fax: 01273 705451   Tel: 01273 277333

PATHE DISTRIBUTION Ltd
Kent House, 14-17 Market Place
Great Titchfield Street, London W1W 8AR
Website: www.pathe.co.uk
Fax: 020-7631 3568   Tel: 020-7323 5151

SONY PICTURES EUROPE HOUSE
25 Golden Square, London W1F 9LU
Fax: 020-7533 1015   Tel: 020-7533 1000

SOUTHERN STAR SALES
, 45-49 Mortimer Street, London W1W 8HX
Fax: 020-7436 7426   Tel: 020-7636 9421

SQUIRREL FILMS DISTRIBUTION Ltd
Grice's Wharf
119 Rotherhithe Street, London SE16 4NF
Website: www.sandsfilms.co.uk
Fax: 020-7231 2119   Tel: 020-7231 2209

UIP (UK)
12 Golden Square, London W1A 2JL
Fax: 020-7534 5202   Tel: 020-7534 5200

UNIVERSAL INTERNATIONAL TELEVISION SEVICES Ltd
5-7 Mandeville Place
London W1U 3AR   Tel: 020-7535 3700

UNIVERSAL PICTURES INTERNATIONAL
Oxford House, 76 Oxford Street, London W1D 1BS
Fax: 020-7307 1301   Tel: 020-7307 1300

WARNER BROS PICTURES
Warner House
98 Theobald's Road, London WC1X 8WB
Fax: 020-7984 5001   Tel: 020-7984 5200

Film Preview Theatres

ACCESS STUDIOS
8-10 Creekside, London SE8 3DX
Website: www.accessstudios.com
e-mail: info@accessstudios.com
Fax: 0870 120 5658   Tel: 020-7231 6185

BRITISH ACADEMY OF FILM & TELEVISION ARTS The
195 Piccadilly, London W1J 9LN
Fax: 020-7734 1792   Tel: 020-7734 0022

BRITISH FILM INSTITUTE
21 Stephen Street, London W1P 2LN
e-mail: roger.young@bfi.org.uk
Fax: 020-7436 7950   Tel: 020-7957 8976

CENTURY THEATRE
(Twentieth Century Fox)
31 Soho Square, London W1D 3AP
e-mail: projection@foxinc.com   Tel: 020-7437 7766

COLUMBIA TRI STAR FILMS (UK)
25 Golden Square, London W1F 9LU
Fax: 020-7533 1015   Tel: 020-7533 1111

DE LANE LEA
75 Dean Street, London W1D 3PU
Website: www.delanelea.com
e-mail: dll@delanelea.com
Fax: 020-7432 3838   Tel: 020-7432 3800

EXECUTIVE THEATRE
(Twentieth Century Fox)
31 Soho Square, London W1D 3AP
e-mail: projection@foxinc.com   Tel: 020-7437 7766

MR YOUNG'S PREVIEW THEATRE
14 D'Arblay Street, London W1F 8DY
Fax: 020-7734 4520   Tel: 020-7437 1771

RIVERSIDE STUDIOS
Crisp Road, London W6 9RL
Website: www.riversidestudios.co.uk
                          Tel: 020-8237 1000

RSA
(Royal Society of Arts)
8 John Adam Street, London WC2N 6EZ
Website: www.theplacetomeet.org.uk
e-mail: conference@rsa.org.uk
Fax: 020-7321 0271   Tel: 020-7839 5049

TRICYCLE CINEMA
269 Kilburn High Road, London NW6 7JR
Website: www.tricycle.co.uk
e-mail: admin@tricycle.co.uk
                          Tel: 020-7328 1000

4MC Ltd
(Post-Production Facilities)
Film House, 142 Wardour Street, London W1V 3AU
Fax: 020-7878 7800   Tel: 020-7878 0000

AC ARTS VIDEO PRODUCTION & EQUIPMENT HIRE
(Showreels, CV-CD Roms & Websites)
Studio B5R Metropolitan Wharf
Wapping Wall, London E1W 3SS
Website: www.ac-arts.co.uk
e-mail: admin@ac-arts.co.uk
                              Tel/Fax: 020-7488 0416

ACTOR'S 'ONE-STOP' SHOP The
(Showreels, Photographs, CVs & Actors' Websites)
54 Belsize Avenue, London N13 4TJ
Website: www.actorsone-stopshop.com
e-mail: info@actorsone-stopshop.com
Fax: 020-8482 7723   Tel: 020-8888 7006

ANVIL POST PRODUCTION
(Studio Manager - Mike Anscombe)
Denham Studios, North Orbital Road
Uxbridge, Middlesex UB9 5HL
Fax: 01895 835006   Tel: 01895 833522

ARK STUDIO Ltd
(Stills - Studio & Location)
Unit 5, 9 Park Hill, London SW4 9NS
e-mail: info@arkstudio.co.uk
Fax: 020-7498 9497   Tel: 020 7622 4000

ARRI MEDIA
4-5 Airlinks, Spitfire Way
Heston, Middlesex TW5 9NR
Website: www.arrimedia.com
e-mail: info@arrimedia.com
Fax: 020-8756 0592   Tel: 020-8573 2255

AUTOMATIVE ACTION STUNTS
(Stunt Rigging & Supplies/Camera Tracking Vehicles)
2 Sheffield House, Park Road
Hampton Hill, Middlesex TW12 1HA
Website: www.carstunts.co.uk
Mobile: 07974 919589   Tel: 020-8977 6186

AXIS FILMS
(Film Equipment Rental)
Shepperton Studios
Studios Road, Middlesex TW17 0QD
Website: www.axisfilms.co.uk
e-mail: info@axisfilms.co.uk
Fax: 01932 592246   Tel: 01932 592244

CHANNEL 20/20 Ltd
Flint House
91-93 Gray's Inn Road, London WC1X 8TX
Fax: 020-7242 4386   Tel: 020-7242 4328

CINE TO VIDEO & FOREIGN TAPE CONVERSION & DUPLICATING
(Peter J Snell Enterprises)
Amp House, Grove Road
Rochester, Kent ME2 4BX
e-mail: pjs-ent@dircon.co.uk
Fax: 01634 726000   Tel: 01634 723838

CLEAR CUT VIDEO EDITING & FILMING
(Peter J Snell Enterprises)
Amp House, Grove Road
Rochester, Kent ME2 4BX
e-mail: pjs-ent@dircon.co.uk
Fax: 01634 726000   Tel: 01634 723838

CONTACT GROUP Ltd
(Conference, Computer Graphic & Video Producers)
Oakridge, Weston Road, Stafford ST16 3RS
e-mail: mail@contactgroup.co.uk
Fax: 01785 610955   Tel: 01785 610966

CREATIVE FILM MAKERS Ltd
(Studio & Video Editing)
Pottery Lane House
34A Pottery Lane, London W11 4LZ
Fax: 020-7229 4999   Tel: 020-7229 5131

CURIOUS YELLOW Ltd
33-37 Hatherley Mews, London, E17 4QP
e-mail: info@curiousyellow.co.uk
Fax: 020-8521 6363   Tel: 020-8521 9595

DE LANE LEA
(Film & TV Sound Dubbing & Editing Suite)
75 Dean Street, London W1D 3PU
Website: www.delanelea.com
e-mail: dll@delanelea.com
Fax: 020-7432 3838   Tel: 020-7432 3800

DENMAN PRODUCTIONS
(3D Computer Animation, Film/Video CD Business
Card Showreels)
5 Holly Road, Twickenham, Middlesex TW1 4EA
Website: www.denman.co.uk
e-mail: info@denman.co.uk   Tel: 020-8891 3461

DIVERSE PRODUCTIONS
(Pre and Post-Production)
6 Gorleston Street, London W14 8XS
Fax: 020-7603 2148   Tel: 020-7603 4567

EXECUTIVE AUDIO VISUAL
(Showreels for Actors & TV Presenters)
80 York Street
London W1H 1QW   Tel: 020-7723 4488

FOUR WHEEL FILMS
(Crews & Equipment, Full Beta SP Kit)
PO Box 1054
Kingston-upon-Thames, Surrey KT2 5YR
e-mail: david@fwfilms.freeserve.co.uk
Fax: 020-8715 5014   Tel: 020-8715 4861

GREENPARK PRODUCTIONS Ltd
(Film Archives)
Illand, Launceston, Cornwall PL15 7LS
e-mail: archives@clips.net
Fax: 01566 782127   Tel: 01566 782107

HULK PRODUCTIONS
(TV Showreels)
PO Box 35762, London E14 8WG
Website: www.hulkproductions.com
e-mail: hulkproductions@aol.com
Fax: 0870 4601686   Mobile: 07970 279277

HUNKY DORY PRODUCTIONS Ltd
(Facilities & Crew)
Cambridge House, 135 High Street
Teddington, Middlesex TW11 8HH
Fax: 020-8977 4464   Tel: 020-8943 3006

INTERACTIVE SHOWREELS
(Showreels & Production)
410 Crown House
North Circular Road, London NW10 7PN
e-mail: interactiveshowreels@btinternet.com
Mobile: 07966 460235   Tel: 020-8838 6800

KINGSTON INMEDIA
Studio K, PO Box 2287
Gerrards Cross, Bucks SL9 8BF
Fax: 01494 876006   Tel: 01494 878297

LENIHAN Sean ASSOCIATES
The Old Chapel, Abbey Hill
Lelant, St Ives
Cornwall TR26 3EB   Tel/Fax: 01736 757557

MAGPIE FILM PRODUCTIONS
31-32 Cheapside, Birmingham B5 6AY
Fax: 0121-666 6077   Tel: 0121-622 5884

MINAMON PRODUCTIONS
(Specialist in Showreels)
117 Downton Avenue, London SW2 3TX
e-mail: minamon.film@virgin.net
Fax: 020-8674 1779   Tel: 020-8674 3957

MOVING PICTURE COMPANY The
(Post-Production)
127-133 Wardour Street, London W1F 0NL
Website: www.moving-picture.com
e-mail: mailbox@moving-picture.com
Fax: 020-7287 5187   Tel: 020-7434 3100

PANAVISION UK
Bristol Road, Greenford, Middlesex UB6 8GD
Fax: 020-8839 7300   Tel: 020-8839 7333

PANTECHNICON
(Audio Visual, Video, Conference Production,
Design for Print)
90 Lots Road, London SW10 0QD
Website: www.pantechnicon.co.uk
e-mail: info@pantechnicon.co.uk
Fax: 020-7351 0667   Tel: 020-7351 7579

PEAK WHITE VIDEO
1 Latimer Road, Teddington, Middlesex TW11 8QA
Website: www.peakwhite.tv
Fax: 020-8977 8357   Tel: 020-8943 1922

PEDIGREE PUNKS
(Interactive CD-Rom & DVD Showreels)
49 Woolstone Road, Forest Hill, London SE23 2TR
Website: www.pedigree-punks.com
e-mail: info@pedigree-punks.com
                          Tel/Fax: 020-8291 5801

PHA CASTING STUDIO
Tanzaro House
Ardwick Green North, Manchester M12 6FZ
Website: www.pha-agency.co.uk
e-mail: studio@pha-agency.co.uk
Fax: 0161-273 4567   Tel: 0161-273 4444

PRO-LINK RADIO SYSTEMS Ltd
(Radio Microphones and Communications)
4 Woden Court, Saxon Business Park
Hanbury Road
Bromsgrove, Worcestershire B60 4AD
Website: http://prolink-radio.com
e-mail: service@prolink-radio.com
Fax: 01527 577757   Tel: 01527 577788

QUADRANT TELEVISION LTD
17 West Hill, London SW18 1RB
Website: www.quadrant-tv.com
e-mail: quadranttv@aol.com   Tel: 020-8870 9933

REPLAY Ltd
(Showreels & Performance Recording)
20 Greek Street, London W1D 4DU
Website: www.replayfilms.co.uk
e-mail: sales@replayfilms.co.uk
Fax: 020-7287 5348   Tel: 020-7287 5334

REYNOLDS GEORGE F
(Videographer & Editor, Video Production)
12 Mead Close
Grays, Essex RM16 2TR
e-mail: g.f.reynolds@talk21.com   Tel: 01375 373886

RIVERSIDE STUDIOS
Crisp Road, London W6 9RL
Website: www.riversidestudios.co.uk
e-mail: info@riversidestudios.co.uk
Fax: 020-8237 1001   Tel: 020-8237 1000

SALON Ltd
(Post Production)
12 Swainson Road, London W3 7XB
Website: www.salonrentals.com
e-mail: hire@salonrentals.com   Tel: 020-8746 7611

SHOWREEL COMPANY The
28 Cleveland Avenue
2 Old Brompton Road, London W4 1SN
e-mail: the.showreelcompany@virgin.net
Tel: 020-8525 0058

SHOWREEL SERVICES
35 Bedfordbury
Covent Garden, London WC2N 4DU
Fax: 020-7379 5210   Tel: 020-7379 6082

SILVER-TONGUED PRODUCTONS
(Specialising in Voice Reels)
Website: www.silver-tongued.co.uk
e-mail: silver-tongued@talk21.com
Tel/Fax: 020-8309 0659

STAR PRODUCTIONS
(Facilities)
Star Studios, 38A Lea Bridge Road
London E5 9QD   Tel: 020-8986 4470

TAKE FIVE
(Showreels)
25 Ganton Street, London W1F 9BP
Website: www.takefivestudio.co.uk
Fax: 020-7287 3035   Tel: 020-7287 2120

TELE-CINE Ltd
(Post Production)
Video House, 48 Charlotte Street, London, W1T 2NS
Fax: 020-7208 2250   Tel: 020-7208 2200

TO BE OR NOT TO BE
(Showreels) (Anthony Barnett)
48 Northampton Road
Kettering, Northants NN15 7JU
Website: http://homepage.ntlworld.com/tobeornottobe
e-mail: tobeornottobe@ntlworld.com
Mobile: 07958 996227   Tel/Fax: 01536 359631

TODD AO UK
(Post Production Film Facilities)
13 Hawley Crescent, London NW1 8NP
Fax: 020-7485 3667   Tel: 020-7284 7900

TV MEDIA SERVICES Ltd
(Video and Broadcast Facilities)
3rd Floor, 420 Sauchiehall Street, Glasgow G2 3JD
e-mail: tvmsmail@aol.com
Fax: 0141-332 9040   Tel: 0141-331 1993

VFG
(Film & TV Equipment Hire)
8 Beresford Avenue, Wembley, Middlesex HA0 1LA
e-mail: info@vfg.co.uk
Fax: 020-8795 3366   Tel: 020-8795 7000

VIDEO CASTING DIRECTORY Ltd
(Production of Performers Showreels)
1 Triangle House
2 Broomhill Road, London, SW18 4HX
e-mail: simon@fightingfilms.com
Fax: 020-8874 8590   Tel: 020-8874 3314

VIDEO INN PRODUCTION
(AV Equipment Hire)
Glebe Farm, Wooton Road
Quinton, Northampton NN7 2EE
Website: www.videoinn.co.uk
e-mail: andy@videoinn.co.uk   Tel: 01604 864868

VIDEOSONICS CINEMA SOUND
(Film & Television Dubbing Facilities)
68A Delancey Street
London NW1 7RY
e-mail: info@videosonics.com
Fax: 020-7419 4470   Tel: 020-7209 0209

VOICE CASTER
(Digital Studio & Video Editing)   Tel: 020-8455 2211

VOICE CLINIC The
(Voice Over Demo's)
99 Cobbold Road, Willesden, London NW10
e-mail: voice_clinic@hotmail.com
Mobile: 07815 782305

VOICE TAPE SERVICES INTERNATIONAL Ltd
(Professional Voice-Over Direction & CDs)
80 Netherlands Road, New Barnet, Herts EN5 1BS
e-mail: info@vsint.co.uk
Fax: 020-8441 4828   Tel: 020-8440 4848

VSI
132 Cleveland Street, London W1T 6AB
Website: www.vsi.tv
e-mail: info@vsi.tv
Fax: 020-7692 7711   Tel: 020-7692 7700

W6 STUDIO
(Video Production & Editing Facilities)
359 Lillie Road, Fulham, London SW6 7PA
Website: www.w6studio.co.uk
e-mail: kaz@w6studio.freeserve.co.uk
Fax: 020-7381 5252   Tel: 020-7385 2272

WILD IRIS FILMS
59 Brewer Street, London W1R 3FB
e-mail: joe@wildiris.co.uk
Fax: 020-7494 1764   Tel: 020-7494 9230

30 BIRD PRODUCTIONS
138A Kingswood Road, Brixton, London SW2 4JL
e-mail: thirtybird.productions@virgin.net
Tel/Fax: 020-8678 7034

4MC
Film House, 142 Wardour Street, London W1V 3AU
Fax: 020-7878 7800   Tel: 020-7878 0000

ACADEMY COMMERCIALS Ltd
16 West Central Street, London WC1A 1JJ
Fax: 020-7240 0355   Tel: 020-7395 4155

ACTION TIME
35-38 Portman Square, London W1H 6NU
Website: www.action-time.com
e-mail: info@actiontime.co.uk
Fax: 020-7612 7524   Tel: 020-7486 6688

AGE FILM & VIDEO
F CV
Fyletts Barn, The Green
Hawstead, Bury St Edmunds
Suffolk INP 5NP   Tel: 01284 386629

AGRAN BARTON TV Ltd
(See HARBOUR PICTURES)

ALGERNON Ltd
15 Cleveland Mansions
Widley Road, London W9 2LA
e-mail: algernon_limited@hotmail.com
Fax: 0870 1388516   Tel/Fax: 020-7266 1582

ALIBI PRODUCTIONS Plc
35 Long Acre, London WC2E 9JT
Fax: 020-7379 70399   Tel: 020-7845 0420

ALOMO PRODUCTIONS Ltd
1 Stephen Street, London W1T 1AL
Website: www.fremantlemedia.com
Fax: 020-7691 6081   Tel: 020-7691 6531

AN ACQUIRED TASTE TV CORP
F TV D
51 Croham Road, South Croydon CR2 7HD
Fax: 020-8686 5928   Tel: 020-8686 1188

ANTELOPE
29B Montague Street, London WC1B 5BH
Website: www.antelope.co.uk
e-mail: antelope@antelope.co.uk
Fax: 020-7209 0098   Tel: 020-7209 0099

APT FILMS
225A Brecknock Road, London N19 5AA
Website: www.aptfilms.com
e-mail: admin@aptfilms.com
Fax: 020-7482 1587   Tel: 020-7284 1695

APTN
The Interchange, Oval Road
Camden Lock, London NW1 7DZ
Fax: 020-7413 8312   Tel: 020-7482 7400

ARENA FILMS Ltd
TV D
2 Pelham Road, London SW19 1SX
Fax: 020-8540 3992   Tel: 020-8543 3990

ARGYLE PRODUCTIONS
TV CV Radio, No Unsolicited CV's
St John's Buildings
43 Clerkenwell Road, London EC1M 5RS
Fax: 020-7608 1642   Tel: 020-7608 2095

ARLINGTON PRODUCTIONS Ltd
TV D Co
Cippenham Court, Cippenham Lane
Cippenham, Nr Slough, Berkshire SL1 5AU
Fax: 01753 691785   Tel: 01753 516767

ART BOX PRODUCTIONS
10 Heatherway, Crowthorne, Berks RG45 6HG
Website: www.tonyhart.nildram.co.uk
e-mail: artbox@nildram.co.uk   Tel/Fax: 01344 773638

ASF PRODUCTIONS Ltd
2 Teal Drive
Ducks Hill Road, Northwood, Middlesex HA6 2PT
e-mail: asfc@genmail.net
Fax: 01923 823310   Tel: 01923 829410

**ASHFORD ENTERTAINMENT
CORPORATION Ltd The**
182 Brighton Road, Coulsdon, Surrey CR5 2NF
Website: www.ashford-entertainment.co.uk
e-mail: info@ashford-entertainment.co.uk
Fax: 020-8763 2558   Tel: 020-8645 0667

ATLANTIC SEVEN PRODUCTIONS Ltd
52 Lancaster Road, London N4 4PR
Fax: 020-7436 9233   Tel: 020-7263 4435

ATP Ltd
TV Ch Docs D
PO Box 24182, London SW18 2WY
e-mail: atpmedia@ukonline.co.uk
Tel/Fax: 020-7738 9886

ATTENBOROUGH Richard PRODUCTIONS Ltd
Twickenham Film Studios
St Margaret's, Twickenham, Middlesex TW1 2AW
Fax: 020-8744 2766   Tel: 020-8607 8873

ATTICUS TELEVISION Ltd
5 Clare Lawn, London SW14 8BH
e-mail: attwiz@aol.com
Fax: 020-8878 3821   Tel: 020-8876 0406

AVALON TELEVISION Ltd
4A Exmoor Street, London W10 6BD
Fax: 020-7598 7281   Tel: 020-7598 7280

BAILEY Catherine Ltd
110 Gloucester Avenue
Primrose Hill, London NW1 8JA
Fax: 020-7483 4541   Tel: 020-7483 2681

BANANA PARK Ltd
(Animation Production Company)
Banana Park, 6 Cranleigh Mews, London SW11 2QL
Fax: 020-7738 1887   Tel: 020-7228 7136

BARFORD FILM COMPANY The
35 Bedfordbury, London WC2N 4DU
Website: www.barford.co.uk
e-mail: info@barford.co.uk
Fax: 020-7379 5210   Tel: 020-7836 1365

BARRATT Michael
Field House, Ascot Road
Maidenhead, Berks SL6 3LD
e-mail: mbarratt@compuserve
Fax: 01628 627737   Tel: 01628 770800

BBC WORLDWIDE Ltd
Woodlands, 80 Wood Lane, London W12 0TT
Fax: 020-8749 0538   Tel: 020-8433 2000

BETTAVISION TV
1 Mount Parade, Cockfosters, Herts EN4 9DD
Fax: 020-8449 8259   Tel: 020-8449 4898

BIRD Martin PRODUCTIONS
TV
Saucelands Barn, Coolham
Horsham, West Sussex RH13 8QG
Website: www.mbptv.com
e-mail: info@mbptv.com
Fax: 01403 741647   Tel: 01403 741620

BIZMANE ENTERTAINMENT Ltd
1st Floor, 787 High Road, London E11 4QS
e-mail: enquiries@bizmane.com
Fax: 020-8558 9891   Tel: 020-8558 4488

BLACK & WHITE PICTURES
Teddington Studios
Teddington, Middlesex TW11 9NT
e-mail: production@blackandwhitepictures.co.uk
Fax: 020-8614 2500   Tel: 020 8614 2344

BLACK CAT FILMS Ltd
(Write)
10-12 High Street, Great Wakering, Essex SS9 1BG
e-mail: mail@blackcatfilms.co.uk

F

BLACKBIRD PRODUCTIONS
6 Molasses Row
Plantation Wharf, Battersea, London SW11 3TW
Fax: 020-7924 4778   Tel: 020-7924 6440

BLUE FISH MEDIA
39 Ratby Close, Lower Earley, Reading RG6 4ER
Website: www.bfmedia.co.uk
e-mail: ideas@bfmedia.co.uk
Fax: 0118-962 0748   Tel: 0118-975 0272

BLUE ORANGE FILMS Ltd
88 Park Avenue South, London N8 8LS
e-mail: ruth@blueorangeltd.demon.co.uk
Fax: 020-8340 9889   Tel: 020-8341 9977

BLUE WAND PRODUCTIONS Ltd
2nd Floor, 12 Weltje Road, London W6 9TG
Website: www.bluewand.co.uk
e-mail: lino@bluewand.co.uk
Mobile: 07885 528743   Tel/Fax: 020-8741 2038

BLUELINE PRODUCTIONS Ltd
Fiord House
10 Reservoir Road, Ruislip, Middlesex HA4 7TU
e-mail: david@blue-line.tv
Fax: 01895 635060   Tel: 01895 635100

BOWE TENNANT PRODUCTIONS
(Specialists Animal Pet Productions)
Applewood House Studio, Ringshall Road
Dagnall, Berkhamsted, Herts HP4 1RN
Fax: 01442 842453   Tel: 01923 213008

BOXCLEVER PRODUCTIONS Ltd
13 Great James Street, London WC1N 3DN
e-mail: chevron@dircon.co.uk
Fax: 020-7831 6606   Tel: 020-7831 1811

BRIDGE LANE THEATRE COMPANY Ltd
(Film Production and Script Development)
The Studio, 49 Ossulton Way
London N2 0JY   Tel/Fax: 020-8444 0505

BRONCO FILMS
F TV D
The Producers' Centre
61 Holland Street, Glasgow G2 4NJ
Website: www.broncofilms.co.uk
e-mail: broncofilm@btinternet.com
Fax: 0141-287 6815   Tel: 0141-287 6817

BROOKSIDE PRODUCTIONS Ltd
TV
Campus Manor, Childwall
Abbey Road, Liverpool L16 0JP
Fax: 0151-722 6839   Tel: 0151-722 9122

BRUNSWICK FILMS Ltd
(Formula One Grand Prix Film Library)
26 Macroom Road, Maida Vale, London W9 3HY
e-mail: brunswick.films@virgin.net
Fax: 020-8960 4997   Tel: 020-8960 0066

BUCKMARK PRODUCTIONS
Commer House, Station Road
Tadcaster, North Yorks LS24 9JF
Website: www.buckmark.co.uk
e-mail: ed@buckmark.co.uk
Fax: 01937 835901   Tel: 01937 835900

BUENA VISTA PRODUCTIONS
3 Queen Caroline Street
Hammersmith, London W6 9PE
Fax: 020-8222 2795   Tel: 020-8222 1000

BURDER FILMS
37 Braidley Road
Meyrick Park, Bournemouth BH2 6JY
Website: www.johnburder.co.uk
e-mail: burderfilms@aol.com   Tel: 01202 295395

CALDERDALE TELEVISION
Dean Clough, Halifax HX3 5AX
e-mail: ctv@calderdaletv.co.uk
Fax: 01422 253101   Tel: 01422 253100

CARAVEL FILM TECHNIQUES Ltd
The Great Barn Studios
Cippenham Lane, Slough, Berks SL1 5AU
e-mail: ajjcaraveltv@aol.com
Fax: 01494 446662   Tel: 01753 534828

CARDINAL BROADCAST
Bishops Lodge
Oakley Green Road, Windsor, Berks SL4 5UL
Fax: 01753 623304   Tel: 01753 623300

CARLTON TELEVISION Ltd
35-38 Portman Square, London W1H 6NU
Fax: 020-7486 1132   Tel: 020-7486 6688

CARNIVAL (FILMS & THEATRE) Ltd
12 Raddington Road, London W10 5TG
Website: www.carnival-films.co.uk
Fax: 020-8968 0155   Tel: 020-8968 0968

CASE TV.COM
204 Mare Street
203-213 Mare Street, London E8 3QE
e-mail: case@casetv.com
Fax: 020-7296 0011   Tel: 020-7296 0010

CASPIAN PRODUCTIONS
15 Ogilvie Terrace, Edinburgh EH11 1NS
e-mail: caspian@blueyonder.co.uk
          Tel/Fax: 0131-346 0283

CELADOR PRODUCTIONS Ltd
39 Long Acre, London WC2E 9LG
Fax: 020-7845 9541   Tel: 020-7240 8101

CELTIC FILMS Ltd
21 Grafton Street, London W1S 4EU
e-mail: celticfilm@aol.com
Fax: 020-7409 2383   Tel: 020-7409 2080

CENTRELINE VIDEO PRODUCTIONS
138 Westwood Road, Tilehurst, Reading RG31 6LL
Website: www.centrelinevideo.com
          Tel: 0118-941 0033

CHAKRA PRODUCTIONS
181 Jersey Road, Osterley, Middlesex TW7 4QJ
Website: www.chakra.co.uk
e-mail: talk@chakra.co.uk
Fax: 020-8737 2987   Tel: 020-8737 1616

CHANNEL 20/20 Ltd
20/20 House, 26-28 Talbot Lane, Leicester LE1 4LR
Fax: 0116-222 1113   Tel: 0116-233 2220

CHATSWORTH TELEVISION Ltd
D Co
97-99 Dean Street, London W1D 3TE
Website: www.chatsworth-tv.co.uk
e-mail: television@chatsworth-tv.co.uk
Fax: 020-7437 3301   Tel: 020-7734 4302

CHILDREN'S FILM & TELEVISION FOUNDATION Ltd
F TV Ch
Elstree Film & TV Studios
Borehamwood, Herts WD6 1JG
e-mail: annahome@cftf.onyxnet.co.uk
Fax: 020-8207 0860   Tel: 020-8953 0844

CHX PRODUCTIONS Ltd
2nd Floor, Highgate Business Centre
33 Greenwood Place, London NW5 1LB
e-mail: firstname.surname@chxp.co.uk
Fax: 020-7428 3998   Tel: 020-7428 3999

CINEMA VERITY PRODUCTIONS Ltd
F TV D Co
11 Addison Avenue, London W11 4QS
Fax: 020-7371 3329   Tel: 020-7460 2777

CLARION TELEVISION
The 1929 Building, Merton Abbey Mills
Watermill Way, London SW10 2RD
Website: www.clariontv.com
e-mail: info@completelycreative.co.uk
Fax: 020-8540 0660   Tel: 020-8540 0110

CLASSIC PICTURES ENTERTAINMENT Ltd
Shepperton Studios, Studios Road
Shepperton, Middlesex TW17 0QD
e-mail: lyn@classicpictures.co.uk
Fax: 01932 592046   Tel: 01932 592016

Film, Radio, Television & Video Production Companies

COLLINGWOOD O'HARE ENTERTAINMENT Ltd
10-14 Crown Street, Acton, London W3 8SB
e-mail: info@crownstreet.co.uk
Fax: 020-8993 9595   Tel: 020-8993 3666

COMMUNICATOR Ltd
199 Upper Street, London N1 1RQ
e-mail: paul@communicator.ltd.uk
Fax: 020-7704 8444   Tel: 020-7704 8333

COMTEC Ltd
Unit 19, Tait Road, Croydon, Surrey CR0 2DP
Website: www.comtecav.co.uk
e-mail: info@comtecav.co.uk
Fax: 020-8684 6947   Tel: 020-8684 6615

CONTACT GROUP Ltd
(Conference Production)
Oakridge, Weston Road, Staffs ST16 3RS
Website: www.contactgroup.co.uk
e-mail: mail@contactgroup.co.uk
Fax: 01785 610955   Tel: 01785 610966

CONVERGENCE PRODUCTIONS Ltd
10-14 Crown Street, Acton, London W3 8SB
e-mail: info@crownstreet.co.uk
Fax: 020-8993 9595   Tel: 020-8993 3666

COURTYARD PRODUCTIONS
TV Ch Co
Little Postlings Farmhouse, Four Elms, Kent TN8 6NA
Fax: 01732 700534   Tel: 01732 700324

CREATIVE CHANNEL Ltd
The Television Centre
La Pouquelaye, St Helier, Jersey JE1 3ZD
e-mail: creative@channeltv.co.uk
Fax: 01534 816889   Tel: 01534 816888

CREATIVE FILM MAKERS Ltd
Pottery Lane House
34A Pottery Lane, London W11 4LZ
Fax: 020-7229 4999   Tel: 020-7229 5131

CREATIVE FILM PRODUCTIONS
68 Conway Road
London N14 7BE   Tel: 020-8447 8187

CREATIVE MEDIA
(Part of the ITM Group)
Latimer Square
White Lion Road, Amersham
Bucks HP7 9JQ   Tel: 020-8515 8252

CREATIVE PARTNERSHIP The
13 Bateman Street, London W1D 3AF
Website: www.creativepartnership.co.uk
Fax: 020-7437 1467   Tel: 020-7439 7762

CROFT TELEVISION & GRAPHICS
Croft House, Progress Business Centre
Whittle Parkway, Slough, Berks SL1 6DQ
Fax: 01628 668791   Tel: 01628 668735

CTVC
Hillside, Merry Hill Road, Bushey, Herts WD23 1DR
Website: www.ctvc.co.uk
e-mail: ctvc@ctvc.co.uk
Fax: 020-8950 1437   Tel: 020-8950 7919

CUTHBERT Tony PRODUCTIONS
7A Langley Street, London WC2H 9JA
Website: www.tonycuthbert.com
e-mail: info@tonycuthbert.com
Fax: 020-7734 6579   Tel: 020-7437 8884

DALTON FILMS Ltd
127 Hamilton Terrace, London NW8 9QR
Fax: 020-7624 4420   Tel: 020-7328 6109

DARLOW SMITHSON PRODUCTIONS Ltd
Fifth Floor, Highgate Business Centre
33 Greenwood Place, London NW5 1LB
e-mail: mail@darlowsmithson.com
Fax: 020-7482 7039   Tel: 020-7482 7027

DAWKINS ASSOCIATES Ltd
PO Box 615, Boughton Monchelsea, Kent ME17 4RN
e-mail: da@ccland.demon.co.uk
Fax: 01622 741731   Tel: 01622 741900

DAWSON FILMS
67 Hillfield Park, London N10 3QU
Fax: 020-8352 4708   Tel: 020-8444 6854

DIFFERENT FILMS
2 Searles Road, London SE1 4YU
Website: www.differentfilms.co.uk
e-mail: info@differentfilms.co.uk
Fax: 0845 4585791   Tel: 0845 4585790

DLT ENTERTAINMENT UK Ltd
10 Bedford Square, London WC1B 3RA
Fax: 020-7636 4571   Tel: 020-7631 1184

DRAGONFLY FILMS Ltd
King's Head Theatre,
115 Upper Street, London N1 1QN
e-mail: brian@dragonflyfilms.co.uk
          Tel: 020-7354 9259

DRAMA HOUSE The
Coach Road Cottages
Little Saxham, Bury St Edmunds, Suffolk IP29 5LE
Website: www.dramahouse.co.uk
e-mail: jack@dramahouse.co.uk
Tel: 01284 811425   Tel: 020-7586 1000

DRAMATIS PERSONAE Ltd
(Nathan Silver, Nicholas Kent)
19 Regency Street, London SW1P 4BY
e-mail: nathan.silver@ntlworld.com
          Tel: 020-7834 9300

DRUMBEAT PRODUCTIONS Ltd
17A Mercer Street, London WC2H 9QT
e-mail: tudorgates@compuserve.com
          Tel: 020-7836 3710

DUCK LANE FILM COMPANY The
5 Carlisle Street, London W1D 3BL
Fax: 020-7437 2260   Tel: 020-7439 3912

EACH WORLD PRODUCTIONS
43 Moormead Road
St Margaret's, Twickenham TW1 1JS
Fax: 020-8744 0676   Tel: 020-8892 0908

ECLIPSE PRESENTATIONS Ltd
3 Croydon Road, Beckenham, Kent BR3 4AA
e-mail: info@eclipse-presentations.co.uk
Fax: 020-8249 6485   Tel: 020-8249 6473

ECOSSE FILMS Ltd
Brigade House, 8 Parsons Green, London SW6 4TN
Website: www.ecossefilms.com
e-mail: info@ecossefilms.com
Fax: 020-7736 3436   Tel: 020-7371 0290

EDGE PICTURE COMPANY Ltd The
7 Langley Street, London WC2H 9JA
Website: www.edgepicture.com
e-mail: ask.us@edgepicture.com
Fax: 020-7836 6949   Tel: 020-7836 6262

EDINBURGH FILM PRODUCTIONS
Keeper's House, Traquair, Innerleithen EH44 6PP
Fax: 01896 831199   Tel: 01896 831188

EDUCATIONAL TRAINING FILMS
17 West Hill
London SW18 1RB   Tel: 020-8870 9933

ELEPHANT PRODUCTIONS
The Studio
2 Rothamsted Avenue, Harpenden, Herts AL5 2DB
Fax: 01582 767532   Tel: 01582 621425

ELMGATE PRODUCTIONS
F TV D
Shepperton Studios
Studios Road, Shepperton, Middlesex
e-mail: elmgate@dial.pipex.com
Fax: 01932 569918   Tel: 01932 562611

ENDEMOL PRODUCTIONS Ltd
(Formerly BAZAL PRODUCTIONS Ltd)
Shepherds Building Central
Charecroft, Shepherds Bush, London W14 0EE
Fax: 0870 3331800   Tel: 0870 3331700

ENLIGHTENMENT PRODUCTIONS
CV
1 Briars Lane, Lathom, Ormskirk, Lancs L40 5TG
Website: www.trainingmultimedia.co.uk
Tel: 01704 896655

EON PRODUCTIONS Ltd
Eon House, 138 Piccadilly, London W1V 9FH
Fax: 020-7408 1236   Tel: 020-7493 7953

EPA INTERNATIONAL MULTIMEDIA Ltd
31A Regent's Park Road, London NW1 7TL
Fax: 020-7267 8852   Tel: 020-7267 9198

EXCELSIOR GROUP PRODUCTIONS
Dorking Road, Tadworth, Surrey KT20 7TJ
Fax: 01737 813163   Tel: 01737 812673

FANTASY FILM COMPANY
74 Vivian Avenue
London NW4 3XG   Tel: 020-8202 4935

FARNHAM FILM COMPANY The
34 Burnt Hill Road, Lower Bourne, Farnham GU10 3LZ
Website: www.farnfilm.com
e-mail: info@farnfilm.com
Fax: 01252 725855   Tel: 01252 710313

FEELGOOD FICTION Ltd
49 Goldhawk Road, London W12 8QP
e-mail: feelgood@feelgoodfiction.co.uk
Fax: 020-8740 6177   Tel: 020-8746 2535

FESTIVAL FILM AND TELEVISION Ltd
Festival House, Tranquil Passage
Blackheath Village, London SE3 0BJ
e-mail: info@festivalfilm.com
Fax: 020-8297 1155   Tel: 020-8297 9999

FILM AND GENERAL PRODUCTIONS Ltd
4 Bradbrook House, Studio Place, London SW1X 8EL
Fax: 020-7245 9853   Tel: 020-7235 4495

FILMS OF RECORD Ltd
2 Elgin Avenue, London W9 3QP
e-mail: films@filmsofrecord.com
Fax: 020-7286 0444   Tel: 020-7286 0333

FIREDOG MOTION PICTURE CORPORATION Ltd The
182 Brighton Road, Coulsdon, Surrey CR5 2NF
Website: www.firedogfilms.co.uk
e-mail: info@firedogfilms.co.uk
Fax: 020-8763 2558   Tel: 020-8660 8663

FIRST CHOICE
F TV D
5 Angler's Lane, London NW5 3DG
Fax: 020-7267 5441   Tel: 020-7485 5000

FLASHBACK TELEVISION Ltd
11 Bowling Green Lane, London EC1R 0BG
Website: www.flashbacktv.com
e-mail: mailbox@flashbacktv.co.uk
Fax: 020-7490 5610   Tel: 020-7490 8996

FLICK FEATURES Ltd
15 Golden Square, London W1F 9JG
Fax: 020-7287 9495   Tel: 020-7734 7979

FLYING COLOURS FILM COMPANY The
11 Charlotte Mews, London W1T 4EQ
e-mail: fc@flyingc.co.uk
Fax: 020-7436 3055   Tel: 020-7436 2121

FLYING DOG PRODUCTIONS
29 Maiden Lane, Covent Garden
London WC2E 7JS   Tel: 020-7692 9203

FOCUS PRODUCTIONS Ltd
PO Box 173
Stratford-upon-Avon, Warwickshire CV37 7ZA
e-mail: maddern@focusproductions.co.uk
Fax: 01789 294845   Tel: 01789 298948

FORSTATER Mark PRODUCTIONS
27 Lonsdale Road, London NW6 6RA
Fax: 020-7624 1124   Tel: 020-7624 1123

FREEHAND PRODUCTIONS Ltd
33-37 Hatherley Mews
Hiltongrove Business Centre, London E17 4QP
Website: www.freehanduk.com
e-mail: freehanduk@yahoo.com
Tel/Fax: 020-8520 7777

FREEWAY FILMS
33A Pembroke Square
London W8 6PD   Tel: 020-7937 9114

FRONT PAGE & CHARISMA FILMS Ltd
Riverbank House, 1 Putney Bridge, London SW6 3JD
Fax: 020-7610 6836   Tel: 020-7610 6830

FUJI INTERNATIONAL PRODUCTIONS (UK) Ltd
2nd Floor, 29 Princes Street, London W1B 2ND
Fax: 020-7734 1197   Tel: 020-7734 8888

FULL WORKS The
Mill Studio, Crane Mead
Ware, Herts SG12 9PY   Tel: 01920 444399

FULMAR TELEVISION & FILM Ltd
Pascoe House
54 Bute Street, Cardiff Bay, Cardiff CF10 5AF
Fax: 029-2045 5111   Tel: 029-2045 5000

GALA PRODUCTIONS Ltd
25 Stamford Brook Road, London W6 0XJ
e-mail: info@galaproductions.co.uk
Fax: 020-8741 2323   Tel: 020-8741 4200

GAMMOND Stephen ASSOCIATES
24 Telegraph Lane, Claygate, Surrey KT10 0DU
e-mail: stephengammond@hotmail.com
Tel: 01372 460674

GARRETTS
F TV Commercials
21 Little Portland Street, London W1W 8BT
e-mail: commercials@garretts.co.uk
Fax: 020-7580 6453   Tel: 020-7580 6452

GATES Martin PRODUCTIONS Ltd
Upper Farm House
Taynton, Nr Burford, Oxon OX18 4UH
Fax: 01993 824471   Tel: 01993 824469

GATEWAY TELEVISION PRODUCTIONS
Gemini House, 10 Bradgate
Cuffley, Herts EN6 4RL   Tel: 01707 872054

GAU John PRODUCTIONS
15 St Albans Mansions
Kensington Court Place, London W8 5QH
e-mail: johngau@hotmail.com
Fax: 020-7938 1429   Tel: 020-7938 1398

GAY Noel TELEVISION Ltd
TV D Ch Co
Shepperton Studios
Studios Road, Shepperton, Middlesex TW17 0QD
e-mail: charles.armitage@virgin.net
Fax: 01932 592172   Tel: 01932 592569

GHA GROUP
1 Great Chapel Street, London W1F 8FA
Website: www.ghagroup.co.uk
e-mail: sales@ghagroup.co.uk
Fax: 020-7437 5880   Tel: 020-7439 8705

GLASS PAGE
27-29 Millstone Lane, Leicester LE1 5JN
Fax: 0116-233 6566   Tel: 0116-233 6565

GODMAN Colin PRODUCTIONS
TV D
41 Trelawney Road, Cotham
Bristol BS6 6DY   Tel: 0117-974 1058

GRADE COMPANY The
17 Albermarle Street, Mayfair, London W1S 4HP
Fax: 020-7408 2042   Tel: 020-7409 1925

GRANT NAYLOR PRODUCTIONS Ltd
Rooms 950-951 The David Lean Building
Shepperton Studios
Studios Road, Shepperton, Middlesex TW17 0QD
Fax: 01932 592484   Tel: 01932 592175

GREAT GUNS Ltd
43-45 Camden Road, London NW1 9LR
e-mail: greatguns@greatguns.com
Fax: 020-7692 4422   Tel: 020-7692 4444

GREENPOINT FILMS
F TV D
7 Denmark Street, London WC2H 8LZ
Fax: 020-7240 7088   Tel: 020-7240 7066

GROOVY MOVIES
(Video Production & Comedy Sketches)
The Dower House
Rocky Lane, Reigate, Surrey RH2 0TA
Website: www.groovymovies.co.uk
Tel/Fax: 01737 643731

GUERILLA FILMS Ltd
35 Thornbury Road, Isleworth, Middlesex TW7 4LQ
Website: www.guerilla-films.com
e-mail: david@guerilla-films.com
Fax: 020-8758 9364   Tel: 020-8758 1716

HAMMERWOOD FILM PRODUCERS & DISTRIBUTORS
110 Trafalgar Road, Portslade, Sussex BN41 1GS
Website: www.filmangel.co.uk
e-mail: ralph@hammerwood.fsnet.co.uk
Fax: 01273 705451   Tel: 01273 277333

HARBOUR PICTURES
11 Langton Street, London SW10 0JL
Website: www.harbourpictures.com
e-mail: info@harbourpictures.com
Fax: 020-7352 3528   Tel: 020-7351 7070

HARTSWOOD FILMS
Twickenham Studios, The Barons
St Margaret's, Twickenham, Middlesex TW1 2AW
Fax: 020-8607 8744   Tel: 020-8607 8736

HASAN SHAH FILMS Ltd
153 Burnham Towers
Adelaide Road, London NW3 3JN
Fax: 020-7483 0662   Tel: 020-7722 2419

HAT TRICK PRODUCTIONS Ltd
TV Co
10 Livonia Street, London W1F 8AF
Fax: 020-7287 9791   Tel: 020-7434 2451

HAWK EYE FILMS
Twickenham Film Studios, The Barons
St Margarets, Twickenham, Middlesex TW1 2AW
Fax: 020-8241 1907   Tel: 020-8607 8873

HEAD Sally PRODUCTIONS
Twickenham Film Studios, The Barons
St Margaret's, Twickenham, Middlesex TW1 2AW
e-mail: admin@shpl.demon.co.uk
Fax: 020-8607 8964   Tel: 020-8607 8730

HEAVY ENTERTAINMENT Ltd
222 Kensal Road, London W10 5BN
Website: www.heavy-entertainment.com
e-mail: info@heavy entertainment.com
Fax: 020-8960 9003   Tel: 020-8960 9001

HELIFILMS
The Cedars
Enborne Street, Enborne, Newbury, Berks RG20 0JS
Website: www.helifilms.com
e-mail: helifilms@msn.com
Fax: 01635 569298   Tel: 01635 569302

HENSON Jim COMPANY
30 Oval Road, Camden, London NW1 7DE
Website: www.henson.com
Fax: 020-7428 4001   Tel: 020-7428 4000

HEWETT Yvonne
Optimum Productions
32 Thames Eyot, Cross Deep
Twickenham TW1 4QL   Tel: 020-8892 1403

HINCHLIFFE Barrie PRODUCTIONS Ltd
Boston House, 36-38 Fitzroy Square, London W1T 9EY
Fax: 020-7631 0255   Tel: 020-7631 1470

HIT ENTERTAINMENT Plc
5th Floor, Maple House
149 Tottenham Court Road, London W1T 7NF
Website: www.hitentertainment.com
e-mail: creative@hitentertainment.com
Fax: 020-7388 9321   Tel: 020-7554 2500

HOBBS LIZ GROUP Ltd
68 Castlegate, Newark, Notts NG24 1BG
Website: www.lizhobbsgroup.com
e-mail: info@lizhobbsgroup.com
Fax: 0870 3337009   Tel: 08700 702702

HOLMES ASSOCIATES & OPEN ROAD FILMS
F TV D
The Studio, 37 Redington Road, London NW3 7QY
e-mail: holmesassociates@blueyonder.co.uk
Fax: 020-7916 9172   Tel: 020-7813 4333

HUDSON FILM Ltd
24 St Leonard's Terrace
London SW3 4QG   Tel/Fax: 020-7730 0002

HUNKY DORY PRODUCTIONS Ltd
TV D Co
Cambridge House, 135 High Street
Teddington, Middlesex TW11 8HH
Fax: 020-8977 4464   Tel: 020-8943 3006

HURLL Michael TELEVISION Ltd
3rd Floor, Beaumont House, Kensington Village
Avonmore Road, London W14 8TS
e-mail: london@uniquegroup.co.uk
Fax: 020-7605 1101   Tel: 020-7605 1100

IAMBIC PRODUCTIONS Ltd
1st Floor, 31 Eastcastle Street, London W1W 8DL
e-mail: team@iambicproductions.com
Fax: 020-7637 7084   Tel: 020-7436 1400

ICON FILMS Ltd
4 West End, Somerset Street, Bristol BS2 8NE
Fax: 0117-942 0386   Tel: 0117-924 8535

ILLUSTRA PRODUCTIONS Ltd
14 Bateman Street, London W1V 6EB
Fax: 020-7734 7143   Tel: 020-7437 9611

IMAGINE MEDIA COMMUNICATIONS Ltd
(Music & TV Production)
9-10 Jew Street, Brighton, East Sussex BN1 1UT
e-mail: marketing@imcproductions.com
Tel/Fax: 01273 883452   Tel: 01273 883543

IMMEDIA TELEVISION COMMUNICATIONS Ltd
Carlton Studios, Lenton Lane, Nottingham NG7 2NA
Website: www.immediagroup.co.uk
e-mail: info@immediagroup.co.uk
Fax: 0115-964 5502   Tel: 0115-964 5505

INFORMATION TRANSFER Ltd
CV (Training Video Packages)
Burleigh House
15 Newmarket Road, Cambridge CB5 8EG
Fax: 01223 310200   Tel: 01223 312227

INITIAL
Shepherds Building Central
Charecroft Way, Shepherds Bush, London W14 0EH
Website: www.endemoluk.com
Fax: 0870 3331800   Tel: 0870 3311700

INTERESTING TELEVISION Ltd
Oakslade Studios, Hatton, Warwick CV35 7LH
Fax: 01926 844045   Tel: 01926 844044

INVISION PRODUCTIONS
8 Barb Mews, London W6 7PA
Fax: 020-7371 2160   Tel: 020-7371 2123

ISIS PRODUCTIONS Ltd
106 Hammersmith Grove, London W6 7HB
e-mail: isis@isis-productions.com
Fax: 020-8748 3046   Tel: 020-8748 3042

ISSITT Erica ASSOCIATES Ltd
27 Sandilands Road, London SW6 2BD
e-mail: erikaissitt@clara.co.uk
Fax: 020-7371 9979   Tel: 020-7287 1080

JACKSON Brian FILMS Ltd
F TV Ch
39-41 Hanover Steps
St George's Fields, Albion Street, London W2 2YG
e-mail: brianjfilm@aol.com
Fax: 020-7262 5736   Tel: 020-7402 7543

JOLL Barrie ASSOCIATES Ltd
58 Frith Street
London W1V 5TA   Tel: 020-7437 9965

JUSTABOUT PRODUCTIONS
4 Northington Street, London WC1N 2JG
Website: www.justabout.tv
e-mail: info@justabout.tv
Fax: 020-7692 9080   Tel: 020-7916 6200

KAYE Tony & PARTNERS
33 Tottenham Street, London W1P 9PE
Fax: 020-7323 1711   Tel: 020-7025 7542
KICK SCREEN Ltd
13 D'Arblay Street, London W1F 8DX
e-mail: kick@thenet.demon.co.uk
Fax: 020-7437 0125   Tel: 020-7287 3757
KINGFISHER TELEVISION
Carlton Studios, Lenton Lane, Nottingham NG7 2NA
Fax: 0115-964 5263   Tel: 0115-964 5262
KNOWLES Dave FILMS
(Also Multimedia Interactive CD-Roms)
34 Ashleigh Close, Hythe SO45 3QP
Website: www.dkfilms.co.uk
e-mail: mail@dkfilms.co.uk
Fax: 023-8084 1600   Tel: 023-8084 2190
LANDSEER FILM & TELEVISION PRODUCTIONS Ltd
140 Royal College Street, London NW1 0TA
Website: www.landseerfilms.com
e-mail: mail@landseerfilms.com
Fax: 020-7485 7573   Tel: 020-7485 7333
LANGTON Jamie KELNAT PRODUCTIONS Ltd
9 Bushey Road, Ickenham Uxbridge
Middlesex UB10 8JP   Tel/Fax: 020-8582 1960
LARGE BEAST PRODUCTIONS Ltd
Unit 4B, The Coda Centre
189 Munster Road, London SW6 6AW
Website: www.largebeastproductions.com
e-mail: e-mail@largebeastproductions.com
Fax: 020-7386 0356   Tel: 020-7381 8228
LE PARK TV Ltd
Windmill Studios
49-51 York Road, Brentford, Middlesex TW8 0QP
Website: www.leparktv.com
e-mail: ian@leparktv.com
Fax: 020-8568 4151   Tel: 020-8568 5855
LENIHAN Sean ASSOCIATES
The Old Chapel, Abbey Hill, Lerant
St Ives, Cornwall TR26 3EB   Tel/Fax: 01736 757557
LIGHT DIVISION
11 Christchurch Gardens, Reading, Berks RG2 7AH
Fax: 0118-931 2123   Tel: 0118-931 3859
LINK ENTERTAINMENT Ltd
Colet Court
100 Hammersmith Road, London W6 7JP
Fax: 020-8762 6299   Tel: 020-8762 6200
LITTLE BIRD COMPANY Ltd
9 Grafton Mews, London W1T 5HZ
e-mail: info@littlebird.co.uk
Fax: 020-7380 3981   Tel: 020-7380 3980
LITTLE KING COMMUNICATIONS
The Studio, 2 Newport Road
Barnes, London SW13 9PE
Fax: 020-8653 2742   Tel: 020-8741 7658
LIVE IN FIVE PRODUCTIONS
14 Kingsmead Road, London SW2 3JB
Website: www.liveinfive.co.uk
e-mail: enquiries@liveinfive.co.uk
Fax: 020-8674 0543   Tel: 020-8674 5964
LONDON COLLEGE OF PRINTING
SCHOOL OF MEDIA
(Film & Video Division)
Media School, 10 Back Hill
Clerkenwell, London EC1R 5LQ
Fax: 020-7514 6848   Tel: 020-7514 6500
LONDON FILMS
71 South Audley Street, London W1K 1JA
Website: www.londonfilms.com
Fax: 020-7499 7994   Tel: 020-7499 7800
LONDON SCIENTIFIC FILMS
Mill Studio, Crane Mead, Ware
Herts SG12 9PY   Tel: 01920 444399

LOOKING GLASS FILMS Ltd
103 Brittany Point
Ethelred Estate, Kennington, London SE11 6UH
e-mail: lookingglassfilm@aol.com
                                 Tel/Fax: 020-7735 1363
LOOP COMMUNICATION AGENCY The
26 Portland Square, Bristol BS2 8RZ
e-mail: stephen.williams@theloopagency.com
Fax: 0117-311 2041   Tel: 0117-311 2040
LOYNES Geoff ANIMATION COMPANY
F TV Ch
Hornbrook Manor Farm House, Appledore Road
Woodchurch, Kent TN26 3TH   Tel: 01233 860252
MAGIC BOX MOTION PICTURES Ltd
Tan-y-Bryn, 51 Highdale Road
Clevedon, North Somerset BS21 7LR
e-mail: magicbox@blueyonder.co.uk
Fax: 01275 544913   Tel: 01275 544741
MAGPIE FILM PRODUCTIONS Ltd
31-32 Cheapside, Birmingham B5 6AY
Fax: 0121-666 6077   Tel: 0121-622 5884
MALLINSON TELEVISION PRODUCTIONS
(TV Commercials)
29 Lynedoch Street, Glasgow G3 6EF
e-mail: shoot@mtp.co.uk
Fax: 0141-332 6190   Tel: 0141-332 0589
MALONE GILL PRODUCTIONS Ltd
27 Campden Hill Road, London W8 7DX
e-mail: malonegill@aol.com
Fax: 020-7376 1727   Tel: 020-7937 0557
MANS Johnny PRODUCTIONS Ltd
PO Box 196, Hoddesdon, Herts EN10 7WG
Fax: 01992 470516   Tel: 01992 470907
MANSFIELD Mike TELEVISION Ltd
5th Floor, 41-42 Berners Street, London W1T 3NB
e-mail: mikemantv@aol.com
Fax: 020-7580 2582   Tel: 020-7580 2581
MANUEL Jo PRODUCTIONS Ltd
11 Keslake Road, London NW6 6DJ
e-mail: jomanuel@cwcom.net
Fax: 020-8933 5475   Tel: 020-8930 0777
MAP FILMS
3 Bourlet Close, London W1W 7BQ
e-mail: mail@mapfilms.com
Fax: 020-7291 7841   Tel: 020-7291 7840
MASON Bill FILMS Ltd
Orchard House, Dell Quay
Chichester, West Sussex PO20 7EE
e-mail: bill.mason@argonet.co.uk Tel: 01243 783558
MAVERICK TELEVISION
The Custard Factory
Gibb Street, Birmingham B9 4AA
e-mail: mail@mavericktv.co.uk
Fax: 0121-771 1550   Tel: 0121-771 1812
MAYA VISION INTERNATIONAL
43 New Oxford Street
London WC1A 1BH   Tel: 020-7836 1113
MELENDEZ FILMS
44 Newman Street
London W1T 1QJ   Tel/Fax: 020-7323 5373
MENTORN
43 Whitfield Street
London W1T 4HA
Fax: 020-7258 6888   Tel: 020-7258 6800
MERCHANT IVORY PRODUCTIONS
46 Lexington Street, London W1F 0LP
Website: www.merchantivory.com
e-mail: miplondon@merchantivory.demon.co.uk
Fax: 020-7734 1579   Tel: 020-7437 1200
MERSEY TELEVISION COMPANY Ltd The
TV
Campus Manor, Childwall
Abbey Road, Liverpool L16 0JP
Fax: 0151-722 6839   Tel: 0151-722 9122

British Film Commission

Promoting the UK as an international production centre to the film and television industries

Harry Potter   Kabhi Khushi Kabhie Gham   Lara Croft: Tomb Raider   Spy Game

If you are an international filmmaker contemplating shooting in the UK, please do not hesitate to contact us for further information:

British Film Commission	Tel:	020 7861 7860
10 Little Portland Street	Fax:	020 7861 7864
London	E-mail:	info@bfc.co.uk
W1W 7JG	Web:	www.bfc.co.uk

The British Film Commission is a division of FILM|COUNCIL

British Film Commission

bfc

MIGHTY MEDIA
Long Boyds House
PO Box 73, Bourne End, Bucks SL8 5FJ
Fax: 01628 526530   Tel: 01628 522002

MINAMON PRODUCTIONS
117 Downton Avenue, London SW2 3TX
e-mail: minamon.film@virgin.net
Fax: 020-8674 1779   Tel: 020-8674 3957

MODUS OPERANDI FILMS
10 Soho Square, London W1V 6NT
Fax: 020-7287 6852   Tel: 020-7434 1440

MOGUL CORPORATION The
60 Aubert Park, London N5 1TS
Fax: 020-7242 2860   Tel: 020-7242 2850

MOGUL TV Ltd
High Pines, Westwood Road, Windlesham
Surrey GU20 6LS   Tel/Fax: 01344 622140

MOONLIGHT COMMUNICATIONS Ltd
48 Vyse Street, Hockley, Birmingham B18 6HF
e-mail: norman.moonlight@btclick.com
Fax: 0121-551 6455   Tel: 0121-523 6221

MORE Alan FILMS
Pinewood Studios
Pinewood Road, Iver, Bucks SL0 0NH
e-mail: almorefilm@aol.com
Fax: 01753 650988   Tel: 01753 656789

MORNINGSIDE PRODUCTIONS INC.
8 Ilchester Place, London W14 8AA
Fax: 020-7602 1047   Tel: 020-7602 2382

MORRISON COMPANY The
302 Clive Court, Maida Vale, London W9 1SF
e-mail: don@morrisonco.com
Fax: 0870 1275065   Tel/Fax: 020-7289 7976

MOSAIC FILMS
The Old Butcher's Shop, St Briavels, Glos GL15 6TA
e-mail: info@mosaicfilms.com
Fax: 01594 530094   Tel: 01594 530708

MOUNTFORD John STUDIOS Ltd
(Radio Commercials & Video Production
Company)
3 Montagu Row, London W1U 6DY
Website: www.jmsradio.co.uk
e-mail: inbox@jmslondon.co.uk
Fax: 020-7224 4035   Tel: 020-7224 1031

Hethersett, Norwich, Norfolk NR9 3DL
e-mail: traffic@jmsradio.co.uk
Fax: 01603 812255   Tel: 01603 811855

MURPHY Patricia FILMS Ltd
40 Frith Street, London W1V 5TS
e-mail: patriciamurphyfilms@cwcom.net
Fax: 020-7388 7231   Tel: 020-7387 9449

MUSIC BOX Ltd
30 Sackville Street, London W1S 3DY
Fax: 020-7478 7403   Tel: 020-7478 7320

NEBRASKA PRODUCTIONS
12 Grove Avenue, London N10 2AR
e-mail: nebraskaprods@aol.com
Fax: 020-8444 2113   Tel: 020-8444 5317

NEWGATE COMPANY
(Radio)
13 Dafford Street, Larkhall, Bath
Somerset BA1 6SW   Tel: 01225 318335

NEXUS PRODUCTIONS Ltd
(Animation for Commercials & Pop Promos)
113-114 Shoreditch High Street, London E1 6JN
Website: www.nexuslondon.com
e-mail: info@nexuslondon.com
Fax: 020-7749 7501   Tel: 020-7749 7500

NUTOPIA FILMS
Number 8
132 Charing Cross Road, London WC2H 0LA
Website: www.nutopia.co.uk
          Tel/Fax: 020-8882 6299

ON COMMUNICATION/ON TV
(Work across all Media in Business Communications,
Museum Prods & Broadcast Docs)
5 East St Helen Street, Abingdon, Oxford OX14 5EG
Website: www.oncomms-tv.co.uk
e-mail: on@oncomms-tv.co.uk
Fax: 01235 530581   Tel: 01235 537400

ON SCREEN PRODUCTIONS Ltd
39 Cardiff Road, Llandaff, Cardiff CF5 2DT
Website: www.onscreenproductions.co.uk
e-mail: action@onscreenproductions.co.uk
Fax: 029-2057 8496   Tel: 029-2056 7593

OPEN MIND PRODUCTIONS
6 Newburgh Street, London W1F 7RQ
e-mail: imogen.robertson@openmind.co.uk
Fax: 020-7434 9256   Tel: 020-7437 0624

OPEN SHUTTER PRODUCTIONS Ltd
100 Kings Road, Windsor
Berks SL4 2AP   Tel/Fax: 01753 841309

**ORCHARD COMMUNICATIONS DESIGN GROUP
Ltd The**
(Interactive Multimedia Production)
Langler House, Market Place
Somerton, Somerset TA11 7LZ
e-mail: lesley@orchardcdg.co.uk
Fax: 01458 274590   Tel: 01458 274589

ORIGINAL FILM & VIDEO PRODUCTIONS Ltd
84 St Dionis Road, London SW6 4TU
e-mail: original.films@btinternet.com
Fax: 020-7731 0027   Tel: 020-7731 0012

OSBORN Peter PRODUCTION Ltd
Square Red Studio
249-251 Kensal Road, London W10 5DB
e-mail: peter@peterosborn.net
Fax: 020-8960 7285   Tel: 020-8960 6069

OVC MEDIA Ltd
88 Berkeley Court, Baker Street, London NW1 5ND
Website: www.ovcmedia.com
e-mail: eliot@ovcmedia.co.uk
Fax: 020-7723 3064   Tel: 020-7402 9111

P4 FILMS
Cheltenham Film Studio
Hatherley Lane, Cheltenham GL51 6PN
Website: www.p4films.com
e-mail: info@p4films.com   Tel/Fax: 01453 872743

PALIN Barry ASSOCIATES
Unit 10, Princeton Court
55 Felsham Road, London SW15 1AZ
e-mail: mail@barrypalinassociates.com
Fax: 020-8785 0440   Tel: 020-8394 5660

PANDER PICTURES Ltd
182 Brighton Road, Coulsdon, Surrey CR5 2NF
Website: www.panderpictures.com
e-mail: info@panderpictures.com
Fax: 020-8763 2558   Tel: 020-8660 8663

PANTECHNICON
90 Lots Road, London SW10 0QD
e-mail: info@pantechnicon.co.uk
Fax: 020-7351 0667   Tel: 020-7351 7579

PAPER MOON PRODUCTIONS
Wychwood House, Burchetts Green Lane
Littlewick Green, Maidenhead, Berks SL6 3QW
e-mail: david@paper-moon.co.uk
Fax: 01628 825949   Tel: 01628 829819

PARADINE David PRODUCTIONS Ltd
1st Floor, 5 St Mary Abbot's Place
Kensington, London W8 6LS
Fax: 020-7602 0411   Tel: 020-7371 3111

PARALLAX INDEPENDENT Ltd
7 Denmark Street, London WC2H 8LZ
Fax: 020-7497 8062   Tel: 020-7836 1478

PARAMOUNT FILM SERVICES Ltd
UIP House, 45 Beadon Road, London W6 0EG
Fax: 020-8563 4266   Tel: 020-8563 4158

PARK VILLAGE Ltd
1 Park Village East, London NW1 7PX
e-mail: reception@parkvillage.co.uk
Fax: 020-7388 3051   Tel: 020-7387 8077

PARLIAMENTARY FILMS Ltd
11A Enterprise House
59-65 Upper Ground, London SE1 9PQ
Fax: 020-7827 9511   Tel: 020-7827 9514

PARTNERS IN PRODUCTION Ltd
Hillview, Hinders Lane, Huntley, Glos GL19 3EZ
Mobile: 07802 967369   Fax: 01452 830500

PASSION PICTURES Ltd
Animation
25-27 Riding House Street, London W1W 7DU
e-mail: info@passion-pictures.com
Fax: 020-7323 9030   Tel: 020-7323 9933

PATHE PICTURES Ltd
Kent House, 14-17 Market Place
Great Titchfield Street, London W1W 8AR
Website: www.pathe.co.uk
Fax: 020-7631 3568   Tel: 020-7323 5151

P.C.I. LIVE DESIGN
(Live Events, Live Design Exhibitions, Film & Video,
2D & 3D Design)
G4 Harbour Yard
Chelsea Harbour, London SW10 0XD
Fax: 020-7352 7906   Tel: 020-7544 7500

PEARSON TELEVISION
1 Stephen Street, London W1T 1AL
Fax: 020-7691 6100   Tel: 020-7691 6000

PICTURE PALACE FILMS Ltd
13 Egbert Street, London NW1 8LJ
Website: www.picturepalace.com
e-mail: info@picturepalace.com
Fax: 020-7586 9048   Tel: 020-7586 8763

PIER PRODUCTIONS Ltd
Lower Ground Floor
1 Marlborough Place, Brighton BN1 1TU
e-mail: pieradmin@mistral.co.uk
Fax: 01273 693658   Tel: 01273 691401

PIEREND PRODUCTIONS
34 Fortis Green, London N2
e-mail: russell@pierend.fsnet.co.uk
                         Tel: 020-8444 0138

POKER Ltd
143B Whitehall Court
London SW1A 2EL   Tel/Fax: 020-7839 6070

POSITIVE IMAGE Ltd
25 Victoria Street, Windsor, Berks SL4 1HE
Fax: 01753 830878   Tel: 01753 842248

PRETTY CLEVER PICTURES
Post 59, Shepperton Studios
Studios Road, Shepperton, Middlesex TW17 0QD
e-mail: pcpics@globalnet.co.uk
Fax: 01932 592454   Tel: 01932 592047

PRINCIPAL PICTURES Ltd
Picture House, 65 Hopton Street, London SE1 9LR
e-mail: pictures@principalmedia.com
Fax: 020-7928 9886   Tel: 020-7928 9287

PRODUCERS The
8 Berners Mews, London W1T 3AW
Website: www.theproducersfilms.co.uk
Fax: 020-7636 4099   Tel: 020-7636 4226

**PROFESSIONAL MEDICAL
COMMUNICATIONS Ltd**
Grosvenor House
1 High Street, Edgware
Middlesex HA8 7TA   Tel: 020-8381 1819

PROMENADE PRODUCTIONS Ltd
6 Russell Grove, London SW9 6HS
e-mail: promenadeproductions@msn.com
Fax: 020-7564 3026   Tel: 020-7582 9354

P.S.A. Ltd
52 The Downs, Altrincham WA14 2QJ
Fax: 0161-924 0022   Tel: 0161-924 0011

PURPLE FROG MEDIA Ltd
The Basement, 34 St Aubyns, Brighton BN3 2TD
e-mail: info@purplefrogmedia.com
Fax: 01273 775787   Tel: 01273 735475

PVA MANAGEMENT Ltd
Hallow Park, Hallow, Worcs WR2 6PG
e-mail: films@pva.co.uk
Fax: 01905 641842   Tel: 01905 640663

QUADRANT TELEVISION Ltd
17 West Hill, London SW18 1RB
Website: www.quadrant-tv.com
e-mail: quadranttv@aol.com   Tel: 020-8870 9933

QUADRILLION
The Old Barn, Kings Lane
Cookham Dean, Berks SL6 9AY
Website: www.quadrillion.tv
e-mail: enq@quadrillion.net
Fax: 01628 487523   Tel: 01628 487522

RAW CHARM Ltd
Ty Cefn, Rectory Road, Cardiff CF5 1QL
e-mail: pam@rawcharm.co.uk
Fax: 029-2066 8220   Tel: 029-2064 1511

READ Rodney
45 Richmond Road
Twickenham, Middlesex TW1 3AW
e-mail: rodney_read@hotmail.com
Fax: 020-8744 9603   Tel: 020-8891 2875

RECORDED PICTURE COMPANY Ltd
24-26 Hanway Street, London W1T 1UH
Fax: 020-7636 2261   Tel: 020-7636 2251

RED ROSE CHAIN
1 Fore Hamlet, Ipswich IP3 8AA
Website: www.redrosechain.co.uk
e-mail: info@redrosechain.co.uk   Tel: 01473 288886

REDWEATHER PRODUCTIONS
Easton Business Centre, Felix Road, Bristol BS5 0HE
Website: www.redweather.co.uk
e-mail: info@redweather.co.uk
Fax: 0117-941 5851   Tel: 0117-941 5854

REEL EDITING COMPANY The
65 Goldhawk Road, London W12 8EH
Fax: 020-8743 2345   Tel: 020-8743 5100

REEL THING Ltd The
182 Brighton Road, Coulsdon, Surrey CR5 2NF
Website: www.reelthing.tv
e-mail: info@reelthing.tv
Fax: 020-8763 2558   Tel: 020-8668 8188

REPLAY Ltd
20 Greek Street, London W1D 4DU
Website: www.replayfilms.co.uk
e-mail: sales@replayfilms.co.uk
Fax: 020-7287 5348   Tel: 020-7287 5334

RESOURCE BASE
Television Centre, Southampton SO14 0PZ
Website: www.resource-base.co.uk
e-mail: post@resource-base.co.uk
Fax: 023-8023 6816   Tel: 023-8023 6806

REUTERS TELEVISION
85 Fleet Street, London EC4P 4AJ
Fax: 020-7542 5401   Tel: 020-7250 1122

REVERE ENTERTAINMENT
91 Berwick Street, London W1F 0NE
Fax: 020-7292 8372   Tel: 020-7292 8370

RIVERSIDE STUDIOS
Crisp Road, London W6 9RL
e-mail: jonfawcett@riversidestudios.co.uk
Fax: 020-8237 1011   Tel: 020-8237 1000

RM ASSOCIATES
Shepherds West, Rockley Road
London W14 0DA   Tel: 020-7605 6600

ROCLIFFE
PO Box 37344, London N1 8YBP
Website: www.rocliffe.com
e-mail: info@rocliffe.com   Tel/Fax: 020-7688 0749

ROGERS Peter PRODUCTIONS Ltd
Pinewood Studios, Iver Heath
Bucks SL0 0NH   Tel: 01753 651700

ROGUE VIDEO
(Video Production)
297 Glyn Road, London E5 0JP
Website: www.roguevideo.com
e-mail: genevieve@roguevideo.com
Mobile: 07711 863573   Tel/Fax: 020-8533 3877

ROOKE Laurence PRODUCTIONS
14 Aspinall House, 155 New Park Road
London SW2 4EY   Tel: 020-8674 3128

ROSE HACKNEY BARBER Ltd
5-6 Kingly Street, London W1B 5PF
Fax: 020-7434 4102   Tel: 020-7439 6697

R.S.A. FILMS
42-44 Beak Street, London W1F 9RH
Fax: 020-7734 4978   Tel: 020-7437 7426

RUSSO Denis ASSOCIATES
F TV Animation
161 Clapham Road, London SW9 0PU
Fax: 020-7582 2725   Tel: 020-7582 9664

SAMUELSON PRODUCTIONS Ltd
13 Manette Street, London W1D 4AW
e-mail: samuelsonp@aol.com
Fax: 020-7439 4901   Tel: 020-7439 4900

SANDS FILMS
Grice's Wharf
119 Rotherhithe Street, London SE16 4NF
Website: www.sandsfilms.co.uk
Fax: 020-7231 2119   Tel: 020-7231 2209

SCALA PRODUCTIONS Ltd
15 Frith Street, London W1D 4RE
e-mail: scalaprods@aol.com
Fax: 020-7437 3248   Tel: 020-7734 7060

SCIMITAR FILMS Ltd
219 Kensington High Street, London W8 6BD
e-mail: winner@ftech.co.uk
Fax: 020-7602 9217   Tel: 020-7734 8385

SCREEN FIRST Ltd
The Studios, Funnells Farm
Down Street, Nutley, East Sussex TN22 3LG
e-mail: info@screenfirst.co.uk
Fax: 01825 713511   Tel: 01825 712034

SCREEN VENTURES
49 Goodge Street
London W1T 1TE   Tel: 020-7580 7448

SEDDON Julian FILMS Ltd
(Commercials)
51-53 Mount Pleasant, London WC1X 0AE
e-mail: julian@julianseddonfilms.com
Fax: 020-7405 3721   Tel: 020-7831 3033

SEPTEMBER FILMS Ltd
Glen House, 22 Glenthorne Road
Hammersmith, London W6 0NG
Fax: 020-8741 7214   Tel: 020-8563 9393

SHART BROS Ltd
52 Lancaster Road, London N4 4PR
Fax: 020-7436 9233   Tel: 020-7263 4435

SHELL FILM & VIDEO UNIT
F CV Docs
Shell Centre, York Road, London SE1 7NA
Fax: 020-7934 4095   Tel: 020-7934 3318

SIGHTLINE
(Videos, Commercials, CD-Rom, DVD, Websites)
Dylan House, Town End Street
Godalming, Surrey GU7 1BQ
Website: www.sightline.co.uk
e-mail: keith@sightline.co.uk
Fax: 01483 861516   Tel: 01483 861555

SILVER PRODUCTIONS Ltd
29 Castle Street, Salisbury, Wilts SP1 1TT
Fax: 01722 336227   Tel: 01722 336221

SIMAGE COMMUNICATIONS
Fulton House, Fulton Road
Wembley Park, Middlesex HA9 0TF
Website: www.simage-comms.co.uk
e-mail: simon@simage-comms.co.uk
Fax: 020-8584 0443   Tel: 020-8584 0444

SIMPLY TELEVISION Ltd
150 Great Portland Street, London W1W 6QD
Website: www.simplytelevision.com
Fax: 020-7307 6167   Tel: 020-7307 6109

SINDIBAD FILMS Ltd
5th Floor, 5 Princes Gate, London SW7 1QJ
Website: www.sindibad.co.uk
e-mail: sindibad@lineone.net
Fax: 020-7823 9137   Tel: 020-7823 7488

SKREBA
7 Denmark Street, London WC2H 8LZ
Fax: 020-7240 7088   Tel: 020-7240 7149

SNEEZING TREE FILMS
C
1-2 Bromley Place, London W1T 6DA
e-mail: sneezingtree@compuserve.com
Fax: 020-7927 9909   Tel: 020-7927 9900

SOMERFILM Ltd
20 Stirling Street, Dundee DD3 6PH
e-mail: somerfilm@aol.com
Fax: 0800 4581901   Tel/Fax: 0800 4581900

SONY PICTURES EUROPE HOUSE
25 Golden Square, London W1F 9LU
Fax: 020-7533 1015   Tel: 020-7533 1000

SOREL STUDIOS
10 Palace Court, Palace Road, London SW2 3ED
e-mail: sorelstudios.co.uk   Tel/Fax: 020-8671 2168

SOUTHERN STAR
45-49 Mortimer Street
London W1W 8HX   Tel: 020-7636 9421

SPACE CITY PRODUCTIONS
77 Blythe Road, London W14 0HP
Website: www.spacecity.co.uk
e-mail: info@spacecity.co.uk
Fax: 020-7371 4001   Tel: 020-7371 4000

SPAFAX
The Pump House
13-16 Jacobswell Mews
London W1U 3DY   Tel: 020-7906 2001

SPEAKEASY PRODUCTIONS Ltd
Wildwood House, Stanley, Perth PH1 4PX
Website: www.speak.co.uk
e-mail: info@speak.co.uk
Fax: 01738 828419   Tel: 01738 828524

SPECIFIC FILMS Ltd
25 Rathbone Street, London W1T 1NQ
e-mail: info@specificfilms.com
Fax: 020-7494 2676   Tel: 020-7580 7476

SPELLBOUND PRODUCTIONS Ltd
90 Cowdenbeath Path, Islington, London N1 0LG
e-mail: phspellbound@hotmail.com
                             Tel/Fax: 020-7713 8066

SPIRAL PRODUCTIONS Ltd
Aberdeen Studios
22 Highbury Grove, London N5 2EA
Fax: 020-7359 6123   Tel: 020-7354 5492

SPIRIT FILMS Ltd
1 Wedgwood Mews
12-13 Greek Street, London W1D 4BA
e-mail: producer@spiritfilms.co.uk
Fax: 020-7734 9850   Tel: 020-7734 6642

STANDFAST FILMS
F TV D
The Studio, 14 College Road, Bromley, Kent BR1 3NS
Fax: 020-8313 0443   Tel: 020-8466 5580

STAR PRODUCTIONS
F CV D
Star Studios, 38 Lea Bridge Road, London E5 9QD
Fax: 020-8533 6597   Tel: 020-8986 4470

STONE PRODUCTIONS
Lakeside Studio
62 Mill Street, St Osyth, Essex CO16 8EW
Fax: 01255 822160   Tel: 01255 822172

STRAWBERRY PRODUCTIONS Ltd
36 Priory Avenue, London W4 1TY
e-mail: strawprod1@aol.com
Fax: 020-8742 7675   Tel: 020-8994 4494

STREETWISE TV
11-15 Betterton Street
Covent Garden, London WC2H 9BP
e-mail: streetwisetv@hotmail.com
Fax: 020-7379 0801   Tel: 020-7470 8825

STUDIO AKA
(Animation)
30 Berwick Street, London W1F 8RH
e-mail: info@studioaka.co.uk
Fax: 020-7437 2309   Tel: 020-7434 3581

SUN DANCE FILMS Ltd
6 Glamorgan Road
Hampton Wick, Kingston, Surrey KT1 4HP
Fax: 020-8977 9441   Tel: 020-8977 1791

SUNFLOWER PRODUCTIONS
(Docs TV)
106 Mansfield Drive, Merstham, Surrey RH1 3JN
Fax: 01737 271231   Tel: 01737 642829

SWIVEL FILMS
4th Floor, 23 Denmark Street, London WC2H 8NA
Fax: 020-7240 4486   Tel: 020-7240 4485

TABARD PRODUCTIONS
Adam House
7-10 Adam Street, London WC2N 6AA
e-mail: johnherbert@tabard.co.uk
Fax: 020-7497 0830   Tel: 020-7497 0850

TABLE TOP PRODUCTIONS
1 The Orchard
Bedford Park, Chiswick, London W4 1JZ
e-mail: berry@tabletopproductions.com
                    Tel/Fax: 020-8742 0507

TAILOR-MADE FILMS
UnitS 16 & 17, Waterside
44-48 Wharf Road, London N1 7UX
Website: www.tailormadefilm.net
e-mail: info@tailormadefilms.net
Fax: 020-7253 1117   Tel: 020-7566 0280

TAKE 3 PRODUCTIONS Ltd
72 Margaret Street, London W1W 8ST
Website: www.take3.co.uk
e-mail: mail@take3.co.uk
Fax: 020-7637 4678   Tel: 020-7637 2694

TAKE FIVE PRODUCTIONS
CV Docs
25 Ganton Street, London W1F 9BP
Website: www.takefivestudio.co.uk
Fax: 020-7287 3035   Tel: 020-7287 2120

TALISMAN FILMS Ltd
5 Addison Place, London W11 4RJ
e-mail: email@talismanfilms.com
Fax: 020-7602 7422   Tel: 020-7603 7474

TALKBACK PRODUCTIONS Ltd
20-21 Newman Street, London W1T 1PG
Fax: 020-7861 8001   Tel: 020-7861 8000

TALKING PICTURES
Swallowtiles, High Street
Drayton, St Leonard, Wallingford OX10 7BQ
Website: www.talkingpictures.co.uk
e-mail: info@talkingpictures.co.uk
Fax: 01865 890504   Tel: 01865 890851

TANDEM TV & FILM Ltd
10 Bargrove Avenue
Hemel Hempstead, Herts HP1 1QP
Website: www.tandemtv.com
e-mail: ttv@tandemtv.com
Fax: 01442 219250   Tel: 01442 261576

TAYLOR David ASSOCIATES Ltd
F CV D Ch
25 Wensley Drive, Hazel Grove
Stockport SK7 6EW   Tel/Fax: 01625 850887

T.B. TV-TONY BASTABLE TELEVISION
The White House, Church Road,
Lingfield, Surrey RH7 6AH
e-mail: tbtv@msn.com
Fax: 01342 834600   Tel: 01342 834588

TELEVISION & THEATRE PROJECTS
17 Lord Roberts Avenue
Leigh-on-Sea, Essex SS9 1ND   Tel: 01702 480488

TELEVISION BUSINESS The
45 Leighton, Orton Malborne
Peterborough PE2 5QB   Tel/Fax: 01733 239082

THIN MAN FILMS
9 Greek Street, London W1D 4DQ
e-mail: info@thinman.co.uk
Fax: 020-7287 5228   Tel: 020-7734 7372

TKO COMMUNICATIONS Ltd
PO Box 130, Hove, Sussex BN3 6QU
e-mail: jskruger@tkogroup.com
Fax: 01273 540969   Tel: 01273 550088

TMB MARKETING COMMUNICATIONS
Milton Heath House
Westcott Road, Docking, Surrey RH4 3NB
e-mail: mail@motivation.co.uk
Website: www.tmbmarcom.com
Fax: 01306 877777   Tel: 01306 877000

TV MEDIA SERVICES Ltd/TVMS
3rd Floor, 420 Sauchiehall Street, Glasgow G2 3JD
e-mail: tvmsmail@aol.com
Fax: 0141-332 9040   Tel: 0141-331 1993

TVE HOUSE
(Broadcast Facilities, Non-Linear Editing)
TVE House, Wick Drive, New Milton, Hants BH25 6RH
e-mail: avid@tvehire.com
Fax: 01425 625021   Tel: 01425 625020

TVF
375 City Road, London EC1V 1NB
Fax: 020-7833 2185   Tel: 020-7837 3000

TWENTIETH CENTURY FOX TELEVISION Ltd
Twentieth Century House
31-32 Soho Square, London W1D 3AP
Fax: 020-7434 2170   Tel: 020-7437 7766

TWO FOUR PRODUCTIONS Ltd
Quay West Studios
Old Newnham, Plymouth PL7 5BH
e-mail: enq@twofour.co.uk
Fax: 01752 344224   Tel: 01752 345424

TWO SIDES TV Ltd
53A Brewer Street, London W1F 9UH
e-mail: twosidestv@clara.net
Fax: 020-7287 2289   Tel: 020-7439 9882

TYBURN FILM PRODUCTIONS Ltd
F
Cippenham Court
Cippenham Lane, Cippenham, Nr Slough
Berkshire SL1 5AU
Fax: 01753 691785   Tel: 01753 516767

TYRO PRODUCTIONS
The Coach House, 20A Park Road
Teddington, Middlesex TW11 0AQ
Fax: 020-8943 4901   Tel: 020-8943 4697

UNGER Kurt
112 Portsea Hall, Portsea Place, London W2 2BZ
Fax: 020-7584 1549   Tel: 020-7584 0542

UNIQUE TELEVISION
3rd Floor, Beaumont House, Kensington Village
Avonmore Road, London W14 8TS
e-mail: london@uniquegroup.co.uk
Fax: 020-7605 1101   Tel: 020-7605 1100

UNITED PRODUCTIONS & LWT PRODUCTIONS
Drama Department, The London Television Centre
London SE1 9LT   Tel: 020-7620 1620

UNIVERSAL PICTURES Ltd/UNIVERSAL STUDIOS
UIP House, 45 Beadon Road, London W6 0EG
Fax: 020-8563 4331   Tel: 020-8563 4329

VERA
3rd Floor, 66-68 Margaret Street, London W1W 8SR
Website: www.vera-media.co.uk
e-mail: rachael@vera.co.uk
Fax: 020-7436 6117   Tel: 020-7436 6116

VERA MEDIA
(Video Production and Training Company)
30-38 Dock Street, Leeds LS10 1JF
e-mail: vera@vera-media.co.uk
Fax: 0113-242 8739   Tel: 0113-242 8646

VIDEO AND FILM PRODUCTION
Robin Hill, The Ridge, Lower Basildon, Reading, Berks
Website: www.videoandfilm.co.uk
e-mail: david.fisher@videoandfilm.co.uk
Fax: 0118-984 4316   Tel: 0118-984 2488

VIDEO ARTS
Dumbarton House
68 Oxford Street, London W1D 1LH
e-mail: info@videoarts.co.uk
Fax: 020-7580 8103   Tel: 020-7637 7288

VIDEO ENTERPRISES
12 Barbers Wood Road
High Wycombe, Bucks HP12 4EP
Website: www.vident.u-net.com
e-mail: maurice@vident.u-net.com
Fax: 01494 534145   Tel: 01494 534144

VIDEOTEL PRODUCTIONS
84 Newman Street, London W1P 3LD
Fax: 020-7299 1818   Tel: 020-7299 1800

VILLAGE PRODUCTIONS
4 Midas Business Centre
Wantz Road, Dagenham, Essex RM10 8PS
e-mail: village@btconnect.com
Fax: 020-8593 0198   Tel: 020-8984 0322

VISAGE TELEVISION Ltd
c/o Instrumental Media
40 New Bond Street, London W1S 2RX
e-mail: television@visagegroup.com
Fax: 020-7629 8785   Tel: 020-7659 1140

W3KTS Ltd
10 Portland Street, York YO31 7EH
e-mail: chris@w3kts.demon.co.uk   Tel: 01904 647822

W6 STUDIO
(The Complete Video Service)
359 Lillie Road, Fulham, London SW6 7PA
Website: www.w6studio.co.uk
e-mail: kaz@w6studio.freeserve.co.uk
Fax: 020-7381 5252   Tel: 020-7385 2272

WALKOVERS VIDEO PRODUCTION
Brook Cottage, Silver Street
Kington Langley, Nr Chippenham Wiltshire SN15 5NU
e-mail: walkoversvideo@msn.com
Fax: 01249 750155   Tel: 01249 750428

WALNUT PARTNERSHIP The
Crown House, Armley Road
Leeds I S12 2EJ
Website: www.walnutpartnership.co.uk
e-mail: mail@walnutpartnership.co.uk
Fax: 08707 427080   Tel: 08707 427070

WALSH BROS. Ltd
24 Redding House, Harlinger Street
King Henry's Wharf, London SE18 5SR
e-mail: walshbros@lycosmail.com
Tel/Fax: 020-8854 5557   Tel/Fax: 020-8858 6870

WARK CLEMENTS & CO Ltd
Studio 7, The Tollgate
Marine Crescent, Glasgow G51 1HD
Website: www.warkclements.com
e-mail: info@warkclements.co.uk
Fax: 0141-429 1751   Tel: 0141-429 1750

WARNER BROS PRODUCTIONS Ltd
FF
Warner Suite
Pinewood Studios, Iver Heath, Bucks SL0 0NH
Fax: 01753 655703   Tel: 01753 654545

WARNER SISTERS FILM AND TELEVISION Ltd
The Cottage, Pall Mall Deposit
124 Barlby Road, London W10 6BL
e-mail: sisters@warnercine.com
Fax: 020-8960 3880   Tel: 020-8960 3550

WEST ONE FILM PRODUCERS Ltd
c/o Richard Hatton Ltd
29 Roehampton Gate, London SW15 5JR
Fax: 020-8876 8278   Tel: 020-8876 6699

WHITE Michael
48 Dean Street, London W1D 5BF
e-mail: contact@michaelwhite.co.uk
Fax: 020-7734 7727   Tel: 020-7734 7707

WHITEHALL FILMS Ltd
10 Lower Common South, London SW15 1BP
e-mail: mwhitehall@email.msn.com
Fax: 020-8788 2340   Tel: 020-8785 3737

WICKES COMPANY The
F TV D
10 Abbey Orchard Street, London SW1P 2LD
e-mail: wickesco@aol.com
Fax: 020-7222 0822   Tel: 020-7222 0820

WILD IRIS FILMS
59 Brewer Street, London W1R 3FB
e-mail: joe@wildiris.co.uk
Fax: 020-7494 1764   Tel: 020-7494 9230

WINNER Michael Ltd
219 Kensington High Street, London W8 6BD
e-mail: winner@ftech.co.uk
Fax: 020-7602 9217   Tel: 020-7734 8385

WORKING TITLE FILMS Ltd
Oxford House, 76 Oxford Street, London W1D 1BS
Fax: 020-7307 3001   Tel: 020-7307 3000

WORLD FILM SERVICES Ltd
Norman House, 105-109 Strand, London WC2R 0AA
Fax: 020-7240 3740   Tel: 020-7240 1444

WORLD PRODUCTIONS Ltd
Norman House, 105-109 Strand, London WC2R 0AA
Website: www.world-productions.com
Fax: 020-7240 3740   Tel: 020-7240 1444

WORLD WIDE PICTURES Ltd
21-25 St Anne's Court, London W1F 0BJ
Website: www.worldwidegroup.ltd.uk
e-mail: info@worldwidegroup.ltd.uk
Fax: 020-7734 0619   Tel: 020-7434 1121

WOT IMAGES Ltd
45 Fitzroy Street, London W1T 6EB
e-mail: jackie.wot@virgin.net
Fax: 020-7387 7303   Tel: 020-7387 4040

XINGU FILMS
12 Cleveland Row, London SW1A 1DH
Fax: 020-7451 0601   Tel: 020-7451 0600

YOUNGER Greg ASSOCIATES
Baron's Croft, Hare Lane
Blindley Heath, Surrey RH7 6JA
Fax: 01342 833768   Tel: 01342 832515

ZAHRA & REMICK
186 Albert Road
London N22 7AH   Tel/Fax: 020-8889 6225

ZENITH ENTERTAINMENT Plc
43-45 Dorset Street, London W1U 7NA
Fax: 020-7224 3194   Tel: 020-7224 2440

ZEPHYR FILMS Ltd
48A Goodge Street, London W1T 4LX
e-mail: pippa@zephyrfilms.co.uk
Fax: 020-7255 3777   Tel: 020-7255 3555

ARTTS SKILLCENTRE
Highfield Grange
Bubwith, North Yorks YO8 6DP
Website: www.artts.co.uk
e-mail: admin@artts.co.uk
Fax: 01757 288253   Tel: 01757 288088

BLAZE THE TRAIL FILM & TELEVISION TRAINING
2nd Floor, 241 High Street, London E17 7BH
Website: www.blaze-the-trail.com
e-mail: bctraining@coralmedia.co.uk
Fax: 020-8520 2358   Tel: 020-8520 4569

BRIGHTON FILM SCHOOL
Member of the National Association for Higher
Education in the Moving Image and the
University Film and Video Association. Part-time
Film Director's courses in Screenwriting,
Cinematography and Editing. Day and Evening
Courses plus Summer Schools.
Admin: 13 Tudor Close, Dean Court Road,
Rottingdean, East Sussex BN2 7DF
Studio: Phoenix Arts Centre, Wellesley House,
10-14 Waterloo Place, Brighton BN2 9NB
Senior Lecturer: Franz von Habsburg MBKS (BAFTA)
Admissions: Meryl von Habsburg BSc MSc Cert Ed
Website: www.brightonfilmschool.org.uk
e-mail: info@brightonfilmschool.org.uk
Fax: 01273 302163   Tel: 01273 302166

LEEDS METROPOLITAN UNIVERSITY
(PG Dip/MA's in Film and Moving Image
Production or Ficton Screenwriting,
HND in Moving Image Production)
The Leeds School of Art Architecture and Design,
H507, Calverley Street, Leeds LS1 3HE
Fax: 0113-283 3139   Tel: 0113-283 2600

LONDON ACADEMY OF RADIO, FILM & TV
American Building
79A Tottenham Court Road
London W1
Website: www.media-courses.com
e-mail: help@radio321.com   Tel: 020-8408 7158

LONDON FILM ACADEMY
The Old Church
52A Walham Grove, London SW6 1QR
Website: www.londonfilmacademy.com
e-mail: info@londonfilmacademy.com
Fax: 020-7381 6116   Tel: 020-7386 7711

LONDON FILM SCHOOL The
(2-year, Full-time Diploma Course in Film Making)
24 Shelton Street
London WC2H 9UB
e-mail: film.school@lfs.org.uk
Fax: 020-7497 3718   Tel: 020-7836 9642

MIDDLESEX UNIVERSITY
(School of Art, Design & Performing Arts)
Cat Hill, Barnet, Herts EN4 8HT
Fax: 020-8440 9541   Tel: 020-8411 5000

NATIONAL FILM & TELEVISION SCHOOL
(Full-time 2-year MA Course specialising in one of:
Directing (Animation, Documentary or Fiction);
Cinematography; Editing; Post-production Sound;
Producing; Screen Design; Screen Music
Screenwriting. One & Two-Year Diploma in Sound.
Part-time producing course. Project Development
Lab for experienced professionals. Short courses
in digital post-production.
Beaconsfield Studios, Station Road
Beaconsfield, Bucks HP9 1LG
Website: www.nftsfilm-tv.ac.uk
e-mail: admin@nftsfilm-tv.ac.uk
Fax: 01494 674042   Tel: 01494 671234

RE:ACTORS
15 Montrose Walk
Weybridge, Surrey KT13 8JN
Website: www.reactors.co.uk
e-mail: michael@reactors.co.uk
Fax: 01932 830248   Tel: 01932 888885

**SURREY INSTITUTE OF ART & DESIGN UNIVERSITY
COLLEGE**
(3-year BA (Hons) Photography, Film & Video &
Production, Time-Based New Media)
Falkner Road
Farnham
Surrey GU9 7DS
Website: www.surrart.ac.uk   Tel: 01252 722441

**UNIVERSITY OF WESTMINSTER SCHOOL
OF COMMUNICATION & CREATIVE INDUSTRIES**
(Degree courses in Film and
Television/Contemporary Media Practice)
Watford Road
Northwick Park
Harrow
Middlesex HA1 3TP   Tel: 020-7911 5000

THE SPOTLIGHT LINK

The *Spotlight Link* is the new electronic connection
that unites agent and casting director.
It is available for casting directors and agents only.

Casting directors can broadcast breakdowns live to agents
and receive suggestions back containing full client details.

When breakdowns arrive, agents review their clients on screen
instantly. They make a suggestion for the role and email an online
CV that includes a photograph, contact details, skills and credits
directly to the casting professionals' desktop.

FREE for agents and subscribers to *Spotlight Interactive*.

*"The Spotlight Link is a valuable tool -
it saves a great deal of
time as it provides immediate
contact with agents and
produces a quick response.
It's simple to create a
breakdown, and easy to view
the suggestions that are made."*

Janie Frazer (Night & Day)

THE SPOTLIGHT ®

7 Leicester Place | London WC2H 7RJ
t +44 (0)20 7437 7631 | f +44 (0)20 7437 5881
e info@spotlightcd.com | www.spotlightcd.com

new < id

Tel: 020 7499 4923/4925

A make over and
photographic
studio run by
stylists and
professionals with
a vast amount of
experience within
the modelling,
dance and
acting industries.
Giving you sound
advice to help
you create your
own unique style
with comp
cards
and portfolios.

1 John Princes St
London W1G 0JS
www.newidstudios.com
Just one minute from
Oxford Circus

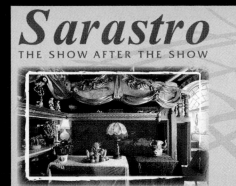

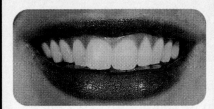

M.V. DIXIE QUEEN

London's largest cruising/static Mississippi-style paddleboat. High 10' ceilings. 2500 sq. ft. of interior space. 2000 ft. exterior space. Additional restaurant deck. Available for Film/TV location work. Experienced personnel on board can assist with all aspects of waterside filming, permissions etc. Call Nigel Scandrett for a good deal and to discuss the potential of using a river venue.

Thames Luxury Charters 020 8780 1562 Website: www.thamesluxurycharters.co.uk

ACCESS STUDIOS
8-10 Creekside, London SE8 3DX
Website: www.accessstudios.com
e-mail: info@accessstudios.com
Fax: 0870 1205658   Tel: 020-7231 6185

ARDMORE STUDIOS Ltd
Herbert Road, Bray, Co. Wicklow, Ireland
e-mail: film@ardmore.ie
Fax: 00 353 1 2861894   Tel: 00 353 1 2862971

BBC SOUTH (ELSTREE)
BBC Elstree Centre
Clarendon Road, Borehamwood
Herts WD6 1JF   Tel: 020-8953 6100

BBC TELEVISION
Television Centre
Wood Lane, Shepherds Bush
London W12 7RJ   Tel: 020-8743 8000

BRAY STUDIOS
Down Place, Water Oakley
Windsor Road, Windsor, Berks SL4 5UG
Fax: 01628 770381   Tel: 01628 622111

CAPITAL STUDIOS
Wandsworth Plain, London SW18 1ET
e-mail: info@capitalstudios.com
Fax: 020-8877 0234   Tel: 020-8877 1234

C F S CHELTENHAM FILM STUDIOS
Arle Court, Hatherley Lane
Cheltenham, Glos GL51 6PN
Website: www.cheltstudio.com
e-mail: info@cheltstudio.com
Fax: 01242 542 701   Tel: 01242 542 700

CORINTHIAN TELEVISION FACILITIES
(TV Post Production, Studios, Transmission)
87 St John's Wood Terrace, London NW8 6PY
Fax: 020-7483 4264   Tel: 020-7483 6000

EALING STUDIOS OPERATIONS Ltd
Ealing Green, London W5 5EP
Website: www.ealingstudios.com
e-mail: info@ealingstudios.com
Fax: 020-8758 8658   Tel: 020-8567 6655

ELSTREE FILM & TELEVISION STUDIOS
Shenley Road, Borehamwood, Herts WD6 1JG
e-mail: info@elstreefilmtv.com
Fax: 020-8905 1135   Tel: 020-8953 1600

HILLSIDE
Merry Hill Road, Bushey, Herts WD23 1DR
Website: www.hillside-studios.co.uk
e-mail: enquiries@hillside-studios.co.uk
Fax: 020-8421 8085   Tel: 020-8950 7919

LONDON STUDIOS The
London Television Centre
Upper Ground, London SE1 9LT
Fax: 020-7928 8405   Tel: 020-7620 1620

PINEWOOD STUDIOS
Pinewood Road, Iver Heath, Bucks SL0 0NH
Website: www.pinewood-studios.co.uk
Fax: 01753 656844   Tel: 01753 651700

REUTERS TELEVISION
85 Fleet Street
London EC4P 4AJ   Tel: 020-7250 1122

RIVERSIDE STUDIOS
Crisp Road, London W6 9RL
Website: www.riversidestudios.co.uk
e-mail: online@riversidestudios.co.uk
Fax: 020-8237 1001   Tel: 020-8237 1000

ROTHERHITHE STUDIOS
119 Rotherhithe Street, London SE16 4NF
Fax: 020-7231 2119   Tel: 020-7231 2209

SANDS FILMS
119 Rotherhithe Street, London SE16 4NF
Fax: 020-7231 2119   Tel: 020-7231 2209

SAVOY HILL STUDIO
Adam House
7-10 Adam Street, London WC2N 6AA
e-mail: savoyhillstudio@tabard.u-net.com
Fax: 020-7520 9023   Tel: 020-7497 0830

SHEPPERTON STUDIOS
Studios Road, Shepperton, Middlesex TW17 0QD
Fax: 01932 568989   Tel: 01932 562611

TEDDINGTON STUDIOS Ltd
Broom Road, Teddington, Middlesex TW11 9NT
Website: www.teddington.co.uk
e-mail: sales@teddington.co.uk   Tel: 020-8977 3252

TWICKENHAM FILM STUDIOS Ltd
The Barons St Margaret's
Twickenham, Middlesex TW1 2AW
Fax: 020-8607 8701   Tel: 020-8607 8888

Good Digs Guide

Compiled By JANICE CRAMER & DAVID BANKS
This is a list of digs recommended by those who have used them.
To keep the list accurate please send recommendations for inclusion to GOOD DIGS GUIDE at The Spotlight.
Thanks to all who did so over the last year.
Entries in Bold have been paid for by the Digs concerned.

ABERDEEN
Mrs A Milne · 5 Sunnyside Walk, Aberdeen AB2 3NZ · 01224 638951
Pat Woods · 62 Union Grove, Aberdeen · 01224 586324

AYR
Sheila Dunn · The Dunn-Thing Guest House, 13 Park Circus, Ayr KA7 2DJ · 01292 284531

BATH
Cecilia Hutton · 25 Claude Avenue, Bath BA2 1AE · 01225 332221
Website: www.bathholidayhomes.co.uk
e-mail: bhh@virgin.net
Mrs G Porter · 95 Shakespeare Avenue, Bath, Avon BA2 4RQ · 01225 420166
Jane Tapley · Camden Lodgings, 3 Upper Camden Place, Bath BA1 5HX · 01225 446561

BELFAST
Mrs Cargill · Eglantine Guest House, 21 Eglantine Avenue, Belfast BT9 6DW · 028-9066 7585
Nora Greer · 59 Rugby Road, Belfast BT7 1PT · 028-9032 2120
Ms S McCully · 28 Eglantine Avenue, Belfast BT9 6DX · 028-9068 2031

BILLINGHAM
Audrey & Reg Bell · 14 The Crescent, Linthorpe, Middlesbrough TS5 6SQ · 01642 822483
Pam & John Fanthorpe · Harker Hill Farm, Seamer, Stokesley, Middlesbrough TS9 5NF · 01642 710431
Anna Farminer · 168 Kennedy Gardens, Billingham, Cleveland TS23 3RJ · 01642 530205
Mrs S Gibson · Northwood, 61 Tunstall Avenue, Billingham · 01642 561071/553125
Mrs Edna Newton · 97 Brendon Crescent, Billingham, Cleveland TS23 2QU · 01642 647958

BIRMINGHAM
Mr N K Baker · 41 King Edward Road, Mosley, Birmingham B13 8EL · 0121-449 8220
John Eccles · 18 Holly Road, Edgbaston, Birmingham B16 9NH · 0121-454 4853
Ms B T Matusiak-Varley · **Red Gables, 69 Handsworth Wood Road
Handsworth Wood, Birmingham B20 2DH** · **0121-686 5942/07771 751105**
Marlene P Mountain · **268 Monument Road, Edgbaston, Birmingham B16 8XF** · **0121-454 5900**
Mrs Wilson · 17 Yew Tree Road, Edgbaston, Birmingham B15 2LX · 0121-440 5182

BLACKPOOL
Brian & Liz Chapman · Hollywood Apartments, 2-4 Wellington Rd, Blackpool FY1 6AR · 01253 341633
Jean Lees · Ascot Flats, 6 Hull Road, Central Blackpool FY1 4QB · 01253 621059
The Proprietor · The Brooklyn Hotel, 7 Wilton Parade, Blackpool FY1 2HE · 01253 627003
The Somerset & Dorset Apartments · 22 Barton Avenue, South Shore, Blackpool FY1 6AP · 01253 346743

BOLTON
Paul Duckworth · 19 Burnham Avenue, Bolton BL1 6DB · 01204 495732
Mrs M Milton-White · 20 Heywood Gardens, Great Lever, Bolton BL3 6RB · 01204 531589

BOURNEMOUTH
James & Maria Dunford · Yew Tree Guest House, 4 Upper Terrace Road, Bournemouth BH2 5NW · 01202 554558

BRADFORD
Michael Calver · **33 Stockhill Fold, Greengates, Bradford BD10 9AY** · **01274 616990**
Theresa Smith · **8 Moorhead Terrace, Shipley, Bradford BD18 4LA** · **01274 778568**

BRIGHTON
Ms Carol Cleveland · 13 Belgrave Street, Brighton BN2 9NS · 01273 602607
Kate Dyson · 28 Victoria Street, Brighton BN1 3FQ · 01273 746505
Mrs Corinne Hamlin · Flat 6, Preston Lodge, Little Preston Street, Brighton BN1 2HQ · 01273 321346
Kate Merrin · 2a Exton House, 4 Second Avenue, Hove BN3 2LG · 07714 672233

BRISTOL
Jinnie Blackburn · 79 Stackpool Road, Southville, Bristol BS3 1NP · 0117-983 3676
Jean Rozario · Manor Lodge, 21 Station Rd, Keynsham, N Somerset BS31 2BH · 0117-986 2191
Mrs E Vibert · 9 Dowry Square, Bristol BS8 4SH · 0117-929 2770

BURY ST EDMUNDS
Mrs S Bird · 30 Crown Street, Bury St Edmunds, Suffolk IP33 1QU · 01284 754492
Sue Harrington-Spier · 39 Well Street, Bury St Edmunds, Suffolk IP33 1EQ · 01284 768986

BUXTON
Mrs M Kitchen · Flat 1, 17 Silverlands, Buxton, Derbyshire SK17 6QH · 01298 78898
Anne & Colin Scruton · Griff Guest House, 2 Compton Road, Buxton SK17 9DN · 01298 23628

CAMBRIDGE
Roger Hones · 25 Magrath Avenue, Cambridge CB4 3AH · 01223 315503

Mrs Anne Walters

Heathcote House, The Courtyard
Main Street, Winster, Matlock, DE4 2DJ Tel: 01629 650342

One bedroom self catering cottage for two people.

CANTERBURY

Mrs Jennifer J Butcher	5 Vernon Place, Canterbury, Kent CT1 3HG	01227 470712
Mrs A Dolan	12 Leycroft Close, Canterbury, Kent CT2 7LD	01227 450064
Nikki Ellen	Crockshard Farmhouse, Wingham, Canterbury CT3 1NY	01227 720464
	Website: www.crockshard.com	
	e-mail: crockshard_bnb@yahoo.com	
Doris Stockbridge	Tudor House, 6 Best Lane, Canterbury, Kent CT1 2JB	01227 765650

CARDIFF

Anne Blade	25 Romilly Road, Canton, Cardiff CF5 1FH	029-2022 5860
Nigel Lewis	66 Donald Street, Roath, Cardiff CF24 4TR	029-2049 4008
Michael Nelmes	**12 Darran Street, Cathays, Cardiff, South Glamorgan CF24 4JF**	**029-2034 2166**
T Taylor & P Chichester	32 Kincraig Street, Roath, Cardiff, South Glamorgan CF24 3HW	029-2048 6785

CHESTERFIELD

Linda & Chris Cook	27 Tennyson Avenue, Chesterfield, Derbyshire	01246 202631/07929 850561
Mr N Connell	Anis Louise Guest House, 34 Clarence Rd, Chesterfield S40 1LN	01246 235412
Mr & Mrs Popplewell	23 Tennyson Avenue, Chesterfield, Derbyshire S40 4SN	01246 201738

CHICHESTER

Tricia & Richard Beeny	Hunston Mill Holiday Homes, Hunston, Nr Chichester PO20 6AU	01243 783375

COVENTRY

Paddy & Bob Snelson	**Banner Hill Farmhouse, Rouncil Lane, Kenilworth CV8 1NN**	**01926 852850**

DARLINGTON

Mrs Bird	Gilling Old Mill, Gilling West, Richmond, N Yorks DL10 5JD	01748 822771
Mr E Barlow	George Hotel, Piercebridge, Darlington DL2 3SW	01325 374576
Mrs Jean Evans	26a Pierremont Crescent, Darlington DL3 9PB	01325 252032
Anne Graham	**Holme House, Piercebridge, Darlington DL2 3SY**	**01325 374280**

DARTFORD

Mrs S Greenwood	8 Sutherland Close, Chalk, Gravesend, Kent DA12 4XJ	01474 350819

DUNDEE

Mrs J Hill	Ash Villa, 216 Arbroth Road, Dundee DD4 7RZ	01382 450831

EASTBOURNE

Peter Allen	Flat 1, 16 Enys Road, Eastbourne BN21 2DN	01323 730235
S Awdry	31 Enys Road, Eastbourne BN21 2DH	01323 416147
David E J Chant	Hamdon, 49 King's Drive, Eastbourne BN21 2NY	01323 722544
Brent Chapman	**13 Warrior Square, Eastbourne BN22 7DB**	**01323 647007**
Mrs J Dawson	14 New Upperton Road, Eastbourne	01323 729988
Mr & Mrs J Weaver	Meads Lodge Holiday Flats	
	1 Jevington Gardens, Eastbourne BN21 4HR	01323 724362

EDINBURGH

Edna Glen Miller	25 Bellevue Road, Edinburgh EH7 4DL	0131-556 4131
Mrs Helen Russell	**9 Lonsdale Terrace, Edinburgh EH3 9HN**	**0131-229 7219/0131-527 8200**
	e-mail: helen.tyrrell@scvo.org.uk	
Joyce Stobbart	84 Bellevue Road, Edinburgh EH7 4DE	0131-226 6881/0131-556 8300

GLASGOW

David W Baird	6 Beaton Road, Maxwell Park, Glasgow G41 4LA	0141-423 1340/570 5420
David Lloyd Jones	3 Whittinghame Drive, Kelvinside, Glasgow G12 0XS	0141-339 3331
Simon Leslie-Carter	52 Charlotte Street, Glasgow G1 5DW	01436 810264/Fax: 01436 810520
	Website: www.52charlottestreet.co.uk	
	e-mail: slc@52charlottestreet.co.uk	
Lesley Robinson	28 Marywood Square, Glasgow G41 2BJ	0141-423 6920

HULL

The Archoc Guesthouse	38 Saner Street, Hull HU3 2TR	01482 211558

INVERNESS

Mrs Blair	McDonald House Hotel, 1 Ardross Terrace, Inverness IV3 5NQ	01463 232878
Jennifer Kerr-Smith	Ardkeen Tower, 5 Culduthel Road, Inverness	01463 233131
Mrs Swart	Abermar Guest House, 25 Fairfield Road, Inverness IV3 5QD	01463 239019

IPSWICH

Bunty Ball	56 Henley Road, Ipswich IP1 3SA	01473 256653
Liz Bennett	Gayfers, Playford, Ipswich IP6 9DR	01473 623343
Anne Hyde-Johnson	64 Benton Street, Hadleigh, Ipswich, Suffolk IP7 5AT	01473 823110

ISLE OF MAN
Mr Holt Mereside Private Hotel, 1 Empire Terrace
Douglas, Isle of Man IM2 4LE 01624 676355
Miss Sue Ogston 'Winward House', 69 Mill Hill Road
Cowes, Isle of Wight PO31 7EQ 01983 280940

KIRKCALDY
Mrs Nicol 44 Glebe Park, Kirkcaldy, Fife KY1 1BL 01592 264531

LEEDS
Mrs M Baker **2 Ridge Mount, (off Cliff Road), Leeds LS6 2HD** **0113-275 8735**
Mrs Kavanagh Novello House, 2 Ladywood Road, Roundhay, Leeds LS8 2QF 0113-265 8330
Bryan & Linda Littlewood 4 Oatland Green, Leeds LS7 1SN 0113-225 3281

LINCOLN
Andrew Carnell Tennyson Court Cottages, 3 Tennyson Street, Lincoln LN1 1LZ 01522 533044
Ye Old Crowne Inn
(Theatre Pub) Clasketgate, Lincoln LN2 1JS 01522 542896
Mavis S Sharpe Bight House, 17 East Bight, Lincoln LN2 1QH 01522 534477

LIVERPOOL
Kate Cowie Flat 5, 2 Fulwood Road, Liverpool L17 5AG 0151-726 0061/709 9434
Ross Double 5 Percy Street, Liverpool L8 7LT 0151-708 8821
Anne Maloney 16 Sandown Lane, Wavertree, Liverpool L15 8HY 0151-734 4839
Damian McGuinness Seapark Apartments, (office)
51 Alexandra Road, Southport, Merseyside PR9 9HD 01704 500444

LLANDUDNO
Alan Bell **Quinton Hotel, 36 Church Walks, Llandudno LL30 2HN** **01492 876879**

LONDON
Mrs I Allen Flat 2, 9 Dorset Square, London NW1 6QB 020-7723 3979
Lise Bird Brixton SW2 07941 346651
Mrs P A Broughton 31 Ringstead Road, Catford, London SE6 2BU 020-8461 0146
Maggie Guess 36 Federal Road, Perivale, Middlesex UB6 7AW 020-8991 0918
Nicholas Mesure 16 St Alfege Passage, Greenwich, London SE10 9JS 020-8853 4337
Lindy Shaw 11 Baronsmede, Acton, London W5 4LS 020-8567 0877

MALVERN
Mrs Emuss Priory Holme, 18 Avenue Road, Malvern WR14 3AR 01684 568455
Mr & Mrs McLeod Sidney House, 40 Worcester Road, Malvern WR14 4AA 01684 574994

MANCHESTER
James & Risa Duff 40 Sunnybank Road, Bury, Lancs BL9 8HF 0161-796 7073/07905 646832
Mrs E Dyson 33 Danesmoor Road, West Didsbury, Manchester M20 3JT 0161-434 5410
Miriam Heaton 59 Tamworth Avenue, Whitefield, Manchester M45 6UA 0161-773 4490
P M Jones 375 Bury New Road, Whitefield, Manchester M45 7SU 0161-766 9243
David Martin & Jez Dolan 86 Stanley Road, Old Trafford, Manchester M16 9DH 0161-848 9231
Fiona & John Prichard 45 Bamford Road, Didsbury, Manchester M20 2QP 0161-434 4877
Rachel Robinson 4 Park View, Ladybarn, Manchester M14 6SY 07810 566524
Mr D Satterthwaite Albany Hotel, 21 Albany Road
Chorton-cum-Hardy, Manchester M21 0AY 0161-881 6774
Susan Twist 45 Osborne Road, Levenshulme, Manchester M19 2DU 0161-225 1591

MILFORD HAVEN
Bruce and Diana **Belhaven House Hotel**
Henricksen **29 Hamilton Terrace, Milford Haven SA73 3JJ 01646 695983/Fax: 01646 690787**
Website: www.westwaleshotels.com
e-mail: hbruceh@aol.com

MOLD
Mr & Mrs Major The Mount, Higher Kinnerton, Chester CH4 9BQ 01244 660275

NEWARK-ON-TRENT
Anne Burns 69 Harcourt Street, Newark-on-Trent, Notts NG24 1RG 01636 702801

NEWCASTLE UPON TYNE
Miss Tot Charlton Ryton Grange, Ryton, Tyne and Wear NE40 3UN 0191-413 3878
Dave Cross
 & Mary Kalaugher 4 Tankerville Terrace, Jesmond, Newcastle upon Tyne NE2 3AH 0191-281 0475
Thomas Guy 11 Rokeby Drive, Gosforth, Newcastle Upon Tyne NE3 4JY 0191-285 7057
Madaleine Moffatt 9 Curtis Road, Fenham NE4 9BH 0191-272 5318
Mrs P Stansfield Rosebury Hotel, 2 Rosebury Crescent, Jesmond
Newcastle Upon Tyne NE2 1ET 0191-281 3363
Miss M E Steele **7 Stoneyhurst Road**
South Gosforth, Newcastle Upon Tyne NE3 1PR **0191-285 7771**

NEWPORT
Mrs Dinah Price 'Great House', Isca Rd, Old Village, Caerleon, Gwent NP18 1QG 01633 420216
Website: www.visitgreathouse.net
e-mail: price.greathouse@tesco.net

Quinton Hotel
AA
B&B
★★★

Comfortable warm rooms, most en-suite with TV, radio, direct dial phones, tea/coffee facilities. Flexible breakfasts, late bar, pool table, darts, piano and karaoke. Free light suppers. Mini-bus service to and from Theatre. Railway and Bus.

36 Church Walks, Llandudno. Tel/Fax: 01492-876879 Email: susanmarybell@yahoo.co.uk

NORTHAMPTON
Lynne Davison | The Stackyard, Holcot Road, Walgrave, Northants | 01604 781803

NORWICH
Julia Edgeley | 8 Chester Street, Norwich NR2 2AY | 01603 612833
Maureen Moore | 63 Surrey Street, Norwich NR1 3PG | 01603 621979
Cathy Much | 128 Southwell Road, Norwich NR1 3RS | 01603 632787

NOTTINGHAM
Barbara Davis | 3 Tattershall Drive, The Park, Nottingham NG7 1BX | 0115-947 4179
Mrs Offord | 5 Tattershall Drive, The Park, Nottingham NG7 1BX | 0115-947 6924
Mrs S Santos | Eastwood Farm, Hagg Lane, Epperstone, Nottingham NG14 6AX | 0115-966 3018
Christine Walker | 18A Cavendish Cresent North, The Park, Nottingham NG7 1BA | 0115-947 2485

OXFORD
Susan Petty | 74 Corn Street, Witney, Oxford OX28 6BS | 01993 703035

PLYMOUTH
Mr & Mrs Carson | 6 Beech Cottages, Parsonage Road, Newton Ferrers, Nr Plymouth PL8 1AX | 01752 872124
John & Sandra Humphreys | Lyttleton Guest House (Self-Catering) 4 Crescent Avenue, Plymouth PL1 3AN | 01752 220176
Julia Noble | Ashgrove Hotel, 218 Citadel Road, The Hoe, Plymouth PL1 3BB | 01752 664046
Hugh & Floise Spencer | 10 Grand Parade, Plymouth PL1 3DF | 01752 664066

POOLE
Mrs Burnett | 63 Orchard Avenue, Parkstone, Poole, Dorset BH14 8AH | 01202 743877
Sarah Moore | Harbour View, 11 Harbour View Road, Poole BH14 0PD | 01202 734763
Mrs Saunders | 1 Harbour Shallows, 15 Whitecliff Road, Poole BH14 8DU | 01202 741637

READING
Estate Office | Mapledurham House and Watermill, Mapledurham Estate, Reading RG4 7TR | 0118-972 3350

SHEFFIELD
J Craig & B Rosen | **59 Nether Edge Road, Sheffield S7 1RW** | **0114-258 1337**
Jane Horton & Lynn Cullumbine | 223 Cemetery Road, Sheffield S11 8FQ | 0114-255 6092
Carole Gillespie | 251 Western Road, Crookes, Sheffield S10 1LE | 0114-266 2666
Liz Godfrey | 12 Victoria Road, Sheffield S10 2DL | 0114-266 9389
Penny Slack | Rivelin Glen Quarry, Rivelin Valley Road, Sheffield S6 5SE | 0114-234 0382/Fax: 0114-234 7630
Website: www.quarryhouse.org.uk e-mail: pennyslack@aol.com

SOUTH SHIELDS, TYNE & WEAR
Pat Underwood | 132 Fort Street, South Shields, Tyne and Wear NE33 2AZ | 0191-422 5066

SOUTHAMPTON
Sandra Cuzzolin | 15 Methuen Street, Inner Avenue, Southampton SO14 6FL | 023-8063 7345

SOUTHSEA & PORTSMOUTH
Wendy Tyrrell | Douglas Cottage, 27 Somerset Road, Southsea PO5 2NL | 023-9282 1453

STIRLING
Mrs N Leighton | 21 Princes Street, Sterling, Fife FK8 1HQ | 01786 473373

STOKE-ON-TRENT
Dorothy Griffiths | 40 Princes Road, Hartshill, Stoke-on-Trent | 01782 416198
Mrs Hindmoor | Verdon Guest House, 44 Charles Street, Hanley, Stoke-on-Trent ST1 3JY | 01782 264244
Mr & Mrs K Meredith | **Bank End Farm Cottages, Hammond Ave, Brown Edge, Stoke-on-Trent Staffs ST6 8QU** | **01782 502160**

STRATFORD UPON-AVON
Mr Maury | Caterham House, 58-59 Rother Street, Stratford-upon-Avon CV37 6LT | 01789 267309

SUNDERLAND
Hazel Clifford | Ravensbourne Guest House, 106 Beach Road, South Shields, Tyne and Wear NE33 2NE | 0191-456 5849
Mrs Henderson | 22 Park Parade, Roker, Sunderland SR6 9LU | 0191-565 6511

SWANSEA
Mr B Richards | 152 Western Street, Swansea SA1 3JY | 01792 464443

Good Digs Guide

TAUNTON

Mike and Diana Jerrold	Oakwood House, Haines Hill, Taunton, Somerset TA1 4HN	01823 322499

TORQUAY

Frank & Irena Lovsey	Silverton Holiday Apts, 217 St Marychurch Rd, Torquay TQ1 3JT	01803 327147

WESTCLIFF

Joy Hussey	42a Ceylon Road, Westclif-on-Sea SS0 7HP	07946 413496
Mark Moulding	24a Elderton Road, Westcliff-on-Sea, Essex	01702 344965
Nicola Swan	7 Old Leigh Road, Leigh, Essex	01702 471600

WINCHESTER

Mrs Fetherston-Dilke	85 Christchurch Road, Winchester SO23 9QY	01962 868661

WOLVERHAMPTON

Julia & Ron Bell	Treetops, The Hem, Shifnal, Shropshire TF11 9PS	01952 460566
Sonia Nixon	39 Stubbs Road, Pennfields, Wolverhampton WV3 7DJ	01902 339744
Peter A Riggs	'Bethesda', 56 Chapel Lane, Codsall, Nr Wolverhampton WV8 2EJ	01902 844068

WORCESTER

Mrs Chris Crossland	Greenlands, Uphampton, Ombersley, Worcester WR9 0JP	01905 620873

WORTHING

Mollie Stewart	School House, 11 Ambrose Place, Worthing BN11 1PZ	01903 206823

YORK

Abbey House Apts	7 St Mary's, Bootham, York YO30 7DD	01765 605133
Tom Blacklock	155 Lowther Street, York YO3 7LZ	01904 620487
Iris & Dennis Blower	Dalescroft Guest House, 10 Southlands Road, York YO23 1NP	01904 626801
Greg Harrand	Hedley House Hotel & Apts, 3 Bootham Terrace, York YO3 7DH	01904 637404

Opera Companies

BROOMHILL OPERA
Wiltons Music Hall
Graces Alley, Wellclose Square, London E1 8JB
e-mail: opera@broomhill.demon.co.uk
Fax: 020-7702 1414   Tel: 020-7702 9555

CARL ROSA OPERA
359 Hackney Road, London E2 8PR
e-mail: mail@carlrosaopera.co.uk
Fax: 020-7613 0859   Tel: 020-7613 0777

D'OYLY CARTE OPERA COMPANY
The Powerhouse
6 Sancroft Street, London SE11 5UD
Website: www.doylycarte.org.uk
e-mail: mail@doylycarte.org.uk
Fax: 020-7793 7300   Tel: 020-7793 7100

DUAL CONTROL INTERNATIONAL THEATRE
Admiral Offices
Historic Dockyard, Chatham, Kent ME4 4TZ
e-mail: info@ellenkentinternational.co.uk
Fax: 01634 819149   Tel: 01634 819141

ENGLISH NATIONAL OPERA
London Coliseum
St Martin's Lane, London WC2N 4ES
Fax: 020-7845 9277   Tel: 020-7836 0111

ENGLISH TOURING OPERA
250A Kennington Lane, London SE11 5RD
Fax: 020-7735 7008   Tel: 020-7820 1131

EUROPEAN CHAMBER OPERA (Echo Opera)
(Incorp. Opera & Concert Productions Worldwide)
60C Kyverdale Road, London N16 7AJ
Website: www.echo-opera.com
e-mail: info@echopera.demon.co.uk
Fax: 020-8806 4465   Tel: 020-8806 4231

GLYNDEBOURNE FESTIVAL OPERA
Glyndebourne, Lewes
East Sussex BN8 5UU   Tel: 01273 812321

GRANGE PARK OPERA
5 Chancery Lane, London EC4 1BU
Website: www.grangeparkopera.co.uk
e-mail: info@grangeparkopera.co.uk
Fax: 020-7320 5429   Tel: 020-7320 5586

KENTISH OPERA
Watermede, Wickhurst Road
Sevenoaks, Weald, Kent TN14 6LX
Website: www.kentishopera.fsnet.co.uk
          Tel: 01732 463284

LONDON OPERA PLAYERS
Broadmeade Copse, Westwood Lane
Wanborough, Near Guildford, Surrey GU3 2JN
Website: www.operaplayers.co.uk
e-mail: operaplayers@gmx.net
Fax: 01483 811721   Tel: 01483 811004

MUSIC THEATRE LONDON
Chertsey Chambers
12 Mercer Street, London WC2H 9QD
Website: www.mtl.org.uk
e-mail: musictheatre.london@virgin.net
Fax: 020-7240 0805   Tel: 020-7240 0919

OPERA DELLA LUNA
7 Cotmore House
Fringford, Bicester, Oxon OX6 9RQ
Website: www.operadellaluna.org
e-mail: operadellaluna@aol.com
Fax: 01869 323533   Tel: 01869 325131

OPERA NORTH
Grand Theatre, 46 New Briggate, Leeds LS1 6NU
Website: www.operanorth.co.uk
Fax: 0113-244 0418   Tel: 0113-243 9999

OPERA PICCOLA
8-14 Orsman Road, London N1 5QS
e-mail: info@operapiccola.com
Fax: 020-7713 6070   Tel: 020-7713 6062

PEGASUS OPERA COMPANY Ltd
The Brix, St Matthew's, Brixton Hill, London SW2 1JF
Website: www.pegopera.org
          Tel/Fax: 020-7501 9501

PIMLICO OPERA
5 Chancery Lane, London EC4A 1BU
e-mail: pimlico@grangeparkopera.co.uk
Fax: 020-7320 5429   Tel: 020-7320 5586

ROYAL OPERA The
Royal Opera House
Covent Garden
London WC2E 9DD   Tel: 020-7240 1200

SCOTTISH OPERA
39 Elmbank Crescent
Glasgow G2 4PT   Tel: 0141-248 4567

WELSH NATIONAL OPERA
John Street, Cardiff CF10 5SP
Website: www.wno.org.uk
e-mail: marketing@wno.org.uk
Fax: 029-2048 3050   Tel: 029-2046 4666

ACTING POSITIVE
22 Chaldon Road, London SW6 7NJ
e-mail: ianflintoff@aol.com   Tel: 020-7385 3800

ACTORCLUB Ltd
17 Inkerman Road, London NW5 3BT
Website: www.actorclub.co.uk
e-mail: johncunningham@actorclub.fsnet.co.uk
Tel: 020-7267 2759

ACTORS' ADVISORY SERVICE
29 Talbot Road, Twickenham
Middlesex TW2 6SJ   Tel: 020-8287 2839

ACTORS' BENEVOLENT FUND
6 Adam Street, London WC2N 6AD
Website: www.actorsbenevolentfund.co.uk
e-mail: office@abf.org.uk
Fax: 020-7836 8978   Tel: 020-7836 6378

ACTORS CENTRE The (LONDON)
1A Tower Street, London WC2H 9NP
Website: www.actorscentre.co.uk
e-mail: act@actorscentre.co.uk
Fax: 020-7240 3896   Tel: 020-7240 3940

ACTORS CENTRE The NORTH-EAST
1st Floor, 1 Black Swan Court
Westgate Road, Newcastle upon Tyne NE1 1SG
Website: www.actorscentrene.com
e-mail: actorscentrene@yahoo.com
Tel: 0191-221 0158

ACTORS CENTRE (NORTHERN)
(See NORTHERN ACTORS CENTRE)

ACTORS' CHARITABLE TRUST
Suite 255-256, Africa House
64-78 Kingsway, London WC2B 6BD
e-mail: admin@tactactors.org
Fax: 020 7242 0234   Tel: 020-7242 0111

ACTORS' CHURCH UNION
St Paul's Church, Bedford Street, London WC2E 9ED
e-mail: actors_church_union@yahoo.co.uk
Tel: 020-7240 0344

ADVERTISING ASSOCIATION
Abford House
15 Wilton Road, London SW1V 1NJ
e-mail: aa@adassoc.org.uk
Fax: 020-7931 0376   Tel: 020-7828 2771

AFTRA (American Federation of Television & Radio Artists)
5757 Wilshire Boulevard, 9th Floor
Los Angeles CA 90036   Tel: (323) 634-8100

AFTRA (American Federation of Television & Radio Artists)
260 Madison Avenue
New York NY 10016
Fax: (212) 545-1238   Tel: (212) 532-0800

AGENTS' ASSOCIATION Ltd (Great Britain)
54 Keyes House, Dolphin Square, London SW1V 3NA
Website: www.agents-uk.com
e-mail: association@agents-uk.com
Fax: 020-7821 0261   Tel: 020-7834 0515

AMATEUR DRAMATICS & OPERATICS DOTCOM
(Worldwide Directory of Amateur
Theatre - Jill Eccleston)
Website: www.amateurdramatics.com
e-mail: editor@amateurdramatics.com
Fax: 0870 1694836   Tel: 01257 450386

ARTS AND ENTERTAINMENT TECHNICAL TRAINING INITIATIVE (AETTI)
Lower Ground
14 Blenheim Terrace
London NW8 0EB
e-mail: aetti@sumack.freeserve.co.uk
Fax: 020-7328 5035   Tel: 020-7328 6174

ARTS & BUSINESS
Nutmeg House
60 Gainsford Street
Butlers Wharf, London SE1 2NY
e-mail: head.office@aandb.org.uk
Fax: 020-7407 7527   Tel: 020-7378 8143

ARTS CENTRE GROUP The
59A Portobello Road, London W11 3DB
Website: www.artscentregroup.org.uk
e-mail: info@artscentregroup.org.uk
Fax: 020-7221 7689   Tel: 020 7243 4550

ARTS COUNCIL OF ENGLAND
14 Great Peter Street
London SW1P 3NQ
Website: www.artscouncil.org.uk
e-mail: enquiries@artscouncil.org.uk
Fax: 020-7973 6590   Tel: 020-7973 6517

ARTS COUNCIL OF NORTHERN IRELAND
MacNeice House
77 Malone Road, Belfast BT9 6AQ
Fax: 028-9066 1715   Tel: 028-9038 5200

ARTS COUNCIL OF WALES
9 Museum Place, Cardiff CF10 3NX
Website: www.ccc-acw.org.uk
e-mail: information@ccc-acw.org.uk
Fax: 029-2022 1447   Tel: 029-2037 6500

ARTSLINE
(Disabled Actors' Information)
54 Chalton Street
London NW1 1HS
e-mail: access@artsline.org.uk
Fax: 020-7383 2653   Tel: 020-7388 2474

ASSOCIATION OF BRITISH THEATRE TECHNICIANS
47 Bermondsey Street, London SE1 3XT
Website: www.abtt.org.uk
Fax: 020-7378 6170   Tel: 020-7403 3778

ASSOCIATION OF LIGHTING DESIGNERS
PO Box 89, Welwyn Garden City AL7 1ZW
Website: www.ald.org.uk
e-mail: office@ald.org.uk   Tel/Fax: 01707 891848

ASSOCIATION OF MODEL AGENTS
122 Brompton Road, London SW3 1JE
Info. Line: 09068 517644   Tel: 020-7584 6466

ASSOCIATION OF PROFESSIONAL THEATRE FOR CHILDREN & YOUNG PEOPLE (APT)
c/o Brian Bishop, Warwick Arts Centre
University of Warwick, Coventry CV4 7AL
e-mail: b.c.bishop@warwick.ac.uk
Fax: 024-7652 3883   Tel: 024-7652 4252

BECTU
(See BROADCASTING ENTERTAINMENT CINEMATOGRAPH & THEATRE UNION)

BRITISH ACADEMY OF COMPOSERS & SONGWRITERS The
2nd Floor, British Music House
26 Berners Street, London W1T 3LR
Website: www.britishacademy.com
e-mail: info@britishacademy.com
Fax: 020-7636 2212   Tel: 020-7636 2929

BRITISH ACADEMY OF FILM & TELEVISION ARTS (LOS ANGELES) The
8533 Melrose Avenue
Suite D, West Hollywood, CA 90069
e-mail: info@baftala.org
Fax: (310) 854-6002   Tel: (310) 652-4121

BRITISH ACADEMY OF FILM & TELEVISION ARTS The
195 Piccadilly, London W1J 9LN
Website: www.bafta.org
e-mail: membership@bafta.org
Fax: 020-7437 0473   Tel: 020-7734 0022

BRITISH ACADEMY OF STAGE AND SCREEN COMBAT
Suite 280, 37 Store Street, London WC1E 7QF
Website: www.bassc.org
e-mail: info@bassc.org   Tel: 020-8352 0605

BRITISH ASSOCIATION OF DRAMA THERAPISTS The
41 Broomhouse Lane, London SW6 3DP
Website: www.badth.co.uk
e-mail: gillian@badth.demon.co.uk
          Tel/Fax: 020-7731 0160

BRITISH BOARD OF FILM CLASSIFICATION
3 Soho Square, London W1D 3HD
Website: www.bbfc.co.uk
Fax: 020-7287 0141   Tel: 020-7440 1570

BRITISH COUNCIL The
(Drama & Dance Unit)
Before July 2003:
11 Portland Place, London W1B 1EJ
Website: www.theatredance.britishcouncil.org.uk
e-mail: theatredance@britishcouncil.org
Fax: 020-7389 3088   Tel: 020-7389 3097
After July 2003:
11 Spring Gardens, London SW1A 2BN

BRITISH FILM COMMISSION
10 Little Portland Street, London W1W 7JG
Website: www.bfc.co.uk
e-mail: info@bfc.co.uk
Fax: 020-7861 7864   Tel: 020-7861 7860

BRITISH FILM INSTITUTE
21 Stephen Street, London W1T 1LN
e-mail: library@bfi.org.uk
Fax: 020-7436 2338   Tel: 020-7255 1444

BRITISH LIBRARY NATIONAL SOUND ARCHIVE
96 Euston Road, London NW1 2DB
Website: www.bl.uk/nsa
e-mail: nsa@bl.uk
Fax: 020-7412 7441   Tel: 020-7412 7440

BRITISH MUSIC HALL SOCIETY
(Secretary: Daphne Masterton)
82 Fernlea Road, London SW12 9RW
Tel: 020-8673 2175   Tel: 01727 768878

BRITISH PERFORMING ARTS MEDICINE TRUST The
196 Shaftesbury Avenue
London WC2H 8JF   Tel: 020-7240 3331

BROADCASTING ENTERTAINMENT CINEMATOGRAPH & THEATRE UNION (BECTU) (Formerly BETA & ACTT)
111 Wardour Street, London W1V 4AY
e-mail: smacdonald@bectu.org.uk
Fax: 020-7437 8268   Tel: 020-7437 8506

CASTING DIRECTORS' GUILD
PO Box 34403, London W6 0YG
Website: www.castingdirectorsguild.co.uk
          Tel/Fax: 020-8741 1951

CATHOLIC STAGE GUILD
(Write SAE)
Ms Molly Steele (Hon Secretary)
1 Maiden Lane
London WC2E 7NB   Tel: 020-7240 1221

CELEBRITY SERVICE Ltd
Room 203-209
93-97 Regent Street, London W1B 4ES
e-mail: celebritylondon@aol.com
Fax: 020-7494 3500   Tel: 020-7439 9840

CHILDREN'S FILM & TELEVISION FOUNDATION Ltd
Elstree Film and Television Studios
Borehamwood, Herts WD6 1JG
e-mail: annahome@cftf.onyxnet.co.uk
Fax: 020-8207 0860   Tel: 020-8953 0844

CINEMA EXHIBITORS' ASSOCIATION
22 Golden Square, London W1F 9JW
e-mail: cea@cinemauk.ftech.co.uk
Fax: 020-7734 6147   Tel: 020-7734 9551

CINEMA & TELEVISION BENEVOLENT FUND (CTBF)
22 Golden Square, London W1F 9AD
Website: www.ctbf.co.uk
e-mail: charity@ctbf.co.uk
Fax: 020-7437 7186   Tel: 020-7437 6567

CLUB FOR ACTS & ACTORS
(Incorporating Concert Artistes Association)
20 Bedford Street, London WC2E 9HP
Office: 020-7836 3172   Members: 020-7836 2884

COI COMMUNICATIONS
(Television)
Hercules Road, London SE1 7DU
e-mail: eileen.newton@coi.gsi.gov.uk
Fax: 020-7261 8776   Tel: 020-7261 8220

COMPANY OF CRANKS
1st Floor, 62 Northfield House
Frensham Street, London SE15 6TN
e-mail: nostring@dircon.co.uk   Tel: 020-7358 0571

Providing a space of energy and inspiration where professional actors can experiment, share creativity, meet new challenges and pursue excellence.

Providing a meeting place where professional actors can develop ideas, exchange information and support one another.

Subsidised Classes

- audition technique
- dialect
- sight reading
- singing
- voice

- Alexander technique
- fencing/stage combat
- movement
- dance

- film
- musical theatre
- poetry reading
- radio
- television
- writing

- career advice
- casting sessions
- financial advice

Tristan Bates Theatre

A vibrant and varied programme of play readings and showcases for invited audiences

The Green Room Bar and Restaurant

Drinks & Snacks

Audition Rooms

Available for hire - ranging from 10 x 15 to 54 x 40
Line - learning service available

If you would like a copy of our current programme please telephone:

020 7240 3940

1A Tower Street Covent Garden WC2H 9NP

or

act@actorscentre.co.uk

Founding Patron: Lord Olivier   **Patron:** Alan Bates CBE
Patron: 1983-94: Sir Alec Guinness   **Artistic Director:** Mark Wing-Davey

CONCERT ARTISTES ASSOCIATION
(See CLUB FOR ACTS & ACTORS)

CONFERENCE OF DRAMA SCHOOLS
(Saul Hyman, Executive Secretary)
PO Box 34252, London NW5 1XJ
e-mail: enquiries@cds.drama.ac.uk
Tel/Fax: 020-7692 0032

**COUNCIL FOR DANCE EDUCATION AND
TRAINING (CDET)**
Toynbee Hall, 28 Commercial Street, London E1 6LS
Website: www.cdet.org.uk
e-mail: info@cdet.org.uk
Fax: 020-7247 3404   Tel: 020-7247 4030

CPMA
(Co-operative Personal Management Association)
The Secretary, c/o 1 Mellor Road, Leicester LE3 6HN
e-mail: cpmauk@yahoo.co.uk
Tel: 0116-233 8432

CRITICS' CIRCLE The
c/o 69 Marylebone Lane, London W1U 2PH
Website: www.criticscircle.org.uk
Tel: 020-7224 1410

DENVILLE HALL
(Nursing Home)
62 Ducks Hill Road, Northwood, Middlesex HA6 2SB
Website: www.denvillehall.org
e-mail: denvillehall@yahoo.com
Fax: 01923 841855   Office: 01923 825843

DEVOTEES OF HAMMER The
(Fan Club)
14 Kingsdale Road, London SE18 2DG
e-mail: 07960969318@one2one.net
Tel: 020-8244 8640

DIRECTORS' AND PRODUCERS' RIGHTS SOCIETY The
Victoria Chambers
16-18 Strutton Ground, London SW1P 2HP
e-mail: info@dprs.org.uk
Fax: 020-7227 4755   Tel: 020-7227 4757

DIRECTORS GUILD OF GREAT BRITAIN
Acorn House
314-320 Gray's Inn Road, London WC1X 8DP
e-mail: guild@dggb.co.uk
Fax: 020-7278 4742   Tel: 020-7278 4343

D'OYLY CARTE OPERA COMPANY
The Powerhouse
6 Sancroft Street, London SE11 5UD
Website: www.doylycarte.org.uk
e-mail: mail@doylycarte.org.uk
Fax: 020-7793 7300   Tel: 020-7793 7100

DRAMA ASSOCIATION OF WALES
(Specialist Drama Lending Library)
The Old Library
Singleton Road, Splott, Cardiff CF24 2ET
Fax: 029-2045 2277   Tel: 029-2045 2200

DRAMATURGS' NETWORK
(Production & Literary Dramaturgy)
139B Tooting Bec Road, London SW17 8BW
Website: www.dramaturgy.co.uk
e-mail: hanna.slattne@dramaturgy.co.uk
Tel: 020-8767 6004

EDINBURGHREVIEW.COM
The Bull Theatre
68 The High Street, Barnet, Herts EN5 5SJ
Website: www.edinburghreview.com
e-mail: mail@edinburghreview.com
Fax: 020-8449 5252   Tel: 020-8449 7800

ENGLISH FOLK DANCE AND SONG SOCIETY
Cecil Sharp House
2 Regent's Park Road, London NW1 7AY
Website: www.efdss.org.info
e-mail: info@efdss.org
Fax: 020-7284 0534   Tel: 020-7485 2206

EQUITY inc Variety Artistes' Federation
Guild House
Upper St Martin's Lane, London WC2H 9EG
Website: www.equity.org.uk
e-mail: info@equity.org.uk
Fax: 020-7379 7001   Tel: 020-7379 6000

**EQUITY inc Variety Artistes' Federation
(North West)**
Conavon Court
12 Blackfriars Street, Salford M3 5BQ
e-mail: info@manchester-equity.org.uk
Fax: 0161-839 3133   Tel: 0161-832 3183

**EQUITY inc Variety Artistes' Federation
(Scotland & Northern Ireland)**
114 Union Street, Glasgow G1 3QQ
e-mail: igilchrist@glasgow.equity.org.uk
Fax: 0141-248 2473   Tel: 0141-248 2472

**EQUITY inc Variety Artistes' Federation
(Wales & South West)**
Transport House, 1 Cathedral Road, Cardiff CF1 9SD
e-mail: info@cardiff-equity.co.uk
Fax: 029-2023 0754   Tel: 029-2039 7971

ETF (Equity Trust Fund)
Suite 222, Africa House
64 Kingsway, London WC2B 6BD
Fax: 020-7831 4953   Tel: 020-7404 6041

F.A.A.
(See FILM ARTISTS ASSOCIATION)

FILM ARTISTS ASSOCIATION
(Amalgamated with B.E.C.T.U.)
373-377 Clapham Road, London SW9
Fax: 020-7437 8268   Tel: 020-7437 8506

GLASGOW FILM FINANCE
(Production Finance for Feature Films)
249 West George Street, Glasgow G2 4QE
Fax: 0141-302 1714   Tel: 0141-302 1757

GRAND ORDER OF WATER RATS
328 Gray's Inn Road, London WC1X 8BZ
Website: www.gowr.net
e-mail: water.rats@virgin.net
Fax: 020-7278 1765   Tel: 020-7278 3248

GROUP LINE
(Group Bookings for London Theatre)
22-24 Torrington Place, London WC1E 7HF
Fax: 020-7436 6287   Tel: 020-7580 6793

GUY Gillian ASSOCIATES
84A Tachbrook Street, London SW1V 2NB
Website: www.show-pairs.co.uk
Fax: 020-7976 5885   Tel: 020-7976 5888

INDEPENDENT TELEVISION COMMISSION (ITC)
33 Foley Street
London W1W 7TL
Website: www.itc.org.uk
e-mail: publicaffairs@itc.org.uk   Tel: 020-7255 3000

INDEPENDENT THEATRE COUNCIL (ITC)
12 The Leathermarket
Weston Street, London SE1 3ER
e-mail: admin@itc-arts.org
Fax: 020-7403 1745   Tel: 020-7403 1727

INSIGHT ARTS TRUST
7-15 Greatorex Street
London E1 5NF
e-mail: iat@insightartstrust.demon.co.uk
Fax: 020-7247 8077   Tel: 020-7247 0778

INTERNATIONAL FEDERATION OF ACTORS (FIA)
Guild House
Upper St Martin's Lane, London WC2H 9EG
Website: www.fia-actors.com
e-mail: office@fia-actors.com
Fax: 020-7379 8260   Tel: 020-7379 0900

INTERNATIONAL THEATRE INSTITUTE
Goldsmiths College, University of London
Lewisham Way, New Cross, London SE14 6NW
Website: http://iti.gold.ac.uk
e-mail: iti@gold.ac.uk
Fax: 020-7919 7277   Tel: 020-7919 7276

INTERNATIONAL VISUAL COMMUNICATION
ASSOCIATION (IVCA)
19 Pepper Street, Glengall Bridge, London E14 9RP
e-mail: info@ivca.org
Fax: 020-7512 0591   Tel: 020-7512 0571

IRISH ACTORS' EQUITY GROUP (SIPTU)
9th Floor, Liberty Hall, Dublin 1
Fax: 00 353 1 8743691   Tel: 00 353 1 8586403

IRVING SOCIETY The
(Michael Kilgariff, Chairman)
10 Kings Avenue, London W5 2SH
e-mail: m.killy@virgin.net   Tel: 020-8566 8301

ITC
(See INDEPENDENT TELEVISION COMMISION)

ITC
(See INDEPENDENT THEATRE COUNCIL)

ITV - NETWORK Ltd
200 Gray's Inn Road, London WC1X 8HF
Fax: 020-7843 8158   Tel: 020-7843 8000

LIAISON OF ACTORS, MANAGEMENTS
& PLAYWRIGHTS (LAMP)
(W Robi)
86A Elgin Avenue
London W9   Tel: 020-7289 3031

LONDON FILM COMMISSION
20 Euston Centre
Regent's Place, London NW1 3JH
Website: www.london-film.co.uk
e-mail: lfc@london-film.co.uk
Fax: 020-7387 8788   Tel: 020-7387 8787

LONDON SCHOOL OF CAPOEIRA The
Units 1 & 2 Leeds Place
Tollington Park, London N4 3RQ
Website: www.londonschoolofcapoeira.co.uk
                            Tel: 020-7281 2020

LONDON SHAKESPEARE WORKOUT The
181A Faunce House
Doddington Grove, Kennington, London SE17 3TB
Website: www.londonshakespeare.org.uk
e-mail: londonswo@hotmail.com
Fax: 020-7735 5911   Tel: 020-7793 9755

MANDER & MITCHENSON THEATRE COLLECTION
Jerwood Library of the Performing Arts
King Charles Building, Old Royal Naval College
Greenwich, London SE10 9JF
e-mail: rmangan@tcm.ac.uk   Tel: 020-8305 3893

MECHANICAL-COPYRIGHT PROTECTION SOCIETY Ltd (MCPS)
Elgar House, 41 Streatham High Road
London SW16 1ER   Tel: 020-8664 4400

MUSICIANS' UNION
60-64 Clapham Road
London SW9 0JJ   Tel: 020-7582 5566

NATIONAL ASSOCIATION OF YOUTH THEATRES (NAYT)
Arts Centre, Vane Terrace, Darlington DL3 7AX
Website: www.nayt.org.uk
e-mail: naytuk@aol.com
Fax: 01325 363313   Tel: 01325 363330

NATIONAL CAMPAIGN FOR THE ARTS
Pegasus House
37-43 Sackville Street, London W1S 3EH
Website: www.artscampaign.org.uk
e-mail: nca@artscampaign.org.uk
Fax: 020-7333 0660   Tel: 020-7333 0375

NATIONAL COUNCIL FOR DRAMA TRAINING
5 Tavistock Place, London WC1H 9SS
Website: www.ncdt.co.uk
e-mail: info@ncdt.co.uk
Fax: 020-7681 4733   Tel: 020-7387 3650

NATIONAL ENTERTAINMENT AGENTS COUNCIL
PO Box 112, Seaford, East Sussex BN25 2DQ
Website: www.neac.org.uk
e-mail: chrisbray@neac.org.uk
Fax: 01323 492234   Tel: 01323 492488

NATIONAL FILM THEATRE
South Bank, Waterloo, London SE1 8XT
Website: www.bfi.org.uk
e-mail: temp.two@bfi.org.uk   Tel: 020-7928 3535

NATIONAL RESOURCE CENTRE FOR DANCE
University of Surrey, Guildford, Surrey GU2 7XH
Website: www.surrey.ac.uk/NRCD
e-mail: nrcd@surrey.ac.uk   Tel: 01483 259316

NATIONAL YOUTH MUSIC THEATRE
5th Floor, The Palace Theatre
Shaftesbury Avenue, London W1D 5AY
Website: www.nymt.org.uk
e-mail: enquiries@nymt.org.uk
Fax: 020-7734 7515   Tel: 020-7734 7478

NODA (National Operatic & Dramatic Association)
1 Crestfield Street, London WC1H 8AU
Website: www.noda.org.uk
e-mail: everyone@noda.org.uk
Fax: 0870 7702490   Tel: 0870 7702480

NORTH AMERICAN ACTORS' ASSOCIATION
1 De Vere Cottages
Canning Place, London W8 5AA
Website: www.naaa.org.uk
e-mail: americanactors@aol.com
Tel/Fax: 020-7938 4722

NORTH WEST PLAYWRIGHTS
18 St Margaret's Chambers
5 Newton Street, Manchester M1 1HL
Website: www.newplaysnw.com
e-mail: newplaysnw@hotmail.com
Tel/Fax: 0161-237 1978

NORTHERN ACTORS' CENTRE
30 St Margaret's Chambers
5 Newton Street, Manchester M1 1HL
Website: www.northernactors.co.uk
Tel/Fax: 0161-236 0041

PACT (PRODUCERS ALLIANCE FOR CINEMA & TELEVISION)
(Trade Association for Independent Television,
Feature Film & New Media Production Companies)
45 Mortimer Street, London W1W 8HJ
Website: www.pact.co.uk
e-mail: enquiries@pact.co.uk
Fax: 020-7331 6700   Tel: 020-7331 6000

PERFORMING RIGHT SOCIETY Ltd
29-33 Berners Street, London W1T 3AB
Fax: 020-7306 4455   Tel: 020-7580 5544

PERSONAL MANAGERS' ASSOCIATION Ltd
Rivercroft, 1 Summer Road, East Molesey
Surrey KT8 9LX
e-mail: info@thepma.com   Tel/Fax: 020-8398 9796

RADIO AUTHORITY The
Holbrook House, 14 Great Queen Street
Holborn, London WC2B 5DG
Fax: 020-7405 7062   Tel: 020-7430 2724

ROYAL TELEVISION SOCIETY
Holborn Hall
100 Gray's Inn Road, London WC1X 8AL
Website: www.rts.org.uk
e-mail: info@rts.org.uk
Fax: 020-7430 0924   Tel: 020-7430 1000

ROYAL THEATRICAL FUND
11 Garrick Street, London WC2E 9AR
e-mail: admin@trtf.com
Fax: 020-7379 8273   Tel: 020-7836 3322

S A G (Screen Actors Guild)
5757 Wilshire Boulevard, Los Angeles, CA 90036-3600
Fax: (323) 549-6656   Tel: (323) 954-1600

1515 Broadway, 44th Floor
New York NY 10036   Tel: (212) 944-1030

SAVE LONDON'S THEATRES CAMPAIGN
Guild House
Upper St Martin's Lane, London WC2H 9EG
Fax: 020-7379 7001   Tel: 020-7670 0270

SCOTTISH ARTS COUNCIL
12 Manor Place, Edinburgh EH3 7DD
Fax: 0131-225 9833   Tel: 0131-226 6051

SCOTTISH SCREEN PRODUCTION & DEVELOPMENT
249 West George Street, Glasgow G2 4QE
Website: www.scottishscreen.com
e-mail: info@scottishscreen.com
Fax: 0141-302 1711   Tel: 0141-302 1700

SCREENWRITER'S WORKSHOP The
Screenwriters' Centre, Suffolk House
1-8 Whitfield Place, London W1T 5JU
Website: www.lsw.org.uk
e-mail: screenoffice@tiscali.co.uk
Tel: 020-7387 5511

SOCIETY FOR THEATRE RESEARCH
c/o The Theatre Museum
1E Tavistock Street, London WC2E 7PR
Website: www.blot.co.uk/str
e-mail: e.cottis@btinternet.com

SOCIETY OF AUTHORS
84 Drayton Gardens, London SW10 9SB
e-mail: info@societyofauthors.org
Tel: 020-7373 6642

SOCIETY OF BRITISH THEATRE DESIGNERS
47 Bermondsey Street, London SE1 3XT
Website: www.theatredesign.org.uk
Fax: 020-7378 6170   Tel: 020-7403 3778

SOCIETY OF LONDON THEATRE (SOLT)
32 Rose Street, London WC2E 9ET
e-mail: enquiries@solttma.co.uk
Fax: 020-7557 6799   Tel: 020-7557 6700

SOCIETY OF TEACHERS OF SPEECH AND DRAMA The
Registered Office:
73 Berry Hill Road, Mansfield, Notts NG18 4RU
Website: www.stsd.org.uk
e-mail: ann.p.jones@btinternet.com
Tel: 01623 627636

SOCIETY OF THEATRE CONSULTANTS
47 Bermondsey Street, London SE1 3XT
Fax: 020-7378 6170   Tel: 020-7403 3778

STAGE CRICKET CLUB
39-41 Hanover Steps
St George's Fields, Albion Street, London W2 2YG
e-mail: brianjfilm@aol.com
Fax: 020-7262 5736   Tel: 020-7402 7543

STAGE GOLFING SOCIETY
Sudbrook Park, Sudbrook Lane, Richmond
Surrey TW10 7AS   Tel: 020-8940 8861

STAGE MANAGEMENT ASSOCIATION
47 Bermondsey Street, London SE1 3XT
Website: www.stagemanagementassociation.co.uk
e-mail: admin@stagemanagementassociation.co.uk
Fax: 020-7378 6170   Tel: 020-7403 6655

STAGECOACH! (WEST MIDLANDS) Ltd
(West Midlands Playwrights - Training & Support)
Broad Street House
212-213 Broad Street, Birmingham B15 1AY
e-mail: stagecoach@playwriting.fsnet.co.uk
                              Tel/Fax: 0121-633 7475

STANDING CONFERENCE OF YOUNG PEOPLES THEATRE (SCYPT)
(Office Manager: Ray Beaumont)
Valleys Kids, Penygraig Community Project
1 Cross Street, Penygraig
Tonypandy, Rhondda Cynon Taff CF40 1LD
Fax: 01443 420877   Tel: 01443 438770

THEATRE INVESTMENT FUND Ltd
32 Rose Street, London WC2E 9ET
Fax: 020-7557 6799   Tel: 020-7557 6737

THEATRE MUSEUM The
1E Tavistock Street, London WC2E 7PR
Website: www.theatremuseum.org
Fax: 020-7943 4777   Tel: 020-7943 4700

THEATRES TRUST The
22 Charing Cross Road, London WC2H 0QL
Website: www.theatrestrust.org.uk
e-mail: info@theatrestrust.org.uk
Fax: 020-7836 3302   Tel: 020 7836 8591

THEATRICAL GUILD The
PO Box 22712, London N22 5AG
Website: www.the-theatrical-guild-org-uk
e-mail: admin@the-theatrical-guild.org.uk
                              Tel: 020-8889 7570

THEATRICAL MANAGEMENT ASSOCIATION
(See TMA)

TMA
(Theatrical Management Association)
32 Rose Street, London WC2E 9ET
e-mail: enquiries@solttma.co.uk
Fax: 020-7557 6799   Tel: 020-7557 6700

UK CHOREOGRAPHERS' DIRECTORY The
c/o Dance UK, Battersea Arts Centre
Lavender Hill, London SW11 5TN
Website: www.danceuk.org
e-mail: info@danceuk.org
Fax: 020-7223 0074   Tel: 020-7228 4990

UK THEATRE CLUBS
54 Swallow Drive, London NW10 8TG
e-mail: uktheatreclubs@aol.com
                              Tel/Fax: 020-8459 3972

UNITED KINGDOM COPYRIGHT BUREAU
110 Trafalgar Road, Portslade, East Sussex BN41 1GS
e-mail: info@copyrightbureau.co.uk
Fax: 01273 705451   Tel: 01273 277333

VARIETY CLUB OF GREAT BRITAIN
Variety Club House
93 Bayham Street, London NW1 0AG
Website: www.varietyclub.org.uk
e-mail: info@varietyclub.org.uk
Fax: 020-7428 8111   Tel: 020-7428 8100

VARIETY & LIGHT ENTERTAINMENT COUNCIL
54 Keyes House, Dolphin Square, London SW1V 3NA
Fax: 020-7821 0261   Tel: 020-7798 5622

WOLFF Peter THEATRE TRUST The
(Neal Foster Executive Director)
Suite 612, 162 Regent Street, London W1B 5TG
e-mail: info@peterwolfftheatretrust.org
Fax: 020-7437 3395   Tel: 020-7494 4662

WOMEN IN FILM AND TELEVISION
6 Langley Street, London WC2H 9JA
e-mail: info@wftv.org.uk
Fax: 020-7379 1625   Tel: 020-7240 4875

WRITERNET
Cabin V, Clarendon Buildings
25 Horsell Road, London N5 1XL
Website: www.writernet.org.uk
e-mail: writernet@btinternet.com
Fax: 020-7609 7557   Tel: 020-7609 7474

WRITERS' GUILD OF GREAT BRITAIN The
430 Edgware Road, London W2 1EH
Website: www.writersguild.org.uk
e-mail: admin@writersguild.org.uk
Fax: 020-7706 2413   Tel: 020-7723 8074

Photographers

Each photographer listed in this section has taken an advertisement in this edition.
Also see Index to Advertisers pages 321-322.

ABACUS PHOTOGRAPHY
Website: www.abacus-photography.co.uk
Tel: 01793 537257

ACTORS'S ONE STOP SHOP
Website: www.actorsone-stopshop.com
Tel: 020-8888 7006

ALLEN Stuart
Website: www.stuartallenphotos.com
Mobile: 07776 258829

ANNAND Simon
Mobile: 07884 446776   Tel: 020-7241 6725

BACON Ric   Mobile: 07970 970799

BAKER Chris   Tel: 020-8441 3851

BAKER Sophie   Tel: 020-8340 3850

BURNETT Sheila
Website: www.sheilaburnett-photography.com
Tel: 020-7289 3058

BURRETT Anthony   Tel: 020-8658 8918

CARPENTER TURNER Robert
Website: www.carpenterturner.co.uk
e-mail: robert@carpenterturner.co.uk
Fax: 020-7624 7773   Tel: 020-7624 2225

CARTER Charlie   Tel: 020-7751 0575

CASSON Jessie   Mobile: 07968 235689

CLARK John
e-mail: clarkdigital@btopenworld.com
Tel: 020-8854 4069

DANCE SCENE PHOTOGRAPHIC
Mobile: 07702 747123   Tel: 01737 552874

DEBAL
Website: www.debal.co.uk   Tel: 020-8568 2122

DE LENG Stephanie
Mobile: 07740 927765   Tel: 0151-476 1563

DEUCHAR Angus
Website: www.actorsphotos.co.uk
Mobile: 07973 600728   Tel: 020-8286 3303

DOCKAR-DRYSDALE Jonathan
Mobile: 07711 006191   Tel: 020-8560 1077

DOMINIC Magnus   Tel: 020-7700 6475

EDDOWES Mike
Website: www.theatre-photography.co.uk
e-mail: mike@photo-publicity.co.uk
Mobile: 07970 141005   Tel: 01903 882525

EVANS Owen   Mobile: 07940 700294

EYRE Anne
Website: www.eyrephoto.co.uk   Tel: 020-7638 1289

FERNANDES David
Website: www.image2film.com
Mobile: 07958 272333

FLETCHER John   Tel: 020-8203 4816

FONTAINE Desi
Website: www.desifontaine.co.uk
Tel: 020-8878 4348

FRANKS Elliott
e-mail: frankse@aol.com
Website: www.elliottfranks.com
Mobile: 07802 537220   Tel: 020-8544 0156

FRENCH Charles
Mobile: 07946 565510   Tel/Fax: 020-8878 2784

GALATEA STUDIO
e-mail: galateastudio@yahoo.com
Mobile: 07957 352832   Tel: 020-7724 4591

GILL James   Tel: 020-7735 5632

GOOD IMAGES
Website: www.goodimages.com
Mobile: 07788 138427

GREENBERG Natasha
Mobile: 07932 618111   Tel: 020-8677 8753

GREGAN Nick
Website: www.nickgregan.com
e-mail: nick@nickgreganphotos.demon.co.uk
Fax: 020-7538 8778
Mobile: 07774 421878   Tel: 020-7358 1249

GRIFFIN Charles
Website: www.charlesgriffinphotography.co.uk
Tel: 01244 535252

GROGAN Claire
Website: www.clairegrogan.co.uk
Mobile: 07932 653381   Tel: 020-7272 1845

HALL Chris
Website: www.chrishallphotography.co.uk
Mobile: 07831 541342   Tel: 020-8845 5229

HALL Peter
e-mail: peter@peterhall.fsnet.co.uk
Tel: 020-8981 2822

HANDZEL
e-mail: richslife@hotmail.com
Mobile: 07855 551382   Tel: 020-8785 9623

HARWOOD-STAMPER Daniel
Mobile: 07966 236865   Tel: 020-7930 1372

HINE Paul
Mobile: 07941 929786   Tel: 020-7240 5020

HOYLE Mike/FOTO-GRAFIX
e-mail: mhoyle6814@aol.com
Mobile: 07790 672681   Tel: 020-7837 1724

IMAGE 2 Ltd
Website: www.image2photo.co.uk
Tel: 01923 775098

INGRAM Winston   Tel: 020-8459 2543

JAMES David
Website: www.djphotos.clara.co.uk
Mobile: 07808 597362

KELLY Luke   Tel: 020-8878 2823

KOPPEL David
Mobile: 07831 838378   Tel: 020-8349 0001

LATIMER Carole
Fax: 020-7229 9306   Tel: 020-7727 9371

LAWTON Steve   Mobile: 07973 307487

LB PHOTOGRAPHY
Mobile: 07885 966192   Tel: 01737 224578

LEVINE David
Website: www.davidlevine.co.uk
Tel: 020-7613 2070

McCREE Jonathan
Mobile: 07789 633061   Tel: 020-7228 3475

Photographers

M.A.D. PHOTOGRAPHY
Website: www.mad-photograpghy.co.uk
Tel: 020-8363 4182

MILES Sally
Website: www.sallymiles.com   Tel: 020-8360 7372

MILES Tom
Website: www.portfolioshoot.com
Mobile: 07770 787249   Tel: 020-7564 0661

NAMDAR Fatimah   Tel: 020-8341 1332

NIXON Kevin
Mobile: 07973 760590   Tel: 020-8340 4598

OAKLEY Stuart
Website: www.oakleystuart.co.uk
e-mail: oakleystuart@hotmail.com
Mobile: 07813 813176

PASSPORT PHOTO SERVICE   Tel: 020-7629 8540

POLLARD Michael
Website: www.michaelpollard.co.uk
Tel: 0161-456 7470

PORTR8T PHOTOGRAPHY (Clare Bourke)
Mobile: 07768 706575   Tel: 020-7733 8678

POTTER David
Website: www.davidpotterphoto.com
Mobile: 07973 579988

RAFIQUE Harry
Website: www.hr-photographer.co.uk
Tel: 020-7266 5398

RENDELL Jeremy
Website: www.jeremyrendell.com
e-mail: jeremy@rendell-photo.demon.co.uk
Mobile: 07860 277411

ROYAL Edd
e-mail: eddroyal@hotmail.com
Mobile: 07814 020808

STJOHN Amanda
Mobile: 07732 771384   Tel: 01892 521282

SAYER Howard
e-mail: howard@howardsayer.com
Mobile: 07860 559891   Tel: 01932 221651

SHAKESPEARE LANE Catherine
Tel: 020-7226 7694

SIMPKIN Peter
e-mail: petersimpkin@aol.com
Mobile: 07973 224084   Tel: 020-8883 2727

SMIT Frans   Mobile: 07813 989372

SMITH Lucy
Website: www.thatlucy.co.uk   Tel: 020-7498 6182

STILL Rosie
Website: www.rosiestillphotography.com
Mobile: 07957 318919   Tel: 020-8857 6920

STRAEGER Anthony
Website: www.straegerphoto.co.uk
Mobile: 07961 184888   Tel: 020-8769 7031

SUMMERS Caroline   Tel: 020-7223 7669

THOMPSON Paul
e-mail: paulthomps@aol.com
Mobile: 07967 800589   Tel: 020-8337 6631

TM PHOTOGRAPHY
Website: www.tmphotography.co.uk
e-mail: tony@tmphotography.co.uk
Mobile: 07931 755252   Tel: 020-8924 4694

TOPSHOTS   Mobile: 07855 586177

TWINNING John
e-mail: iron.stone@btopenworld.com
Tel: 0121-515 2906

VANDYCK Katie
Website: www.iphotou.co.uk
Mobile: 07941 940259   Tel: 020-7733 9297

WAITE Charlie
Website: landscape@charliewaite.com
Mobile: 07831 364764   Tel: 020-7622 5353

WILKINSON Mark   Mobile: 07713 219648

WILL C
Website: www.billysnapper.com
e-mail: billy_snapper@hotmail.com Tel/Fax: 020-8438 0202

WILLIAMS Colin
Website: www.photocol.co.uk
Mobile: 07957 188983

WOOLNOUGH Laura
Mobile: 07941 018957   Tel: 020-8674 3078

WORKMAN Robert
Website: www.robertworkman.demon.co.uk
Tel: 020-7385 5442

Press Cutting Agencies

BROADCAST MONITORING COMPANY The
89½ Worship Street
London EC2A 2BF
Fax: 020-7377 6103   Tel: 020-7377 1742

DURRANTS
(Media Monitoring Agency)
Discovery House, 28-42 Banner Street
London EC1Y 8QE
Website: www.durrants.co.uk
e-mail: sales@durrants.co.uk
Fax: 020-7674 0222   Tel: 020-7674 0200

INFORMATION BUREAU The
51 The Business Centre
103 Lavender Hill, London SW11 5QL
Website: www.infobureau.co.uk
e-mail: infobureau@dial.pipex.com
Fax: 020-7738 2513   Tel: 020-7924 4414

INTERNATIONAL PRESS-CUTTING BUREAU
224-236 Walworth Road
London SE17 1JE
e-mail: ipcb2000@aol.com
Fax: 020-7701 4489   Tel: 020-7708 2113

McCALLUM MEDIA MONITOR
Tower House
10 Possil Road, Glasgow G4 9SY
Website: www.press-cuttings.com
Fax: 0141-333 1811   Tel: 0141-333 1822

TNS MEDIA INTELLIGENCE
6th Floor
292 Vauxhall Bridge Road
London SW1V 1AE
Fax: 020-7963 7609   Tel: 020-7963 7605

07000 BIG TOP
(Big Top, Seating, Circus)
The Arts Exchange, Congleton, Cheshire CW12 1JG
Website: www.circus-online.co.uk
e-mail: phillipgandey@netcentral.co.uk
Fax: 01260 270777   Tel: 01260 276627

10 OUT OF 10 PRODUCTIONS Ltd
(Lighting, Sound, AV Hire, Sales and Installation)
Unit 14 Forest Hill Business Centre
Clyde Vale, London SE23 3JF
Website: www.10outof10.co.uk
e-mail: sales@10outof10.co.uk
Fax: 020-8699 8968   Tel: 020-8291 6885

20TH CENTURY FUNFAIR FACTORY
(Fun Fair Locations, Equipment and Prop Hire)
Plot 24 The Plantation
West Park Road, New Chapel, Surrey RH7 6HT
Mobile: 07976 297735   Tel: 01342 717707

3D CREATIONS
(Production Design, Scenery Contractors,
Prop Makers & Scenic Artists)
9 Keppel Road, Gorleston-on-Sea
Great Yarmouth, Norfolk NR31 6SN
Website: www.3d-creations.co.uk
e-mail: 3dcreations@rjt.co.uk
Fax: 01493 443124   Tel: 01493 652055

A. S. DESIGNS
(Theatrical Designer, Sets, Costumes,
Heads, Masks, Puppets etc)
Website: www.astheatricaldesign.co.uk
e-mail: maryannscadding@btinternet.com
Fax: 01279 435642   Tel: 01279 722416

fREEDALE PRESS
36 HEDLEY STREET
MAIDSTONE
KENT
ME14 5AD

For All Your Printing Requirements Please Contact
MICHAEL FREEMAN
or
MARK DALE
TELEPHONE: (01622) 200123
MOBILE: (07836) 225919
FAX: (01622) 200131
e-mail: freedalepress@cableinet.co.uk

ACROBAT PRODUCTIONS
(Artistes & Advisors)
The Circus Space
Coronet Street, Hackney, London N1 6HD
Website: www.acrobatsunlimited.com
e-mail: info@acrobatproductions.co.uk
Tel/Fax: 020-7613 5259

ADAMS ENGRAVING
Unit G1A, The Mayford Centre
Mayford Green, Woking GU22 0PP
Website: www.adamsengraving@pncl.co.uk
Fax: 01483 751787   Tel: 01483 725792

AERONAUTIC
(Function Balloons)
46 Burrage Place, Plumstead, London SE18 7BE
Website: www.aeronautic.org.uk
e-mail: sales@aeronautic.org.uk
Fax: 020-8317 1515   Mobile: 07956 369890

AFX (UK) Ltd
(Flying Systems & Specialist Aerial Effects Rigging)
8 Greenford Avenue, Hanwell, London W7 3QP
Website: www.afxuk.com
e-mail: info@afxuk.com
Mobile: 07958 285608   Tel: 020-8723 8552

AIRBOURNE SYSTEMS INTERNATIONAL
(All Skydiving Requirements Arranged.
Parachute Hire - Period & Modern)
8 Burns Crescent
Chelmsford, Essex CM2 0TS   Tel: 01245 268772

ALCHEMICAL LABORATORIES ETC
(Medieval Science and Technology Recreated for
Museums and Films)
Oldwood Pits, Tanhouse Lane
Yate, Bristol BS37 7PZ
Website: www.jackgreene.co.uk   Tel: 01454 227164

ALL SCENE ALL PROPS
(Scenery, Props & Painters)
443-445 Holloway Road, London N7 6LW
e-mail: allscene@hotmail.com
Tel/Fax: 020-7561 9231

ANCHOR MARINE FILM & TELEVISION
(Boat Location, Charter, Maritime Co-ordinators)
Spikemead Farm, Poles Lane
Lowfield Heath, West Sussex RH11 0PX
e-mail: amsfilm@aol.com
Fax: 01293 551558   Tel: 01293 538188

ANELLO & DAVIDE
(Theatrical Footwear)
Shop: 47 Beauchamp Place
Chelsea, London SW3 1NX
Fax: 020-7225 3375   Tel: 020-7225 2468

ANGLO PACIFIC INTERNATIONAL PLC
(Freight Forwarders & Removal Services)
Unit 1, Bush Industrial Estate
Standard Road, North Acton, London NW10 6DF
Fax: 020-8965 4954   Tel: 020-8965 1955

ANIMAL ARK
(Animals & Natural History Props)
The Studio
29 Somerset Road, Brentford, Middlesex TW8 8BT
Website: www.animal-ark.co.uk
e-mail: info@animal-ark.co.uk
Fax: 020-8560 5762   Tel: 020-8560 3029

AQUARIUS
(Film and TV Stills Library)
PO Box 5, Hastings TN34 1HR
Website: www.aquariuscollection.com
e-mail: aquarius.lib@clara.net
Fax: 01424 717704   Tel: 01424 721196

AQUATECH
(Camera Boats)
Epney, Gloucestershire GL2 7LN
Website: www.aquatech-uk.com
e-mail: office@aquatech-uk.com
Tel: 01452 740559   Fax: 01452 741958

ARCHERY CENTRE The
(Archery Tuition)
PO Box 39, Battle
East Sussex TN33 0ZT   Tel: 01424 777183

ARMS & ARCHERY
(Armour, Weaponry, Chainmail, X-bows, Longbows)
The Coach House
London Road, Ware, Herts SG12 9QU
e-mail: tgou104885@aol.com
Fax: 01920 461044   Tel: 01920 460335

ART
(Art Consultant, Supplier of Paintings and Sculpture)
66 Josephine Avenue, London SW2 2LA
Website: www.artstar.co.uk
e-mail: h_artstar@hotmail.com
Fax: 07970 455956   Tel: 07967 294985

ART DIRECTORS & TRIP PHOTO LIBRARY
(Colour Slides - All Subjects)
57 Burdon Lane, Cheam, Surrey SM2 7BY
Website: www.artdirectors.co.uk
e-mail: images@artdirectors.co.uk
Fax: 020-8395 7230   Tel: 020-8642 3593

ASH Riky
(Equity Registered Stunt Performer/Co-ordinator)
c/o 65 Britania Avenue, Nottingham NG6 0EA
Website: www.fallingforyou.co.uk
Mobile: 07850 471227   Tel: 0115-849 3470

ATP EUROPE Ltd
(Print & Repro)
ATP House, 12 Sovereign Park, London NW10 7QP
e-mail: info@atpeurope.com
Fax: 020-8961 7743   Tel: 020-8961 0001

BAD DOG DESIGN
(3D Models, Props, Sets)
Fir Tree Cottage
Fish Pool Hill, Brentry, Bristol BS10 6SW
e-mail: baddog@dircon.co.uk
Fax: 0117-959 1245   Tel: 0117-959 2011

BAPTY 2000 Ltd
(Weapons, Dressing, Props etc)
Witley Works, Witley Gardens
Norwood Green, Middlesex UB2 4ES
e-mail: hire@bapty.demon.co.uk
Fax: 020-8571 5700   Tel: 020-8574 7700

BARHAM ASSOCIATES
(65 Foot Classic Motor Yacht available for water
Based Events, Cowes Week etc)
6 Liberty Row, The Square
Hamble, Southampton SO31 4RR
Website: www.classicyachtcharter.co.uk
e-mail: info@classicyachtcharter.co.uk
          Tel/Fax: 023-8045 8778

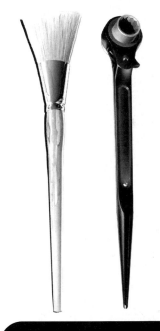

BARNES CATERERS Ltd
9 Ripley Drive, Normanton
Wakefield, West Yorks WF6 1QT
Fax: 01924 223730   Tel: 01924 892332

BARTON Joe
(Puppeteer, Model & Prop Maker)
7 Brands Hill Avenue
High Wycombe, Bucks   Tel: 01494 439056

BASINGSTOKE PRESS The
Digital House
The Loddon Centre
Wade Road, Basingstoke, Hants RG24 8QW
Website: www.basingstokepress.co.uk
e-mail: sales@baspress.co.uk
Fax: 01256 840383   Tel: 01256 467771

BBC VISUAL EFFECTS DEPARTMENT
Room G14, Park Western
41-44 Kendal Avenue, London W3 0RP
e-mail: visual.effects@bbc.co.uk
Fax: 020-8993 8741   Tel: 020-8993 9434

BEAT ABOUT THE BUSH
(Musical Instruments)
Unit 23, Enterprise Way, Triangle Business Centre
Salter Street, London NW10 6UG
Fax: 020-8969 2281   Tel: 020-8960 2087

BENSON'S JUMPAROUND ACTIVITY CENTRES
(Chester Benson Inflatables & Soft Play Equipment,
Bouncy Castles)
PO Box 4227, Worthing BN11 5ST
Website: www.davebensonphillips.co.uk
e-mail: davebensonphillips@yahoo.com
Fax: 01903 700389   Tel: 01903 248258

BIANCHERI The
(The Lampie's Coolest Tool)
T & D House, 7 Woodville Road, London E17 7ER
Mobile: 07973 663154   Tel: 020-8521 6408

BIANCHI AVIATION FILM SERVICES
(Historic and other Aircraft)
Wycombe Air Park, Booker Marlow, Bucks SL7 3DP
e-mail: info@bianchiaviation.com
Fax: 01494 461236   Tel: 01494 449810

BIDDLES Ltd
(Quality Book Binders & Printers)
Woodbridge Park Estate, Woodbridge Road,
Guildford, Surrey GU1 1DA
Website: www.biddles.co.uk
e-mail: enquiries@biddles.co.uk
Fax: 01483 576150   Tel: 01483 502224

BLACKOUT Ltd
280 Weston Road, London SW19 2QA
Website: www.tabtrack.com
e-mail: info@blackout-tabtrack.com
Fax: 020-8687 8500   Tel: 020-8687 8400

BLUEBELL RAILWAY Plc
(Steam Locomotives, Pullman Coaches,
Period Stations, Much Film Experience)
Sheffield Park Station, East Sussex TN22 3QL
Website: www.bluebell-railway.co.uk
Fax: 01825 720804   Tel: 01825 720800

BOSCO LIGHTING
(Design/Technical Consultancy)
63 Nimrod Road, London SW16 6SZ
e-mail: boscolx@lineone.net   Tel: 020-8769 3470

BRISTOL (UK) Ltd
(Scenic Paint & StageFloor Duo Suppliers)
12 The Arches, Maygrove Road, London NW6 2DS
Fax: 020-7372 5242   Tel: 020-7624 4370

BRISTOL OLD VIC HIRE SERVICE
(Furniture Props)
Wapping Wharf, Cumberland Road, Bristol BS1 6UP
Website: www.bristol-old-vic.co.uk/hire
e-mail: bov-hire-dept@lineone.net
Fax: 0117-929 1665   Tel: 0117-934 9350

BRODIE & MIDDLETON Ltd
(Theatrical Suppliers, Paints, Powders, Glitter etc)
68 Drury Lane, London WC2B 5SP
e-mail: info@brodies.net
Fax: 020-7497 8425   Tel: 020-7836 3289

BUXWORTH STEAM GROUP
Tower Farm, Boarstall, Nr Thame
Aylesbury, Bucks   Tel: 01844 239302

CANDLE MAKERS SUPPLIES
The Wax & Dyecraft Centre
28 Blythe Road, London W14 0HA
Website: www.candlemakers.co.uk
e-mail: candles@candlemakers.co.uk
Fax: 020-7602 2796   Tel: 020-7602 4031

CAPITAL ORGANISATION Ltd The
Capital House
804 Oxford Avenue, Slough, Berks SL1 4LN
Fax: 01753 696401   Tel: 01753 696410

CHALFONT CLEANERS & DYERS Ltd
(Dry Cleaners, Launderers & Dyers
Stage Curtains & Costumes)
222 Baker Street
London NW1 5RT   Tel: 020-7935 7316

CHEVALIER EVENT DESIGN & CONTEMPORARY CUISINE
(Corporate Hospitality Caterers)
Studio 4-5, Garnett Close, Watford, Herts WD24 7GN
Website: www.chevalier.co.uk
e-mail: enquiries@chevalier.co.uk
Fax: 01923 211704   Tel: 01923 211703

CHRISANNE Ltd
(Specialist Fabrics & Accessories for Theatre & Dance)
Chrisanne House
14 Locks Lane, Mitcham, Surrey CR4 2JX
Website: www.chrisanne.co.uk
e-mail: sales@chrisanne.co.uk
Fax: 020-8640 2106   Tel: 020-8640 5921

CIRCUS MANIACS
(Circus Equipment, Rigging & Training)
Office 8A, The Kingswood Foundation
Britannia Road, Kingswood, Bristol BS15 8DB
e-mail: info@circusmaniacs.com
Mobile: 07977 247287   Tel/Fax: 0117-947 7042

CIRCUS PROMOTIONS
(Entertainers)
36 St Lukes Road, Tunbridge Wells
Kent TN4 9JH   Tel: 01892 537964

CLARK DAVIS & CO Ltd
(Stationery & Office Equipment)
Excelda House, Unit D, Six Bridges Trading Estate
Marlborough Grove, London SE1 5JT
e-mail: steve@clarkdavis.sol.co.uk
Fax: 020-7240 2106   Tel: 020-7836 5703

CLARKE Donald
(Historical Interpreter, Role Playing)
80 Warden Avenue
Rayners Lane, Harrow, Middlesex HA2 9LW
Mobile: 07811 606285   Tel: 020-8866 2997

CLEANING & FLAME RETARDING SERVICE The
Unit 3, Grange Farm Industrial Units
Grange Road, Tiptree, Essex CO5 0QQ
Website: www.flameretarding.co.uk
e-mail: email@flameretarding.co.uk
Fax: 01621 819803   Tel: 01621 818477

CLEVELAND COLLEGE OF ART & DESIGN
Green Lane, Linthorpe, Middlesbrough TS5 7RJ
Website: www.ccad.ac.uk
Fax: 01642 288828   Tel: 01642 288000

COMPTON Mike & Rosi
(Costumes, Props & Models)
11 Woodstock Road, Croydon, Surrey CR0 1JS
Fax: 020-8681 3126   Tel: 020-8680 4364

CONCEPT ENGINEERING Ltd
(Smoke, Fog, Snow, etc)
7 Woodlands Business Park
Woodlands Park Avenue
Maidenhead, Berks SL6 3UA
Fax: 01628 826261   Tel: 01628 825555

COOK Sheila
(Period Jewellery, Textiles, Costumes and Accessories for Hire/Sale)
283 Westbourne Grove, London W11 2QA
e-mail: sheilacook@sheilacook.co.uk
Fax: 020-7229 3855   Tel: 020-7792 8001

CRESTA BLINDS Ltd
(Supplier of Vertical Blinds)
Crown Walks, Tetnall Street, Dudley DY2 8SA
Website: www.crestablindsltd.co.uk
e-mail: info@crestablindsltd.co.uk
Fax: 01384 457675   Tel: 01384 255523

CROCKSHARD FARMHOUSE
(Bed & Breakfast, Contact: Nicola Ellen)
Wingham, Canterbury, Kent CT3 1NY
e-mail: crockshard_bnb@yahoo.com
Fax: 01227 721929   Tel: 01227 720464

CROFTS ANDREW
(Book Writing Services)
Westlands Grange
West Grinstead, Horsham, West Sussex RH13 8LZ
Website: www.andrewcrofts.com
Tel/Fax: 01403 864518

CUE ACTION POOL PROMOTIONS
(Advice for UK & US Pool, Snooker, Trick Shots)
PO Box 3941, Colchester, Essex CO2 8HN
Website: www.cueaction.com
e-mail: sales@cueaction.com
Fax: 01206 729480   Tel: 07000 868689

DARK SIDE
(Photographic Repro Service)
4 Helmet Row, London EC1V 3QJ
e-mail: info@darksidephoto.co.uk
Fax: 020-7250 1771   Tel: 020-7250 1200

DAVEY Brian
(See NOSTALGIA AMUSEMENTS)

DAY LIGHT DESIGNS UK Ltd
(Theatre Lantern Conversions/Recolourings &
Restoration)
3 Chesnut Grange, Broughton Astley
Leics LE9 6PT   Mobile: 07802 376212

DEAN Audrey Vincente
(Soft Dolls, Toys & Figures to Order, No Hire)
76 Burlington Avenue, Kew, Surrey TW9 4DH
e-mail: audreymiller@waitrose.com
                              Tel: 020-8876 6441

DESIGN ASYLUM
(Design, Web & Print)
Crown House, North Circular Road
Park Royal, London NW10 7PN
Website: www.2dwp.net
e-mail: info@2dwp.net   Tel/Fax: 020-8838 3555

DESIGN PROJECTS
Perrysfield Farm
Broadham Green, Old Oxted, Surrey RH8 9PG
Fax: 01883 723707   Tel: 01883 730262

DEVEREUX K W & Sons
(Removals)
Daimler Drive, Cowpen Industrial Estate, Billingham,
Cleveland TS23 4JD
e-mail: devereux@onyxnet.co.uk
Fax: 01642 566664   Tel: 01642 560854

DIRECTFOODS.UK.COM
(British Food Export Service for British People
Working Overseas)
46 Burrage Place, Plumstead, London SE18 7BE
Website: www.directfoods.uk.com
e-mail: sales@directfoods.uk.com
                              Tel/Fax: 020-8317 1515

DONOGHUE Phil PRODUCTIONS
Bridge House, Three Mills Island Studios
Three Mill Lane, Bromley-by-Bow, London E3 3DU
Mobile: 07802 179801   Tel/Fax: 020-8215 0169

DORANS PROPMAKERS/SET BUILDERS
53 Derby Road, Ashbourne, Derbyshire DE6 1BH
e-mail: props@dorans.demon.co.uk
                              Tel/Fax: 01335 300064

DRIVING CENTRE The
(Expert Driving Instructors on All Vehicles)
6 Marlott Road, Poole, Dorset BH15 3DX
Mobile: 07860 290437   Tel: 01202 666001

DURRENT Peter
(Audition & Rehearsal Pianist, Cocktail Pianist,
Composer, Vocal Coach)
Blacksmiths Cottage, Bures Road
Little Cornard, Sudbury
Suffolk CO10 0NR   Tel: 01787 373483

EAGLES Steve
(International Sharpshooter & Firearms Lecturer)
Wivenhoe, 46 Hartwood Road
Southport, Merseyside PR9 9AW
e-mail: sn03@dial.pipex.com
Mobile: 07721 464611   Tel/Fax: 01704 547884

EAT TO THE BEAT
(Production Location Caterers)
Studio 4-5, Garnett Close, Watford
Herts WD24 7GN
Website: www.eattothebeat.com
e-mail: tony@eattothebeat.com
Fax: 01923 211704   Tel: 01923 211702

EATON'S SEASHELLS
30 Forest Drive West, London E11 1LA
Website: www.eatonsseashells.co.uk
                              Tel/Fax: 020-8539 5288

ECCENTRIC TRADING COMPANY Ltd
(Antique Furniture & Props) incorporating
COMPUHIRE (Computer Hire)
Unit 2, Frogmore Estate
Acton Lane, London NW10 7NQ
Website: www.compuhire.com
e-mail: info@compuhire.com   Tel: 020-8453 1125

ELECTRO SIGNS Ltd
97 Vallentin Road, London E17 3JJ
Fax: 020-8520 8127   Tel: 020-8521 8066

ELMS LESTERS PAINTING ROOMS
1-5 Flitcroft Street
London WC2H 8DH
e-mail: office@elms-lesters.demon.co.uk
Fax: 020-7379 0789   Tel: 020-7836 6747

ENCHANTING FOREST
Unit 6, Machin Industrial Estate
Gotham
Nottingham NG11 0HH   Tel/Fax: 0115-983 0777

ESCORT GUNLEATHER
(Custom Leathercraft)
602 High Road
Benfleet, Essex SS7 5RW
Website: www.escortgunleather.com
e-mail: info@escortgunleather.com
Fax: 01268 566775   Tel: 01268 792769

EVANS Peter STUDIOS Ltd
(Scenic Embellishment, Vacuum Forming)
(Catalogue Available)
1 Frederick Street, Luton, Beds LU2 7QW
Fax: 01582 481329   Tel: 01582 725730

FAB 'N' FUNKY
(Prop Hire Specialist 50's - 70's)
18-20 Brunel Road, London W3 7XR
Website: www.fabnfunky.co.uk
Fax: 020-8743 2662   Tel: 020-8746 7746

FACADE
(Musical Production Services)
43A Garthorne Road
London SE23 1EP   Tel: 020-8699 8655

FAIRGROUNDS TRADITIONAL
Halstead, Fovant, Salisbury, Wilts SP3 5NL
Website: www.pozzy.co.uk
e-mail: s-vpostlethwaite@fovant.fsnet.co.uk
Mobile: 07701 287251   Tel: 01722 714786

**FALCONS STUNT DISPLAY TEAM COMBAT
THROUGH THE AGES**
(Medieval Displays, Combat Display Team,
Stunt Action Specialists)
110 Trafalgar Road, Portslade
East Sussex BN41 1GS
Tel: 01273 430323   Tel: 01273 411862

FILM MEDICAL SERVICES
Units 5 & 7, Commercial Way, Park Royal
London NW10 7XF
Website: www.filmmedical.co.uk
e-mail: filmmed@aol.com
Fax: 020-8961 7427   Tel: 020-8961 3222

FIND ME ANOTHER
(Prop Hire/Location Finder specialising in
Gardenalia/Farming/Bygones/Kitchenalia)
c/o Mills Barnes, Tenzing Grove, Luton, Beds LU1 5JJ
Website: www.findmeanother.co.uk
e-mail: info@findmeanother.co.uk
Mobile: 07885 777751   Tel/Fax: 01582 415834

FIREBRAND
(Flambeaux Hire & Sales)
Leac na ban, By Lochgilphead, Argyll PA31 8PF
e-mail: alex@firebrand.fsnet.co.uk
                              Tel/Fax: 01546 870310

FLAMENCO PRODUCTIONS
(Entertainers)
Sevilla 4 Cormorant Rise
Lower Wick
Worcester WR2 4BA   Tel: 01905 424083

FLINT HIRE & SUPPLY Ltd
Queen's Row, London SE17 2PX
Website: www.flints.co.uk
e-mail: sales@flints.co.uk
Fax: 020-7708 4189   Tel: 020-7703 9786

FLYING BY FOY
(Flying Effects for Theatre, TV, Corporate Events etc)
Unit 4, Borehamwood Enterprise Centre
Theobald Street, Borehamwood, Herts WD6 4RQ
Website: www.flyingbyfoy.co.uk
e-mail: mail@flyingbyfoy.co.uk
Fax: 020-8236 0235   Tel: 020-8236 0234

FOXTROT PRODUCTIONS Ltd
(Armoury Services, Firearms, Weapons &
Costume Hire)
Unit 46 Canalot Production Studios
222 Kensal Road
London W10 5BN   Tel: 020-8964 3555

FREEDALE PRESS
(Printing)
36 Hedley Street, Maidstone, Kent ME14 5AD
Fax: 01622 200131   Tel: 01622 200123

FROST John NEWSPAPERS
(Historical Newspaper Service)
22B Rosemary Avenue, Enfield, Middlesex EN2 0SS
Website: www.johnfrostnewspapers.com
e-mail: andrew@johnfrostnewspapers.com
Tel: 020-8366 1392

GAMBA
(Theatrical Shoes and Wholesale Dancewear)
1 Northfield Industrial Estate
Beresford Avenue, Wembley HA0 1XS
Fax: 020-8903 6669   Tel: 020-8903 8177

GAMBA
(Dancewear & Ballet Shoes)
3 Garrick Street, Covent Garden, London WC2E 9BF
Fax: 020-7497 0754   Tel: 020-7437 0704

GAV NICOLA THEATRICAL SHOES
1A Suttons Lane, Hornchurch, Essex RM12 6RD
e-mail: sales@gavnicola.freeserve.co.uk
Mobile: 07961 974278   Tel/Fax: 01708 438584

GET STUFFED
(Taxidermy)
105 Essex Road, London N1 2SL
Website: www.thegetstuffed.co.uk
e-mail: taxidermy@thegetstuffed.co.uk
Fax: 020-7359 8253   Tel: 020-7226 1364

GLOBAL CEILINGS & TILES
(Designers, Suppliers, Installers)
1B Argyle Road
Argyle Corner, Ealing, London W13 0LL
Website: www.globalceiling.co.uk
Mobile: 07976 159402   Tel: 020-8810 5914

GORGEOUS GOURMETS
(Caterers and Equipment Hire)
Gresham Way, Wimbledon SW19 8ED
Website: www.gorgeousgourmets.co.uk
e-mail: events@gorgeousgourmets.co.uk
Fax: 020-8946 1639   Tel: 020-8944 7771

GOULD Gillian ANTIQUES
(Scientific & Marine Antiques & Collectables)
18A Belsize Park Gardens
Belsize Park, London NW3 4LH
Website: www.gilliangouldantiques.co.uk
e-mail: gillgould@dealwith.com
Fax: 020-7419 0400   Tel: 020-7419 0500

GRADAV HIRE & SALES Ltd
(Lighting & Sound Hire/Sales)
Units C6 & C9 Hastingwood Trading Estate
Harbet Road, Edmonton, London N18 3HR
e-mail: office@gradav.co.uk
Fax: 020-8803 5060   Tel: 020-8803 7400

GRAY Robin COMMENTARIES
(Saddles, Bridles, Racing Colours & Hunting Attire)
Comptons, Isington
Alton, Hants GU34 4PL   Tel/Fax: 01420 23347

GREENPROPS
(Prop Suppliers, Artificial Trees, Plants, Fruit, Grass etc)
West Bovey Farm, Waterrow, Somerset TA4 2BA
Website: www.greenprops.com
e-mail: trevor@greenprops.com
Fax: 01398 361307   Tel: 01398 361531

HANDS ON SECURITY SERVICE
65 Farnham Road
Harold Hill
Romford, Essex RM3 8ED   Tel/Fax: 01708 342186

HARLEQUIN Plc
(Floors for Stage, Opera, Dance, Concert,
Shows & Events)
Bankside House, Vale Road
Tonbridge, Kent TN9 1SJ
Website: www.harlequinfloors.com
e-mail: sales@harlequinfloors.co.uk
Fax: 01732 367755   Tel: 01732 367666

HARLEQUIN PROMOTIONS
(Fun Casinos, Scalextric & Race Nights)
Harlequin House
13 Gurton Road, Coggleshall, Essex CO6 1QL
e-mail: john@harlequin-casinos.co.uk
Tel: 01376 563385

HAWES Joanne
(Children's Administrator for Theatre, Film & TV)
21 Westfield Road, Maidenhead, Berkshire SL6 5AU
e-mail: jo.hawes@virgin.net
Fax: 01628 672884   Tel: 01628 773048

HERON & DRIVER
(Scenic Furniture & Prop Makers)
Unit 7, Dockley Road Industrial Estate
Rotherhithe, London SE16 3SF
Website: www.herondriver.co.uk
e-mail: mail@herondriver.co.uk
Fax: 020-7394 8680   Tel: 020-7394 8688

HEWER Richard
(Props Maker)
7 Sion Lane
Bristol BS8 4BE   Tel/Fax: 0117-973 8760

HI-FLI (Flying Effects)
4 Boland Drive
Manchester M14 6DS
e-mail: mikefrost@hi-fli.co.uk   Tel/Fax: 0161-224 6082

HOLME VALLEY WAREHOUSE
(Period Furniture, Household Equipment and
Accessories. Prop Hire/Purchase)
Westgate, Honley, Nr Huddersfield, West Yorkshire
Fax: 01484 687241   Tel: 01484 667915

HOTEL BROKERS
(Conference & Accommodation Consultants)
19 Bakery Place
119 Altenburg Gardens, London SW11 1JQ
e-mail: dbriant@hotelbrokers.co.uk
Fax: 020-7228 4460   Tel: 020-7924 3663

HOWARD Rex DRAPES Ltd
Acton Park Industrial Estate
Eastman Road, The Vale, London W3 7QS
Fax: 020-8740 5994   Tel: 020-8740 5881

IMAGERY
(Painting & Decoration)
420 G, 9 Sims House
Commercial Road, London E1 1LD
e-mail: chrispro@freenetnames.co.uk
Mobile: 07956 512074

IMPACT DISTRIBUTION & MARKETING
(Leaflet & Poster Distribution & Display)
Tuscany Wharf, 4B Orsman Road, London N1 5QJ
Website: www.impact@uk.com
e-mail: admin@impact.uk.com
Fax: 020-7729 5994   Tel: 020-7729 5978

IMPACT PERCUSSION
(Percussion Instruments for Sale)
Unit 7 Goose Green Trading Estate
47 East Dulwich Road, London SE22 9BN
e-mail: sales@impactpercussion.com
Fax: 020-8299 6704   Tel: 020-8299 6700

INTERNATIONAL CLOWNS DIRECTORY The
(Salvo The Clown)
13 Second Avenue
Kingsleigh Park, Thundersley
Essex SS7 3QD   Tel: 01268 745791

JAPAN PROMOTIONS
(Organise Japanese Events)
200 Russell Court
3 Woburn Place
London WC1H 0ND   Tel/Fax: 020-7278 4099

JESSAMINE Bob
(Scene Painting, Prop Making)
4 Matlock Avenue, Birkdale
Southport, Merseyside PR8 5EZ
Website: www.rscsjessamine.supernet.com
e-mail: rscsjessamine@supanet.com
                                          Tel: 01704 564521

JULIETTE DESIGNS
(Diamante Jewellery Mmanufacturer,
Necklaces, Crowns etc)
90 Yerbury Road, London N19 4RS
Website: www.stagejewellery.com
Fax: 020-7281 7326   Tel: 020-7263 7878

K & D
(Footwear)
Unit 7A, Thames Road Industrial Estate
Thames Road, Silvertown, London E16 2EZ
Website: www.shoemaking.co.uk
e-mail: k&d@shoemaking.co.uk
Fax: 020-7476 5220   Tel: 020-7474 0500

KEW BRIDGE STEAM MUSEUM
(Steam Museum)
Green Dragon Lane, Brentford, Middlesex TW8 0EN
Website: www.kbsm.org
e-mail: info@kbsm.org
Fax: 020-8569 9978   Tel: 020-8568 4757

KIEVE Paul
(Magical Effects for Theatre & Film)
23 Terrace Road, South Hackney, London E9 7ES
Website: www.stageillusion.com
e-mail: mail@stageillusion.com
                                        Tel/Fax: 020-8985 6188

KIRBY'S AFX (LONDON)
8 Greenford Avenue, Hanwell, London W7 3QP
Website: www.kirbysflying.co.uk
e-mail: info@kirbysflying.co.uk
Mobile: 07958 285608   Tel/Fax: 020-8723 8552

231

KIRBY'S AFX (SCOTLAND)
c/o 8 Greenford Avenue, Hanwell, London W7 3QB
Website: www.kirbysflying.co.uk
e-mail: info@kirbysflying.co.uk
Mobile: 07767 464224   Tel/Fax: 0141-423 4672

KNEBWORTH HOUSE
(Stately Home & Country Park)
Hertfordshire   Tel: 01438 812661

KNIGHT Robert/TOP OF THE BILL Ltd
Unit 1B, Mill Street Industrial Estate
Slough, Berkshire SL2 5DD
Fax: 01753 535775   Tel: 01753 535758

K. W. PROPS
(Propmaking)
Unit J304, Tower Bridge Business Complex
100 Clements Road, London SE16 4DG
e-mail: kwprops@gmx.co.uk
Tel/Fax: 020-8299 67858

LAREDO Alex
(Expert with Ropes, Bullwhips, Shooting, Riding)
29 Lincoln Road, Dorking
Surrey RH4 1TE   Tel: 01306 889423

LAREDO WILD WEST TOWN
(Wild West Entertainments)
19 Surrenden Road
Staplehurst, Tonbridge, Kent TN12 0LY
Website: www.laredo.org.uk
e-mail: enquiries@laredo.org.uk
Tel: 01474 706129   Tel: 01580 891790

LEES-NEWSOME Ltd
(Manufacturers of Flame Retardant Fabrics)
Ashley Street, Westwood, Oldham OL9 6LS
e-mail: info@leesnewsome.co.uk
Fax: 0161-627 3362   Tel: 0161-652 1321

LEIGHTON HALL
(Historic House)
Carnforth, Lancs LA5 9ST
Website: www.leightonhall.co.uk
e-mail: leightonhall@yahoo.co.uk
Fax: 01524 720357   Tel: 01524 734474

LEVRANT Stephen - HERITAGE ARCHITECTURE Ltd
(Historic Buildings & Interiors Consultants)
363 West End Lane
West Hampstead, London NW6 1LP
e-mail: levrant@aol.com
Fax: 020-7794 9712   Tel: 020-7435 7502

LONDON BUSINESS EQUIPMENT
(Authorised Canon Dealer)
527-529 High Road, Leytonstone, London E11 4PB
Fax: 020-8556 4865   Tel: 020-8558 0024

LONDON UNDERWATER CENTRE
(Pre-holiday Scuba Courses in Victoria)
QMSC 223 Vauxhall Bridge Road
London SW1V 1EL   Tel/Fax: 020-7630 7443

LONG Alan
(Gun Hire and Weapons Armourer)
PO Box 6079, Birmingham B28 0FF
Fax: 0121-624 9060   Mobile: 07976 953375

LYON EQUIPMENT
(Petzl & Beal Rope Access Equipment (PPE) for
Industrial & Theatrical Work)
Rise Hill Mill, Dent, Sedbergh, Cumbria LA10 5QL
Website: www.lyon.co.uk
e-mail: info@lyon.co.uk
Fax: 01539 625454   Tel: 01539 625493

M A C
(Sound Hire)
1-2 Attenburys Park
Park Road, Altrincham, Cheshire WA14 5QE
Website: www.macsound.co.uk
e-mail: hire@macsound.co.uk
Fax: 0161-962 9423   Tel: 0161-969 8311

MACKIE Sally LOCATIONS
(Location Finding & Management)
Cownham Farm, Broadwell
Moreton-in-Marsh, Glos GL56 0TT
Website: www.sallymackie-locations.com
e-mail: sallymackie@lokations.freeserve.co.uk
Fax: 01451 832442   Tel: 01451 830294

MADDERMARKET THEATRE
(Furniture, Props, Costumes & Accessories)
(Contact Rhett Davies, Resident Stage Manager)
St John's Alley, Norwich NR2 1DR
Website: www.maddermarket.freeserve.co.uk
e-mail: theatre@maddermarket.freeserve.co.uk
Fax: 01603 661357   Tel: 01603 626560

MAGICAL MART
(Magic, Ventriloquists' Dolls, Punch & Judy,
Hire & Advising. Callers by Appointment)
42 Christchurch Road, Sidcup, Kent DA15 7HQ
Website: www.johnstylesentertainer.co.uk
Tel/Fax: 020-8300 3579

MANSON TRASH
(Ex-Guards Drill Instructor)
Make your soldiers look and sound real.
Tel: 020-8747 3510

MARINE UNDERWATER EQUIPMENT
(Watersports Equipment)
Ocean Leisure (Main Branch)
11-14 Northumberland Avenue, London WC2N 5AQ
e-mail: info@oceanleisure.co.uk
Fax: 020-7930 3032   Tel: 020-7930 5050

MARKSON PIANOS
8 Chester Court, Albany Street, London NW1 4BU
Fax: 020-7224 0957   Tel: 020-7935 8682

McDONALD ROWE (SCULPTURE) Ltd
20 Southfield Way, St Albans, Herts AL4 9JJ
e-mail: mcdonald@stalbans01.freeserve.co.uk
Tel: 01727 765277

MIDNIGHT ELECTRONICS
(Sound Hire)
Off Quay Building
Foundry Lane, Newcastle NE6 1LH
Website: www.midnightelectronics.co.uk
e-mail: dx@compuserve.com
Fax: 0191-224 0080   Tel: 0191-224 0088

MODEL BOX Ltd
(Computer Aided Design & Design Services)
20 Merton Industrial Park
Jubilee Way, London SW19 3WL
Website: www.modelbox.co.uk
e-mail: info@modelbox.co.uk
Fax: 020-8254 4721   Tel: 020-8254 4720

MORTON G & L
(Horses/Farming)
Hashome Carr
Holme-on-Spalding Moor
Yorks YO43 4BD   Tel: 01430 860393

NEWENS Chas MARINE CO Ltd
(Boats for Sale/Hire Marine Props etc)
The Boathouse
Embankment, Putney, London SW15 1LB
Fax: 020-8780 2339   Tel: 020-8788 4587

NEWMAN HIRE CO
16 The Vale, Acton
London W3 7SB
e-mail: info@newman-hire.co.uk   Tel: 020-8743 0741

NORTHERN LIGHT
Assembly Street, Leith, Edinburgh EH6
Website: www.northernlight.co.uk
e-mail: enquiries@northernlight.co.uk
Fax: 0131-553 3296   Tel: 0131-553 2383

NOSTALGIA AMUSEMENTS
(Brian Davey)
22 Greenwood Close, Thames Ditton, Surrey KT7 0BG
Mobile: 07973 506869   Tel: 020-8398 2141

NOTTINGHAM JOUSTING ASSOCIATION SCHOOL OF NATIONAL EQUITATION Ltd
(Jousting & Medieval Tournaments,
Horses & Riders for Films & TV)
Bunny Hill Top, Costock
Loughborough, Leics LE12 6XE
Website: www.bunny-hill.co.uk
e-mail: Info@bunny-hill.co.uk
Fax: 01509 856067   Tel: 01509 852366

OCEAN LEISURE
(Scuba Diving, Watersports)
11-14 Northumberland Avenue, London WC2N 5AQ
Fax: 020-7930 3032   Tel: 020-7930 5050

OFFSTAGE
(Theatre & Film Bookshop)
37 Chalk Farm Road, London NW1 8AJ
e-mail: offstagebookshop@aol.com
Fax: 020-7916 8046   Tel: 020-7485 4996

PALAVA ARTS
(Digital Media, Musical Composition &
Production Services)
43 Kingsway Avenue, Kingswood, Bristol BS15 8DB
e-mail: sam@palava-arts.com
Mobile: 07733 228864   Tel/Fax: 0117-961 6858

PATERSON Helen
(Typing Services)
40 Whitelands House, London SW3 4QY
e-mail: pater@waitrose.com   Tel: 020-7730 6428

PENDLEBURYS CANDLE CO.
(Church Candles & Requisites)
Church House
Portland Avenue, Stamford Hill, London N16 6HJ
e-mail: books@pendleburys.demon.co.uk
Tel/Fax: 020-8809 4922

PERIOD PROPS AND LIGHTING Ltd
17-23 Stirling Road, London W3 8DJ
Website: www.periodpropsandlighting.co.uk
e-mail: pplprops@supanet.com
Fax: 020-8993 4637   Tel: 020-8992 6901

PHOSPHENE
(Lighting, Sound & Accessories. Design, Sales, Hire)
Milton Road South, Stowmarket, Suffolk IP14 1EZ
Website: www.phosphene.co.uk
e-mail: cliff@phosphene.freeserve.co.uk
Tel: 01449 770011

PHOTOGRAPHIC RETOUCHER
(Steve McAllister)
50-54 Beak Street
London W1F 9RN   Tel: 020-7250 0951

PHYSICALITY
(Physical Skills Specialists)
265-267 Ilford Lane, Ilford, Essex IG1 2SD
Website: www.physicality.co.uk
e-mail: info@physicality.co.uk
Fax: 020-8491 2801   Tel: 020-8491 2800

PICKFORDS Ltd
Heritage House
345 Southbury Road, Enfield EN1 1UP
Fax: 020-8219 8001   Tel: 020-8219 8000

PICTURES PROPS CO Ltd
(TV, Film & Stage Hire)
12-16 Brunel Road, London W3 7XR
Fax: 020-8740 5846   Tel: 020-8749 2433

PINK POINTES DANCEWEAR
1A Suttons Lane, Hornchurch, Essex RM12 6RD
e-mail: sales@gavnicola.freeserve.co.uk
Tel/Fax: 01708 438584

PLASTIC WARRIOR
(Model Figures)
38A Horsell Road, London N5 1XP
e-mail: figsculpt@aol.com
Fax: 020-7700 4624   Tel: 020-7700 7036

PLAYBOARD PUPPETS
2 Ockendon Mews
London N1 3JL   Tel/Fax: 020-7226 5911

POLAND Anna: SCULPTOR AND MODELMAKER
(Sculpture, Models, Puppets, Masks etc)
Salterns, Old Bursledon
Southampton, Hampshire SO31 8DH
Fax: 023-8045 6364   Tel: 023-8040 5166

POLLEX PROPS / FIREBRAND
(Prop Makers)
Leac na Ban, Tayvallich
Lochgilphead, Argyll PA31 8PF
e-mail: alex@firebrand.fsnet.co.uk
Tel/Fax: 01546 870310

PRAETORIAN ASSOCIATES
(Personal Safety & Anti-Stalking Consultancy)
Suite 501, 2 Old Brompton Road, London SW7 3DG
Website: www.praetorianasc.com
e-mail: e17one@aol.com
Fax: 020-8923 7177   Tel: 020-8923 9075

PRAETORIAN PROCUREMENT SERVICES - SA
(Providing Services for the Film/TV Industry
within South Africa)
Suite 501, 2 Old Brompton Road, London SW7 3DG
Website: www.praetorianasc.com
e-mail: e17one@aol.com
Fax: 020-8923 7177   Tel: 020-8923 9075

PRO-ACRO
(Acrobats/Circus Skills & Speciality Acts)
Springvale, Tutland Road
North Baddesley, Hampshire SO52 9FL
Website: www.2ma.co.uk
e-mail: mo@2ma.co.uk
Fax: 023-8074 1355   Tel: 023-8074 1354

PRO BLOOD
11 Mount Pleasant, Framlingham
Suffolk IP13 9HQ   Tel/Fax: 01728 723865

PROFESSOR PATTEN'S PUNCH & JUDY
(Hire & Performances/Advice on Traditional Show)
14 The Crest, Goffs Oak
Herts EN7 5NP   Tel: 01707 873262

PROFILE PRINTS
(Photographic Processing)
Courtwood Film Service Ltd
Freepost TO55, Penzance, Cornwall TR18 2BF
Website: www.courtwood.co.uk
e-mail: people@courtwood.co.uk
Fax: 01736 350203   Tel: 01736 365222

PROP FARM Ltd
(Pat Ward)
Grange Farm, Elmton
Nr Creswell, North Derbyshire S80 4LX
e-mail: pat/les@propfarm.free-online.co.uk
Fax: 01909 721465   Tel: 01909 723100

PROP ROTATION
41 Trelawney Road, Cotham
Bristol BS6 6DY   Tel: 0117-974 1058

PROPS GALORE
(Period Textiles/Jewellery)
15 Brunel Road, London W3 7XR
e-mail: propsgalore@farley.co.uk
Fax: 020-8354 1866   Tel: 020-8746 1222

PUNCH & JUDY PUPPETS & BOOTHS
(Hire & Advisory Service, Callers by Appointment)
42 Christchurch Road, Sidcup, Kent DA15 7HQ
Website: www.johnstylesentertainer.co.uk
Tel/Fax: 020-8300 3579

RAINBOW PRODUCTIONS Ltd
(Manufacture & Handling of Costume Characters)
Rainbow House
56 Windsor Avenue
London SW19 2RR
Website: www.rainbowproductions.co.uk
e-mail: info@rainbowproductions.co.uk
Fax: 020-8545 0777   Tel: 020-8545 0700

RENTABOOK (Norma & Ray Feather)
74 Park Chase, Wembley
Middlesex HA9 8EH   Tel: 020-8902 3659

RENT-A-CLOWN
(Mattie Faint)
37 Sekeforde Street, Clerkenwell
London EC1R 0HA   Tel/Fax: 020-7608 0312

RENT-A-SWORD
(Alan M Meek)
180 Frog Grove Lane
Wood Street Village
Guildford, Surrey GU3 3HD
Fax: 01483 236684   Tel: 01483 234084

REPLAY Ltd
(Showreels & TV Facilities Hire)
20 Greek Street
London W1D 4DU
Website: www.replayfilms.co.uk
e-mail: sales@replayfilms.co.uk
Fax: 020-7287 5348   Tel: 020-7287 5334

RETROGRAPH NOSTALGIA ARCHIVE
(Posters & Packaging 1880-1970, Picture Library/
Photo Stills/Ephemera/Fine Arts 1870-1970)
164 Kensington Park Road
Notting Hill, London W11 2ER
Website: www.retrograph.com
e-mail: retropix1@aol.com
Fax: 020-7229 3395   Tel: 020-7727 9378

RICO THE CIRCUS CLOWN
66 Queen Elizabeth's Drive, Addington
Croydon, Surrey CR0 0HE   Tel: 01689 846887

RITCHIE Alison ASSOCIATES
16 Chessing Court, Fortis Green, London N2 9ER
Fax: 020-8883 3156   Tel: 020-8444 5983

ROOTSTEIN Adel Ltd
(Mannequin Hire)
9 Beaumont Avenue
London W14 9LP
Fax: 020-7381 3263   Tel: 020-7381 1447

ROYAL HORTICULTURAL HALLS & CONFERENCE CENTRE
(Film Location: Art Deco & Edwardian Buildings)
80 Vincent Square, London SW1P 2PE
Website: www.horticultural-halls.co.uk
e-mail: maugiel@rhs.org.uk
Fax: 020-7834 2072   Tel: 020-7828 4125

ROYAL SHAKESPEARE COMPANY COSTUME HIRE WARDROBE
Timothy's Bridge Road, Stratford-upon-Avon
Warks CV37 9UY   Tel: 01789 205920

ROYER Hugo INTERNATIONAL Ltd
(Hair & Wig Materials)
10 Lakeside Business Park
Swan Lake, Sandhurst, Berkshire GU47 9DN
Website: www.royer.co.uk
e-mail: enquiries@royer.co.uk
Fax: 01252 878852   Tel: 01252 878811

RUDKIN DESIGN
(Design Consultants, Brochures, Advertising,
Corporate etc)
Bishop Crewe House, North Street
Daventry, Northamptonshire NN11 5PN
e-mail: studio@rudkindesign.com
Fax: 01327 872728   Tel: 01327 301770

RUMBLE Jane
(Props to Order, No Hire)
121 Elmstead Avenue
Wembley, Middlesex HA9 8NT   Tel: 020-8904 6462

S + H TECHNICAL SUPPORT GROUP
(Star Cloths, Drapes)
Unit A The Old Laundry, Chambercombe Road
Ilfracombe, Devon EX34 9PH
Website: www.starcloth.co.uk
e-mail: enquiries@starcloth.co.uk
Fax: 01271 865423   Tel: 01271 866832

SABAH
(Stylist/Designer/Co-ordinator/Wardrobe/Sets/Props)
Bay Colony Club Condo, Bay Club Drive-Bldg 5
Apt 6267-3, Fort Lauderdale, Florida 33308 USA
e-mail: sabah561@aol.com

SAPEX SCRIPTS
Millennium Studios
5 Elstree Way, Borehamwood, Herts WD6 1SH
Website: www.sapex.co.uk
e-mail: scripts@sapex.co.uk
Fax: 020-8236 1591   Tel: 020-8236 1600

SCENA PRODUCTIONS Ltd
240 Camberwell Road, London SE5 0DP
e-mail: scena@pro.com
Fax: 020-7703 7012   Tel: 020-7703 4444

SCENE TWO HIRE
(Film & TV Props Hire)
18-20 Brunel Road, Acton, London W3 7XR
Fax: 020-8743 2662   Tel: 020-8740 5544

SCENICS
Copse Field Farm
Cawlow Lane, Warslow
Buxton SK17 0HE   Tel: 01298 84762

SCHULTZ & WIREMU FABRIC EFFECTS
(Dyeing/Printing/Distressing)
Unit B202 Faircharm Studios
8-12 Creekside, London SE8 3DX
Website: www.schultz-wiremufabricfx.co.uk
e-mail: schultz_wiremfx@onetel.net.uk
          Tel/Fax: 020-8469 0151

SCRIPTRIGHT
(S.C. Hill - Script/Manuscript Typing Services/
Script Reading Services)
6 Valetta Road, London W3 7TN
e-mail: samc.hill@virgin.net
Fax: 020-8740 6486   Tel: 020-8740 7303

SCRIPTS AT ARGYLE
(Play, Film & Book. Word Processing,
Copying & Binding)
St John's Buildings
43 Clerkenwell Road, London EC1M 5RS
e-mail: scripts.typing@virgin.net
Fax: 020-7608 1642   Tel: 020-7608 2095

SHAOLIN WAY
(Martial Arts, Lion Dance & Martial Arts Supplies)
10 Little Newport Street, London WC2H 7JJ
e-mail: shaolinway@btclick.com
Fax: 020-7287 6548   Tel: 020-7734 6391

SHER SYSTEM The
(Helping Skin with Acne & Rosacea)
30 New Bond Street, London W1S 2RN
Website: www.sher.co.uk/skincare/
e-mail: skincare@sher.co.uk
Fax: 020-7629 7021   Tel: 020-7499 4022

SHIRLEY LEAF & PETAL CO
(Flower Makers Museum)
58A High Street, Old Town, Hastings
East Sussex TN34 3EN   Tel/Fax: 01424 427793

SHOP FITTINGS DIRECT
Unit 3 The Interchange
Colonial Way, Watford, Herts WD24 4PR
Fax: 01923 232326   Tel: 01923 232425

SIDE EFFECTS
(Props, Models & FX)
Unit 4, Camberwell Trading Estate
117 Denmark Road, London SE5 9LB
e-mail: sfx@lineone.net
Fax: 020-7738 5198   Tel: 020-7738 5199

SILVER Sam KENSINGTON Ltd
(Special Eye Effects)
37 Kensington Church Street, London W8 4LL
e-mail: samsilveropticians@btinternet.com
Fax: 020-7937 8969   Tel: 020-7937 8282

SMITH Tom
(Blacksmith)
Unit 2, Lopen Works
Lopen Road, Edmonton
London N18 1PU   Tel/Fax: 020-8884 2626

SNOW BUSINESS
(Snow/Winter Effects on Any Scale)
The Snow Mill
Bridge Road, Ebley, Stroud, Glos GL5 4TR
Website: www.snowfx.com
e-mail: snow@snowbusiness.com
                       Tel/Fax: 01453 840077

SOFT PROPS
(Costume & Modelmakers)
Unit 4, Camberwell Trading Estate
117-119 Denmark Road, London SE5 9LB
e-mail: jackie@softprops.co.uk
Fax: 020-7738 5198   Tel: 020-7738 6324

STEELDECK RENTALS
(Theatre & Staging Equipment)
King's Cross Freight Depot, York Way, London N1 0UZ
e-mail: lynda@steeldeck.ndo.co.uk
Fax: 020-7278 3403   Tel: 020-7833 2031

STEELDECK SALES Ltd
(Modular Staging)
King's Cross Freight Depot, York Way, London N1 0UZ
e-mail: jo@steeldeck.ndo.co.uk
Fax: 020-7278 3403   Tel: 020-7833 2031

STILTS & STUFF!
(Circus Skills/Entertainers)
Kaos Towers
346 Tunbridge Road, Maidstone
Kent ME16 8TG   Tel/Fax: 01622 727433

STIRLING Rob
(Carpentry & Joinery)
Copse Field Farm, Cawlow Lane
Warslow, Buxton SK17 0HE   Tel: 01298 84762

STUDIO FOUR COSTUMES
4 Warple Mews
Warple Way, Acton
London W3 0RF   Tel/Fax: 020-8749 6569

STUDIO & TV HIRE
3 Ariel Way, Wood Lane, White City
London W12 7SL
Website: www.stvhire.com
e-mail: enquiries@stvhire.com
Fax: 020-8740 9662   Tel: 020-8749 3445

STUNT ACTION SPECIALISTS (S.A.S.)
(Corporate Stunt Work)
110 Trafalgar Road, Portslade, Sussex BN41 1GS
Fax: 01273 708699   Tel: 01273 430323

SUPERSCRIPTS
14 Cambridge Grove Road, Kingston, Surrey KT1 3JJ
Mobile: 07890 972595   Tel: 020-8546 9824

SUPERSCRIPTS
(Audio Typing, Rushes, Post-Prod Scripts)
56 New Road, Hanworth, Middlesex TW13 6TQ
e-mail: jackie@superscripts.fsnet.co.uk
Mobile: 07971 671011   Tel: 020-8898 7933

TAYLOR Charlotte
(Stylist/Props Buyer)
18 Eleanor Grove, Barnes SW13 0JN
e-mail: charlotte-taylor@breathemail.net
Mobile: 07836 708904   Tel/Fax: 020-8876 9085

TECHNIQUES
(Property Makers)
15 Danehurst Avenue
Leicester LE3 6DB   Tel/Fax: 0116-285 7294

TELESCRIPT PROMPTING Ltd
The Barn, Handpost Farmhouse
Maidens Green, Bracknell, Berks RG42 6LD
Fax: 01344 890655   Tel: 01344 890470

TESTMAN P.A.T.
(Portable Electrical Appliance Testing,
Specialists in Theatre)
7 Woodville Road, London E17 7ER
Mobile: 07973 663154   Tel: 020-8521 6408

THEATRESEARCH
(Theatre Consultants)
Dacre Hall, Dacre, North Yorkshire HG3 4ET
Website: www.theatresearch.co.uk
e-mail: info@theatresearch.co.uk
Fax: 01423 781957   Tel: 01423 780497

THEME TRADERS Ltd
(Props)
The Stadium, Oaklands Road, London NW2 6DL
Website: www.themetraders.com
e-mail: mailroom@themetraders.com
Fax: 020-8450 7322   Tel: 020-8452 8518

TOMLIN Mick DRAPES
(Curtain Makers)
213 Westmount Road, Eltham
London SE9 1XZ   Tel/Fax: 020-8850 8073

TOP SHOW
(Props & Scenery, Conference Specialists)
North Lane, Huntington
York YO32 9SU   Tel/Fax: 01904 750022

TRANSCRIPTS
(Audio + LTC/Post-prod)
#2, 6 Cornwall Gardens, London SW7 4AL
e-mail: lucy@transcripts.demon.co.uk
Mobile: 07973 200197   Tel: 020-7584 9758

TRAPEZE & AERIAL COACH/CHOREOGRAPHER
(Jacqueline Welbourne)
43 Kingsway Avenue, Kingswood, Bristol BS15 8DB
e-mail: jackie@welbourne.co.uk
Mobile: 07977 247287   Tel/Fax: 0117-947 7042

TROPICAL SURROUNDS Ltd
(Distributors and Installers of Natural Theming
Materials)
The Old Grain Store, Redenham Park Farm,
Redenham, Nr Andover, Hampshire SP11 9AQ
Fax: 01264 773660   Tel: 01264 773009

TRYFONOS Mary
(Mask Maker)
59 Shaftesbury Road, London N19 4QW
e-mail: marytryfonos@aol.com
Mobile: 07764 587433   Tel: 020-7561 9880

GREENPROPS
Trees ▪Plants▪Flowers▪Fruit & Grass
Tel: 01398 361531
Fax 01398 361307   www.greenprops.com
e mail:trevor@greenprops.com
The artificial STAGE SUPPLIERS, serving The West End, The UK and Europe

TURN ON LIGHTING
(Antique Lighting c.1840-1940)
116-118 Islington High Street
Camden Passage
London N1 8EG   Tel/Fax: 020-7359 7616

UFX
(Event Design & Production Management)
Studio A,
14 Ayres Street, Flat Iron Yard, London SE1 1ES
Website: www.ufxltd.com
e-mail: ufx@dial.pipex.com
Fax: 020-7403 6511   Tel: 020-7403 6510

VENTRILOQUIST DOLLS HOME
(Hire & Helpful Hints, Callers by Appointment)
42 Christchurch Road
Sidcup, Kent DA15 7HQ
Website: www.johnstylesentertainer.co.uk
                                 Tel/Fax: 020-8300 3579

VENTRILOQUIST DUMMY HIRE
(Dennis Patten - Hire & Advice)
14 The Crest, Goffs Oak
Herts EN7 5NP   Tel: 01707 873262

VENYFLEX COMPANY
(Drapes, Tabs, Blinds)
1 Holly Road, Hampton Hill
Middlesex TW12 1QF   Tel: 020-8977 3780

VINMAG ARCHIVE Ltd
84-90 Digby Road, London E9 6HX
Website: www.vinmag.com
e-mail: piclib@vinmag.com
Fax: 020-8533 7283   Tel: 020-8533 7588

VIRGIN ATLANTIC AIRWAYS Ltd
(Reservations)
The Office, Crawley Business Quarter
Manor Royal, West Sussex RH10 9NU
Fax: 01293 444123   Tel: 01293 747747

VISUALEYES IMAGING SERVICES
(Photographic Reproduction)
11 West Street, London WC2H 9NA
Website: www.visualeyes.ltd.uk
e-mail: imaging@visualeyes.ltd.uk
Fax: 020-7240 0050   Tel: 020-7836 3004

VOCALEYES
(Suppliers of Audio Description for Theatrical
Performance)
25 Short Street, London SE1 8LJ
Website: www.vocaleyes.co.uk
e-mail: enquiries@vocaleyes.co.uk
Fax: 020-7928 2225   Tel: 020-7261 9199

WEBBER Peter HIRE/RITZ STUDIOS
(Music Equipment Hire, Rehearsal Studios)
110-112 Disraeli Road, London SW15 2DX
Fax: 020-8877 1036   Tel: 020-8870 1335

WESTED LEATHERS CO
(Suede & Leather Suppliers/Manufacturers)
Little Wested House
Wested Lane, Swanley, Kent BR8 8EF
e-mail: wested@compuserve.com
Fax: 01322 667039   Tel: 01322 660654

WESTWARD Lynn
(Window Blind Specialist)
273 The Vale, Acton, London W3 7QA
Fax: 020-8740 9836   Tel: 020-8740 8756

WHITEHORN Simon
(Sound Design)
57 Acre Lane, London SW2 5TN
e-mail: simon@orbitalsound.co.uk
Fax: 020-7501 6869   Tel: 020-7501 6868

WILLIAMS Frank
(Bottles & Jars 1870 - 1940)
33 Enstone Road, Ickenham, Uxbridge, Middlesex
e-mail: wllmsfrn4@aol.com   Tel: 01895 672495

WILTSHIRE A. F.
(Agricultural Engineers)
The Agricultural Centre
Alfold Road, Dunsfold, Surrey GU8 4NP
e-mail: team@afwiltshire.fsnet.co.uk
Fax: 01483 200491   Tel: 01483 200516

WINSHIP Geoff
The Knights of Merrie England Ltd
153 Salisbury Road, Burton, Christchurch BH23 7JS
Website: www.medievaljousting.com
e-mail: geoff@medievaljousting.com
Fax: 01202 483666   Tel: 01202 483777

WOODEN CANAL BOAT SOCIETY
(Historic Canal Boats)
5 Oaken Clough Terrace
Limehurst, Ashton-under-Lyne, Lancs OL7 9NY
Website: www.wcbs.org.uk
e-mail: chris@widdershins.fsnet.co.uk
Mobile: 07855 601589   Tel: 0161-330 2315

WORBEY Darryl STUDIOS
(Specialist Puppet Design)
e-mail: dworbey@freewire.co.uk
Fax: 020-7635 6397   Tel: 020-7639 8090

WORLD OF FANTASY
(Props and Costumes)
Swansnest, Rear of 2 Windmill Road
Hampton Hill, Middlesex TW12 1RH
e-mail: swansflight@aol.com
Fax: 020-8783 1366   Tel: 020-8941 1595

WORLD OF ILLUSION
4 Sunnyside, Wimbledon SW19 4SL
Fax: 020-8946 0228   Tel: 020-8946 9478

WWW.PUPPETSPRESENT.COM
c/o Peter Charlesworth & Associates
68 Old Brompton Road, London SW7 3LD
Website: www.puppetspresent.com
e-mail: puppetspresent@btinternet.com
                                 Tel: 020-7581 2478

237

ACADEMY PLAYERS DIRECTORY
1313 N. Vine Street, Hollywood, CA 90028
Website: www.playersdirectory.com
e-mail: players@oscars.org
Fax: (310) 550-5034   Tel: (310) 247-3000

A & C BLACK (Publicity Dept)
37 Soho Square, London W1D 3QZ
e-mail: publicity@acblack.com
Fax: 020-7758 0222   Tel: 020-7758 0200

A C I D PUBLICATIONS
Suite 247, 37 Store Street, London WC1E 7BS
e-mail: acidnews@aol.com   Tel/Fax: 07050 205206

ACTING: A DRAMA STUDIO SOURCE BOOK
(Peter Owen Publishers)
73 Kenway Road
London SW5 0RE
Website: www.peterowen.com
e-mail: admin@peterowen.com   Tel: 020-7373 5628

ACTORS' HANDBOOK
(Bloomsbury Publishing Plc)
38 Soho Square, London W1D 3HB
Website: www.bloomsbury.com
e-mail: webmaster@bloomsbury.com
Fax: 020-7434 0151   Tel: 020-7494 2111

AMATEUR STAGE MAGAZINE & COMMUNITY ARTS DIRECTORY
(Platform Publications Ltd)
Hampden House
2 Weymouth Street, London W1W 5BT
e-mail: cvtheatre@aol.com
Fax: 020-7636 2323   Tel: 020-7636 4343

ANNUAIRE DU CINEMA BELLEFAYE
(French Actors Directory, Production, Technicians & All Technical Industries & Suppliers)
38 rue Etienne Marcel, 75002 Paris
Website: www.bellefaye.com
e-mail: contact@bellefaye.com
Fax: 00 331 42 33 39 00   Tel: 00 331 42 33 52 52

ARTISTES & AGENTS
(Richmond House Publishing Co)
Douglas House
3 Richmond Buildings, London W1D 3HE
Website: www.rhpco.co.uk
e-mail: sales@rhpco.co.uk
Fax: 020-7287 3463   Tel: 020-7437 9556

AUDITION NOW
(Weekly Casting Publication)
Lifegroup Ltd, Garden Studios
11-15 Betterton Street, Covent Garden
London WC2H 9BP   Tel: 0800 0966144

AURORA METRO PRESS (1979)
(Drama, Fiction, Reference & International Literature in English Translation)
4 Osier Mews, Chiswick,
London W4 2NT
Website: www.aurorametro.com
e-mail: ampress@netcomuk.co.uk
Fax: 020-8742 2925   Tel: 020-8747 1953

BRITISH NATIONAL FILM & VIDEO CATALOGUE
(British Film Institute)
21 Stephen Street, London W1T 1LN
Website: www.bfi.org.uk
e-mail: maureen.brown@bfi.org.uk
Fax: 020-7436 7950   Tel: 020-7957 4706

BRITISH PERFORMING ARTS YEARBOOK
(Rhinegold Publishing)
241 Shaftesbury Avenue
London WC2H 8TF
Website: www.rhinegold.co.uk
e-mail: bpay@rhinegold.co.uk   Tel: 020-7333 1721

BRITISH THEATRE DIRECTORY
(Richmond House Publishing Co)
Douglas House
3 Richmond Buildings, London W1D 3HE
Website: www.rhpco .co.uk
e-mail: sales@rhpco.co.uk
Fax: 020-7287 3463   Tel: 020-7437 9556

BROADCAST
33-39 Bowling Green Lane, London EC1R 0DA
Website: www.broadcastnow.co.uk
Fax: 020-7505 8020   Tel: 020-7505 8014

CALDER PUBLICATIONS
51 The Cut, London SE1 8LF
e-mail: info@calderpublications.com
Fax: 020-7928 5930   Tel: 020-7633 0599

CASTCALL & CASTFAX
(Casting Information Services)
106 Wilsden Avenue, Luton LU1 5HR
Website: www.castcall.co.uk
e-mail: admin@castcall.co.uk
Fax: 01582 480736   Tel: 01582 456213

CASTWEB
7 St Luke's Avenue, London SW4 7LG
Website: www.castweb.co.uk
e-mail: castweb@netcomuk.co.uk
Fax: 020-7720 2879   Tel: 020-7720 9002

CELEBRITY BULLETIN The
Rooms 203-209
93-97 Regent Street, London W1B 4ES
e-mail: celebritylondon@aol.com
Fax: 020-7494 3500   Tel: 020-7439 9840

CELEBRITY SERVICE Ltd
Rooms 203-209
93-97 Regent Street, London W1B 4ES
e-mail: celebritylondon@aol.com
Fax: 020-7494 3500   Tel: 020-7439 9840

CHAPPELL OF BOND STREET
(Sheet Music, Musical Instruments, Pianos, Synthesizers, Keyboards)
50 New Bond Street, London W1S 1RD
Fax: 020-7491 0133   Tel: 020-7491 2777

CONFERENCE & INCENTIVE TRAVEL MAGAZINE
174 Hammersmith Road, London W6 7JP
Fax: 020-8267 4192   Tel: 020-8267 4307

CREATIVE HANDBOOK
(Reed Business Information)
Windsor Court, East Grinstead House
East Grinstead, West Sussex RH19 1XA
Website: www.chb.com
e-mail: phewson@reedinfo.co.uk
Fax: 01342 332072   Tel: 01342 332022

DANCE EXPRESSION
(A. E. Morgan Publications Ltd)
51 Earl's Court Square, London SW5 9DG
Website: www.danceexpressionsmag.co.uk
                              Tel: 020-7370 7324

DIRECTING DRAMA
(Peter Owen Publishers)
73 Kenway Road
London SW5 0RE
Website: www.peterowen.com
e-mail: admin@peterowen.com   Tel: 020-7373 5628

EQUITY JOURNAL
Guild House
Upper St Martin's Lane, London WC2H 9EG
Website: www.equity.org.uk
e-mail: info@equity.org.uk
Fax: 020-7379 6074   Tel: 020-7379 5185

FILMLOG
(Subscriptions)
PO Box 100, Broadstairs, Kent CT10 1UJ
Tel: 01843 860885   Tel: 01843 866538

FORESIGHT
(The Profile Group)
6-7 St Cross Street, London EC1N 8UA
Website: www.foresightonline.co.uk
Fax: 020-7430 1089   Tel: 020-7405 4455

GETTING INTO FILM & TV
(John Burder Films)
37 Braidley Road
Meyrick Park
Bournemouth BH2 6JY   Tel: 01202 295395

GRAPEVINE The
9 Greville Hall, Greville Place
London NW6 5JS   Tel/Fax: 020-7625 2213

HOLLYWOOD REPORTER The
Endeavour House
189 Shaftesbury Avenue, London WC2H 8TJ
Fax: 020-7420 6015   Tel: 020-7420 6003

KAY'S UK & EUROPEAN PRODUCTION MANUALS
Pinewood Studios
Pinewood Road, Iver Heath, Bucks SL0 0NH
Website: www.kays.tv
e-mail: info@kays.co.uk
Fax: 01753 652665   Tel: 01753 651171

KEMP'S FILM, TV & VIDEO
(Reed Business Information)
East Grinstead House
East Grinstead, West Sussex RH19 1XA
Website: www.cht.com
e-mail: phewson@reedinfo.co.uk
Fax: 01342 332072   Tel: 01342 332022

KNOWLEDGE The
Riverbank House
Angel Lane, Tonbridge, Kent TN9 1SE
Website: www.theknowledgeonline.com
e-mail: knowledge@cmpinformation.com
Fax: 01732 368324   Tel: 01732 377591

LIMELIGHT The
(Limelight Publications, Contacts and Casting
Directory)
Postal Address: PO Box 760
Randpark Ridge, 2156, Gauteng, South Africa
Website: www.llmelight.co.za
e-mail: barbara@limelight.co.za
Tel/Fax: 00 27 11 793 7231

MAKING OF THE PROFESSIONAL ACTOR The
(Peter Owen Publishers)
73 Kenway Road
London SW5 0RE
Website: www.peterowen.com
e-mail: admin@peterowen.com   Tel: 020-7373 5628

MUSICAL STAGES
(Musical Theatre Magazine)
Box 8365, London W14 0GL
Website: www.musicalstage.co.uk
e-mail: editor@musicalstages.co.uk
Tel/Fax: 020-7603 2221

MUSIC WEEK DIRECTORY
United Business Media Entertainment Group
Ludgate House
245 Blackfriars Road
London SE1 9UR   Tel: 020-7579 4192

OFFICIAL LONDON SEATING PLAN GUIDE The
(Richmond House Publishing Co)
Douglas House
3 Richmond Buildings, London W1D 3HE
Website: www.rhpco.co.uk
e-mail: sales@rhpco.co.uk
Fax: 020-7287 3463   Tel: 020-7437 9556

PA LISTINGS Ltd
292 Vauxhall Bridge Road
Victoria, London SW1V 1AE
Website: www.pa.press.net
e-mail: arts@listings.press.net
Fax: 020-7963 7800   Tel: 020-7963 7707

PANTOMIME BOOK The
(Peter Owen Publishers)
73 Kenway Road
London SW5 0RE
Website: www.peterowen.com
e-mail: admin@peterowen.com   Tel: 020-7373 5628

PCR
(See PRODUCTION & CASTING REPORT)

PERFORMING ARTS YEARBOOK FOR EUROPE (PAYE)
(Arts Publishing International Ltd)
Unit A, 402A Tower Bridge Business Complex
100 Clements Road, London SE16 4DG
e-mail: paye@api.co.uk
Fax: 020-7394 8753   Tel: 020-7232 5800

PLAYERS' GUIDE
(In association with THE SPOTLIGHT &
BREAKDOWN SERVICES Ltd USA)
123 West 44th Street, #2J, New York NY 10036
e-mail: playersguide@breakdownservices.com
Fax: (212) 302-3495   Tel: (212) 302-9474

PLAYS INTERNATIONAL
33A Lurline Gardens
London SW11 4DD   Tel/Fax: 020-7720 1950

PRESENTER'S CONTACT FILE THE/PRESENTER'S YEAR PLANNER The
Presenter Promotions
123 Corporation Road, Gillingham, Kent ME7 1RG
Website: www.presenterpromotions.com
e-mail: info@presenterpromotions.com
Fax: 01634 316771   Tel: 01634 851077

PRESENTERS SPOTLIGHT
7 Leicester Place, London WC2H 7RJ
Website: www.spotlightcd.com
e-mail: info@spotlightcd.com
Fax: 020-7437 5881   Tel: 020-7437 7631

PRESS PLANNER
(The Profile Group)
6-7 St Cross Street, London EC1N 8UA
Website: www.forwardplanning.co.uk
e-mail: info@pressplanner.co.uk
Fax: 020-7405 4347   Tel: 020-7405 4455

PRODUCERS ALLIANCE FOR CINEMA & TELEVISION
(Pact Directory of Independent Producers/
Art of the Deal/Rights Clearance)
45 Mortimer Street, London W1W 8HJ
Website: www.pact.co.uk
e-mail: enquiries@pact.co.uk
Fax: 020-7331 6700   Tel: 020-7331 6000

PRODUCTION & CASTING REPORT
(Editorial)
PO Box 11, London N1 7JZ
Website: www.pcrnewsletter.com
Fax: 020-7566 8284   Tel: 020-7566 8282

PRODUCTION & CASTING REPORT
(Subscriptions)
PO Box 100, Broadstairs, Kent CT10 1UJ
Website: www.pcrnewsletter.com
Tel: 01843 860885   Tel: 01843 866538

RADIO TIMES
80 Wood Lane, London W12 0TT
e-mail: radio.times@bbc.co.uk
Fax: 020-8433 3923   Tel: 0870 6084455

RICHMOND HOUSE PUBLISHING COMPANY Ltd
Douglas House
3 Richmond Buildings, London W1D 3HE
Website: www.rhpco.co.uk
e-mail: sales@rhpco.co.uk
Fax: 020-7287 3463   Tel: 020-7437 9556

SCREEN INTERNATIONAL
33-39 Bowling Green Lane, London EC1R 0DA
Website: www.screeninternational.com
e-mail: screeninternational@compuserve.com
Fax: 020-7505 8117   Tel: 020-7505 8080

SCRIPT BREAKDOWN SERVICE Ltd
Suite 1, 16 Sidmouth Road, London NW2 5JX
e-mail: casting@sbsltd.demon.co.uk
Fax: 020-8459 7442   Tel: 020-8451 2852

SHOWCALL
47 Bermondsey Street, London SE1 3XT
Website: www.showcall.co.uk
e-mail: info@thestage.co.uk
Fax: 020-7378 0480   Tel: 020-7403 1818

SHOWCAST: THE AUSTRALASIAN CASTING DIRECTORY
PO Box 2001, Leumeah, NSW 2560 Australia
Website: www.showcast.com.au
e-mail: brian@showcast.com.au
Fax: 02 4647 4167   Tel: 02 4647 4166

SIGHT & SOUND
(British Film Institute)
21 Stephen Street, London W1T 1LN
Website: www.bfi.org.uk/sightandsound/
e-mail: s&s@bfi.org.uk
Fax: 020-7436 2327   Tel: 020-7255 1444

SPEECH FOR THE SPEAKER
(Peter Owen Publishers)
73 Kenway Road
London SW5 0RE
Website: www.peterowen.com
e-mail: admin@peterowen.com   Tel: 020-7373 5628

SPOTLIGHT CASTING DIRECTORY The
7 Leicester Place, London WC2H 7RJ
Website: www.spotlightcd.com
e-mail: info@spotlightcd.com
Fax: 020-7437 5881   Tel: 020-7437 7631

STAGE BY STAGE
(Drama/Theatre Studies/History/Reference)
(Peter Owen Publishers)
73 Kenway Road, London SW5 0RE
e-mail: admin@peterowen.com
Fax: 020-7373 6760   Tel: 020-7373 5628

STAGECAST: IRISH STAGE & SCREEN DIRECTORY
15 Eaton Square
Monkstown, Dublin   Tel/Fax: 00 353 1 2808968

STAGE NEWSPAPER Ltd The
47 Bermondsey Street, London SE1 3XT
Website: www.thestage.co.uk
e-mail: editor@thestage.co.uk
Fax: 020-7357 9287   Tel: 020-7403 1818

TANGO REVIEW
(Academia Nacional del Tango UK Ltd)
51 Earl's Court Square
London SW5 9DG   Tel: 020-7370 7324

TELEVISUAL
12-26 Lexington Street, London W1R 4HQ
Website: www.televisual.com
Fax: 020-7970 6733   Tel: 020-7970 6541

THEATRE RECORD
305 Whitton Dene, Isleworth, Middlesex TW7 7NE
Website: www.theatrerecord.com
e-mail: editor@theatrerecord.demon.co.uk
Fax: 020-8893 9677   Tel: 020-8737 8489

THEATRE REPORT
(Subscriptions)
PO Box 100, Broadstairs, Kent CT10 1UJ
Website: www.pcrnewsletter.com
Tel: 01843 860885   Tel: 01843 866538

TIME OUT GROUP Ltd
Universal House
251 Tottenham Court Road
London W1T 7AB
e-mail: net@timeout.co.uk
Fax: 020-7813 6001   Tel: 020-7813 3000

TV TIMES
IPC Magazines
Kings Reach Tower, Stamford Street, London SE1 9LS
Fax: 020-7261 7888   Tel: 020-7261 7000

VARIETY NEWSPAPER
7th Floor, 84 Theobalds Road, London WC1X 8RR
Website: www.variety.com
Fax: 020-7611 4581   Tel: 020-7611 4580

VOICE BOOK The
(Michael McCallion, published by Faber & Faber)
Macmillan Distribution
e-mail: mdl@macmillan.co.uk   Tel: 01256 302699

WHITE BOOK The
Bank House, 23 Warwick Road
Coventry CV1 2EW   Tel: 024-7655 9590

ARTHUR Anna PRESS & PR
52 Tottenham Street, London W1T 4RN
e-mail: name@aapr.co.uk
Fax: 020-7637 2984   Tel: 020-7637 2994

ASSOCIATES The
(Film & Video Publicity Specialists)
39-41 North Road, London N7 9DP
Website: www.the-associates.co.uk
e-mail: info@the-associates.co.uk
Fax: 020-7609 2249   Tel: 020-7700 3388

AVALON PUBLIC RELATIONS
(Marketing/Arts)
4A Exmoor Street, London W10 6BD
e-mail: edt@avalonuk.com
Fax: 020-7598 7223   Tel: 020-7598 7222

BARLOW Tony ASSOCIATES
(Press & Marketing for Music, Dance & Theatre)
3 Choumert Square, London SE15 4RE
Website: www.tonybarlowuk.co.uk
e-mail: artspublicity@hotmail.com
Mobile: 07774 407385   Tel/Fax: 020-7358 9291

BETTER ENGLISH PROOF-READING
6 Hornsey Lane Gardens, Highgate, London N6 5PB
Website: www.better-english.net
e-mail: infocom@dial.pipex.com
                                        Tel/Fax: 020-8374 6040

BOLTON Erica & QUINN Jane Ltd
10 Pottery Lane, London W11 4LZ
e-mail: e.mail@boltonquinn.com
Fax: 020-7221 8100   Tel: 020-7221 5000

BORKOWSKI Mark PR & IMPROPERGANDA Ltd
2nd Floor, 12 Oval Road, London NW1 7DH
Website: www.borkowski.co.uk
e-mail: vicki@borkowski.co.uk
Fax: 020-7482 5400   Tel: 020-7482 4000

CAHOOTS PRODUCTION & PR
(Denise Silvey, Martin Rumble)
32 Champion Grove, London SE5 8BW
e-mail: cahootstheatreco@aol.com
                                        Tel/Fax: 020-7738 4250

CELEBRATE
(Creative Events Promotion)
22 Brownhill Lane
Holmfirth, West Yorkshire HD9 2QW
e-mail: info@celebrateprojects.co.uk
                                        Tel: 01484 688219

CENTRESTAGE PUBLIC RELATIONS
Yeates Cottage, 27 Wellington Terrace
Knaphill, Woking, Surrey GU21 2AP
e-mail: dellayedwards@hotmail.com
                                        Tel: 01483 487808

CHAPMAN Emma PUBLICITY
2nd Floor
18 Great Portland Street, London W1W 8QP
e-mail: pr@ecpub.com
Fax: 020-7637 0660   Tel: 020-7637 0990

CHAPMAN Guy ASSOCIATES
33 Southampton Street
Covent Garden, London WC2E 7HE
e-mail: admin@g-c-a.co.uk
Fax: 020-7379 8484   Tel: 020-7379 7474

CHESTON Judith PUBLICITY
30 Telegraph Street
Shipston-on-Stour, Warks CV36 4DA
e-mail: cheston@shipstononstour1.freeserve.co.uk
Fax: 01608 663772   Tel: 01608 661198

COWAN SYMES & ASSOCIATES
83 Charlotte Street, London W1T 4PR
Fax: 020-7323 1070   Tel: 020-7323 1200

CUE CONSULTANTS
18 Barrington Court, London N10 1QG
e-mail: jmin@globalnet.co.uk
Fax: 020-8883 4197   Tel: 020-8444 6533

DAVEY Christine Ltd
29 Victoria Road
Eton Wick, Windsor, Berkshire SL4 6LY
Fax: 01753 851123   Tel: 01753 852619

DAVIDSON Dennis ASSOCIATES
Royalty House
72-74 Dean Street, London W1D 3SG
Fax: 020-7437 6358   Tel: 020-7439 6391

EILENBERG Charlotte ASSOCIATES
6 Balfour Road, London N5 2HB
e-mail: charlotte.eilenberg@dial.pipex.com
                                        Tel/Fax: 020-7354 2155

ELSON Howard PROMOTIONS
16 Penn Avenue
Chesham, Buckinghamshire HP5 2HS
e-mail: helson1029@aol.com
Fax: 01494 784760   Tel: 01494 785873

GADABOUTS Ltd
(Theatre Marketing & Promotions)
54 Friary Road, London N12 9PB
Website: www.gadabouts.co.uk
e-mail: events@gadabouts.fsnet.co.uk
Tel/Fax: 020-8445 5450   Tel: 020-8445 4793

GAYNOR Avril ASSOCIATES
76 Probyn House, Page Street, London SW1P 4BQ
e-mail: gaynorama@aol.com
                                        Tel/Fax: 020-7976 6522

GOODMAN Deborah PUBLICITY
44 Pembroke Road, London N10 2HT
e-mail: dg.pr@virgin.net
Fax: 020-8365 3557   Tel: 020-8444 2607

HATTON & RAE-SMITH
91 Southwood Lane
London N6 5TB   Tel: 020-8340 5942

HYMAN Sue ASSOCIATES Ltd
Suite 1, Waldorf Chambers
11 Aldwych, London WC2B 4DA
e-mail: sue.hyman@btinternet.com
Fax: 020-7379 4944   Tel: 020-7379 8420

IMPACT AGENCY
3 Bloomsbury Place, London WC1A 2QL
e-mail: mail@impactagency.co.uk
Fax: 020-7580 7200   Tel: 020-7580 1770

KEAN LANYON
(Sharon Kean)
Rose Cottage, The Aberdeen Centre
22-25 Highbury Grove, London N5 2EA
e-mail: sharon@keanlanyon.com
Fax: 020-7359 0199   Tel: 020-7354 3574

Publicity & Press Representatives

KELLER Don ARTS MARKETING
65 Glenwood Road, Harringay, London N15 3JS
e-mail: donkeller@waitrose.com
Fax: 020-8809 6825   Tel: 020-8800 4882

KWPR
(Kevin Wilson Public Relations)
Studio 310 The Chandlery
50 Westminster Bridge Road, London SE1 7QY
Website: www.kwpr.co.uk
e-mail: kwshout@aol.com
Fax: 020-7721 7640   Tel: 020-7721 7621

LAKE-SMITH GRIFFIN ASSOCIATES
15 Maiden Lane
Covent Garden, London WC2E 7NG
e-mail: lakesmithgriffin@aol.com
Fax: 020-7836 1040   Tel: 020-7836 1020

LAVER Richard PUBLICITY
3 Troy Court
High Street Kensington, London W8 7RA
e-mail: richardlaver@btconnect.com
Fax: 020-7937 7322   Tel: 020-7937 7322

LEE Phillip
(Marketing, Press and Publicity)
Top Floor, 21 Denmark Street, London WC2H 8NA
e-mail: philip@leep.biz
Fax: 020 7916 0031   Tel: 020 7916 0030

MAYER Anne PR
82 Mortimer Road, London N1 4LH
e-mail: johnxbird@aol.com
Fax: 020-7254 8227   Tel: 020-7254 7391

McDONALD Charles
(See McDONALD & RUTTER)

McDONALD & RUTTER
34 Bloomsbury Street, London WC1B 3QJ
e-mail: info@mcdonaldrutter.com
Fax: 020-7637 3690   Tel: 020-7637 2600

MITCHELL Jackie
(JM Communications)
4 Sims Cottages
The Green Claygate, Surrey KT10 0JH
e-mail: pr@jackiem.com
Fax: 01372 471073   Tel: 01372 465041

MITCHELL Sarah PARTNERSHIP The
Third Floor, 87 Wardour Street, London W1F 0VA
Website: www.thesmp.com
e-mail: sarah@thesmp.com
Fax: 020-7434 1954   Tel: 020-7434 1944

MORGAN Jane ASSOCIATES
(Media & Marketing)
8 Heathville Road, London N19 3AJ
e-mail: morgans@dircon.co.uk
Fax: 020-7263 9877   Tel: 020-7263 9867

MORGAN Kim MEDIA & MARKETING
2 Averill Street, Hammersmith, London W6 8EB
e-mail: kim@kimmorgan-pr.com
Mobile: 07939 591403   Tel/Fax: 020-7381 4115

NEWLEY Patrick ASSOCIATES
45 Kingscourt Road, London SW16 1JA
e-mail: patricknewley@yahoo.com
Tel/Fax: 020-8677 0477

PARKER James ASSOCIATES
67 Richmond Park Road, London SW14 8JY
e-mail: jimparkerjpa@hotmail.com
Tel/Fax: 020-8876 1918

POWELL Martin COMMUNICATIONS
1 Lyons Court, Long Ashton Business Park
Yanley Lane, Bristol BS41 9LB
Fax: 01275 393933   Tel: 01275 394400

PREMIER PR
91 Berwick Street, London W1F 0NE
Fax: 020-7734 2024   Tel: 020-7494 3478

PR PEOPLE The
1 St James Drive, Sale, Cheshire M33 7QX
e-mail: pr.people@btinternet.com
Fax: 0161-976 2758   Tel: 0161-976 2729

PUBLIC EYE COMMUNICATIONS Ltd
Suite 318, Plaza, 535 Kings Road, London SW10 0SZ
e-mail: reception@publiceye.co.uk
Fax: 020-7351 1010   Tel: 020-7351 1555

RKM PUBLIC RELATIONS
(London. Los Angeles)
83 Replingham Road, London SW18 5LU
Website: www.rkmpr.com
e-mail: info@rkmpr.com
Fax: 020-8516 8909   Tel: 020-8516 9669

SAPIEKA Joy
Premier PR, 91 Berwick Street, London W1F 0NE
e-mail: jsa.press@easynet.co.uk
Fax: 020-7586 3200   Tel: 020-7586 3100

SHIPPEN Martin MARKETING AND MEDIA
91 Dyne Road, London NW6 7DR
e-mail: m.shippen@virgin.net
Mobile: 07956 879165   Tel/Fax: 020-7372 3788

SINGER Sandra ASSOCIATES
(Corporate Services)
21 Cotswold Road, Westcliff on Sea, Essex SS0 8AA
Website: www.sandrasinger.com
e-mail: sandrasingeruk@aol.com
Fax: 01702 339393   Tel: 01702 331616

S & X MEDIA
405F The Big Peg, Vyse Street, Birmingham B18 6NF
e-mail: roulla@sx-media.com
Fax: 0121-694 6494   Tel: 0121-604 6366

TAYLOR Annie
(Festival Management and Marketing)
Spring, Washwells, Box, Wiltshire SN13 8DA
Website: www.greateventcompany.co.uk
e-mail: info@greateventcompany.co.uk
                        Mobile: 07720 444045

TAYLOR HERRING COMMUNICATIONS Ltd
107 Freston Road, London W11 4BD
Website: www.taylorherring.com
e-mail: james@taylorherring.com
Fax: 020-7313 2550   Tel: 020-7313 2551

THOMPSON Peter ASSOCIATES
Flat One, 12 Bourchier Street, London W1V 5HN
Fax: 020-7439 1202   Tel: 020-7439 1210

THORNBORROW Bridget
110 Newark Street, London E1 2ES
e-mail: bthornborrow@aol.com
Fax: 020-7247 4144   Tel: 020-7247 4437

TOWN HOUSE PUBLICITY Ltd
(Theatre & Television PR)
45 Islington Park Street, London N1 1QB
e-mail: thp@townhousepublicity.co.uk
Fax: 020-7359 6026   Tel: 020-7226 7450

TRE-VETT Eddie
Brink House
Avon Castle, Ringwood
Hants BH24 2BL   Tel: 01425 475544

WILLIAMS Tei PRESS & ARTS MARKETING
7 Acre End Street, Eynsham, Oxon OX29 4PE
e-mail: tei@artsmarketing.demon.co.uk
Fax: 01865 884240   Tel: 01865 883139

WILSON Stella PUBLICITY
130 Calabria Road, London N5 1HT
e-mail: stella@starmaker.demon.co.uk
Fax: 020-7354 2242   Tel: 020-7354 5672

WINGHAM Maureen PRESS & PUBLIC RELATIONS
PO Box 125, Stowmarket, Suffolk IP14 1PB
e-mail: mjw.wingham@virgin.net
Fax: 01449 771400   Tel: 01449 771200

WRIGHT Peter
(See CUE CONSULTANTS)

BBC RADIO, Broadcasting House, London W1A 1AA
Tel: 020-7580 4468 (Main Switchboard)

■ DRAMA

BBC Radio Drama
Bush House
The Aldwych, London WC2B 4PH
Tel: 020-7580 4468 (Main Switchboard)
Production

Head	Gordon House
Production Executive	Rebecca Wilmhurst
Co-ordinator Radio	
Drama Company	Cynthia Fagan

Executive Producers

World Service	Marion Nancarrow
London	David Hunter
	Jeremy Mortimer
Manchester	Sue Roberts
Birmingham	Vanessa Whitburn

Senior Producers

Ned Chaillet	David Hitchinson (Westway)
Sally Avens	Sue Wilson (Birmingham)
Cherry Cookson	Keri Davies (Archers)

Producers - London

Jonquil Panting	Pam Fraser Solomon
Tracey Neale	Janet Whitaker
Mary Peate	Claire Grove
Duncan Minshull	Peter Kavanagh
Rishi Sankar (World Service)	Ros Ward

Producers - Manchester

Polly Thomas	Pauline Harris
Jim Poyser	Nadia Molinari

Producers Birmingham

Peter Wild	Julie Beckett (Archers)

Diversity Development

Director	Topher Campbell

Development Producers

Toby Swift	Naylah Ahmed (Birmingham)
Izzy Mant	Liz Webb

Writers Room

Director	Kate Rowland
Co-ordinator	Jessica Dromgoole

BROADCAST

Radio Drama - BBC Scotland

Head	Patrick Rayner
Editor, Radio Drama	Bruce Young
Management Assistant	Sue Meek
Producers	
Gaynor Macfarlane	David Jackson Young
Lu Kemp	

Radio Drama - BBC Wales

Geri Thomas	Allison Hindell

Radio Drama - BBC Northern Ireland

All enquiries to Anne Simpson

■ LIGHT ENTERTAINMENT/RADIO PRODUCTION

Head, Light Entertainment Radio	
	John Pidgeon
Finance Manager	Sally Kirkby

Producers

Lucy Armitage	Claire Jones
Ashley Blaker	Carol Smith
Adam Bromley	Mario Stylianides
Steve Doherty	Danny Wallace
Richard Edis	Helen Williams
Maria Esposito	

Radio Administrator	Sarah Wright

■ NEWS AND CURRENT AFFAIRS

BBC News (Television & Radio)
Television Centre
Wood Lane, London W12 7RJ
Tel: 020-8576 7178   Fax: 020-8576 7120

Director News	Richard Sambrook
Deputy Director News	Mark Damazer
Head of Television News	Roger Mosey
Deputy Head of Television News	Rachel Atwell
Head of Radio News	Stephen Mitchell
Head of Political Programmes	Francesca Unsworth
Head of News Resources	Julia Nelson

■ RADIO SPORT

Head of Sport	Gordon Turnbull

■ CONTROLLERS

Director, BBC Radio	Jenny Abramsky

RADIO 1

Controller	Andy Parfitt

RADIO 2

Controller	Jim Moir

RADIO 3

Controller	Roger Wright

RADIO 4

Controller	James Boyle

■ BBC NEW WRITING

The Writersroom
Room 222
BBC Broadcasting House
London W1A 1AA   Tel: 020-7765 2703
e-mail: new.writing@bbc.co.uk
Website: www.bbc.co.uk/writersroom

Creative Director	Kate Rowland
Newwriting Co-ordinator	Jessica Dromgoole

245

R

BBC RADIO BRISTOL
PO Box 194, Bristol BS99 7QT
Fax: 0117-923 8323   Tel: 0117-974 1111
Managing Editor: Jenny Lacey
News Editor: Dawn Trevett

BBC CAMBRIDGE
Broadcasting House
104 Hills Road, Cambridgeshire CB2 1LD
Fax: 01223 460832   Tel: 01223 259696
Managing Editor: David Martin
Assistant Editor: Patrick Davies

BBC RADIO CLEVELAND
PO Box 95 FM, Middlesbrough TS1 5DG
Website: www.bbc.co.uk/tees
Fax: 01642 211356   Tel: 01642 225211
Managing Editor: Andrew Glover

BBC RADIO CORNWALL
Phoenix Wharf, Truro, Cornwall TR1 1UA
Fax: 01872 275045   Tel: 01872 275421
Managing Editor: Pauline Causey

BBC COVENTRY & WARWICKSHIRE
Holt Court, 1 Greyfriars Road, Coventry CV1 2WR
Fax: 024-7657 0100   Tel: 024-7686 0086
Senior Broadcast Journalist: Sue Curtis

BBC RADIO CUMBRIA
Annetwell Street, Carlisle, Cumbria CA3 8BB
Fax: 01228 511195   Tel: 01228 592444
Managing Editor: Nigel Dyson

BBC RADIO DERBY
PO Box 104.5, Derby DE1 3HL   Tel: 01332 361111
Managing Editor: Simon Cornes

BBC RADIO DEVON
Linkmail 123 Plymouth, PO Box 5, Plymouth PL3 5YQ
Fax: 01752 234564   Tel: 01752 260323
Managing Editor: John Lilley

BBC ESSEX
PO Box 765, Chelmsford
Essex CM2 9XB   Tel: 01245 616000
Managing Editor: Margaret Hyde

BBC RADIO GLOUCESTERSHIRE
London Road
Gloucester GL1 1SW   Tel: 01452 308585
Managing Editor: Mark Hurrell

BBC LONDON LIVE 94.9
35C Marylebone High Street, London W1A 4FL
Fax: 020-7486 4045   Tel: 020-7208 9200
Managing Editor: David Robey
Assistant News Editor: Wyn Baptist
Assistant Editor General Programmes: Paul Leaper

BBC GMR
PO Box 951, Oxford Road
Manchester M60 1SD   Tel: 0161-200 2000
Editor: Steve Taylor

BBC RADIO GUERNSEY
Commerce House, Les Banques
St Peter Port, Guernsey, Channel Islands GY1 2HS
e-mail: radio.guernsey@bbc.co.uk
Fax: 01481 713557   Tel: 01481 728977
Senior Broadast Journalist: Kay Longlois

BBC HEREFORD & WORCESTER
Hylton Road
Worcester WR2 5WW   Tel: 01905 748485
Managing Editor: James Coghill

BBC RADIO HUMBERSIDE
9 Chapel Street, Hull HU1 3NU
e-mail: radio.humberside@bbc.co.uk
Fax: 01482 226409   Tel: 01482 323232
Executive Managing Editor: Helen Thomas

BBC RADIO JERSEY
18 Parade Road, St Helier, Jersey JE2 3PL
Fax: 01534 732569   Tel: 01534 870000
Senior Broadcast Journalist: Matthew Price
News Editor: Sarah Scriven

BBC RADIO KENT
The Great Hall, Mount Pleasant Road
Tunbridge Wells, Kent TN1 1QQ   Tel: 01892 670000
Managing Editor: Robert Wallis

BBC RADIO LANCASHIRE
20-26 Darwen Street, Blackburn
Lancs BB2 2EA   Tel: 01254 262411
Editor: John Clayton

BBC RADIO LEEDS
Broadcasting House
Woodhouse Lane, Leeds LS2 9PN
Fax: 0113-242 0652   Tel: 0113-244 2131
Managing Editor: Richard Whitaker

BBC RADIO LEICESTER
Epic House, Charles Street, Leicester LE1 3SH
Fax: 0116-251 1463   Tel: 0116-251 6688
Editor: Liam McCarthy

BBC RADIO LINCOLNSHIRE
PO Box 219, Newport, Lincoln LN1 3XY
Fax: 01522 511058   Tel: 01522 511411
Station Editor: Charlie Partridge

BBC RADIO MERSEYSIDE
55 Paradise Street, Liverpool L1 3BP
Website: www.bbc.co.uk/liverpool
e-mail: radio.merseyside@bbc.co.uk
Managing Editor: Mick Ord   Tel: 0151-708 5500

BBC RADIO NEWCASTLE
Broadcasting Centre, Barrack Road
Fenham, Newcastle upon Tyne NE99 1RN
Fax: 0191-232 5082   Tel: 0191-232 4141
Editor: Sarah Drummond
Senior Producer: Jon Harle

BBC RADIO NORFOLK
Norfolk Tower, Surrey Street, Norwich NR1 3PA
Website: www.bbc.co.uk/norfolk
e-mail: david.clayton@bbc.co.uk
Fax: 01603 667949   Tel: 01603 617411
Managing Editor: David Clayton

BBC NORTHAMPTON
Broadcasting House
Abington Street, Northampton NN1 2BH
e-mail: northampton@bbc.co.uk
Fax: 01604 230709   Tel: 01604 239100
Manager: David Clargo
Senior Broadcast Journalists: Mike Day, Jo Griffith

BBC RADIO NOTTINGHAM
London Road, Nottingham NG2 4UU
Fax: 0115-902 1985   Tel: 0115-955 0500
Editor: Mike Bettison
Editor News Gathering: Lisa Lambden

BBC RADIO SHEFFIELD
54 Shoreham Street, Sheffield S1 4RS
Fax: 0114-267 5454   Tel: 0114-273 1177
Managing Editor: Gary Keown
Senior Broadcast Journalist News: David Holmes

BBC RADIO SHROPSHIRE
2-4 Boscobel Drive, Shrewsbury, Shropshire SY1 3TT
e-mail: radio.shropshire@bbc.co.uk
Fax: 01743 271702   Tel: 01743 248484
Editor: Tony Fish
Senior Broadcast Journalist News: John Shone

BBC RADIO SOLENT
Broadcasting House
Havelock Road, Southampton SO14 7PW
e-mail: solent@bbc.co.uk
Fax: 023-8033 9648   Tel: 023-8063 1311
Managing Editor: Mia Cóstello

Radio (BBC Local)

BBC SOUTHERN COUNTIES RADIO
Broadcasting Centre, Guildford, Surrey GU2 5AP
e-mail: southern.counties.radio@bbc.co.uk
Fax: 01483 304952   Tel: 01483 306306
Managing Editor: Mike Hapgood
Head of Output: Sara David

BBC RADIO STOKE
Cheapside, Hanley
Stoke-on-Trent, Staffs ST1 1JJ
Website: www.bbc.co.uk/radiostoke
e-mail: radio.stoke@bbc.co.uk
Fax: 01782 289115   Tel: 01782 208080
Managing Editor: Mark Hurrell

BBC RADIO SUFFOLK
Broadcasting House
St Matthews Street, Ipswich IP1 3EP
Website: www.bbc.co.uk/suffolk
e-mail: radiosuffolk@bbc.co.uk
Editor: David Peel   Tel: 01473 250000

BBC THREE COUNTIES RADIO
PO Box 3CR, Luton LU1 5XL
e-mail: 3cr@bbc.co.uk
Fax: 01582 401467   Tel: 01582 637400
Managing Editor: Mark Norman

BBC RADIO WM (WEST MIDLANDS)
PO Box 206, Birmingham B5 7SD
Fax: 0121-472 3174   Tel: 0121-432 9000
Editor Local Services: Keith Beech

BBC WILTSHIRE SOUND
Broadcasting House, 56-58 Prospect Place
Swindon SN1 3RW
Fax: 01793 513650   Tel: 01793 513626
Manager: Tony Worgan

BBC RADIO YORK
20 Bootham Row, York YO30 7BR
Website: www.bbc.co.uk/radioyork
e-mail: radio.york@bbc.co.uk
Fax: 01904 610937   Tel: 01904 641351
Managing Editor: Barrie Stephenson

Radio (Independent Local)

ABERDEEN North Sound Radio
45 Kings Gate, Aberdeen AB15 4EL
e-mail: northsound@srh.co.uk   Tel: 01224 337000

AYR West Sound and West FM
Radio House, 54 Holmston Road, Ayr KA7 3BE
e-mail: westfm@srh.co.uk   Tel: 01292 283662

BELFAST City Beat 96.7 FM
PO Box 967, Belfast BT9 5DF
Fax: 028-9020 0023   Tel: 028-9020 5967

Downtown Radio
Newtownards, Co Down BT23 4ES
e-mail: alastair.mcdowell@downtown.co.uk
                                Tel: 028-9181 5555

BIRMINGHAM BRMB Radio & Capital Radio
9 Brindley Place, Birmingham B1 2DJ
Fax: 0121-245 5245   Tel: 0121-245 5000

BORDERS Radio Borders Ltd
Tweedside Park, Galashiels TD1 3TD
Fax: 0845 3457080   Tel: 01896 759444

BRADFORD Sunrise Radio
30 Chapel Street
Little Germany, Bradford BD1 5DN
Fax: 01274 728534   Tel: 01274 735043

BRADFORD, HUDDERSFIELD, HALIFAX, KEIGHLEY & DEWSBURY
The Pulse/West Yorkshire's Classic Gold
Forster Square, Bradford BD1 5NE
e-mail: general@pulse.co.uk   Tel: 01274 203040

BRIGHTON, EASTBOURNE & HASTINGS Southern FM
Radio House, PO Box 2000
Brighton BN41 2SS   Tel: 01273 430111

BRISTOL GWR FM & Classic Gold 1260
1 Passage Street, PO Box 2000
Bristol BS99 7SN   Tel: 0117-984 3200

CAMBRIDGE & NEWMARKET Q 103 FM
PO Box 103, The Vision Park
Chivers Way, Histon
Cambridge CB4 9WW   Tel: 01223 235255

CARDIFF & NEWPORT
Red Dragon FM & Capital Gold
Atlantic Wharf, Cardiff Bay, Cardiff CF10 4DJ
e-mail: mail@reddragonfm.co.uk
                                Tel: 029-2066 2066

CHESTER, NORTH WALES & WIRRAL
MFM & Marcher Gold
The Studios Mold Road, Wrexham LL11 4AF
Website: www.mfmradio.co.uk
e-mail: sarah.smithard@musicradio.com
                                Tel: 01978 752202
Managing Director: Sarah Smithard

COVENTRY Mercia FM
Hertford Place Coventry CV1 3TT   Tel: 024-7686 8200

KIX 96.2 FM
Watch Close, Spon Street
Coventry CV1 3LN   Tel: 024-7652 5656

DUMFRIES West Sound FM
Unit 40, The Loreburn Centre
High Street, Dumfries DG1 2BD   Tel: 01387 250999

DUNDEE & PERTH Tay FM & Radio Tay AM
PO Box 123, 6 North Isla Street, Dundee DD3 7JQ
Website: www.radiotay.co.uk
e-mail: tayfm@radiotay.co.uk   Tel: 01382 200800

EDINBURGH Radio Forth Ltd
Forth House, Forth Street, Edinburgh EH1 3LE
Website: www.forthonline.co.uk
e-mail: info@radioforth.co.uk   Tel: 0131-556 9255

EXETER & TORBAY Gemini Radio Ltd
Hawthorn House, Exeter Business Park
Exeter EX1 3QS   Tel: 01392 444444

FALKIRK Central FM
201-203 High Street
Falkirk FK1 1DU   Tel: 01324 611164

GLASGOW Radio Clyde FM1 & Clyde 2 AM
3 South Avenue, Clydebank Business Park
Glasgow G81 2RX   Tel: 0141-565 2200

GLOUCESTER & CHELTENHAM
Severn Sound, FM & Classic Gold
Bridge Studios, Eastgate Centre
Gloucester GL1 1SS   Tel: 01452 313200

GREAT YARMOUTH & NORWICH
Radio Broadland FM & Classic Gold Digital
St Georges Plain, 47-49 Colegate
Norwich NR3 1DB   Tel: 01603 630621

GUILDFORD
96.4 The Eagle FM & County Sound 1566 MW
County Sound Radio Network Ltd, Dolphin House
3 North Street, Guildford, Surrey GU1 4AA
e-mail: eagle@countysound.co.uk
                                Tel: 01483 300964

HEREFORD & WORCESTER Wyvern FM
5-6 Barbourne Terrace, Worcester WR1 3JZ
Website: www.koko.com   Tel: 01905 612212

INVERNESS Moray Firth Radio
PO Box 271, Scorguie Place, Inverness IV3 8UJ
e-mail: mfr@mfr.co.uk
Fax: 01463 243224   Tel: 01463 224433

IPSWICH SGR-FM
Radio House, Alpha Business Park
Whitehouse Road
Ipswich IP1 5LT   Tel: 01473 461000

ISLE OF WIGHT Isle of Wight Radio
Dodnor Park Newport, Isle of Wight PO30 5XE
e-mail: admin@iwradio.co.uk
Fax: 01983 821690   Tel: 01983 822557

KENT Invicta FM & Capital Gold
Radio House, John Wilson Business Park
Whitstable, Kent CT5 3QX
e-mail: info@invictafm.com   Tel: 01227 772004

KETTERING & CORBY Connect FM 97.2 & 107.4 FM
Centre 2000, Robinson Close
Telford Way Industrial Estate, Kettering
Northants NN16 8PU   Tel: 01536 412413

LEEDS 96.3 Radio Aire & Magic 828
PO Box 2000, 51 Burley Road
Leeds LS3 1LR   Tel: 0113-283 5500

LEICESTER Leicester Sound 105.4 FM
Granville House, Granville Road Leicester LE1 7RW
Tel: 0116-256 1300

LEICESTER, NOTTINGHAM & DERBY
96 Trent FM & Classic Gold GEM
29-31 Castle Gate
Nottingham NG1 7AP   Tel: 0115-952 7000

LIVERPOOL Radio City
St Johns Beacon
1 Houghton Street, Liverpool L1 1RL
Website: www.radiocity.co.uk
                                 Tel: 0151-472 6800

LONDON
Capital Radio Plc
30 Leicester Square
London WC2H 7LA   Tel: 020-7766 6000

Choice FM
291-299 Borough High Street
London SE1 1JG   Tel: 020-7378 3969

Classic FM
7 Swallow Place, Oxford Circus
London W1B 2AG   Tel: 020-7343 9000

Heart 106.2 FM
The Chrysalis Building, Bramley Road
London W10 6SP   Tel: 020-7468 1062

ITN Radio
200 Gray's Inn Road
London WC1X 8XZ   Tel: 020-7430 4814

Jazz FM 102.2
26-27 Castlereagh Street, London W1H 5DL
Website: www.jazzfm.com
e-mail: info@jazzfm.com   Tel: 020-7706 4100

Kiss 100
Mappin House, 4 Winsley Street
London W1W 8HF
Website: www.kiss100.com   Tel: 020-7617 9100

London Greek Radio
Florentia Village, Vale Road, Haringey
London N4 1TD   Tel: 020-8800 8001

Magic 105.4 FM
Mappin Houset, 4 Winsley Street
London W1W 8HF   Tel: 020-7436 1515

Millennium 106.8 FM
2 Basildon Road
London SE2 0EW   Tel: 020-8311 3112

Virgin Radio
1 Golden Square
London W1F 9DJ   Tel: 020-7434 121

LUTON & BEDFORD
97.6 Chiltern FM & Classic Gold 792/828
Broadcast Centre, Chiltern Road
Dunstable LU6 1HQ   Tel: 01582 676200

MANCHESTER Key 103 FM & Magic 1152
Piccadilly Radio Ltd, Castle Quay, Castle Field
Manchester M15 4PR   Tel: 0161-288 5000

MILTON KEYNES FM 103 Horizon
14 Vincent Avenue
Milton Keynes Broadcast Centre, Crownhill
Milton Keynes MK8 0AB   Tel: 01908 269111

NORTHAMPTON Northhants 96/Classic Gold 1557
Northamptonshire Digital
19-21 St Edmunds Road, Northampton NN1 5DY
e-mail: reception@northants96.musicradio.com
                                 Tel: 01604 795600

NOTTINGHAM & DERBY 96 Trent FM
29-31 Castle Gate, Nottingham NG1 7AP
e-mail: admin@musicradio.com
                                 Tel: 0115-952 7000

OXFORD & BANBURY Fox FM
Brush House, Pony Road
Oxford OX4 2XR   Tel: 01865 871000

PETERBOROUGH
102.7 Hereward FM & Classic Gold
PO Box 225, Queensgate Centre
Peterborough PE1 1XJ   Tel: 01733 460460

PLYMOUTH Plymouth Sound
Earl's Acre, Alma Road
Plymouth PL3 4HX   Tel: 01752 227272

PORTSMOUTH & SOUTHAMPTON
Ocean Radio Group
Radio House, Whittle Avenue
Segensworth West, Fareham
Hants PO15 5SH   Tel: 01489 589911

PRESTON Red Rose Radio Ltd
PO Box 301, St Paul's Square, Preston
Lancs PR1 1YE   Tel: 01772 47770

READING, BASINGSTOKE & ANDOVER 2-Ten FM
PO Box 2020, Reading
Berks RG31 7FG   Tel: 0118-945 4400

REIGATE & CRAWLEY 102.7 Mercury FM
9 The Stanley Centre, Kelvin Way
Manor Royal, Crawley, West Sussex RH10 9SE
e-mail: name@musicradio.com   Tel: 01293 519161

SOMERSET Orchard FM
Haygrove House, Shoreditch
Taunton TA3 7BT   Tel: 01823 338448

SOUTH MANCHESTER Imagine FM
Regent House, Heaton Lane
Stockport, Cheshire SK4 1BX
e-mail: recipient@imaginefm.net
                                 Tel: 0161-609 1400

SOUTHEND Essex Radio Group
(Essex FM/The Breeze/Ten 17/Vibe FM/96.6 Oasis
FM/KFM/Mercury & Fame)
Radio House, 19-20 Clifftown Road
Southend-on-Sea, Essex SS1 1SX
Fax: 01702 345224   Tel: 01702 333711

STOKE-ON-TRENT & STAFFORD Signal Radio
Stoke Road, Stoke-on-Trent, Staffordshire ST4 2SR
Website: www.signaonelradio.co.uk
e-mail: info@signalradio.com   Tel: 01782 747047

SWANSEA 96.4 FM The Wave
Victoria Road, Gowerton
Swansea SA4 3AB   Tel: 01792 511964

TEESSIDE TFM 96.6 & Magic 1170
Yale Crescent Thornaby, Stockton on Tees
Cleveland TS17 6AA   Tel: 01642 888222

TYNE & WEAR & NORTHUMBERLAND, DURHAM
Metro Radio
Newcastle upon Tyne NE99 1BB   Tel: 0191-420 0971

WOLVERHAMPTON & BLACK COUNTRY/
SHREWSBURY & TELFORD Beacon FM & Classic Gold
267 Tettenhall Road
Wolverhampton WV6 0DE   Tel: 01902 461300

YORKSHIRE Hallam FM & Magic AM
Radio House, 900 Herries Road
Hillsborough Sheffield S6 1RH   Tel: 0114-209 1000

YORKSHIRE & LINCOLNSHIRE
96.9 Viking FM & Magic 1161 AM
Commercial Road
Hull HU1 2SG   Tel: 01482 325141

4MC
Film House, 142 Wardour Street, London W1V 3AU
e-mail: anna.billington@4mc.co.uk
Fax: 020-7439 0700   Tel: 020-7439 0600

A1 VOX Ltd
(Specialising in Voices, Audio Editing,
Voice-Over Training and Demo CDs)
20 Old Compton Street, London W1D 4TW
Website: www.a1vox.com
e-mail: info@a1vox.com
Fax: 020-7434 4414   Tel: 020-7434 4404

ABBEY ROAD STUDIOS
3 Abbey Road, St John's Wood, London NW8 9AY
Website: www.abbeyroad.com
e-mail: info@abbeyroad.com
Fax: 020-7266 7250   Tel: 020-7266 7000

AIR-EDEL RECORDING STUDIOS Ltd
18 Rodmarton Street, London W1U 8BJ
e-mail: trevorbest@air-edel.co.uk
Fax: 020-7224 0344   Tel: 020-7486 6466

AIR STUDIOS (LYNDHURST) Ltd
Lyndhurst Hall, Lyndhurst Road, London NW3 5NG
Fax: 020-7794 8518   Tel: 020-7794 0660

ANGEL RECORDING STUDIOS Ltd
311 Upper Street, London N1 2TU
e-mail: angel@angelstudio.co.uk
Fax: 020-7226 9624   Tel: 020-7354 2525

BATTERY STUDIOS
1 Maybury Gardens, London NW10 2NB
Website: www.battery-studios.co.uk
e-mail: amanda.todd@batterystudios.co.uk
Fax: 020-8459 8732   Tel: 020-8967 0013

BLACKHEATH HALLS
23 Lee Road, Blackheath, London SE3 9RQ
Website: www.blackheathhalls.com
e-mail: mail@blackheathhalls.com
Fax: 020-8852 5154   Tel: 020-8318 9758

CHANNEL 20/20 Ltd
20/20 House, 26-28 Talbot Lane, Leicester LE1 4LR
Fax: 0116-222 1113   Tel: 0116-233 2220

CRYING OUT LOUD
(Voice-Over Specialists/Voice-Over Demo CDs)
e-mail: simon.cryer@rab.co.uk
Mobile: 07946 533108   Mobile: 07796 266265

DB POST PRODUCTIONS Ltd
1-8 Batemans Buildings
Soho Square, London W1V 5TW
Website: www.dbpost.com
e-mail: general@dbpost.com
Fax: 020-7287 9143   Tel. 020-7434 0097

DE LANE LEA SOUND
(Post Production, Re-Recording Studios)
75 Dean Street, London W1D 3PU
Website: www.delanelea.com
e-mail: dll@delanelea.com
Fax: 020-7432 3838   Tel: 020-7432 3800

ELMS STUDIOS DIGITAL
(Mac G4/Logic Platinum/Emu Systems, 02R,
Music Composing/Scoring & VO's)
Addiscombe, 10 Empress Avenue, London E12 5ES
Website: www.impulse-music.co.uk/elms-studio
e-mail: phillawrence@elmsstudios.com
Fax: 020-8532 9333   Tel: 020-8518 8629

ESSENTIAL MUSIC
20 Great Chapel Street, London W1F 8FW
e-mail: essentialmusic@hotmail.com
Fax: 020-7287 3597   Tel: 020-7439 7113

HEAVY ENTERTAINMENT Ltd
222 Kensal Road, London W10 5BN
Website: www.heavy-entertainment.com
e-mail: info@heavy-entertainment.com
Fax: 020-8960 9003   Tel: 020-8960 9001

R

ISLAND 41
(Voice-Over Recording Studio)
29 Ash Grove, London W5 4AX
Website: www.island41.com
e-mail: info@island41.com
Fax: 020-8567 5183   Tel: 020-8567 5140

KONK STUDIOS
84-86 Tottenham Lane, London N8 7EE
Fax: 020-8348 3952   Tel: 020-8340 7873

LANSDOWNE RECORDING STUDIOS Ltd
Lansdowne House
Lansdowne Road, London W11 3LP
Website: www.cts-lansdowne.co.uk
e-mail: info@cts-lansdowne.co.uk
Fax: 020-7792 8904   Tel: 020-7727 0041

MAKING TRACKS RECORDING STUDIO
(Voice Tapes/Open Reel &
Digital Multi-Track Recording)
52 St Swithins Road, Tankerton, Kent CT5 2HX
Website: www.young-sounds.com/makingtracks.html
e-mail: jfield@young-sounds.com
Fax: 01277 277851   Tel: 01277 275120

MOTIVATION SOUND STUDIOS Ltd
35A Broadhurst Gardens, London NW6 3QT
e-mail: info@motivationmultimedia.co.uk
Fax: 020-7624 4879   Tel: 020-7328 8305

ORANGE ROOM MUSIC
4 Kendal Court, Railway Road
Newhaven, East Sussex BN9 0AY
e-mail: orangeroommusic@aol.com
Fax: 01273 612811   Tel: 01273 612825

OTHERWISE STUDIOS
61D Gleneldon Road, London SW16 2BH
e-mail: voicedemos@hotmail.com
                          Tel: 020-8769 7793

SARM STUDIOS WEST Ltd
8-10 Basing Street, London W11 1ET
Fax: 020-7221 9247   Tel: 020-7229 1229

SHAW Bernard
(Specialist in Recording & Directing Voice Tapes)
Horton Manor, Canterbury CT4 7LG
Website: www.bernardshaw.co.uk
e-mail: bernard@bernardshaw.co.uk
                          Tel/Fax: 01227 730843

SILVER-TONGUED PRODUCTIONS
(Specialising in Voice Reels)
Website: silver-tongued.co.uk
e-mail: silver-tongued@talk21.com
                          Tel/Fax: 020-8309 0659

SONY MUSIC
31-37 Whitfield Street, London W1T 2SS
Fax: 020-7580 0543   Tel: 020-7636 3434

SOUND COMPANY The
2 Lord Hills Road, London W2 6PD
Website: www.thesoundcompany.net
e-mail: info@thesoundcompany.net
Fax: 020-7286 7377   Tel: 020-7286 7277

SOUND CONCEPTION
82-84 York Road, Bristol BS3 4AL
e-mail: k-dubb@talk21.com
Fax: 0117-963 5059   Tel: 0117-966 2932

SOUND HOUSE POST PRODUCTION Ltd The
10th Floor, Astley House
Quay Street, Manchester M3 4AE
Fax: 0161-832 7266   Tel: 0161-832 7299

STERLING SOUND
(Voice Over Demo CD's, Jingles & Commercials)
8A Barry Road, London SE22 0HU
e-mail: bob@mintman.co.uk
Fax: 020-8693 2976   Tel: 020-8637 0351

STUDIO AVP
82 Clifton Hill, London NW8 0JT
Fax: 020-7624 9112   Tel: 020-7624 9111

TOUCHWOOD AUDIO PRODUCTIONS
6 Hyde Park Terrace, Leeds, W Yorks LS6 1BJ
e-mail: bruce.w@appleonline.net
                          Tel: 0113-278 7180

TOUCHWOOD PRODUCTION STUDIOS
(Voice-Over Showreels, Digital Editing etc)
Knightsbridge House
229 Acton Lane, Chiswick, London W4 5DD
Website: www.touchwoodstudios.co.uk
e-mail: info@touchwoodstudios.co.uk
Fax: 020-8995 2144   Tel: 020-8995 3232

UNIVERSAL SOUND (JUST PLAY) Ltd
16 Aintree Road, Perivale, Middlesex UB6 7LA
Fax: 020-8991 9461   Tel: 020-8998 1619

VOICE CASTER
(Voice-Over Demo Tapes and Commercial
Production)   Tel: 020-8455 2211

VOICE OVER DEMOS
61 Cropley Street, London N1 7JB
Website: www.voiceoverdemos.co.uk
e-mail: daniel@voiceoverdemos.co.uk
                          Tel: 020-7684 1645

W.F.S. Ltd
(Sound Transfer/Optical & Magnetic)
Warwick Sound
111A Wardour Street, London W1F 0UJ
Website: www.warwicksound.com
e-mail: info@warwicksound.com
Fax: 020-7439 0372   Tel: 020-7437 5532

WORLDWIDE SOUND Ltd
21-25 St Anne's Court, Soho, London W1F 0BJ
Website: www.worldwidegroup.ltd.uk
e-mail: sound@worldwidegroup.ltd.uk
Fax: 020-7734 0619   Tel: 020-7434 1121

ACRE LANE INTERNATIONAL REHEARSAL COMPLEX
57 Acre Lane
Brixton, London SW2 5TN
Fax: 020-7501 6869   Tel: 020-7501 6868

ACTORS CENTRE The (LONDON)
(Audition Space Only)
1A Tower Street, London WC2H 9NP
e-mail: admin@actorscentre.co.uk
Fax: 020-7240 3896   Tel: 020-7240 3940

ADI The
218 Lambeth Road, London SE1 7JY
e-mail: info@adiplay.org.uk
Fax: 020-7401 2816   Tel: 020-7928 6160

ALFORD HOUSE
Aveline Street
London SE11 5DQ   Tel: 020-7735 1519

ALRA (Academy of Live and Recorded Arts)
Royal Victoria Patriotic Building
Fitzhugh Grove, Trinity Road London SW18 3SX
Website: www.alra.demon.co.uk/events
e-mail: acting@alra.demon.co.uk
Fax: 020-8875 0789   Tel: 020-8870 6475

AMADEUS CENTRE The
50 Shirland Road,
Little Venice, London W9 2JA
Fax: 020-7266 1225   Tel: 020-7286 1686

AMERICAN CHURCH IN LONDON The
Whitefield Memorial Church
79A Tottenham Court Road, London W1T 4TD
Website: www.amchurchuk.com
e-mail: latchcourt@amchurch.fsnet.co.uk
Fax: 020-7580 5013   Tel: 020-7580 2791

ARTSADMIN
(Toynbee Studios)
28 Commercial Street
London E1 6LS
Website: www.artsadmin.co.uk
e-mail: space@artsadmin.co.uk
Fax: 020-7247 5103   Tel: 020-7247 5102

BAC
Lavender Hill, London SW11 5TN
Website: www.bac.org.uk
e-mail: mailbox@bac.org.uk
Fax: 020-7978 5207   Tel: 020-7223 6557

BELSIZE MUSIC ROOMS
(Casting, Auditioning, Filming)
67 Belsize Lane
Hampstead
London NW3 5AX
Website: www.belsize-music-rooms.co.uk
e-mail: info@belsize-music-rooms.co.uk
Fax: 020-7916 0222   Tel: 020-7916 0111

BIG CITY STUDIOS
Montgomery House
159-161 Balls Pond Road
Islington, London N1 4BG
Website: www.pineapple-agency.com
Fax: 020-7241 3006   Tel: 020-7241 6655

BLACKHEATH HALLS
23 Lee Road, Blackheath
London SE3 9RQ
Website: www.blackheathhalls.com
e-mail: mail@blackheathhalls.com
Fax: 020-8852 5154   Tel: 020-8318 9758

BRIXTON ST VINCENTS COMMUNITY CENTRE
Talma Road, London SW2 1AS
Fax: 020-7326 1713   Tel: 020-7326 4417

CASTING CABIN The
19 Denmark Street
London WC2H 8NA
Fax: 020-7379 5444   Tel: 020-7379 0444

CASTING STUDIOS INTERNATIONAL Ltd
Ramillies House, 1-2 Ramillies Street, London W1F 7LN
Website: www.castingstudios.com
e-mail: info@castingstudios.co.uk
Fax: 020-7437 2080   Tel: 020-7437 2070

CASTING SUITE The
10 Warwick Street, London W1R 5RA
e-mail: sadiejenour@lineone.net
Fax: 020-7494 0803   Tel: 020-7434 2331

CECIL SHARP HOUSE
(Nicola Elwell)
2 Regent's Park Road, London NW1 7AY
Website: www.efdss.org
e-mail: hire@efdss.org
Fax: 020-7284 0534   Tel: 020-7485 2206

CENTRAL LONDON GOLF CENTRE
Burntwood Lane, London SW17 0AT
Fax: 020-8874 7447   Tel: 020-8871 2468

CENTRAL STUDIOS
470 Bromley Road, Bromley, Kent BR1 4PN
Fax: 020-8697 8100   Tel: 020-8698 8880

CHATS PALACE ARTS CENTRE
42-44 Brooksby's Walk
Hackney, London E9 6DF
Fax: 020-8985 6878   Tel: 020-8533 0227

CHELSEA THEATRE
World's End Place
King's Road, London SW10 0DR
Website: www.chelseatheatre@btinternet.com
Fax: 020-7352 2024   Tel: 020-7352 1967

CIRCUS MANIACS
(Circus Skills Rehearsal & Casting Facilities)
Office 8A, The Kingswood Foundation
Britannia Road, Kingswood, Bristol BS15 8DB
e-mail: rehearse@circusmaniacs.com
Mobile: 07977 247287   Tel/Fax: 0117-947 7042

CLAPHAM COMMUNITY PROJECT
St Anne's Hall
Venn Street, London SW4 0BN
Website: www.claphamcommunityproject.org.uk
e-mail: admin@claphamcommunityproject.org.uk
                              Tel/Fax: 020-7720 8731

CLEAN BREAK CENTRE FOR THEATRE & THE ARTS
2 Patshull Road, London NW5 2LB
e-mail: general@cleanbreak.org.uk
Fax: 020-7482 8611   Tel: 020-7482 8600

CLUB FOR ACTS & ACTORS
(Incorporating Concert Artistes Association)
20 Bedford Street
London WC2E 9HP   Tel: 020-7836 3172

COPTIC STREET STUDIO Ltd
9 Coptic Street, London WC1A 1NH
Fax: 020-7636 1414   Tel: 020-7636 2030

253

The Cameron Mackintosh **REHEARSAL STUDIO** *9x15 metres*

★ **Production Office also available** ★ **Bar & Cafe open daily**

⊖ Kilburn ⇌ Brondesbury   Buses: 16, 31, 32, 98, 189, 206, 316, 328

The Tricycle, 269 Kilburn High Road, London NW6 7JR Telephone: 020 7372 6611 Fax: 020 7328 0795

**COVENT GARDEN CASTING SUITES
& AUDITION ROOMS**
29 Maiden Lane, Covent Garden
London WC2E 7JS   Tel: 020-7240 1438

CRAGRATS Ltd
The Mill
Dunford Road, Holmfirth Huddersfield HD9 2AR
Website: www.cragrats.com
e-mail: lindsay@cragrats.com
Fax: 01484 686212   Tel: 01484 686451

CUSTARD FACTORY The
Gibb Street, Digbeth, Birmingham B9 4AA
e-mail: dance@clara.co.uk
Fax: 0121-604 8888   Tel: 0121-693 7777

DANCE ATTIC STUDIOS
368 North End Road
London SW6   Tel: 020-7610 2055

DANCE COMPANY The
(Sue Hann)
76 High Street
Beckenham, Kent BR3 1ED
e-mail: dancecomp@aol.com
Fax: 020-8402 1414   Tel: 020-8402 2424

DANCEWORKS
16 Balderton Street, London W1K 6TN
Fax: 020-7499 9087   Tel: 020-7629 6183

DIAMOND DANCE STUDIO
6-8 Vestry Street, London N1 7RE
Website: www.diamondstudio.co.uk
e-mail: gem@diamonddance.com
Fax: 020-7251 8379   Tel: 020-7251 8858

DIORAMA ARTS
34 Osnaburgh Street, London NW1 3ND
Website: www.diorama-arts.org.uk
e-mail: admin@diorama-arts.org.uk
Fax: 020-7813 3116   Tel: 020-7916 5467

DRILL HALL The
16 Chenies Street, London WC1E 7EX
Website: www.drillhall.co.uk
e-mail: admin@drillhall.co.uk
Fax: 020-7307 5062   Tel: 020-7307 5061

EALING STUDIOS
Ealing Green, London W5 5EP
Website: www.ealingstudios.com
e-mail: gabrielle.kane@ealingstudios.com
Fax: 020-8758 8658   Tel: 020-8567 6655

ENGLISH FOLK DANCE & SONG SOCIETY
Cecil Sharp House
2 Regent's Park Road, London NW1 7AY
Website: www.efdss.org
e-mail: info@efdss.org
Fax: 020-7284 0534   Tel: 020-7485 2206

ENGLISH NATIONAL OPERA
Lilian Baylis House
165 Broadhurst Gardens, London NW6 3AX
Website: www.eno.org
e-mail: receptionlbh@eno.org
Fax: 020-7625 3398   Tel: 020-7624 7711

ESSEX HALL
Unitarian Headquarters
1-6 Essex Street, London WC2R 3HY
Fax: 020-7240 3089   Tel: 020-7240 2384

ETCETERA THEATRE
265 Camden High Street, London NW1 7BU
e-mail: etceteratheatre@hotmail.com
Fax: 020-7482 0378   Tel: 020-7482 4857

FSU LONDON STUDY CENTRE
98-104 Great Russell Street, London WC1B 3LA
Fax: 020-8202 6797   Tel: 020-7813 3223

HAMILTON ROAD CENTRE
1 Hamilton Road, Stratford, London E15 3AE
Fax: 020-7476 0050   Tel: 020-7473 0395

HAMPSTEAD THEATRE
Eton Avenue, Swiss Cottage, London NW3 3EU
Website: www.hampstead-theatre.co.uk
e-mail: admin@hampstead-theatre.com
Fax: 020-7722 3860   Tel: 020-7722 1189

HEN & CHICKENS THEATRE
Unrestricted View
Above Hen & Chickens Theatre Bar
109 St Paul's Road, London N1 2NA
Website: www.henandchickens.com
e-mail: james@henandchickens.com
                         Tel: 020-7704 2001

HER MAJESTY'S THEATRE
Haymarket, London SW1Y 4QL   Tel: 020-7494 5200

HOLY INNOCENTS CHURCH
Paddenswick Road, London W6 0UB
Fax: 020-8563 8735   Tel: 020-8748 2286

HOPE STREET Ltd
13a Hope Street, Liverpool L1 9BQ
Website: www.hope-street.org
e-mail: arts@hopest.u-net.com
Fax: 0151-709 3242   Tel: 0151-708 8007

ISLINGTON ARTS FACTORY
2 Parkhurst Road, London N7 0SF
Website: www.islingtonartsfactory.org.uk
e-mail: islington@artsfactory.fsnet.co.uk
Fax: 020-7700 7229   Tel: 020-7607 0561

JACKSONS LANE ARTS CENTRE
(Various Spaces inc. Rehearsal Rooms
& Theatre Hire)
269A Archway Road, London N6 5AA
Website: www.jacksonslane.org.uk
e-mail: mail@jacksonslane.org.uk
                         Tel: 020-8340 5226

Commercial & Film Casting Studio

Mobile Casting, Showreels

Take Five Casting Studio
25 Ganton St • London W1F 9BP
Tel: 020 7287 2120 • Fax: 020 7287 3035

JERWOOD SPACE
171 Union Street, London SE1 0LN
Website: www.jerwoodspace.co.uk
e-mail: space@jerwoodspace.co.uk
Fax: 020-7654 0172   Tel: 020-7654 0171

K M C AGENCIES
PO Box 122, 48 Great Ancoats Street
Manchester M4 5AB
Website: www.kmcagencies.co.uk
e-mail: studios@kmcagencies.co.uk
Fax: 0161-237 9812   Tel: 0161-237 3009

LA MAISON VERTE
31 Avenue Henri Mas, 34320 Roujan, France
e-mail: nicole.russell@wanadoo.fr
Fax: 00 334 67246998   Tel: 00 334 67248852

LIVE THEATRE The
27 Broad Chare
Quayside, Newcastle-upon-Tyne NE1 3DQ
Website: www.live.org.uk
e-mail: info@live.org.uk   Tel: 0191-261 2694

LONDON BUBBLE THEATRE COMPANY Ltd
5 Elephant Lane, London SE16 4JD
e-mail: admin@londonbubble.org.uk
Fax: 020-7231 2366   Tel: 020-7237 4434

LONDON SCHOOL OF CAPOEIRA
Units 1 & 2 Leeds Place
Tollington Park, London N4 3RQ
Website: www.londonschoolofcapoeira.co.uk
                    Tel: 020-7281 2020

LONDON STUDIO CENTRE
42-50 York Way, London N1 9AB
e-mail: enquire@london-studio-centre.co.uk
Fax: 020-7837 3248   Tel: 020-7837 7741

LONDON WELSH TRUST Ltd
157-163 Gray's Inn Road, London WC1X 8UE
Fax: 020-7837 6268   Tel: 020-7837 3722

LOUNGE The
7th Floor, 4 Golden Square, London W1F 9HT
e-mail: info@thelounge.uk.com
Tel: 020-7494 9901   Fax: 020-7494 9933

MACKINTOSH Cameron REHEARSAL STUDIO
The Tricycle
269 Kilburn High Road, London NW6 7JR
e-mail: admin@tricycle.co.uk
Fax: 020-7328 0795   Tel: 020-7372 6611

MADDERMARKET THEATRE
St John's Alley, Norwich, Norfolk NR2 1DR
Website: www.maddermarket.freeserve.co.uk
e-mail: theatre@maddermarket.freeserve.co.uk
Fax: 01603 661357   Tel: 01603 626560

MARMALADE STUDIO
Studio B5R Metropolitan Wharf
Wapping Wall, London E1W 3SS
Website: www.marmaladeonline.co.uk
e-mail: admin@marmaladeonline.co.uk
                    Tel/Fax: 020-7702 2193

MARYMOUNT COLLEGE
22 Brownlow Mews, London WC1N 2LA
e-mail: vhedges.marymt@btconnect.com
Fax: 020-7831 7185   Tel: 020-7242 7004

MOBERLY SPORTS & EDUCATION CENTRE
Kilburn Lane, London W10 4AH
Fax: 020-7641 5878   Tel: 020-7641 4807

MOTIVATION SOUND STUDIOS Ltd
35A Broadhurst Gardens, London NW6 3QT
e-mail: info@motivationmultimedia.co.uk
Fax: 020-7624 4879   Tel: 020-7328 8305

MOUNTVIEW
Academy of Theatre Arts
The Ralph Richardson Memorial Studios
Kingfisher Place, Clarendon Road
London N22 6XF
Website: www.mountview.ac.uk
e-mail: enquiries@mountview.ac.uk
Fax: 020-8829 0034   Tel: 020-8881 2201

NATIONAL YOUTH THEATRE OF GREAT BRITAIN
443-445 Holloway Road, London N7 6LW
Website: www.nyt.org.uk
e-mail: info@nyt.org.uk
Fax: 020-7281 8246   Tel: 020-7281 3863

NEAL'S YARD MEETING ROOMS
14 Neal's Yard
Covent Garden, London WC2H 9DP
Website: www.nealsyardmeetingrooms.com
e-mail: info@nealsyardmeetingrooms.com
Fax: 020-7836 6489   Tel: 020-7379 0141

NETTLEFOLD The
West Norwood Library Centre
1 Norwood High Street, London SE27 9JX
Fax: 020-7926 8071   Tel: 020-7926 8070

NORTH LONDON PERFORMING ARTS CENTRE
(Production & Casting Office Facilities)
76 St James Lane, Muswell Hill, London N10 3DF
Website: www.nlpac.co.uk
e-mail: nlpac@compuserve.com
Fax: 020-8444 4040   Tel: 020-8444 4544

NORTH PADDINGTON REHEARSAL ROOMS
235 Lanark Road
London W9 1RA   Tel: 020-7624 4089

OCTOBER GALLERY
24 Old Gloucester Street, London WC1N 3AL
Website: www.theoctobergallery.com
e-mail: rentals@ukgateway.net
Fax: 020-7405 1851   Tel: 020-7831 1618

OLD VIC THEATRE
Waterloo Road
London SE1 8NB   Tel: 020-7928 2651

OPEN DOOR COMMUNITY CENTRE
Keevil Drive, Beaumont Road, Wimbledon SW19 6TF
e-mail: opendoor@wandsworth.gov.uk
                    Tel/Fax: 020-8871 8174

OUT OF JOINT
7 Thane Works
Thane Villas, London N7 7PH
Website: www.outofjoint.co.uk
e-mail: ojo@outofjoint.co.uk
Fax: 020-7609 0203   Tel: 020-7609 0207

OVAL HOUSE
52-54 Kennington Oval
London SE11 5SW
Website: www.ovalhouse.com
e-mail: info@ovalhouse.com   Tel: 020-7582 0080

PAINES PLOUGH AUDITION SPACE
4th Floor, 43 Aldwych
London WC2B 4DN
Website: www.painesplough.com
e-mail: office@painesplough.com
Fax: 020-7240 4534   Tel: 020-7240 4533

PEOPLE SHOW
People Show Studios
Pollard Row, London E2 6NB
Website: www.peopleshow.co.uk
e-mail: people@peopleshow.co.uk
Fax: 020-7739 0203   Tel: 020-7729 1841

PINEAPPLE STUDIOS
7 Langley Street
London WC2H 9JA
Fax: 020-7836 0803   Tel: 020-7836 4004

PLACE The (CONTEMPORARY DANCE TRUST)
17 Duke's Road
London WC1H 9PY
Fax: 020-7383 4851   Tel: 020-7387 0161

PLAY Ltd
(See ADI The)

PLAYGROUND PERFORMING ARTS STUDIO The
Unit 8, Latimer Road
London W10 6RQ
Website: www.the-playground.co.uk
e-mail: info@the-playground.co.uk
                            Tel/Fax: 020-8960 0110

POOR SCHOOL The
242 Pentonville Road
London N1 9JY   Tel: 020-7837 6030

QUESTORS THEATRE EALING The
12 Mattock Lane
London W5 5BQ
Website: www.questors.org.uk
e-mail: paul@questors.org.uk
Fax: 020-8567 8736   Tel: 020-8567 0011

QUICKSILVER THEATRE
The Glass House
4 Enfield Road, London N1 5AZ
Website: www.quicksilvertheatre.org
e-mail: talktous@quicksilvertheatre.org
Fax: 020-7254 3119   Tel: 020-7241 2942

RAMBERT DANCE COMPANY
(Patricia Bakewell)
94 Chiswick High Road, London W4 1SH
e-mail: rdc@rambert.org.uk
Fax: 020-8747 8323   Tel: 020-8630 0600

REALLY USEFUL THEATRES
Manor House
21 Soho Square, London W1D 3QP
Fax: 020-7434 1217   Tel: 020-7494 5200

ROOFTOP STUDIO THEATRE
Rooftop Studio, Somerfield Arcade
Stone, Staffordshire ST15 8AU   Tel: 01785 818176

ROTHERHITHE STUDIOS
119 Rotherhithe Street
London SE16 4NF
Website: www.sandsfilms.co.uk
Fax: 020-7231 2119   Tel: 020-7231 2209

ROYAL ACADEMY OF DANCING
36 Battersea Square, London SW11 3RA
Website: www.rad.org.uk
e-mail: info@rad.org.uk
Fax: 020-7924 3129   Tel: 020-7326 8000

ROYAL SHAKESPEARE COMPANY
35 Clapham High Street
London SW4 7TW
Fax: 020-7498 0472   Tel: 020-7720 9941

SCHER Anna THEATRE
70-72 Barnsbury Road
Islington, London N1 0ES
Fax: 020-7833 9467   Tel: 020-7278 2101

SCREEN WEST
136-142 Bramley Road
London W10 6SR
e-mail: sarah.alliston@fbcp.co.uk
Fax: 020-7565 3077   Tel: 020-7565 3102

SEA CADET DRILL HALL
Fairways, Off Broom Road
Teddington   Tel: 01784 241020

SHARED EXPERIENCE THEATRE
The Soho Laundry
9 Dufours Place, London W1F 7SJ
e-mail: admin@setheatre.co.uk
Fax: 020-7287 8763   Tel: 020 7734 8570

SOHO GYMS
Camden Town Gym
193 Camden High Street, London NW1 7JY
Fax: 020-7267 0500   Tel: 020-7482 4524

SOHO GYMS
Clapham Common Gym
95-97 Clapham High Street
London SW4 7TB   Tel: 020-7720 0321

SOHO GYMS
Covent Garden Gym
12 Macklin Street
London WC2B 5NF
Fax: 020-7242 0899   Tel: 020-7242 1290

SOHO GYMS
Earl's Court Gym
254 Earl's Court Road, London SW5 9AD
Fax: 020-7244 6893   Tel: 020-7370 1402

SOHO THEATRE & WRITERS' CENTRE
21 Dean Street, London W1D 3NE
Website: www.sohotheatre.com
e-mail: mail@sohotheatre.com
Fax: 020-7287 5061   Tel: 020-7287 5060

SOUTHALL COMMUNITY CENTRE
(Rehearsal/Location Work)
20 Merrick Road, Southall, London UB2 4AU
Fax: 020-8574 3459   Tel: 020-8574 3458

S.P.A.C.E. The
(Studios for Performing Arts & Creative Enterprise)
Forsyth House
3rd Floor, 111 Union Street
Glasgow G1 3TA
e-mail: info@thespace.fsbusiness.co.uk
Fax: 0141-353 6385   Tel: 0141-331 2519

SPOTLIGHT The
2nd Floor
7 Leicester Place WC2H 7RJ
Website: www.spotlightcd.com/rooms
e-mail: info@spotlightcd.com
Fax: 020-7437 5881   Tel: 020-7437 7631

STEADFAST SEA CADET CORPS
(Modern Hall Available)
Thames Side
Kingston-upon-Thames KT1 1PX   Tel: 01276 485819

ST GILES'S CHURCH HALL
81 Camberwell Church Street
London SE5 8RB   Tel: 020-7701 9319

ST JAMES'S CHURCH PICCADILLY
197 Piccadilly
London W1J 9LL
Fax: 020-7734 7449   Tel: 020-7734 4511

ST JOHN'S CHURCH
Waterloo Road
Southbank
London SE1 8TY
Fax: 020-7928 4470   Tel: 020-7928 2003

Artsadmin
Toynbee Studios

28 Commercial Street, London E1 6LS

Artsadmin have rehearsal spaces available in Toynbee Studios, Aldgate East. There are five spaces for hire, one of which is a 240 seat theatre with basic lighting rig and p.a. facilities. Competitive daily and weekly rates are available and bookings of more than three weeks qualify for a discount on the weekly rate.

Artsadmin Video Resource offers a range of camera and editing equipment for hire. Membership is required and Artsadmin reserve the right to refuse membership.

The Arts Cafe is on site serving light snacks, meals and a selection of drinks.

For further information see www.artsadmin.co.uk/aaresources.co.uk
or contact Gill Lloyd at Artsadmin
Tel: 020 7247 5102   Fax: 020 7247 5103   e-mail: admin@artsadmin.co.uk

ST JOHN'S METHODIST CHURCH
9-11 East Hill, Wandsworth
London SW18 2HT
Tel: 020-8874 4780   Tel: 020-8871 9124

ST MARY ABBOTS HALL
Vicarage Gate
Kensington
London W8 4HN
Website: www.stmaryabbots.freeserve.co.uk
e-mail: terry.pritchard@gmx.net
Fax: 020-7368 6505   Tel: 020-7937 8885

ST MARY NEWINGTON CHURCH HALL
(Peter Edwards)
The Rectory
57 Kennington Park Road
London SE11 4JQ   Tel: 020-7735 1894

ST MARY'S CHURCH HALL PADDINGTON
c/o Bill Kenwright Ltd
106 Harrow Road
London W2 1RR
e-mail: info@kenwright.com
Fax: 020-7446 6222   Tel: 020-7446 6200

TAKE FIVE CASTING STUDIO
(Casting Suite)
25 Ganton Street
London W1F 9BP
Fax: 020-7287 3035   Tel: 020-7287 2120

THEATRE ROYAL DRURY LANE
Catherine Street
London WC2B 5JF   Tel: 020-7494 5200

**THRESH Melody MANAGEMENT
ASSOCIATES Ltd (MTM)**
MTM House
29 Ardwick Green North
Manchester M12 6DL
e-mail: melody.thresh@melody-thresh-management.co.uk
Fax: 0161-273 5455   Tel: 0161-273 5445

TRESTLE ARTS BASE
(Home of Trestle Theatre Company)
Russet Drive
St Albans, Herts AL4 0JQ
Website: www.trestle.org.uk
e-mail: admin@trestle.org.uk
Fax: 01727 855558   Tel: 01727 850150

TRICYCLE The
269 Kilburn High Road
London NW6 7JR
Website: www.tricycle.co.uk
e-mail: admin@tricycle.co.uk
Fax: 020-7328 0795   Tel: 020-7372 6611

TWICKENHAM SEA CADETS
Fairways, Off Broom Road
Teddington
Middlesex TW11 9PL   Tel: 01784 241020

UCL BLOOMSBURY The
15 Gordon Street
London WC1H 0AH
Website: www.thebloomsbury.com
e-mail: blooms.theatre@ucl.ac.uk
                                          Tel: 020-7679 2777

UNION CHAPEL PROJECT
Compton Avenue
London N1 2XD
Website: www.unionchapel.org.uk
e-mail: spacehire@unionchapel.org.uk
Fax: 020-7354 8343   Tel: 020-7226 3750

UNION THEATRE The
204 Union Street
Southwark, London SE1 0LX
e-mail: sasha@uniontheatre.freeserve.co.uk
                                   Tel/Fax: 020-7261 9876

URDANG ACADEMY The
20-22 Shelton Street
Covent Garden
London WC2H 9JJ
Website: www.urdang-academy.co.uk
e-mail: info@theurdangacademy.com
Fax: 020-7836 7010   Tel: 020-7836 5709

WATERMANS
40 High Street
Brentford, Middlesex TW8 0DS
Fax: 020-8232 1030   Tel: 020-8232 1020

WILDITCH COMMUNITY CENTRE
48 Culvert Road
Battersea
London SW11 5BB
Website: www.wandsworth.gov.uk/playservices/community/htm
e-mail: wilditch@wandsworth.gov.uk
                                   Tel/Fax: 020-8871 8172

Y TOURING
10 Lennox Road
Finsbury Park
London N4 3JQ
e-mail: d.jackson@ytouring.org.uk
Fax: 020-7272 8413   Tel: 020-7272 5755

YOUNG Sylvia THEATRE SCHOOL
Rossmore Road
Marylebone
London NW1 6NJ
e-mail: sylvia@youngunsagency.co.uk
Fax: 020-7723 1040   Tel: 020-7723 0037

It is essential that anyone undertaking a journey to the studios below, double checks these routes. Owing to constant changes of rail/bus companies/operators routes may change.

BBC TELEVISION

UNDERGROUND — CENTRAL LINE to WHITE CITY. Turn left from tube, cross zebra crossing. Studios outside station.

BBC South (Elstree) — BOREHAMWOOD

Trains from KINGS CROSS - Thames Link. Take stopping train to Elstree then walk (7/8 mins down Shenley High St.)
UNDERGROUND — NORTHERN LINE to EDGWARE or HIGH BARNET. 107 & 292 BUSES FROM EDGWARE VIA HIGH BARNET TO BOREHAMWOOD.

BRAY STUDIOS (BRAYSWICK)

BR Train from PADDINGTON to MAIDENHEAD. Then take taxi to studios
BR WATERLOO - WINDSOR RIVERSIDE. Take taxi. Coach from VICTORIA to WINDSOR. Take taxi.

HILLSIDE STUDIOS

Train from EUSTON (Network SE) — WATFORD JUNCTION, then taxi. UNDERGROUND — METROPOLITAN LINE to WATFORD, then taxi. Fast Trains from the Midlands & the North also stop at Watford Junction.
If catching slow train get off at Bushey/Oxhey then catch taxi from rank outside, or JUBILEE LINE to STANMORE then a taxi. METROPOLITAN LINE, change at Baker Street or Wembley.

THE LONDON STUDIOS
(LONDON TELEVISION CENTRE)

UNDERGROUND (Bakerloo, Jubilee and Northern Lines) to WATERLOO then follow signs to Royal National Theatre then two buildings along.

PINEWOOD

UNDERGROUND — METROPOLITAN or PICCADILLY LINE to UXBRIDGE. Taxi rank outside station takes about 10 minutes. BRITISH RAIL WESTERN REGION — PADDINGTON to SLOUGH. Taxis from SLOUGH or BUS TO IVER HEATH.

RIVERSIDE STUDIOS

UNDERGROUND — HAMMERSMITH and CITY, DISTRICT or PICCADILLY LINE to HAMMERSMITH — then short walk to studios (behind the London Apollo Hammersmith). Numerous BUS ROUTES from the WEST END. 5 minutes from Hammersmith Broadway.

ROTHERHITHE STUDIOS

UNDERGROUND — DISTRICT LINE to WHITECHAPEL — then change to EAST LONDON LINE to ROTHERHITHE. JUBILEE LINE to CANADA WATER then EAST LONDON LINE to ROTHERHITHE. (5 mins walk) BUS — 188 from EUSTON STATION via WATERLOO or 47 from LONDON BRIDGE or 381 from WATERLOO (best one to catch stops outside Studios).

SHEPPERTON STUDIOS

BRITISH RAIL — SOUTHERN REGION WATERLOO to SHEPPERTON then BUS Route 218 to studios

TEDDINGTON STUDIOS
(THAMES TELEVISION)

BRITISH RAIL — WATERLOO to TEDDINGTON. Cross over footbridge at station. Come out of Station Road entrance. Left past Garden Centre. Nat West at right hand side TURN RIGHT walk 10 mins, then to set of lights, go over into Ferry Road, follow road then come to Studios (next to Anglers Pub on river). UNDERGROUND — DISTRICT LINE to RICHMOND — then take taxi or Bus R68 to TEDDINGTON to top of Ferry Road. Ask for Landmark Centre. Then go back to traffic lights, go across, past the Tide End Public House to Anglers Pub etc.

TWICKENHAM

BRITISH RAIL — SOUTHERN REGION — WATERLOO to ST MARGARET'S. UNDERGROUND — DISTRICT LINE to RICHMOND then SOUTHERN REGION or BUS 37 to ST MARGARET'S.

3D SET COMPANY
(Sets & Scenery Design & Construction)
Unit Q1, Buffalo Courts
Weston Park, Salford Quays
Manchester M50 2QL
Fax: 0161-876 4148   Tel: 0161-888 2225

AHEAD PRODUCTION SERVICES
Charles Taylor Works
43 Bartholomew Street
Digbeth, Birmingham B5 5QN
Website: www.aheadps.co.uk
e-mail: craig@aheadps.freeserve.co.uk
Mobile: 07957 470728   Tel/Fax: 0121-633 7366

ALBEMARLE OF LONDON
(Suppliers of Scenery & Costumes Construction/Hire)
74 Mortimer Street, London W1N 7DF
Website: www.freespace.virgin.net/albemarle.productions
e-mail: albemarle.productions@virgin.net
Fax: 020-7323 3074   Tel: 020-7631 0135

ALL SCENE ALL PROPS
(Scenery, Props & Painters)
443-445 Holloway Road
London N7 6LW
e-mail: allscene@hotmail.com
                          Tel/Fax: 020-7561 9231

BBC VISUAL EFFECTS
41-44 Kendal Avenue
Acton, London W3 0RP
Fax: 020-8993 8741   Tel: 020-8993 9434

BLACKOUT TRIPLE E Ltd
(Unitrack Track Systems, Automation,
Drape & Rigging)
280 Weston Road
London SW19 2QA
Website: www.blackout-tabtrack.comm
e-mail: info@blackout-tabtrack.com
Fax: 020-8687 8500   Tel: 020-8687 8400

BRISTOL (UK) Ltd
(Scenic Paint & StageFloor Duo Suppliers)
12 The Arches
Maygrove Road, London NW6 2DS
Website: www.bristolpaint.com
e-mail: tech.sales@bristolpaint.com
Fax: 020-7372 5242   Tel: 020-7624 4370

CCT LIGHTING Ltd
(Lighting, Dimmers, Sound & Stage Machinery)
Hindle House
Traffic Street
Nottingham NG2 1NE
Website: www.cctlighting.com
e-mail: office@cctlighting.co.uk
Fax: 0115-986 2546   Tel: 0115-986 2722

DAYLIGHT DESIGNS (UK) Ltd
(Conversions, Re-colouring &
Restoration of Luminaires)
3 Chestnut Grove, Boughton Astley
Leics LE9 6PT   Mobile: 07802 376212

DISCO ENTERTAINMENTS
(Disc Jockeys/Mobile Discos)
12 Mead Close, Grays, Essex RM16 2TR
e-mail: disco-entertainments@talk21.com
                          Tel: 01375 373886

DOVETAIL SPECIALIST SCENERY
(Scenery, Prop & Furniture Builders)
42-50 York Way
London N1 9AB
e-mail: daria@ntlworld.com Tel/Fax: 020-7278 7379

FISHER Charles STAGING Ltd
Unit 4, Redhouse Farm
Bridgehewick, Ripon
North Yorks HG4 5AY
Website: www.charlesfisher.co.uk
e-mail: info@charlesfisher.co.uk   Tel: 01765 601604

FUTURIST Ltd
Trinity Business Park
Turner Way, Wakefield
West Yorks WF2 8EF
Fax: 01924 298700   Tel: 01924 298900

GRANT INTERNATIONAL
(Period Furniture)
Dengmarsh Road
Lydd, Romney Marsh, Kent TN29 9JH
Fax: 01797 321754   Tel: 01797 321999

HARLEQUIN (British Harlequin Plc)
Bankside House
Vale Road, Tonbridge, Kent TN9 1SJ
Website: www.harlequinfloors.com
e-mail: sales@harlequinfloors.co.uk
Fax: 01732 367755   Tel: 01732 367666

HENSHALL John
(Director of Lighting & Photography)
68 The High Street
Stanford in the Vale, Oxon SN7 8NL
e-mail: john@epi-centre.com   Tel: 01367 710191

HERON & DRIVER
(Scenic Furniture & Structural Prop Makers)
Unit 7, Dockley Road Industrial Estate
Rotherhithe, London SE16 3SF
Website: www.herondriver.co.uk
e-mail: mail@herondriver.co.uk
Fax: 020-7394 8680   Tel: 020-7394 8688

KIMPTON WALKER Ltd
(Scenery Contractors)
10 Ellerslie Square, London SW2 5DZ
Website: www.kimptonwalker.co.uk
e-mail: awalker@kwscenic@aol.com
Fax: 020-7738 5517   Tel: 020-7738 3222

KNIGHT Robert/TOP OF THE BILL Ltd
Unit 1B, Mill Street Industrial Estate
Slough, Berkshire SL2 5DD
Fax: 01753 535775   Tel: 01753 535758

LEE LIGHTING Ltd
Wycombe Road, Wembley, Middlesex HA0 1QD
e-mail: info@lee.co.uk
Fax: 020-8902 5500   Tel: 020-8900 2900

LIGHTING TECHNOLOGY GROUP
2 Tudor Estate, Abbey Road
Park Royal, London NW10 7UY
e-mail: info@lighting-tech.com
Fax: 020-8965 0950   Tel: 020-8965 6800

LIGHT WORKS Ltd
2A Greenwood Road
London E8 1AB
Fax: 020-7254 0306   Tel: 020-7249 3627

LITE IT
27 Victoria Road
Chichester
West Sussex PO19 4MY   Mobile: 07973 942027

MALTBURY Ltd
(Portable Staging Sales & Consultancy)
11 Hollingbury Terrace
Brighton BN1 7JE
Website: www.maltbury.com
e-mail: info@maltbury.com   Tel/Fax: 0845 308881

MARPLES Ken CONSTRUCTION
(Scenery & Props)
11 Coombe Road
Chiswick, London W4 2HR
e-mail: ken@marplesk.freeserve.co.uk
Fax: 020-8995 4434   Mobile: 07831 281574

MASSEY Bob ASSOCIATES
(Electrical & Mechanical Stage Consultants)
9 Worrall Avenue
Arnold, Notts NG5 7GN
Website: www.bobmasseyassociates.co.uk
e-mail: bm.associates@virgin.net
    Tel/Fax: 0115-967 3969

MODELBOX
(Computer Aided Design & Design Services)
20 Merton Industrial Park
Jubilee Way
London SW19 3WL
Website: www.modelbox.co.uk
e-mail: info@modelbox.co.uk
Fax: 020-8254 4721   Tel: 020-8254 4720

MURPHY Terry SCENERY Ltd
Western Wharf
Livesey Place
Peckham Park Road
London SE15 6SL
Fax: 020-7277 5147   Tel: 020-7277 5156

NEED Paul J
(Lighting Designer)
Unit 14, Forest Hill Business Centre
Clyde Vale, London SE23 3JF
Website: www.10outof10.co.uk
e-mail: paul@10outof10.co.uk
Fax: 020-8699 8968   Tel: 020-8291 6885

NORTHERN LIGHT
(Lighting, Sound, Communications &
Stage Equipment)
Assembly Street
Leith, Edinburgh EH6 7RG
Website: www.northernlight.co.uk
e-mail: enquiries@northernlight.co.uk
Fax: 0131-553 3296   Tel: 0131-553 2383

ORBITAL
(Sound Hire & Design)
57 Acre Lane
Brixton, London SW2 5TN
e-mail: hire@orbitalsound.co.uk
Fax: 020-7501 6869   Tel: 020-7501 6868

P.L. PARSONS SCENERY MAKERS
King's Cross Freight Depot
York Way
London N1 0UZ
Fax: 020-7278 3403   Tel: 020-7833 2031

RED SHIFT LIGHTING
(Lighting Design & Hire Services)
South East London
Website: www.redshiftlighting.co.uk
e-mail: ben@redshiftlighting.co.uk
Mobile: 07816 879561   Tel/Fax: 020-7701 4593

RETROGRAPH NOSTALGIA ARCHIVE
(Posters/Prints/Ephemera for Interiors/
Exteriors 1880-1970)
164 Kensington Park Road, Notting Hill, London W11 2ER
Website: www.retrograph.com
e-mail: retropix1@aol.com
Fax: 020-7229 3395   Tel: 020-7727 9378

S

RWS ELECTRICAL AND AUDIO CONTRACTORS
1 Spinners Close
Biddenden, Kent TN27 8AY
Website: www.rwselectrical.com   Tel: 01580 291764

SCENERY JESSEL
(Scenery Builders/Stage Supplies)
Unit B
New Baltic Wharf
Oxestalls Road
Deptford, London SE8 5RJ
e-mail: sceneryjessel@ntlworld.com
Fax: 020-8694 2430   Tel: 020-8469 2777

SCOTT FLEARY Ltd
(Creative Construction Company)
Unit 2
Southside Industrial Estate
Havelock Terrace
London SW8 4AS
e-mail: scenery@scottflearyltd.com
Fax: 020-7622 0322   Tel: 020-7978 1787

SCOTT MYERS ASSOCIATES
(Theatre Sound Design)
36 Madras Road
Cambridge CB1 3PX
Website: www.sound.design.freeuk.com
e-mail: sound.design@freeuk.com
Fax: 01223 562542   Tel: 01223 562262

SOUND COMPANY The
(Sound Hire, Design & Installation)
2 Lord Hills Road
London W2 6PD
Website: www.thesoundcompany.net
e-mail: info@thesoundcompany.net
Fax: 020-7286 7377   Tel: 020-7286 7477

STAGE SYSTEMS
(Designers and Suppliers of Modular Staging,
Tiering & Auditorium Seating)
Stage House
Prince William Road
Loughborough LE11 5GU
Website: www.stagesystems.co.uk
e-mail: info@stagesystems.co.uk
Fax: 01509 233146   Tel: 01509 611021

STAGECRAFT Ltd
(Hire & Sales of Lighting, Sound, Audio Visual for
Conference & Live Events)
Ashfield Trading Estate
Salisbury, Wilts SP2 7HL
Website: www.stagecraft.co.uk
e-mail: hire@stagecraft.co.uk
Fax: 01722 414076   Tel: 01722 326055

STORM LIGHTING Ltd
Unit 6 Wintonlea Industrial Estate
Monument Way West
Woking, Surrey GU21 5EN
e-mail: info@stormlighting.co.uk
Fax: 01483 757710   Tel: 01483 757211

STRAND LIGHTING Ltd
(Lighting Equipment for Stage, Studio and Film & TV)
Unit 3, Hammersmith Studios
Yeldham Road, London W6 8JF
e-mail: sales@stranduk.com
Fax: 020-8735 9799   Tel: 020-8735 9790

SUFFOLK SCENERY
28 The Street
Brettenham
Ipswich, Suffolk IP7 7QP
Website: www.suffolkscenery.co.uk
e-mail: piehatch@aol.com
Fax: 01449 737620   Tel: 01449 736679

SUPOTCO GROUP
(Production - Lighting,
Set Construction & Scenery)
3-5 Valentine Place
London SE1 8QH
Fax: 020-7928 6082   Tel: 020-7928 5474

THEME PARTY COMPANY The
(Set Design Backdrops & Props)
21-37 Third Avenue
London E13 8AW
Fax: 020-8471 2111   Tel: 020-8471 3111

TOBEM SERVICES
(Theatrical Lighting)
Glen Orrin, Felcourt
East Grinstead
West Sussex RH19 2LE
e-mail: valerieandterry@btclick.com
                            Tel: 01342 870438

TOP SHOW
(Props, Scenery, Conference Specialists)
North Lane
Huntington, York YO32 9SU   Tel: 01904 750022

TURN ON LIGHTING
(Antique Lighting c1840-1940)
116-118 Islington High Street
Camden Passage
London N1 8EG   Tel/Fax: 020-7359 7616

WEST John ASSOCIATES
(Designers & Scenic Artists - Film, TV & Display)
103 Abbotswood Close
Winyates Green
Redditch, Worcestershire B98 0QF
e-mail: johnwest@dial.pipex.com
Mobile: 07753 637451   Tel/Fax: 01527 516771

WHITEHORN Simon
(Sound Design)
57 Acre Lane
London SW2 5TN
e-mail: simon@orbitalsound.co.uk
Fax: 020-7501 6869   Tel: 020-7501 6868

WHITE LIGHT (Electrics) Ltd
(Stage & TV Lighting)
20 Merton Industrial Park
Jubilee Way
London SW19 3WL
Website: www.whitelight.ltd.uk
e-mail: info@whitelight.ltd.uk
Fax: 020-8254 4601   Tel: 020-8254 4600

WOOD Rod
(Scenic Artist, Backdrops, Scenery,
Props & Design)
41 Montserrat Road
London SW15 2LD
Mobile: 07887 697646   Tel: 020-8788 1941

BBC Television, Wood Lane, London W12 7RJ
Tel: 020-8743 8000

■ TALENT RIGHTS GROUP

BBC PRODUCTION
172 - 178 Victoria Road, W3 6UL

Head of Rights Group   Simon Hayward-Tapp

LITERARY COPYRIGHT
Rights Manager   Ben Green
Rights Executives   Ann Kelly
                                  Sue Dickson
                                  Sally Millwood
                                  Julie Gallagher
                                  James Dundas
                                  Andrew Downey
                                  Gail Finn
                                  Sharon Cowley
                                  Fiona Nerberg
                                  David Knight
                                  Hilary Sagar
                                  Sarah Wade

FACTUAL, ARTS & CLASSICAL MUSIC
Rights Manager   Simon Brown

Rights Executives   Lorraine Clark
                                  Tristan Evans
                                  Gay Hedani-Palin
                                  Ken McHale
                                  Annie Pollard
                                  Shelagh Morrison
                                  John Hunter
                                  Pamela Wise
                                  Shirley Noel
                                  Cathy Holmes
            Penelope Davies/Allson Johnston
              Hilary Dodds/Caroline Edwards
                                  Costas Tanti

MUSICAL COPYRIGHT
Senior Rights Manager, Music Claire Jarvis
Rights Executives   Nicky Bignell
                                  Peter Bradbury
                                  Sally Dunsford
                                  Liz Evans
                                  Catherine Grimes
                                  Debbie Rogerson

DRAMA ENTERTAINMENT & CHILDRENS
Rights Manager Performance   John Holland
Rights Executives   Maggie Anson
                                  Stephanie Beynon
                                  Mike Bickerdike
                                  Jo Buckingham
                                  Sally Dean

Rights Executives continued
                                  Lisa Guthrie
                                  Marie-Louise Hagan
                                  Amanda Kimpton
                                  Lesley Longhurst
                                  David Marum
                                  Thalia Reynolds
                                  Lloyd Shepherd

ENGLISH REGIONS:

BIRMINGHAM - Pebble Mill
Contracts Manager   Janet Brookes

BRISTOL
Contracts Manager
 (Acting)   David Crockford

MANCHESTER
Contracts Executive   Alison Ripley

■ DRAMA

Controller, Continuing Series   Mal Young
Head of Films &
    Single Drama   David Thompson
Head of Drama Serials   Laura Mackie

Executive Producers
Ruth Caleb   Katherine Hutchinson
Serena Cullen   Simon Lewis
Alexei de Keyser   Hilary Salmon
Kate Harwood   Tracey Scoffield
Sally Haynes   John Yorke
Sue Hogg   Mervyn Watson

Producers
Chris Ballentyne   Liza Marshall
Kate Bartlett   Paul Rutman
Beverley Dartnall   Diederick Santer
Victoria Fea   David Snodin
Deborah Jones   Pier Wilkie

■ COMMISSIONING

Controller Factual Commissioning
                                  Nicola Moody
Controller Entertainment Commissioning
                                  Jane Lush
Controller Drama Commissioning   Jane Tranter
Head of Drama Commissioning, Development
                                  Pippa Harris
Head of Drama Commissioning, Independents
                                  Gareth Neame

■ NEWS AND CURRENT AFFAIRS

BBC News (Television & Radio)
Television Centre
Wood Lane, London W12 7RJ
Tel: 020-8576 7178   Fax: 020-8576 7120

Director News	Richard Sambrook
Deputy Director News	Mark Damazer
Head of Television News	Roger Mosey
Deputy Head of Television News	Rachel Atwell
Head of Radio News	Stephen Mitchell
Head of Political Programmes	
	Francesca Unsworth
Head of News Resources	Julia Nelson

■ DOCUMENTARIES

Controller of Documentaries Group	
	Anne Morrison
Head of Production	Steve Wallis
Managing Editor	Donna Taberer
Creative Director	Alex Holmes
Creative Director	Owen Gay
Acting Creative Director	Lisa Ausden
General Documentaries	Tessa Finch

■ FACTUAL & LEARNING

Controller Daytime	Alison Sharman
Creative Directors	Owen Gay
	Jonnine Waddell
	Nick Vaughan-Barratt
	Andy Batten-Foster
	Vicki Barrass
	Mark Hill
Head of Development	Rachel Innes-Lursden

■ ARTS

Creative Director	Franny Moyle
Editor Arena	Antony Wall
Editor, Arts Series	Kim Thomas
Editor Arena	Anthony Wall
Editor Omnibus	Basil Comely
Editor Talk & Events	David Okuefuna

■ MUSIC

Head of Classical Music	Peter Maniura

■ CHILDREN'S PROGRAMMES

Controller CBBC	Nigel Pickard
Head of Programming, CBBC	Dorothy Prior
Editor, Blue Peter	Steve Hocking
Editor, CBBC On-Line	Rebecca Shallcross
Head of Acquisitions, CBBC	
	Theresa Plummer-Andrews
Head of Drama, CBBC	Elaine Sperber
Head of Children's Entertainment, CBBC	
	Chris Bellinger
Executive Producer	Camilla Lewis
Head of CBBC News	Roy Milani
Head of Children's Programmes, Scotland	
	Claire Mundell
Head of Pre-School Programmes	Clare Elstow
Executive Producer - Schools, CBBC	Sue Natt
Production Development Executive	
	Amanda Gabbitas
Head of Future TV, CBBC	Greg Childs

■ SPORT

Director of Sport	Peter Salmon
Director, Sports Rights & Finance	Dominic Coles
Controller Radio Five Live	Bob Shennan
Head of Major Events	Dave Gordon
Head of Football & Boxing	Niall Sloane
Head of Programmes & Planning	Pat Younge
Head of General Sports	Barbara Slater
Head of Radio Sport	Gordon Turnbull
Head of New Media, Sports News	
& Development	Andrew Thompson

■ SCIENCE

Creative Director for Science	John Lynch
Series Producer	Cameron Balbirnie
Development Executive	Sacha Baveystock
Deputy Editor Horizon	Mathew Barrett
Executive Producer	Michael Mosley
Editor Tomorrow's World	Tina Fletcher

■ NEW WRITING

The Writersroom
Room 222
BBC Broadcasting House
London W1A 1AA   Tel: 020-7765 2703
e-mail: new. writing@bbc.co.uk
Website: www.bbc.co.uk/writersroom

Creative Director	Kate Rowland
New Writing Co-ordinator	Jessica Dromgoole

■ BBC BRISTOL

Broadcasting House
Whiteladies Road
Bristol BS8 2LR   Tel: 0117-973 2211

NETWORK TELEVISION AND RADIO
FEATURES
Creative Directors   Andy Batten-Foster
                                           Mark Hill
Executive Producers   Michael Poole
                                        Dick Colthurst

TELEVISION
Producers
Robert Bayley   Peter Lawrence
Mark Bristow   Christopher Lewis
Kathryn Broome   Kim Littlemore
Michelle Burgess   Jane Lomas
Roy Chapman   Susan McDermott
Linda Cleeve   Julian Mercer
Peter Firstbrook   Martin Pallthorpe
Trevor Hill   Ian Pye
Jeremy Howe   Amanda Reilly
Chris Hutchins   Colin Rose
David Hutt   Miranda Steed
Sarah Johnson

RADIO
Unit Manager, Radio   Kate Chaney
Editors   Elizabeth Burke
                                    Fiona Cooper
Producers
Viv Beesby   Jane Greenwood
John Byrne   Jeremy Howe
Frances Byrnes   Kate McCall
Sara Davies   David Olusoga
Tim Dee   Lucy Willmore
Paul Dodgson

NATURAL HISTORY UNIT
Head of Natural History Unit   Keith Scholey
Editor The Natural World   Mike Gunton

Television Producers
Paul Appleby   Liz Green
Melinda Barker   Martin Hughes-Games
Miles Barton   Mark Jacobs
Karen Bass   Hilary Jeffkins
Vanessa Belowitz   Mark Linfield
Mike Beynon   Neil Lucas
Lucy Bowden   Sue McMillan
Andrew Byatt   Patrick Morris
Paul Chapman   Stephen Moss
Mary Colwell   Mike Salisbury
Huw Cordey   Jo Sarsby
Peter Crawford   Tim Scoones
Yvonne Ellis   Mary Summerhill
Mark Flowers   Dale Templar
Sara Ford   James Walton

Managing Editor NHU Radio   Julian Hector
Director of Development   Michael Bright

■ BBC WEST

Whiteladies Road
Bristol BS8 2LR   Tel: 0117-973 2211

Head of Regional and Local Programmes,
including BBC West, Radio Bristol & Somerset
Sound, Radio Gloucestershire & BBC Wiltshire
    Sound   Andrew Wilson
Series Producer, Current Affairs Documentaries
                                 James MacAlpine
Editor, Political Unit   Paul Cannon
Editors, Output   Stephanie Marshall
                                  Jane Kingham

■ BBC SOUTH WEST

Seymour Road
Mannamead
Plymouth PL3 5BD   Tel: 01752 229201

Head of Local & Regional
    Programmes   Leo Devine
Editor TV Current Affairs   Simon Willis
Senior Assistant News Editor   Simon Read

■ BBC SOUTH

Havelock Road
Southampton SO14 7PU   Tel: 023-8022 6201

Head of Regional & Local
    Programmes   Eve Turner
Managing Editor, BBC Oxford ,   Phil Ashworth
Editor Local Services   Mia Costello

■ BBC LONDON

PO Box 94.9
London W1A 6FL   Tel: 020-7208 9200

BBC London:
TV: Newsroom South East & (Political
Programme) Metropol
Radio: London Live 94.9 FM

Executive Editor   Jane Mote
News/Output Editor   Sandy Smith
Executive Producer, First Sight Dippy Chaudhray
Managing Editor BBC
    London Live 94.9FM   David Robey
Politcal Editor   Jon Craig

■ BBC SOUTH EAST

c/o BBC Radio Kent
The Great Hall, Mount Pleasant Road
Tunbridge Wells
Kent TN1 1QQ   Tel: 01892 670000

Head of Regional & Local
    Programmes   Laura Ellis
Output Editor   Rod Beards
Editor Local Services   Michael Hapgood
Editor   David Farwig

■ BBC NORTH WEST

New Broadcasting House
Oxford Road
Manchester M60 1SJ   Tel: 0161-200 2020

Entertainment & Features

Head of Entertainment Group   Wayne Garvie
Editor Factual & Entertainment   Alan Brown
Editor   Phil Parsons

Religious Broadcasting

Executive Producer, Talks/Debate David Coomes
Head of Religious Ethics   Alan Bookbinder

Network News & Current Affairs

Editor News & Current Affairs   Dave Stanford
Editor File on Four   David Ross

Regional & Local Programmes

Head of Regional
    & Local Programmes   Martin Brooks

Leeds

Head of Regional
    & Local Programmes   Colin Philpott

Newcastle

Head of Regional
    & Local Programmes   Olwyn Hocking

■ BBC BIRMINGHAM

BBC Birmingham
Pebble Mill Road
Birmingham B5 7QQ
Fax: 0121-432 8634   Tel: 0121-432 8888

English Regions

Controller, English Regions. Head of Centre
    (Birmingham)   Andy Griffee
Head of New Services, English Regions John Allen
Head of Finance, English Regions Julie Bertolini
Chief Press & Public Relations Officer
    English Regions   Simon Channon
Secretary, English Regions   Louise Hall
Head of Regional & Local
    Programmes West Midlands and Director of
    Mailbox Project   Roy Roberts

Leisure and Factual Entertainment, BBC Birmingham

Head of Programmes   Tessa Finch
Managing Editor   Paresh Solanki

Network Radio

Editor, Factual Radio & Rural Affairs
                               Andrew Thorman
Editor, Specialist Programmes, Radio 2
                                David Barber

Drama

Head of Production BBC
    Birmingham   Trevor West
Editor Radio Drama
    & The Archers   Vanessa Whitburn

■ SCOTLAND

Glasgow
Broadcasting House
Queen Margaret Drive
Glasgow G12 8DG   Tel: 0141-339 8844

SCOTTISH DIRECTION GROUP

Controller Scotland   John McCormick
Head of Network Programmes   Colin Cameron
Head of Comedy & Entertainment Mike Bolland
Executive Editor New Media   Julie Adair
Commissioning Editor, TV   Ewan Angus

Head of Radio   Maggie Cunningham
Head of Programmes Scotland   Ken McQuarrie
Head of TV Drama, Scotland   Barbara McKissack
Head of Gaelic   Donalda Mackinnon
Head of News and Current Affairs Blair Jenkins
Head of Factual, Scotland   Andrea Millar
Head of Sport   Neil Fraser
Head of North   Andrew Jones
Creative Director, Childrens   Claire Mundell

Head of Finance & Business Affairs Irene Tweedie
Head of Production   Nancy Braid
Head of Human Resources and Internal
    Communications   Steve Ansell
Head of Marketing and Communications
                              Mairead Ferguson
Secretary and Head of Public Policy
                               Mark Leishman

Edinburgh

The Tun
Holyrood Road
Edinburgh EH8 8JF   Tel: 0131-557 5677

Aberdeen

Broadcasting House
Beechgrove Terrace
Aberdeen AB15 5ZT   Tel: 01224 625233

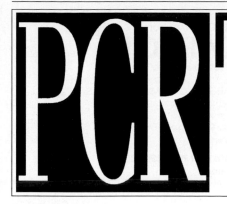

Dumfries
BBC Dumfries
Elmbank, Lovers Walk
Dumfries DG1 1NZ   Tel: 01387 268008

Dundee
66 Nethergate
Nethergate Centre
Dundee DD1 4ER   Tel: 01382 202481

Inverness
BBC Inverness
Broadcasting House
7 Culduthel Road
Inverness IV2 4AD   Tel: 01463 720720

Orkney
BBC Radio Orkney
Castle Street
Kirkwall
Orkney KW15 1DF   Tel: 01856 873939

Portree
Clydesdale Bank Buildings
Somerled Square
Portree
Isle of Skye IV51 9BT   Tel: 01478 612005

Selkirk
BBC Selkirk
Old Municipal Buildings
High Street
Selkirk TD7 4JX   Tel: 01750 21884

Shetland
BBC Shetland
Pitt Lane
Lerwick
Shetland ZE1 0DW   Tel: 01595 694747

Stornoway
Radio nan Gaidheal
Rosebank
Church Street
Stornoway
Isle of Lewis HS1 2LS   Tel: 01851 705000

■ WALES
Broadcasting House
Llandaff
Cardiff CF5 2YQ   Tel: 029-2032 2000

Controller	Menna Richards
Head of Programmes (Welsh)	Keith Jones
Head of Programmes (English)	Clare Hudson
Head of Public Affairs	Manon Williams
Head of Marketing & Communication	tba
Head of News & Current Affairs	Aled Eirug
Head of Personnel	Keith Rawlings
Head of Finance	Gareth Powell
Head of Drama	Matthew Robinson
Head of Sport	Nigel Walker
Head of North Wales	Marian Wyn Jones
Head of Factual	Adrian Davies
Head of Education	Eleri Wyn-Lewis
Editor Radio Wales	Julie Barton
Editor Radio Cymru	Aled Glynne-Davies

■ NORTHERN IRELAND

Belfast
Ormeau Avenue
Belfast BT2 8HQ   Tel: 028-9033 8000

Controller	Anna Carragher
Head of Broadcasting	Tim Cooke
Head of News & Current Affairs	Andrew Colman
Head of Drama	Robert Cooper
Head of Factual & Learning	Bruce Batten
Head of Entertainment & Events	Mike Edgar
Head of Finance & Business Affairs	Crawford Maclean
Head of Personnel	Liz Torrans
Head of Marketing & Development	Peter Johnston
Head of Resources	Stephen Beckett

Londonderry
BBC Radio Foyle   Tel: 028-7126 2244

Editor Foyle   Ana Leddy

ANGLIA TELEVISION LTD
Head Office
Anglia House Norwich NR1 3JG
Fax: 01603 631032   Tel: 01603 615151
East of England: Weekday & Weekend

Regional News Centres

Cambridge
26 Newmarket Road Cambridge CB5 8DT
Fax: 01223 467106   Tel: 01223 467076
Reporter: Matthew Hudson

Chelmsford
64-68 New London Road Chelmsford CM1 0YU
Fax: 01245 267228   Tel: 01245 357676
Reporter: Timothy Evans

Luton
16 Park Street Luton LU1 3EP
Fax: 01582 401214   Tel: 01582 729666
Reporter: Charlotte Fisher

Northampton
77B Abington Street Northampton NN1 2BH
Fax: 01604 629856   Tel: 01604 624343
Reporter: Karl Heidel

Peterborough
6 Bretton Green Village
Rightwell Bretton Peterborough PE3 8DY
Fax: 01733 269424   Tel: 01733 269440
Reporter: Piers Hopkirk

Ipswich
Hubbard House Civic Drive Ipswich IP1 2QA
Fax: 01473 233279   Tel: 01473 226157
Reporters: Lindsay Brooke, Rebecca Atherstone

BORDER TELEVISION PLC
Head Office & Studios
The Television Centre
Carlisle CA1 3NT   Tel: 01228 525101
*Southern Scotland, North-West England,
North Northumberland and the Isle of Man;
Weekday and Weekend*

Chairman   Charles Allen
Managing Director   Paddy Merrall
Director of Programmes   Neil Robinson

CARLTON COMMUNICATIONS
25 Knightsbridge
London SW1X 7RZ
Fax: 020-7663 6300   Tel: 020-7663 6363
Chairman   Michael Green

CARLTON TELEVISION
London
101 St Martin's Lane
London WC2N 4RF
Fax: 020-7240 4171   Tel: 020-7240 4000
Chief Executive of Carlton Channels
                            Clive Jones
Director of Programmes and
   Managing Director of Carlton Productions
                            Steve Hewlett
Chief Executive, Carlton Sales   Martin Bowley
Finance Director   Mike Green
Director of Regional & Public Affairs
                            Hardeep Kalsi

PRODUCTION
London
35-38 Portman Square, London W1H 0NU
Fax: 020-7486 1132   Tel: 020-7486 6688

Director of Programmes and
Managing Director of Carlton Productions
                            Steve Hewlett
Controller, Business Affairs   Martin Baker
Director of Drama &
   Co-production   Jonathan Powell
Executive Producer, Drama   Sharon Bloom
Controller, Children's & Young
   People's Programmes   David Mercer
Controller of Light Entertainment   Mark Wells
Controller, Factual Entertainment   Nick Bullen
Director of Factual Group   Polly Bide
Director of Factual Programmes
                            Richard Clemmow
Head of Regional Programmes
   (Based at 101 St. Martins Lane, London)
                            Emma Barker
Head of Regional Programmes
   (Based at Gas Street, Birmingham)
                            Duncan Rycroft
Director of Programmes, HTV Wales
   (Based at Culverhouse Cross, Cardiff)
                            Ellis Owen

East Midlands
Carlton Studios, Lenton Lane
Nottingham NG7 2NA
Fax: 0115-964 5552   Tel: 0115-986 3322

Westcountry
Western Wood Way
Langage Science Park, Plymouth PL7 5BQ
Fax: 01752 333444   Tel: 01752 333333
Director of Programmes - Westcountry
   & HTV West   Jane McCloskey

BROADCASTING
Carlton Broadcasting
London:
101 St Martin's Lane
London WC2N 4RF
Fax: 020-7240 4171   Tel: 020-7240 4000

London Television Centre
Upper Ground, London SE1 9LT
                            Tel: 020-7620 1620

Central Broadcasting
West Midlands:
Central Court, Gas Street, Birmingham B1 2JT
                            Tel: 0121-643 9898
East Midlands:
Carlton Studios, Lenton Lane
Nottingham NG7 2NA
Fax: 0115-964 5552   Tel: 0115-986 3322
South Midlands:
Windrush Court, Abingdon Business Park
Abingdon, Oxon OX1 1SA
Fax: 01235 524024   Tel: 01235 554123

Westcountry Television:
Western Wood Way, Langage Science Park
Plymouth PL7 5BQ
Fax: 01752 333444   Tel: 01752 333333

Chairman   Clive Jones
Managing Director, HTV West & Wales
                              Jeremy Payne
Managing Director, Carlton Broadcasting
                            Colin Stanbridge
Managing Director, Carlton Broadcasting
   Central Region   Ian Squires
Managing Director, Carlton Broadcasting
   West Country Region   Mark Haskell
Controller of Features &
   Programme Development   Caroline Righton
Controller Broadcasting   Coleena Reid
Head of Regional Acquisitions & Planning
                                David Joel
Head of Presentation   Wendy Chapman
Head of Presentation & Programme
   Planning (Central)   David Burge
Controller, Sport   Gary Newbon
Controller, News & Operations Laurie Upshon
Editor, Central News West   Dan Barton
Editor, Central News East   Mike Blair
Editor, Central News South   Ian Rumsey
Controller of News &
   Current Affairs, West Country Phil Carrodus
Head of News, HTV West   Steve Eggington
Head of News, HTV Wales   John G Williams
Finance Director of Carlton Broadcasting
                               Ian Hughes

FACILITIES AND STUDIOS
Outside Broadcasting
Carlton 021
12-13 Gravelly Hill Industrial Estate
Birmingham B24 8HZ
Fax: 0121-327 7021   Tel: 0121-327 2021
Managing Director   Ed Everest

Carlton Studios
Lenton Lane, Nottingham NG7 2NA
Fax: 0115-964 5552   Tel: 0115-986 3322
Managing Director   Ian Squires

SALES
London
101 St Martin's Lane
London WC2N 4RF
Fax: 020-7240 4171   Tel: 020-7240 4000

Manchester
1st Floor Brazenose House West
Lincoln Square
Manchester M2 5AS
Fax: 0161-835 8001   Tel: 0161-835 8001

Westcountry
Western Wood Way
Langage Science Park
Plymouth PL7 5BQ
Fax: 01752 333444   Tel: 01752 333333

Birmingham
Central Court, Gas Street
Birmingham B1 2JT   Tel: 0121-643 9898

HTV
Culverhouse Cross, Cardiff CF5 6XJ
Fax: 029-2059 7183   Tel: 029-2059 7183

Chief Executive of Carlton Sales Martin Bowley
Managing Director of Carlton Sales Steve Platt
Sales Director   Gary Digby
Director of Marketing, Sales   Fran Cassidy

CHANNEL TELEVISION LTD
Registered Office
The Television Centre
La Pouquelaye
St Helier Jersey JE1 3ZD
Channel Islands

Fax: 01534 816817   Tel: 01534 816816

Channel Islands: Weekday and Weekend

Managing Director	Michael Lucas
Director of Programmes	Karen Rankine
Director of Sales	Gordon de Ste.Croix
Director of Transmission & Resources	Kevin Banner
Director of Finance	Amanda Trotman
News Editor	Allan Watts

b adler@ channel4.
co.uk

CHANNEL FOUR TELEVISION CORPORATION
London Office
124 Horseferry Road
London SW1P 2TX

Fax: 020-7306 8116   Tel: 020-7396 4444

Members of the Board

Chairman	Vanni Treves
Deputy Chairman	Barry Cox
Chief Executive	Mark Thompson
Managing Director	David Scott
Director of Programmes	Tim Gardam
Commercial Director	Andy Barnes
Director of Strategy & Development	David Brook
Director of Finance & Business Affairs	Janet Walker
Managing Director 4 Ventures Ltd	Rob Woodward

Non-Executive Directors

Millie Banerjee	Robin Miller
Peter Bazalgette	Ian Ritchie
Barry Cox	Joe Sinyor
Andrew Graham	Vanni Treves

Company Secretary: Andrew Brann

Heads of Department

Head of Airtime Management	Merlin Inkley
Head of Commercial Development & Research	Hugh Johnson
Head of Agency Sales	Matt Shreeva
Head of Information Systems	Ian Dobb
Controller of Human Resources	Peter Meier
Head of Presentation	Steve White
MD, 124 Facilities	David Mann
Head of Business Affairs	Andrew Brann
Head of Programme Finance	Maureen Semple-Piggot
Head of Legal & Compliance	Jan Tomalin
Group Controller of Finance	Tony Moore
MD 4 Learning Ltd	Heather Rabbatts
Managing Editor Commissioning & Head of Factual	Janey Walker
Head of Programmes (Nations & Regions)	Stuart Cosgrove
Controller of Programme Acquisition	June Dromgoole
Head of Science & Education	Sara Ramsden
Head of News, Current Affairs & Business	David Lloyd
Head of Entertainment	Daniella Lux
Head of Drama	Tessa Ross
Director of Marketing & Commercial Development	Polly Cochrane
Chief Executive - FilmFour Ltd	Paul Webster
Head of Corporate Relations	John Newbigin
Controller Broadcasting	Rosemary Newell
Head of Press & Publicity	Matt Baker

Commissioning Editors

Documentaries	Peter Dale
Art & Religion	Janice Hadlow
Multicultural (Docs & Factual)	Yasmin Anwar
Independent Film & Video	Jess Seouch
Daytime	Jo McGrath
4 Learning	Paula Snyder
Schools Programmes	John Richmond
Adult Interactive Learning	Paula Snyder
News, Current Affairs & Business	Dorothy Byrne
Entertainment	Caroline Leddy
Drama	Lucy Richer

THE SPOTLIGHT ®

The most celebrated casting directory in the world

CHANNEL 5 BROADCASTING
22 Long Acre
London WC2E 9LY
Fax: 020-7550 5554   Tel: 020-7550 5555
Website: www.channel5.co.uk

Chief Executive	Dawn Airey
Director of Programmes	Kevin Lygoe
Marketing Director	David Pullan
Deputy Chief Executive	Nick Milligan
Director of Finance	Grant Murray
Director of Legal & Business Affairs	
	Colin Campbell
Director of Broadcasting	Ashley Hill
Director of Acquisitions	Jeff Ford
Senior Programme Controller	
News & Current Affairs	Chris Shaw
Controller of Entertainment	Andrew Newman
Controller of Factual	Dan Chambers
Controller of Factual Entertainment	Sue Murphy
Controller of Youth, Music & Interactive	
	Sham Sandhu
Controller of Drama	Corinne Hollingworth
Controller of Sport	Robert Charles
Controller of Children's	Nick Wilson
Controller of Daytime, Arts & Religion	Kim Peat

GMTV
London Television Centre
Upper Ground
London SE1 9TT
Fax: 020-7827 7001   Tel: 020-7827 7000

Chairman	Nigel Walmsley
Managing Director	Paul Corley
Director of Programmes	Peter McHugh
Finance Director	Rhian Walker
Director of Sales	Clive Crouch
Head of Press	Nikki Johnceline
Managing Editor	John Scammell
Editor	Martin Frizell
Chief Engineer	Geoff Wright

GRAMPIAN TELEVISION
Head Office & Studios
Queen's Cross
Aberdeen AB15 3XJ
Fax: 01224 846800   Tel: 01224 846846
Website: www.grampiantv.co.uk

Managing Director	Derrick Thomson
Head of News & Current Affairs	Henry Fagles
Production Resources Manager	Karen Murphy

The London Television Centre
Upper Ground
London SE1 9LT   Tel: 020-7620 1620

LWT
London Television Centre
Upper Ground
London SE1 9LT   Tel: 020-7620 1620

Granada Television
Quay Street
Manchester M60 9EA   Tel: 0161-832 7211

Yorkshire Television
Television Centre
Leeds LS3 1JS   Tel: 0113-243 8283

Tyne Tees Television
City Road
Newcastle-Upon-Tyne NE1 2AL
    Tel: 0191-261 0181

Anglia TV
Anglia House
Norwich NR1 3JG   Tel: 01603 615151

Meridian Broadcasting
Television Centre
Southampton SO14 0PZ   Tel: 02380 222555

Border Television
TV Centre
Carlisle CA1 3NT   Tel: 01228 525101

Granada Animation
2nd Floor, 16 Hatfields
London SE1 8DJ   Tel: 020-7620 1620

Granada Continued...

Granada Wild
One Whiteladies Road
Bristol BS8 1NU — Tel: 01179 745803

Granada Sport
Television Centre
Southampton SO14 0PZ — Tel: 023-8071 2307

Granada Film
48 Leicester Square
London WC2H 7FB — Tel: 020-7491 1441

Granada Learning
Granada Television
Quay Street
Manchester M60 9EA — Tel: 0161-827 2927

Letts Education
Auld Dine House, Auld Dine Place
London W12 8AW — Tel: 020-8740 2266

Granada International
48 Leicester Square
London WC2H 7FB — Tel: 020-7491 1441

Granada Commercial Ventures
200 Grays Inn Road
London WC1X 8X2 — Tel: 020-7396 6000

Granada plc - Executive Board

Executive Chairman	Charles Allen
Chief Executive	Steve Morrison
Finance Director & Deputy Chairman, Media Ventures	Henry Staunton
Commercial Director	Graham Parrott
Managing Director Operations	Jules Burns
Managing Director, Granada Content	Simon Shaps
Chief Executive, Enterprises	Mick Desmond

HTV GROUP LTD

Television Centre, Culverhouse Cross
Cardiff CF5 6XJ — Tel: 029-2059 0590

Television Centre, Bath Road
Bristol BS4 3HG — Tel: 0117-972 2722

Wales/West of England: All week

Group Managing Director	Jeremy Payne
Controller, HTV Wales	Elis Owen
Director of Programmes	Jane McCloskey
HTV Wales Head of Drama Development	Peter Edwards
HTV Wales Head of Factual Development	Paul Calverley

INDEPENDENT TELEVISION NEWS

200 Gray's Inn Road
London WC1X 8XZ — Tel: 020-7833 3000

Chief Executive	Stewart Purvis
Editor-in-Chief	Richard Tait
Editor, ITV News	Nigel Dacre
Editor, Channel 4 News	Jim Gray
Editor 5 News	Gary Rogers
Marketing Director	David Robinson
Director of Public Affairs	Mark Gallagher

LWT

LWT HOLDINGS PLC

The London Television Centre
Upper Ground
London SE1 9LT — Tel: 020-7620 1620
London 5.10 pm Friday to 6 am Monday

Executives of the LWT Group

Controller of Arts & Features LWT	Melvyn Bragg
Controller of Drama LWT & United Productions	Michelle Buck
Controller of Factual, LWT	Will Smith

Directors

Executive Chairman, Granada	Charles Allen
Chief Executive, Granada	Steve Morrison
Managing Director, LWT	Christy Swords

MERIDIAN

MERIDIAN BROADCASTING LTD
Television Centre, Southampton SO14 0PZ
Fax: 023-8033 5050   Tel: 023-8022 2555

Board
Chairman	Charles Allen
MD Granada Broadcasting	Stewart Butterfield
Finance Director,	
Granada Broadcasting	Mike Fegan
Director of Sales,	
Granada Enterprises	David Croft
Managing Director, Meridian	Linsay Charlton
Director of Broadcasting	Mark Southgate
Director of News	Andy Cooper
Director of Regional &	
Commercial Affairs	Martin Morrall

Executives
Managing Director, Meridian	Linsay Charlton
Director of Broadcasting	Mark Southgate
Director of News	Andy Cooper
Director of Regional &	
Commercial Affairs	Martin Morrall
General Manager	Jan Beal
Controller of Sport	Tony Baines
Controller of Personnel	Peter Ashwood
Finance Manager	Sian Harvey
Controller of Network	
Factual & Development	Trish Powell

S4C-THE WELSH FOURTH CHANNEL
Parc Tŷ Glas, Llanisien, Cardiff CF14 5DU
Fax: 029-2075 4444   Tel: 029-2074 7444
e-mail: s4c@s4c.co.uk

The Welsh Fourth Channel Authority
Chair	Elan Closs Stephens
Members	Cefin Campbell
Enid Rowlands	Eira Davies
Huw Wynne-Griffiths	Janet Lewis Jones
Nic Parry	Dr. Christopher Llewelyn

Senior Staff
Chief Executive	Huw Jones
Director of Corporate Affairs	Alun Davies
Director of Programming	Huw Eirug
Director of Engineering	Arshad Rasul
Director of Marketing	Eleri Twynog Davies
Director of Finance	Kathryn Morris
Director of Commercial Affairs	Wyn Innes
Head of Press	Hannah Thomas
Director of Personnel	Ifan Roberts

scottish tv

SCOTTISH TELEVISION (Part of SMG Group)
Glasgow Office
200 Renfield Street, Glasgow G2 3PR
Fax: 0141-300 3580   Tel: 0141-300 3000
Website: www.scottishtv.co.uk
Chief Executive, Television	Donald Emslie
Managing Director, Scottish TV	Sandy Ross
Head of News & Current Affairs	Paul McKinney

London Office
3 Waterhouse Square, 138-142 Holborn
London EC1N 2YN
Fax: 020-7882 1014   Tel: 020-7882 1010

tv productions   Part of 'SMG Group'

London Office
1 Golden Square
London W1F 9DJ   Tel: 020-7663 2300

Glasgow Office
Glasgow G2 3PR
Fax: 0141-300 3580   Tel: 0141-300 3000
Managing Director   Elizabeth Partyka

TYNE TEES TELEVISION

TYNE TEES TELEVISION
The Television Centre, City Road
Newcastle upon Tyne NE1 2AL
Fax: 0191-261 2302   Tel: 0191-261 0181

Teeside Studio
Pavilion 13 Belasis Hall Technology Park
Greenwood Rd
Billingham
Cleveland TS23 4EG
Fax: 01642 566560   Tel: 01642 566999

*North East and North Yorkshire:
Weekday and Weekend*

Chairman	Charles Allen
Managing Director	Margaret Fay
Controller of Programmes	Graeme Thompson
Managing Editor, News	Graham Marples
Head of Network Features	Mark Robinson
Head of Sport	Roger Tames
Head of New MEdia	Malcolm Wright
Editor, Current Affairs	
& Features	Jane Bolesworth

275

ULSTER TELEVISION PLC

Havelock House
Ormeau Road
Belfast BT7 1EB
Fax: 028-9024 6695   Tel: 028-9032 8122

Northern Ireland: Weekday and Weekend

Chairman   J B McGuckian BSc (Econ)
Managing Director   J McCann BSc, FCA
Financial Director   Jim Downey
Director of Programming   A Bremner
Head of Press & Public Relations Orla McKibbin
Head of News & Current Affairs   R Morrison
Sales Director   P Hutchinson

YORKSHIRE TELEVISION LTD

The Television Centre
Leeds LS3 1JS
Fax: 0113-244 5107   Tel: 0113-243 8283

London Office

London Television Centre
Upperground
London SE1 9LT   Tel: 020-7620 1620

Hull Office

23 Brook Street
The Prospect Centre
Hull HU2 8PN   Tel: 01482 24488

Sheffield Office

Charter Square
Sheffield S1 3EJ   Tel: 0114-272 3262

Lincoln Office

88 Bailgate
Lincoln LN1 3AR   Tel: 01522 530738

Grimsby Office

Margaret Street
Immingham
North East Lincs DN40 1LE Tel: 01469 510661

York Office

8 Coppergate
York YO1 1NR   Tel: 01904 610066

Executives

Managing Director   David M B Croft
Controller of Programmes (YTV)   Clare Morrow
Controller, Features   Bridget Boseley
Director of Business Affairs   Filip Cieslik
Head of News   Will Venters
Controller of Drama, YTV   Carolyn Reynolds
Controller of Comedy Drama
  & Drama Features   David Reynolds
Controller of Drama, Yorkshire-Tyne Tees
  Productions   Keith Richardson
Director of Finance, Yorkshire-Tyne Tees
  Productions   Ian Roe
Controller, Documentaries &
  Factual Programmes   Helen Scott
Director of Broadcasting   Helen Stevens
Director of Programmes   John Whiston
Head of Regional Features   Mark Witty

SKY Satellite Television
BRITISH SKY BROADCASTING LIMITED (BSkyB)

6 Centaurs Business Park
Grant Way
Isleworth
Middlesex TW7 5QD
Fax: 020-7705 3030   Tel: 020-7705 3000

Chief Executive   Tony Ball
Chief Operating Officer   Richard Freudenstein
Managing Director, Sky Sports   Vic Wakeling
Director of Broadcasting
  & Production   Mark Sharman
Head of Sky News   Nick Pollard
Director of Public Affairs   Ray Gallagher
Director of Communications   Julian Eccles

30 BIRD PRODUCTIONS
138A Kingswood Road, Brixton, London SW2 4JL
e-mail: thirtybird.productions@virgin.net
Tel: 020-8678 7034

ACORN ENTERTAINMENTS Ltd
PO Box 64, Cirencester, Glos GL7 5YD
Website: www.huttrussell.org.com
e-mail: acornents@btconnect.com
Fax: 01285 642291   Tel: 01285 644622

ACT PRODUCTIONS Ltd
20-22 Stukeley Street, London WC2B 5LR
Website: www.actproductions.co.uk
e-mail: info@act.tt
Fax: 020-7242 3548   Tel: 020-7438 9500

ACTORS OF DIONYSUS
Suite No 5, 44-46 Old Steine, Brighton BN1 1NH
Website: www.actorsofdionysus.com
e-mail: info@actorsofdionysus.com
Fax: 01273 320385   Tel: 01273 320384

ACTORS TOURING COMPANY (ATC)
Alford House, Aveline Street, London SE11 5DQ
Website: www.atc-online.com
e-mail: atc@atc-online.com   Tel: 020-7735 8311

ADMIRATION THEATRE
PO Box 448, London WC2B 5US
Website: www.admirationtheatre.co.uk
e-mail: enquiries@admirationtheatre.co.uk
Tel/Fax: 020-7692 3698

AD PRODUCTIONS
(See HILTON Adrian Ltd)

AKA PRODUCTIONS
Gloucester Mansions
140A Shaftesbury Avenue, London WC2H 8HD
Website: www.akauk.com
e-mail: aka@akauk.om
Fax: 020-7836 8787   Tel: 020-7836 4747

ALBERY Ian
c/o Sadler's Wells Theatre
Rosebery Avenue, London EC1R 4TN
e-mail: ceo@sadlerwells.com
Fax: 020-7863 8031   Tel: 020-7863 8034

AMBASSADOR THEATRE GROUP
Duke of York's Theatre
104 St Martin's Lane, London WC2N 4BG
e-mail: atglondon@theambassadors.com
Fax: 020-7854 7001   Tel: 020-7854 7000

ANDROMEDA PRODUCTIONS
4 The Old School, 146 York Way
London N1 0AE   Tel/Fax: 020-7278 3799

ARENA PRODUCTIONS
111 Blackfriars Foundry
156 Blackfriars Road, London SE1 8EN
Fax: 020-7721 8541   Tel: 020-7721 8540

ARTS MANAGEMENT
Pinewood Studios
Iver Heath, Bucks SL0 0NH
Fax: 01753 785443   Tel: 01753 785444

A. T. P. Ltd
PO Box 24182, London SW18 2WY
e-mail: prompt@atpmedia.com
Tel/Fax: 020-7738 9886

ATTIC THEATRE COMPANY (LONDON) Ltd
Wimbledon Theatre
The Broadway, London SW19 1QG
Website: www.attictheatre.com
e-mail: info@attictheatre.com
Tel/Fax: 020-8543 7838

BACCHAI PRODUCTIONS
(Write)
10-12 High Street, Great Wakering, Essex SS3 0EQ
e-mail: mail@bacchai.com

BACKGROUND Ltd
Third Floor, Lafone House
11-13 Leathermarket Street, London SE1 3HN
e-mail: insight@background.co.uk
Fax: 020-7357 9520   Tel: 020-7357 9515

BARKING PRODUCTIONS/INSTANT WIT
(Comedy Improvisation/Corporate Entertainment &
Training)
PO Box 597, Bristol BS99 2BB
Website: www.barkingproductions.co.uk
e-mail: info@barkingproductions.co.uk
Fax: 0117-908 5384   Tel: 0117-939 3171

BEE & BUSTLE ENTERPRISES
32 Exeter Road, London NW2 4SB
Website: www.beeandbustle.co.uk
e-mail: info@beeandbustle.co.uk
Fax: 020-8450 1057   Tel: 020-8450 0371

BHJ Ltd
(Brian Hewitt-Jones)
The Studio, No. 1 Barrington Road, London N8 8QR
Fax: 020-8374 5163   Tel: 020-8374 6970

BIG DOG PRODUCTIONS Ltd
(Martin Roddy)
16 Kirkwick Avenue, Harpenden, Herts AL5 2QN
e-mail: bigdog@kirkwick.demon.co.uk
Fax: 01582 467349   Tel: 01582 467344

BLACK THEATRE CO-OPERATIVE
(See NITRO)

BLUE ORANGE THEATRE COMPANY The
43 Mendip Court
Riverside Plaza, Chatfield Road, London SW11 3UZ
e-mail: blueorangetc@aol.com
Tel/Fax: 020-7223 1100

BORDERLINE THEATRE COMPANY
North Harbour Street, Ayr KA8 8AA
e-mail: enquiries@borderlinetheatre.co.uk
Tel: 01292 281010

BREAKWITH PRODUCTIONS Ltd
7 London Court, Frogmore
London SW18 1HH   Tel/Fax: 020-8871 4999

BRIDGE LANE THEATRE COMPANY Ltd
The Studio, 49 Ossulton Way
London N2 0JY   Tel/Fax: 020-8444 0505

**BRIGHTON REVUE COMPANY The
(BRC PRODUCTIONS)**
139 Freshfield Road, Brighton BN2 2YE
Website: www.brightonrevue.fsnet.co.uk
e-mail: enquiries@brightonrevue.fsnet.co.uk
Fax: 01273 672646

BRIGHTON THEATRE EVENTS
40 Upper Gardner Street, Brighton BN1 4AN
Website: www.brigthontheatreevents.supanet.com
e-mail: brightontheatreevents@supanet.com
Tel/Fax: 01273 819184

BRITISH ACTORS THEATRE COMPANY Ltd The
28 Stanmer Avenue, Saltdean
Brighton BN2 8QL   Tel: 01273 308737

BRITISH STAGE PRODUCTIONS
Victoria Buildings, 1B Sherwood Street
Scarborough, North Yorks YO11 1SR
e-mail: britishstage@aol.com
Fax: 01723 501328   Tel: 01723 507186

BROADHOUSE PRODUCTIONS Ltd
38 Stourcliffe Close
Stourcliffe Street, London W1H 5AR
e-mail: admin@broadhouse.co.uk
Fax: 020-7402 2173   Tel: 020-7402 0624

BROOKS Sacha Ltd
3rd Floor, 55 Greek Street, London W1D 3DT
Fax: 020-7437 0930   Tel: 020-7437 2900

BROOKE Nick Ltd
The Penthouse, 7 Leicester Place, London WC2H 7RJ
e-mail: info@nickbrooke.com
Fax: 020-7734 7185   Tel: 020-7851 0393

B & R PRODUCTIONS Ltd
1st Floor
66A Great Titchfield Street, London W1W 7QH
Fax: 020-7436 6603   Tel: 020-7580 5277

BUSH THEATRE
Shepherd's Bush Green, London W12 8QD
Website: www.bushtheatre.co.uk
e-mail: info@bushtheatre.co.uk
Fax: 020-7602 7614   Tel: 020-7602 3703

CAPRICORN STAGE (& SCREEN) DIRECTIONS
1A Wedderburn House
Wedderburn Road, Hampstead
London NW3 5QR   Tel: 020-7794 5843

CASSANDRA THEATRE COMPANY
(Vanessa Mildenberg, Clare Bloomer)
Flat 3, 30 Ephraim Road, London SW16 1LW
e-mail: cassandraprod@hotmail.com
Mobile: 07796 264828   Tel: 020-7372 0733

CAVALCADE THEATRE COMPANY Ltd
(Plays, Musicals & Tribute Shows
Cabaret, Children's Shows)
57 Pelham Road, London SW19 1NW
Fax: 020-8540 2243   Tel: 020-8540 3513

CELEBRATION
(Theatre Company for the Young)
48 Chiswick Staithe
London W4 3TP   Tel: 020-8994 8886

CENTRELINE PRODUCTIONS
Unit 7, 93 Paul Street, London EC2A 4NY
Website: www.c-line.dircon.co.uk
e-mail: c-line@dircon.co.uk
Fax: 020-7251 9255   Tel: 020-7251 9251

CHANNEL THEATRE COMPANY
Central Studios
130 Grosvenor Place, Margate, Kent CT9 1UY
Website: www.channel-theatre.co.uk
e-mail: info@channel-theatre.co.uk
Fax: 01843 280088   Tel: 01843 280077

CHAPMAN Duggie ASSOCIATES
(Pantomime, Concerts, Musicals)
The Old Coach House
202 Common Edge Road, Blackpool FY4 5DG
e-mail: etmmgt@aol.com
Fax: 0115-946 1831   Tel: 01253 691823

CHAPMAN Guy PRODUCTIONS
33 Southampton Street, London WC2E 7HE
e-mail: guy@g-c-a.co.uk
Fax: 020-7379 8484   Tel: 020-7379 7474

CHICHESTER FESTIVAL THEATRE
Oaklands Park, Chichester, West Sussex PO19 4AP
Website: www.cft.org.uk
e-mail: admin@cft.org.uk
Fax: 01243 787288   Tel: 01243 784437

CHURCHILL THEATRE BROMLEY Ltd
Churchill Theatre
High Street, Bromley, Kent BR1 1HA
Website: www.churchilltheatre.co.uk
Fax: 020-8290 6968   Tel: 020-8464 7131

CITY CONCERT ORGANISATION Ltd The
PO Box 3145, Lichfield WS13 6YN
Website: www.cityconcert.com
e-mail: admin@cityconcert.com
Tel/Fax: 01543 262286

CLEAR CHANNEL GROUP
35 Grosvenor Street, London W1R 4QX
Fax: 020-7529 4301   Tel: 020-7529 4300

CLOSE FOR COMFORT THEATRE COMPANY
34 Boleyn Walk, Leatherhead
Surrey KT22 7HU   Tel: 01372 378613

CODRON Michael PLAYS Ltd
Aldwych Theatre Offices, London WC2B 4DF
Fax: 020-7240 8467   Tel: 020-7240 8291

COGO-FAWCETT Robert
58 Hythe Road, Brighton BN1 6JS
e-mail: robertcogo_fawcett@hotmail.com
Mobile: 07973 938634

COLE KITCHENN Ltd
Nederlander House
7 Great Russell Street, London WC1B 3NH
Fax: 020-7580 2992   Tel: 020-7580 2772

COMPASS THEATRE COMPANY
Carver Street Institute
24 Rockingham Lane, Sheffield S1 4FW
Website: www.compasstheatrecompany.com
e-mail: info@compasstheatrecompany.com
Fax: 0114-278 6931   Tel: 0114-275 5328

CONCORDANCE
(Neil McPherson)
7 Defoe House, Barbican, London EC2Y 8DN
Website: www.concordance.org.uk
e-mail: admin@concordance.org.uk
Tel/Fax: 020-7638 9073

CONTEMPORARY STAGE COMPANY
3 Etchingham Park Road, Finchley, London N3 2DU
Website: www.contemporarystage.co.uk
e-mail: contemp.stage@britishlibrary.net
Fax: 020-8349 2458   Tel: 020-8349 4402

CONWAY Clive ASSOCIATES & THE ENGLISH CHAMBER THEATRE
32 Grove Street, Oxford OX2 7JT
Website: www.celebritytheatre.co.uk
e-mail: clive.conway@ntlworld.com
Fax: 01865 514409   Tel: 01865 514830

COONEY Ray PLAYS
Everglades
29 Salmons Road, Chessington, Surrey KT9 2JE
e-mail: alan@raycooneyplays.co.uk
Fax: 020-8397 0070   Tel: 020-8397 0021

CRISP THEATRE
8 Cornwallis Crescent, Clifton, Bristol BS8 4PL
e-mail: crisptheatre@hotmail.com
Tel/Fax: 0117-973 7106

C T G COTSWOLD THEATRE GROUP
Sandford Cottage, Shipton Road
Milton-under-Wychwood
Oxon OX7 6JT   Fax: 01993 776071

DAVID GRAHAM ENTERTAINMENT Ltd
3-5 Latimer Road, Teddington, Middlesex TW11 8QA
Website: www.davidgraham.co.uk
e-mail: info@davidgraham.co.uk
Fax: 020-8977 6909   Tel: 020-8977 8707

DAVIES Alma
2 Turnberry Place, 2857 S. Paradise Road
Unit 1001, Las Vegas NV 89109
e-mail: divaalmadavies@aol.com
Fax: (702) 341-5681   Tel: (702) 341-5631

DEAD EARNEST THEATRE
57 Burton Street, Sheffield S6 2HH
e-mail: info@deadearnest.co.uk   Tel: 0114-233 4579

DEAN Lee
PO Box 10703, London WC2H 9ED
Fax: 020-7836 6968   Tel: 020-7497 5111

DELFONT MACKINTOSH THEATRES Ltd
(Theatre Owners)
Prince of Wales Theatre
Coventry Street, London W1D 6AS
e-mail: info@delfont-mackintosh.com
Fax: 020-7930 8970   Tel: 020-7930 9901

DISNEY Walt THEATRICAL (UK) Ltd
The Lyceum Theatre
21 Wellington Street, London WC2E 7DA
Fax: 020-7845 0999   Tel: 020-7845 0900

DONNA MARIA COMPANY
16 Bell Meadow, Dulwich, London SE19 1HP
Website: www.donna-marias-world.co.uk
e-mail: info@donna-marias-world.co.uk
                               Tel: 020-8670 7814

DOODAH THEATRE
27 St Peter's Way, Ealing, London W5 2QR
e-mail: doodahtc@aol.com
Fax: 020-8997 9757   Tel: 020-8991 5903

DORE Katharine MANAGEMENT & PRODUCTIONS Ltd (KDM)
Horseshoe Wharf, 6A Clink Street, London SE1 9FD
Website: www.kdmanagement.co.uk
e-mail: info@kdmanagement.co.uk
Fax: 020-7357 8002   Tel: 020-7357 6633

DRAMATIS PERSONAE Ltd
(Nathan Silver, Nicolas Kent)
19 Regency Street, London SW1P 4BY
e-mail: nathan.silver@ntlworld.com
                               Tel: 020-7834 9300

DUAL CONTROL OPERA & BALLET INTERNATIONAL
Admiral's Office
Historic Dockyard, Chatham, Kent ME4 4TZ
e-mail: info@ellenkentinternational.co.uk
Fax: 01634 819149   Tel: 01634 819141

EACH WORLD PRODUCTIONS
43 Moormead Road
St Margaret's, Twickenham TW1 1JS
Fax: 020-8744 0676   Tel: 020-8892 0908

EASTERN ANGLES THEATRE COMPANY
(Touring)
Sir John Mills Theatre
Gatacre Road, Ipswich, Suffolk IP1 2LQ
Website: www.easternangles.co.uk
e-mail: admin@easternangles.co.uk
Fax: 01473 384999   Tel: 01473 218202

Richard Jordan Productions Ltd

- Producing
- General Management
  UK and International Productions,
  and International Festivals
- Consultancy

Richard Jordan Productions Ltd
Mews Studios, 16 Vernon Yard
London W11 2DX

Tel: 020 7243 9001
Fax: 020 7313 9667
e-mail: richard.jordan@virgin.net

ELLIOTT Paul Ltd
(Triumph Entertainment Ltd), Suite 3
Waldorf Chambers, 11 Aldwych, London WC2B 4DG
e-mail: pelliott@paulelliott.ltd.uk
Fax: 020-7379 4860   Tel: 020-7379 4870

EMPTY SPACE THEATRE COMPANY
32 Kenbrook House
Leighton Road, Kentish Town, London NW5 2QN
e-mail: estc@dircon.co.uk
Fax: 0870 9090103   Tel: 0870 9090102

ENGLISH CHAMBER THEATRE
18 The Crooked Billet
London SW19 4RQ   Tel: 020-8946 9898

ENGLISH NATIONAL OPERA
London Coliseum
St Martin's Lane, London WC2N 4ES
Fax: 020-7845 9277   Tel: 020-7836 0111

ENGLISH STAGE COMPANY Ltd
Royal Court, Sloane Square, London SW1W 8AS
Website: www.royalcourttheatre.com
e-mail: info@royalcourttheatre.com
Fax: 020-7565 5001   Tel: 020-7565 5050

ENGLISH THEATRE COMPANY Ltd
(TMA Member)
Nybrogatan 35, 114 39 Stockholm, Sweden
Website: www.englishtheatre.se
e-mail: etc.ltd@telia.com
Fax: 00 46 8660 1159   Tel: 00 46 8662 4133

ENGLISH TOURING THEATRE
25 Short Street, London SE1 8LJ
Website: www.englishtouringtheatre.co.uk
e-mail: admin@englishtouringtheatre.co.uk
Fax: 020-7450 1991   Tel: 020-7450 1990 Ext 304

ENTERTAINMENT BUSINESS Ltd The
199 Piccadilly, London W1J 9HA
Fax: 020-7287 5144   Tel: 020-7734 8555

EUROPEAN THEATRE COMPANY The
39 Oxford Avenue, London SW20 8LS
Website: www.europeantheatre.co.uk
e-mail: admin@europeantheatre.co.uk
Fax: 020-8544 1999   Tel: 020-8544 1994

FACADE
(Musicals)
43A Garthorne Road
London SE23 1EP   Tel: 020-8699 8655

FACE TO FACE THEATRE PRODUCTIONS Ltd
(Write)
10 St Fillans Road, Stepps, Glasgow G33 6LW
e-mail: robinfacetoface@hotmail.com

FARRAH Paul PRODUCTIONS
Strand Theatre Offices, London WC2B 4LD
e-mail: pfpltd@aol.com
Fax: 020-7240 4451   Tel: 020-7240 4431

FAT BLOKE PRODUCTIONS
187 Drury Lane, London WC2B 5QD
e-mail: f@tbloke.com
Fax: 020-7405 6262   Tel: 020-7405 6161

FELL Andrew Ltd
7 Upper St Martin's Lane, London WC2H 9DL
e-mail: hq@andrewfell.co.uk
Fax: 020-7240 2499   Tel: 020-7240 2420

FIELDING Harold
69 Strand on the Green
London W4 3PF   Tel: 020-8673 4323

FIERY ANGEL Ltd
22-24 Torrington Place, London WC1E 7HF
Website: www.fiery-angel.com
e-mail: admin@fiery-angel.com
Fax: 020-7580 6652   Tel: 020-7907 7040

FLEIGHTON PRODUCTIONS Ltd
Suite 11, 33 Rushworth Street, London SE1 0RB
Fax: 020-7928 2328   Tel: 020-7928 2333

FLUXX
(Improvised Theatre)
Sebbon Street Centre
Sebbon Street, London N1 2DZ
Website: www.fluxx.co.uk
e-mail: admin@fluxx.co.uk   Tel: 020-8348 3658

FORD Vanessa PRODUCTIONS Ltd
Upper House Farm
Upper House Lane
Shamley Green, Surrey GU5 0SX
Website: www.vfpltd.com
e-mail: vanessa@vfpltd.fsnet.co.uk
Tel/Fax: 01483 278203   Tel: 01483 268530

FOX Robert Ltd
6 Beauchamp Place, London SW3 1NG
e-mail: rf@robertfoxltd.com
Fax: 020-7225 1638   Tel: 020-7584 6855

FREEDMAN Bill Ltd
Room 311, Bedford Chambers
The Piazza, Covent Garden, London WC2E 8HA
Fax: 020-7836 9903   Tel: 020-7836 9900

FUTURA MUSIC (PRODUCTIONS) Ltd
(Write only)
29 Emanuel House
Rochester Row, London SW1P 1BS

GALE PRODUCTIONS
24 Wimbledon Park Road, London SW18 1LT
e-mail: gale.prod@which.net
Fax: 020-8875 1582   Tel: 020-8870 1149

GALLEON THEATRE COMPANY Ltd
Greenwich Playhouse
Greenwich BR Station Forecourt
189 Greenwich High Road, London SE10 8JA
Website: www.galleontheatre.co.uk
e-mail: boxoffice@galleontheatre.co.uk
Fax: 020-8969 2910   Tel: 020-8858 9256

GLASS David ENSEMBLE
59 Brewer Street, London W1F 9UN
Website: www.davidglassensemble.com
e-mail: dg.ensemble@virgin.net
Fax: 020-7734 0365   Tel: 020-7734 6030

GOOD COMPANY
46 Quebec Street, Brighton, Sussex BN2 9UZ
e-mail: gco@goodcompany.idps.co.uk
Fax: 01273 606926   Tel: 01273 606652

GOSS Gerald Ltd
Dudley House, 169 Piccadilly, London W1J 9EH
Fax: 020-7499 7227   Tel: 020-7499 7447

GRAEAE THEATRE COMPANY
Interchange Studios, Hampstead Town Hall Centre
213 Haverstock Hill, London NW3 4QP
Website: www.graeae.org
e-mail: info@graeae.org
Fax: 020-7681 4756   Tel: 020-7681 4755

GREEN & LENAGAN Ltd
140 Buckingham Palace Road, London SW1W 9SA
e-mail: postbox@greenandlenagan.co.uk
Fax: 020-7881 9661   Tel: 020-7881 9660

HALE Ivan Ltd
5 Denmark Street, London WC2H 8LP
e-mail: ivanhaleltd@hotmail.com
Fax: 01923 492772   Tel: 01923 492992

HAMPSTEAD THEATRE PRODUCTIONS Ltd
Eton Avenue, Swiss Cottage, London NW3 3EU
Website: www.hampstead-theatre.co.uk
e-mail: admin@hampstead-theatre.com
Fax: 020-7722 3860   Tel: 020-7722 9224

HANDSTAND PRODUCTIONS
13 Hope Street, Liverpool L1 9BH
Website: www.handstand-uk.com
e-mail: info@handstand-uk.com
Fax: 0151-709 3515   Tel: 0151-708 7441

HARLEY CINE LIBRE PRODUCTIONS
68 New Cavendish Street, London W1G 8TE
e-mail: harleyprods@aol.com
Fax: 020-8202 8863   Tel: 020-7580 3247

HAYMARKET THEATRE CO Ltd
Wote Street, Basingstoke, Hants RG21 7NW
Website: www.haymarket@org.uk
e-mail: info@haymarket.org.uk
Fax: 01256 357130   Tel: 01256 323073

HAZEMEAD Ltd
(Entertainment Consultants)
Camellia House, 38 Orchard Road
Sundridge Park
Bromley, Kent BR1 2PS   Tel: 0870 2402082

HENDERSON Glynis PRODUCTIONS
69 Charlotte Street, London W1T 4PJ
e-mail: info@ghmp.co.uk
Fax: 020-7436 1489   Tel: 020-7580 9644

HESTER John PRODUCTIONS
(INTIMATE MYSTERIES THEATRE COMPANY)
105 Stoneleigh Park Road, Epsom, Surrey KT19 0RF
e-mail: hester92@hotmail.com
                                      Tel/Fax: 020-8393 5705

HILTON Adrian Ltd
(Write Only)
Priory House
Amersham Road, Beaconsfield, Bucks HP9 2HA

HISS & BOO COMPANY Ltd The
(Ian Liston)
Nyes Hill, Wineham Lane
Bolney, West Sussex RH17 5SD
Website: www.hissboo.co.uk
e-mail: ian@hissboo.co.uk
Fax: 01444 882057   Tel: 01444 881707

HOLMAN Paul ASSOCIATES Ltd
20 Deane Avenue, South Ruislip, Middlesex HA4 6SR
e-mail: paulholmanassociates@blueyonder.co.uk
Fax: 020-8582 2557   Tel: 020-8845 9408

HOLT Thelma Ltd
Waldorf Chambers, 11 Aldwych, London WC2B 4DG
Website: www.thelmaholt.co.uk
e-mail: thelma@dircon.co.uk
Fax: 020-7836 9832   Tel: 020-7379 0438

HOUSE OF GULLIVER
(Write)
77 Longfield Road, Tring, Herts HP23 4DF

HULL TRUCK THEATRE
Spring Street, Hull HU2 8RW
Website: www.hulltruck.co.uk
e-mail: admin@hulltruck.co.uk
Fax: 01482 581182   Tel: 01482 224800

HUTT RUSSELL PRODUCTIONS Ltd
PO Box 64, Cirencester, Glos GL7 5YD
Website: www.huttrussellorg.com
e-mail: shows@huttrussellorg.com
Fax: 01285 642291   Tel: 01285 644622

IMAGE MUSICAL THEATRE
23 Sedgeford Road
Shepherd's Bush, London W12 0NA
Website: www.imagemusicaltheatre.co.uk
e-mail: brianthresh@image-theatre-co.demon.uk
Fax: 020-8749 9294   Tel: 020-8743 9380

IMAGINATION ENTERTAINMENTS
25 Store Street, South Crescent, London WC1E 7BL
Website: www.imagination.com
e-mail: entertainments@imagination.com
Fax: 020-7323 5801   Tel: 020-7323 3300

IMPACT UK Ltd
Hope Bank House, Woodhead Road
Honley, Huddersfield HD9 6PF
Fax: 08700 111266   Tel: 08700 111288

INCISOR
30 Brondesbury Park, London NW6 7DN
Website: www.festival-edinburgh.com
e-mail: enquiries@startek-uk.com
Fax: 020-8830 4992   Tel: 020-8830 0074

INDIGO ENTERTAINMENTS
Tynymynydd, Bryneglwys
Corwen, Denbighshire LL21 9NP
Website: www.indigoentertainments.com
e-mail: info@indigoentertainments.com
Tel: 01978 790211

INSIDE INTELLIGENCE
(Musical and Contemporary Opera Products)
13 Athlone Close, London E5 8HD
Website: www.inside-intelligence.nildram.co.uk
e-mail: admin@inside-intelligence.org.uk
Tel/Fax: 020-8986 8013

INTERNATIONAL THEATRE & MUSIC Ltd
(Piers Chater Robinson)
Shakespeare House
Theatre Street, London SW11 5ND
e-mail: inttheatre@aol.com
Fax: 020-7801 6317   Tel: 020-7801 6316

ISLEWORTH ACTORS COMPANY
38 Eve Road, Isleworth, Middlesex TW7 7HS
Tel/Fax: 020-8891 1073   Tel/Fax: 020-8892 4207

JACKSON Richard
48 William Mews
London SW1X 9HQ   Tel/Fax: 020-7235 3759

JAMES Bruce PRODUCTIONS Ltd
68 St. Georges Park Avenue
Westcliff-on-Sea, Essex SS0 9UD
Website: www.brucejamesproductions.co.uk
e-mail: info@brucejamesproductions.co.uk
Tel/Fax: 01702 335970

JOHNSON David
85B Torriano Avenue, London NW5 2RX
e-mail: david@johnsontemple.co.uk
Tel: 020-7284 3733

JOHNSON Gareth Ltd
Plas Hafren, Egwyswrw
Crymych, Pembrokeshire SA41 3UL
e-mail: gjltd@macunlimited.net
Tel/Fax: 01239 891368

JORDAN Andy PRODUCTIONS Ltd
24 Well's House Road, East Acton, London NW10 6EE
e-mail: andyjandyjordan@aol.com
Fax: 020-8838 4482   Tel: 020-8963 9171

JORDAN Richard PRODUCTIONS Ltd
Mews Studios, 16 Vernon Yard, London W11 2DX
e-mail: richard.jordan@virgin.net
Fax: 020-7313 9667   Tel: 020-7243 9001

KARUSHI PROMOTIONS
Golden Cross House
8 Duncannon Street, London WC2N 4JF
Website: www.karushi.com
e-mail: ed@karushi.com
Fax: 020-7484 5151   Tel: 020-7484 5040

KENWRIGHT Bill Ltd
BKL House, 106 Harrow Road
Off Howley Place, London W2 1RR
e-mail: info@kenwright.com
Fax: 020-7446 6222   Tel: 020-7446 6200

KING'S HEAD THEATRE PRODUCTION Ltd
115 Upper Street, London N1 1QN
Fax: 020-7226 8507   Tel: 020-7226 8561

KIRK David
12 Panmuir Road, Wimbledon SW20 0PZ
Fax: 020-8944 1810   Tel: 020-8947 0130

KNIGHTSBRIDGE THEATRICAL PRODUCTIONS Ltd
21 New Fetter Lane, London EC4A 1JJ
Fax: 020 7583 1040   Tel: 020-7583 8687

LEWIS Richard PRODUCTIONS Ltd
Limelight, Trident International
40 Victoria Way, London SE7 7QS
Fax: 020-8305 2684   Tel: 020-8858 6141

LINNIT PRODUCTIONS Ltd
123A Kings Road, London SW3 4PL
Fax: 020-7352 3450   Tel: 020-7352 7722

LIVE THEATRE COMPANY
7-8 Trinity Chare, Quayside
Newcastle upon Tyne NE1 3DF
Website: www.live.org.uk   Tel: 0191-261 2694

LLOYD-JAMES Adrian
310 Cowley Mansions
Mortlake High Street, London SW14 8SL
e-mail: tabsproductions@bushinternet.com
Fax: 020-8255 1632   Tel: 020-8255 1332

LONDON BUBBLE THEATRE COMPANY Ltd
5 Elephant Lane, London SE16 4JD
Website: www.londonbubble.org.uk
e-mail: admin@londonbubble.org.uk
Fax: 020-7231 2366   Tel: 020-7237 4434

**LONDON COMPANY
INTERNATIONAL PLAYS Ltd The**
(No CV's please)
PO Box 4458, London SW1X 8XP
e-mail: derek@glynnes.co.uk
Fax: 020-7486 2164   Tel: 020-7486 3166

LONDON GREEK THEATRE GROUP The
(Write)
7 Breantmead Gardens, London NW10 7DT

LONDON PRODUCTIONS Ltd
PO Box 10703, London WC2H 9ED
Fax: 020-7836 6968   Tel: 020-7497 5111

LYRIC HAMMERSMITH PRODUCTIONS
58 Hythe Road, Brighton BN1 6JS
e-mail: robertcogo_fawcett@hotmail.com
                          Mobile: 07973 938634

MACKINTOSH Cameron Ltd
1 Bedford Square, London WC1B 3RB
Fax: 020-7436 2683   Tel: 020-7637 8866

MACNAGHTEN Marianne
Dundarave, Bushmills, Co. Antrim, N Ireland BT57 8ST
Fax: 028-2073 2575   Tel: 028-2073 1215

MALCOLM Christopher Ltd
1 Calton Road, Bath BA2 4PP
Website: www.rockyhorror.co.uk
e-mail: cmalcolm@btconnect.com
Fax: 01225 427778   Tel: 01225 445459

MANS Johnny PRODUCTIONS Ltd
PO Box 196, Hoddesdon, Herts EN10 7WG
Fax: 01992 470516   Tel: 01992 470907

MASTERSON Guy PRODUCTIONS
(Write)
The Bull Theatre, 68 High Street, Barnet, Herts EN5 5SJ
Website: www.guymasterson.com
e-mail: admin@guymasterson.com
Fax: 020-8449 5252   Tel: 020-8449 7800

MEADOW Jeremy
(See TEG PRODUCTIONS Ltd)

MENZIES Lee Ltd
118-120 Wardour Street, London W1V 3LA
Website: www.leemenzies.co.uk
e-mail: leemenzies@leemenzies.co.uk
Fax: 020-7734 4224   Tel: 020-7734 9559

METRO ENTERTAINMENT Ltd
Strand Theatre Offices, London WC2B 4LD
e-mail: info@metroentertainmentltd.com
Fax: 020-7240 4451   Tel: 020-7240 4431

METRO PRODUCTIONS
11 Keyford Place, Frome
Somerset BA11 1JE   Tel: 01373 462812

MICHAEL ROSE Ltd
The Old Dairy, Throop Road, Holdenhurst,
Bournemouth, Dorset BH8 0DL
e-mail: mrl@mrltheatre.u-net.com
Fax: 01202 522311   Tel: 01202 522711

MIDDLE GROUND THEATRE COMPANY
3 Gordon Terrace
Malvern Wells, Malvern, Worcs WR14 4ER
e-mail: middleground@tinyworld.co.uk
Fax: 01684 574472   Tel: 01684 577231

MILLENNIUM ARTISTES MANAGEMENT Ltd
(Personal Management & Event Co-ordinators)
PO Box 2001, Caterham, Surrey CR3 6UA
e-mail: mamltd@ntlworld.com
                          Tel/Fax: 01883 347790

MILLFIELD THEATRE
Silver Street, Edmonton, London N18 1PJ
Website: www.millfieldtheatre.co.uk
e-mail: info@millfieldtheatre.co.uk
                          Tel: 020-8807 6186

MITCHELL Matthew Ltd
Flat 5, 65 Cumberland Street, London SW1V 4LY
e-mail: mmitch@dircon.co.uk
Fax: 020-7834 8738   Tel: 020-7630 8881

MOVING THEATRE
16 Laughton Lodge
Laughton, Nr Lewes, East Sussex BN8 6BY
Website: www.movingtheatre.com
e-mail: info@movingtheatre.com
Fax: 01323 815736   Tel: 01323 815726

MU-LAN THEATRE COMPANY
The Albany, Douglas Way, London SE8 4AG
Website: www.mu-lan.org
e-mail: mailbox@mu-lan.org
Fax: 020-8694 0618   Tel: 020-8694 0557

MUSIC THEATRE LONDON
Chertsey Chambers
12 Mercer Street, London WC2H 9QD
Website: www.mtl.org.uk
e-mail: musictheatre.london@virgin.net
Fax: 020-7240 0805   Tel: 020-7240 0919

NEW SHAKESPEARE COMPANY Ltd The
Open Air Theatre, The Iron Works
Inner Circle, Regent's Park, London NW1 4NR
Website: www.open-air-theatre.org.uk
Fax: 020-7487 4562   Tel: 020-7935 5756

NEW VIC THEATRE OF LONDON INC.
Suite 42, 91 St Martin's Lane
London WC2H 0DL   Tel/Fax: 020-7240 2929

NEW VIC WORKSHOP Ltd
15 Bedford Place, Brighton BN1 2PT
e-mail: newvicworkshop@lineone.net
Fax: 01273 776663   Tel: 01273 775126

NEWPALM PRODUCTIONS
26 Cavendish Avenue, London N3 3QN
Fax: 020-8346 8257   Tel: 020-8349 0802

NITRO
(Formerly Black Theatre Co-operative)
6 Brewery Road, London N7 9NH
Website: www.nitro.co.uk
e-mail: btc@dircon.co.uk
Fax: 020-7609 1221   Tel: 020-7609 1331

**NORTHERN STAGE
(THEATRICAL PRODUCTIONS) Ltd**
Newcastle Playhouse
Barras Bridge, Newcastle upon Tyne NE1 7RH
Website: www.northernstage.com
e-mail: info@northernstage.com
Fax: 0191-261 8093   Tel: 0191-232 3366

NORWELL LAPLEY ASSOCIATES
Lapley Hall, Lapley, Staffs ST19 9JR
Website: www.norwelllapley.co.uk
e-mail: norwelllapley@freeuk.com
Fax: 01785 841992   Tel: 01785 841991

NOT THE NATIONAL THEATRE
(Write) (Small/Mid-Scale Touring - UK & Abroad)
101 Broadhurst Gardens, London NW6 3BJ

NTC TOURING THEATRE COMPANY
The Playhouse, Bondgate Without
Alnwick, Northumberland NE66 1PQ
Website: www.ntc-touringtheatre.co.uk
e-mail: admin@ntc-touringtheatre.co.uk
Fax: 01665 605837   Tel: 01665 602586

O'BRIEN Barry (1968) Ltd
26 Cavendish Avenue, London N3 3QN
Fax: 020-8346 8257   Tel: 020-8346 8011

OFF THE CUFF THEATRE COMPANY
First Floor, 52 Crowndale Road, London NW1 1TP
Website: www.offthecuffonline.com
e-mail: otctheatre@aol.com   Tel: 020-7691 1577

OPEN AIR THEATRE
(See NEW SHAKESPEARE COMPANY Ltd The)

OPERA AND BALLET INTERNATIONAL Ltd
(International Opera & Ballet Producers)
Admiral's Offices
The Historic Dockyard
Chatham, Kent ME4 4TZ
e-mail: info@ellenkentinternational.co.uk
Fax: 01634 819149   Tel: 01634 819141

OUT OF JOINT
7 Thane Works, Thane Villas, London N7 7PH
Website: www.outofjoint.co.uk
e-mail: ojo@outofjoint.co.uk
Fax: 020-7609 0203   Tel: 020-7609 0207

OUT OF THE BLUE PRODUCTIONS Ltd
48 Conduit Street, London W1S 2YR
Website: www.otbp.com
e-mail: info@otbp.com
Fax: 020-7734 3678   Tel: 020-7734 1345

OVATION
1 Prince of Wales Passage, London NW1 3EF
Website: www.ovationproductions.com
e-mail: events@ovationproductions.com
Fax: 020-7380 0404   Tel: 020-7387 2342

OXFORD STAGE COMPANY
131 High Street, Oxford OX1 4DH
Website: www.oxfordstage.co.uk
e-mail: info@oxfordstage.co.uk
Fax: 01865 790625   Tel: 01865 723238

PAINES PLOUGH
Fourth Floor, 43 Aldwych, London WC2B 4DN
Website: www.painesplough.com
e-mail: office@painesplough.com
Fax: 020-7240 4534   Tel: 020-7240 4533

PARASOL PRODUCTIONS
Garden House, 4 Sunnyside, Wimbledon SW19 4SL
Fax: 020-8946 0228   Tel: 020-8946 9478

PENDLE PRODUCTIONS
39 Ermine Close, Blackburn BB2 3UW
Website: www.pendleproductions.co.uk
e-mail: theatre@pendle.u-net.com
      Tel/Fax: 01254 59590

PENTABUS
(National Touring Company for New Writing)
Bromfield, Ludlow, Shropshire SY8 2JU
Website: www.pentabus.co.uk
e-mail: firstname@pentabus.co.uk
Fax: 01584 856254   Tel: 01584 856564

PEOPLE SHOW
People Show Studios, Pollard Row, London E2 6NB
Website: www.peopleshow.co.uk
e-mail: people@peopleshow.co.uk
Fax: 020-7739 0203   Tel: 020-7729 1841

PERFORMANCE BUSINESS The
15 Montrose Walk, Weybridge, Surrey KT13 8JN
Website: www.reactors.co.uk
e-mail: michael@theperformancebusiness.com
Fax: 01932 830248   Tel: 01932 888885

PERICLES
(Paddy Wilson)
6-7 Buckingham House
Buckingham Street, London WC2N 6BU
e-mail: periclesdevelopments@genie.co.uk
Fax: 020-7925 0965   Tel: 020-7925 0964

PLANTAGENET PRODUCTIONS
(Drawing Room Recitals)
Westridge (Open Centre)
Star Lane, Andover Road
Highclere, Nr Newbury RG20 9PJ   Tel: 01635 253322

PLUNGE PRODUCTIONS Ltd
9 Whittington Road, London N22 8YS
e-mail: info@plungeproductions.com
      Tel/Fax: 020-8888 6608

POLKA THEATRE FOR CHILDREN
240 The Broadway, Wimbledon SW19 1SB
Website: www.polkatheatre.com
e-mail: admin@polkatheatre.com
Fax: 020-8545 8365   Tel: 020-8545 8320

POSTER Kim
The Penthouse, Charles House
7 Leicester Place, London WC2H 7RJ
Fax: 020-7734 7185   Tel: 020-7734 0710

PROMENADE PRODUCTIONS Ltd
6 Russell Grove, London SW9 6HS
e-mail: promenadeproductions@msn.com
Fax: 020-7564 3026   Tel: 020-7582 9354

P&S PRODUCTIONS
Top Flat, 51 Norroy Road
London SW15 1PQ
e-mail: timsawers@msn.com   Tel/Fax: 020-8780 9115

PUGH David Ltd
Canaletto Yard, 41-45 Beak Street, London W1F 9SB
e-mail: dpl@davidpughltd.com
Fax: 020-7287 8856   Tel: 020-7434 9757

PURSUED BY A BEAR PRODUCTIONS
6 Glenluce Road, Blackheath, London SE3 7SB
Website: www.pbab.org
e-mail: pbab@pbab.org   Tel/Fax: 020-8480 9514

PW PRODUCTIONS Ltd
The Penthouse, 7 Leicester Place, London WC2H 7RJ
Website: www.pwprods.co.uk
Fax: 020-7734 7185   Tel: 020-7734 7184

QDOS ENTERTAINMENT (THEATRE) Ltd
8 King Street, London WC2E 8HN
Fax: 020-7379 4892   Tel: 020-7836 2795

Qdos House, Queen Margaret's Road
Scarborough, North Yorks YO11 2SA
Fax: 01723 361958   Tel: 01723 500038

QUANTUM THEATRE
Unit S9, The Shakespeare Centre
245A Coldharbour Lane, London SW9 8RR
Website: www.quantumtheatre.co.uk
e-mail: quantumtheatre@btinternet.com
      Tel: 020-7733 8150

RAGGED RAINBOW PRODUCTIONS Ltd
45 Nightingale Lane, Crouch End, London N8 7RA
e-mail: rainbowrp@onetel.net.uk
      Tel/Fax: 020-8341 6241

RAGS & FEATHERS THEATRE COMPANY
80 Summer Road, Thames Ditton, Surrey KT7 0QP
e-mail: jill@ragsandfeathers.freeserve.co.uk
Mobile: 07958 724374   Tel: 020-8224 2203

RAIN OR SHINE T.C.
25 Paddock Gardens
Longlevens, Gloucester GL2 0ED
Website: www.rainorshine.co.uk
e-mail: theatre@rainorshine.co.uk
Fax: 01452 521575   Tel: 01452 521575

REALLY USEFUL GROUP Ltd The
22 Tower Street, London WC2H 9TW
Fax: 020-7240 1204   Tel: 020-7240 0880

REALLY USEFUL THEATRES
(Theatre Operators)
Manor House, 21 Soho Square, London W1D 3QP
Website: www.rutheatres.com
e-mail: info@rutheatres.com
Fax: 020-7434 1217   Tel: 020-7494 5200

RED LEAF
Ground Floor
384 Hanworth Road, Hounslow
Middlesex TW3 3SN   Tel/Fax: 020-8577 5138

RED ROSE CHAIN
1 Fore Hamlet, Ipswich IP3 8AA
Website: www.redrosechain.co.uk
e-mail: info@redrosechain.co.uk   Tel: 01473 288886

RED SHIFT THEATRE COMPANY
TRG2 Trowbray House
108 Weston Street, London SE1 3QB
Website: www.redshifttheatreco.co.uk
e-mail: mail@redshifttheatreco.co.uk
Fax: 020-7378 9789   Tel: 020-7378 9787

REDINGTON Michael Ltd
10 Maunsel Street, London SW1P 2QL
Fax: 020-7828 6947   Tel: 020-7834 5119

RELEASE THEATRE COMPANY
(Small Scale, Fringe Venues, TIE Touring)
PO Box 34512, London SE15 2FZ
Website: www.releasetheatrecompany.co.uk
e-mail: releasetheatreco@yahoo.co.uk
                         Mobile: 07720 600126

REVEAL THEATRE COMPANY
40 Pirehill Lane, Walton, Stone, Staffordshire ST15 0JN
e-mail: revealtheatre@hotmail.com
                         Tel: 01785 814052

RHO DELTA Ltd
(Greg Ripley-Duggan)
52 Tottenham Street
London W1T 4RN
e-mail: ripleyduggan@aol.com   Tel: 020-7436 1392

RICHMOND PRODUCTIONS
47 Moor Mead Road, St Margaret's
Twickenham TW1 1JS   Tel/Fax: 020-8891 2280

ROCKET THEATRE COMPANY
245 Broadfield Road, Manchester M14 7JT
Website: www.rockettheatre.co.uk
e-mail: martin@rockettheatre.co.uk
Mobile: 07788 723570   Tel: 0161-226 8788

ROSENTHAL Suzanna Ltd
PO Box 40001, London N6 4YA
e-mail: admin@suzannarosenthal.com
                         Tel/Fax: 020-8340 4421

ROYAL COURT THEATRE PRODUCTIONS Ltd
Sloane Square, London SW1W 8AS
Website: www.royalcourttheatre.com
e-mail: info@royalcourttheatre.com
Fax: 020-7565 5001   Tel: 020-7565 5050

ROYAL EXCHANGE THEATRE COMPANY
St Ann's Square, Manchester M2 7DH
Website: www.royalexchange.co.uk
                         Tel: 0161-833 9333

ROYAL NATIONAL THEATRE
South Bank, London SE1 9PX
Website: www.nationaltheatre.org.uk
e-mail: marketing@nationaltheatre.org.uk
Fax: 020-7452 3344   Tel: 020-7452 3333

ROYAL SHAKESPEARE COMPANY
1 Earlham Street, London WC2H 9LL
Website: www.rsc.org.uk
Fax: 020-7845 0505   Tel: 020-7845 0500

ROYAL SHAKESPEARE THEATRE
Stratford-upon-Avon CV37 6BB
Fax: 01789 294810   Tel: 01789 296655

SANDPIPER PRODUCTIONS Ltd
49A Ossington Street, London W2 4LY
e-mail: harold@sanditen.fsworld.co.uk
Fax: 020-7229 6710   Tel: 020-7229 6708

SHARED EXPERIENCE THEATRE
(National/International Touring)
The Soho Laundry, 9 Dufour's Place, London W1F 7SJ
Website: www.setheatre.co.uk
e-mail: admin@setheatre.co.uk
Fax: 020-7287 8763   Tel: 020-7434 9248

SHARLAND Elizabeth
Suite 12
30 New Compton Street
London WC2H 8DN   Tel: 020-7836 4203

SHAW Vincent ASSOCIATES Ltd
51 Byron Road, London E17 4SN
Website: www.vincentshaw.com
e-mail: info@vincentshaw.com
Fax: 020-8521 1588   Tel: 020-8509 2211

SHOW OF STRENGTH
74 Chessel Street, Bedminster, Bristol BS3 3DN
Fax: 0117-902 0196   Tel: 0117-902 0235

SINDEN Marc PRODUCTIONS
11 Garrick Street, London WC2E 9AR
Website: www.sindenproductions.com
e-mail: mail@sindenproductions.com
Fax: 020-7836 3669   Tel: 020-7836 3667

SOHO THEATRE COMPANY
21 Dean Street, London W1D 3NE
Website: www.sohotheatre.com
e-mail: mail@sohotheatre.com
Fax: 020-7287 5061   Tel: 020-7287 5060

SPHINX THEATRE COMPANY The
25 Short Street, London SE1 8LJ
Website: www.sphinxtheatre.co.uk
Fax: 020-7401 9995   Tel: 020-7401 9993

SPIEGEL Adam PRODUCTIONS
2nd Floor, 20-22 Stukeley Street, London WC2B 5LR
e-mail: claudia@adamspiegel.demon.co.uk
Fax: 020-7438 9577   Tel: 020-7438 9565

SPLATS ENTERTAINMENT
5 Denmark Street, London WC2H 8LP
Fax: 020-7240 8409   Tel: 020-7240 8400

STACEY Barrie UK PRODUCTIONS Ltd
Flat 8, 132 Charing Cross Road, London WC2H 0LA
Fax: 020-7836 2949   Tel: 020-7836 4128

STAGE FURTHER PRODUCTIONS Ltd
Westgate, Stansted Road
Eastbourne, East Sussex BN22 8LG
e-mail: garthsfp@aol.com   Tel/Fax: 01323 739478

STAGE PRESENCE
(Mark Bentley)
PO Box 7579, London NW3 1WA
e-mail: mark.bentley@btinternet.com
                         Tel: 020-7794 9140

STANHOPE PRODUCTIONS Ltd
The Penthouse, Charles House
7 Leicester Place, London WC2H 7RJ
Fax: 020-7734 7185   Tel: 020-7734 0710

STEAM INDUSTRY The
The Finborough Theatre
118 Finborough Road
London SW10 9ED
Website: www.steamindustry.co.uk
e-mail: admin@steamindustry.co.uk
Fax: 020-7835 1853   Tel: 020-7244 7439

STIGWOOD Robert ORGANISATION Ltd The
(Write)
Barton Manor
Whippenham, East Cowes
Isle of Wight PO32 6LB

STRAYDOGS
55 Monmouth Street
London WC2H 9DG
Website: www.straydogs.org.uk
e-mail: info@straydogs.org.uk
Fax: 020-7395 6110   Tel: 020-7395 6113

SUTHERLAND Martin PRODUCTIONS
430 Merton Road
London SW18 5AE
Website: www.martinsutherland.co.uk
e-mail: info@martinsutherland.co.uk
                Tel: 020-8875 0220

SWALLOW PRODUCTIONS (UK) Ltd
32 Blenheim Gardens
Wembley Park, Middlesex HA9 7NP
e-mail: swproduk@aol.com   Tel/Fax: 020-8904 7024

TABS PRODUCTIONS
310 Cowley Mansions
Mortlake High Street
London SW14 8SL
e-mail: tabsproductions@bushinternet.com
Fax: 020-8255 1632   Tel: 020-8255 1332

TALAWA THEATRE COMPANY
23-25 Great Sutton Street
London EC1V 0DN
Website: www.talawa.com
e-mail: hq@talawa.com
Fax: 020-7251 5969   Tel: 020-7251 6644

TAMASHA THEATRE COMPANY Ltd
Unit E, 11 Ronalds Road, London N5 1XJ
Website: www.tamasha.org.uk
e-mail: info@tamasha.org.uk
Fax: 020-7609 2722   Tel: 020-7609 2411

TAMBAR Ltd
PO Box LB689, London W1A 9LB
e-mail: tambarltd@hotmail.com   Tel: 020-7833 8953

TBA MUSIC Ltd
24 Clifton Hill, London NW8 0QG
e-mail: mail@tbamusic.freeserve.co.uk
Fax: 020-7372 0802   Tel: 0845 1203722

TEG PRODUCTIONS Ltd
11-15 Betterton Street, London WC2H 9BP
e-mail: teg@plays.demon.co.uk
Fax: 020-7836 9454   Tel: 020-7379 1066

Winnington Hall
Winnington, Northwich, Cheshire CW8 4DU
Fax: 01606 872701   Tel: 01606 872700

TEMPLE Richard PRODUCTIONS
Revolver House
15 Kensington High Street
London W8 5NP
e-mail: name@richardtempleproductions.com
Fax: 020-7376 0916   Tel: 020-7376 0915

TEN PENCE PRODUCTIONS
Ground Floor
384 Hanworth Road
Hounslow, Middlesex TW3 3SN
e-mail: tenpenceproductions@yahoo.co.uk
                Tel/Fax: 020-8577 5138

TENTH PLANET PRODUCTIONS
75 Woodland Gardens, London N10 3UD
Website: www.tenthplanetproductions.com
e-mail: admin@tenthplanetproductions.com
Tel: 020-8442 2659   Fax: 020-8883 1708

THEATRE ABSOLUTE
57-61 Corporation Street, Coventry CV1 1GQ
e-mail: julia@theatreabsolute.demon.co.uk
                Tel: 024-7625 7380

THEATRE DE COMPLICITE
14 Angler's Lane, London NW5 3DE
e-mail: email@complicite.org
Fax: 020-7485 7701   Tel: 020-7485 7700

THEATRE OF COMEDY COMPANY Ltd
Shaftesbury Theatre
210 Shaftesbury Avenue, London WC2H 8DP
Fax: 020-7836 8181   Tel: 020-7379 3345

THEATRE ROYAL STRATFORD EAST
Gerry Raffles Square, Stratford, London E15 1BN
Website: www.stratfordeast.com
e-mail: theatreroyal@stratfordeast.com
                Tel: 020-8534 7374

THEATRE SANS FRONTIERES
The Queen's Hall Arts Centre
Beaumont Street, Hexham NE46 3LS
e-mail: admin@tsfront.co.uk
Fax: 01434 607206   Tel: 01434 652484

THEATRE SET-UP Ltd
(International Touring)
12 Fairlawn Close, Southgate
London N14 4JX
Website: www.ts-u.co.uk   Tel/Fax: 020-8886 9572

THEATRE TOURS INTERNATIONAL
The Bull Theatre
68 The High Street, Barnet, Herts EN5 5SJ
Website: www.theatretoursinternational.com
e-mail: mail@theatretoursinternational.com
Fax: 020-8449 5252   Tel: 020-8449 7800

THRESHOLD THEATRE COMPANY Ltd
Flat 5, 65 Cumberland Street, London SW1V 4LY
Fax: 020-7834 8738   Tel: 020-7630 8881

TRADING FACES
(Mask & Physical Theatre)
2 Bridge View, Bridge Street, Abingdon OX14 3HN
Website: www.tradingfaces.demon.co.uk
e-mail: office@tradingfaces.demon.co.uk
Fax: 01235 553403   Tel: 01235 550829

TRENDS PRODUCTIONS Ltd
54 Lisson Street, London NW1 5DF
e-mail: info@trendsgroup.co.uk
Fax: 020-7258 3591   Tel: 020-7723 8001

TRESTLE THEATRE COMPANY
(Touring Mask Theatre)
Trestle Arts Base, Russet Drive, St Albans AL4 0JQ
Website: www.trestle.org.uk
e-mail: admin@trestle.org.uk
Fax: 01727 855558   Tel: 01727 850950

**TRIUMPH ENTERTAINMENT Ltd
(DUNCAN C. WELDON)**
Suite 4, Waldorf Chambers
11 Aldwych, London WC2B 4DC
e-mail: dcwtpp@aol.com
Fax: 020-7343 8801   Tel: 020-7343 8800

TROY PRODUCTIONS
17 Talbot Meadows
Talbot Village, Poole, Dorset BH12 5DG
e-mail: lulu_2013@yahoo.co.uk
Mobile: 07710 431741   Tel: 01202 780346

TURTLE KEY ARTS
Ladbroke Hall, 79 Barlby Road, London W10 6AZ
e-mail: turtlek@globalnet.co.uk
Fax: 020-8964 4080   Tel: 020-8964 5060

TWO HATS MIDLANDS THEATRE COMPANY
2 The Countess' Croft
Coventry CV3 5ET
e-mail: twohatz@yahoo.com   Tel: 024-7650 5098

TWO'S COMPANY
244 Upland Road, London SE22 0DN
e-mail: 2scompany@britishlibrary.net
Fax: 020-8299 3714   Tel: 020-8299 4593

UK ARTS INTERNATIONAL
2nd Floor, 6 Shaw Street, Worcester WR1 3QQ
e-mail: janryan@ukarts.com
Fax: 01905 22868   Tel: 01905 26424

UNRESTRICTED VIEW
Above Hen & Chickens Theatre Bar
109 St Paul's Road, London N1 2NA
Website: www.henandchickens.com
e-mail: james@henandchickens.com
                            Tel: 020-7704 2001

VANCE Charles
CV Productions Ltd
Hampden House
2 Weymouth Street, London W1W 5BT
e-mail: cvtheatre@aol.com
Fax: 020-7636 2323   Tel: 020-7636 4343

VANDER ELST Anthony PRODUCTIONS
The Studio, 14 College Road, Bromley, Kent BR1 3NS
Fax: 020-8313 0443   Tel: 020-8466 5580

VENUS PRODUCTIONS
51 Church Road, London SE19 2TE
e-mail: venusfilms@yahoo.com   Tel: 020-8653 7735

VOLCANO THEATRE COMPANY Ltd
176 Hanover Street, Swansea SA1 6BP
Website: www.volcanotheatre.co.uk
e-mail: volcano.tc@virgin.net
Fax: 01792 467563   Tel: 01792 472772

WALLBANK John ASSOCIATES
60 Barclay Road, London E11 3DG
Fax: 020-8928 0339   Tel: 020-8530 7386

WAREHOUSE THEATRE COMPANY
Dingwall Road, Croydon CR0 2NF
e-mail: warehous@dircon.co.uk
Fax: 020-8688 6699   Tel: 020-8681 1257

WAX Kenneth H Ltd
The Penthouse
7 Leicester Place, London WC2H 7RJ
Fax: 020-7734 7185   Tel: 020-7734 7184

WEAVER-HUGHES ENSEMBLE
12B Carholme Road
London SE23 2HS
Website: www.weaverhughensemble.co.uk
e-mail: ensemble@weaverhughesensemble.co.uk
                        Tel/Fax: 020-8693 5614

WHITALL Keith
10 Woodlands Avenue
West Byfleet, Surrey KT14 6AT   Tel: 01932 343655

WHITE Michael
48 Dean Street, London W1D 5BF
e-mail: contact@michaelwhite.co.uk
Fax: 020-7734 7727   Tel: 020-7734 7707

WILDCARD THEATRE COMPANY
PO Box 267, High Wycombe, Bucks HP11 2WB
Website: www.wildcardtheatre.org.uk
e-mail: admin@wildcardtheatre.org.uk
Fax: 07092 024967   Tel: 01494 439375

WILLIAMS Anthony PRODUCTIONS (IOM) Ltd
The Vollan
24 Albany Road, Douglas, Isle of Man IM2 3NG
e-mail: awpsolutions@aol.com
Fax: 01624 673738   Tel: 01624 675640

WILLIAMS Anthony PRODUCTIONS Ltd
Unit 4, The Studio
Throstle Mill, Bacup, Lancashire OL13 0AY
e-mail: awpsolutions@aol.com
Fax: 01706 871729   Tel: 01706 871720

WILLS Newton MANAGEMENT
The Studio
29 Springvale Avenue, Brentford
Middlesex TW8 9QH
e-mail: newtonwills@aol.com
Fax: 00 33 2418 23108   Mobile: 07989 398381

WIZARD PRESENTS
2 Lord Hills Road, London W2 6PD
e-mail: info@wizardpresents.co.uk
Fax: 020-7286 7377   Tel: 020-7286 7277

WOMENS PLAYHOUSE TRUST (WPT)
Wapping Hydraulic Power Station
Wapping Wall, London E1W 3ST
e-mail: info@wapping-wpt.com
Fax: 020-7680 2081   Tel: 020-7680 2096

WOOD Kevin PRODUCTIONS
5 Archery Square, Walmer, Deal, Kent CT14 7JA
e-mail: kevin.wood.organisation@dial.pipex.com
Fax: 01304 381192   Tel: 01304 365515

WORTMAN Neville
48 Chiswick Staithe, London W4 3TP
e-mail: nevillewortman@beeb.net
Mobile: 07976 805976   Tel: 020-8994 8886

WRESTLING SCHOOL The
(The Howard Baker Company)
42 Durlston Road, London E5 8RR
Website: www.members.aol.com/wrestles
                        Tel/Fax: 020-8442 4229

X-PRODUCTIONS AT THE SHAW THEATRE
The Bernard Shaw Park Plaza Hotel
100-100 Euston Road, London NW1 2AJ
Website: www.shawtheatre.com
e-mail: nina@shawtheatre.com
Tel: 020-7383 4887 (Hire)   Tel: 020-7387 6864 (BO)

YELLOW EARTH THEATRE
Diorama Arts Centre
34 Osnaburgh Street
London NW1 3ND
Website: www.yellowearth.org
e-mail: admin@yellowearth.org
Fax: 0870 1319775   Tel: 020-7209 2326

YOUNG VIC COMPANY
66 The Cut, London SE1 8LZ
Website: www.youngvic.org
e-mail: info@youngvic.org
Fax: 020-7928 1585   Tel: 020-7633 0133

6.15 THEATRE COMPANY
22 Brookfield Mansions
Highgate West Hill, London N6 6AS
Website: www.six15@dircon.co.uk
e-mail: six15@dircon.co.uk
Fax: 020-8340 5696   Tel: 020-8342 8239

7:84 THEATRE COMPANY SCOTLAND
333 Woodlands Road, Glasgow G3 6NG
Website: www.784theatre.com
e-mail: admin@784theatre.com
Fax: 0141-334 3369   Tel: 0141-334 6686

ABERYSTWYTH ARTS CENTRE
Penglais, Aberystwyth, Ceredigion SY23 3DE
Website: www.aber.ac.uk/artscentre
e-mail: lla@aber.ac.uk
Fax: 01970 622883   Tel: 01970 622882

ACTORCLUB Ltd
17 Inkerman Road
London NW5 3BT   Tel: 020 7267 2759

AGE EXCHANGE THEATRE TRUST
The Reminiscence Centre
11 Blackheath Village, London SE3 9LA
Website: www.age-exchange.org.uk
e-mail: age-exchange@lewisham.gov.uk
Fax: 020-8318 0060   Tel: 020-8318 9105

ALLEGRESSE
3 Hampden Road, Muswell Hill, London N10 2HP
e-mail: sara@allegresse.demon.co.uk
          Tel: 020-8883 8596

ALBANY The
Douglas Way, Deptford, London SE8 4AG
Fax: 020-8469 2253   Tel: 020-8692 0231

ALTERNATIVE ARTS
Top Studio, Bethnal Green Training Centre,
Deal Street, London E1 5HZ
e-mail: info@alternativearts.co.uk
Fax: 020-7375 0484   Tel: 020-7375 0441

ANGLES THEATRE The
Alexandra Road, Wisbech, Cambs PE13 1HQ
Fax: 01945 481768   Tel: 01945 585587

ASHCROFT YOUTH THEATRE
Ashcroft Academy of Dramatic Art
Bellenden Old School
Bellenden Road, London SE15 4DG
Website: www.ashcroftacademy.co.uk
          Tel/Fax: 020-8693 8088

ATTIC THEATRE COMPANY (LONDON) Ltd
Wimbledon Theatre
The Broadway, London SW19 1QG
Website: www.attictheatre.com
e-mail: info@attictheatre.com
          Tel/Fax: 020-8543 7838

BANNER THEATRE
Friends Institute, 220 Moseley Road
Highgate, Birmingham B12 0DG
e-mail: voices@btinternet.com
Fax: 0121-440 0459   Tel: 0121-440 0460

BLUNDERBUS THEATRE COMPANY Ltd
The Mick Jagger Centre
Shepherds Lane, Dartford DA1 2JZ
Website: www.blunderbus.co.uk
e-mail: admin@blunderbus.co.uk
Fax: 01322 286285   Tel: 01322 286284

BORDERLINE THEATRE COMPANY
North Harbour Street, Ayr KA8 8AA
Fax: 01292 263825   Tel: 01292 281010

BRAVE NEW WORLD THEATRE COMPANY
(Write) 2nd Floor, 79 Highbury Hill, London N5 1SX
e-mail: spencer.hinton@virgin.net

BRIGHTON THEATRE EVENTS
40 Upper Gardner Street, Brighton BN1 4AN
e-mail: brightontheatreevents@supanet.com
          Tel: 01273 819184

BRISTOL EXPRESS THEATRE COMPANY Ltd
24 Well's House Road
East Acton, London NW10 6EE
e-mail: andyjandyjordan@aol.com
Fax: 020-8838 4482   Tel: 020-8963 9171

BRITISH ASIAN THEATRE COMPANY
Star Studios, 38 Leabridge Road
London E5 9QD   Tel: 020-8986 4470

BRUVVERS THEATRE COMPANY
(Touring on Tyneside)
The Fun Palace
36 Lime Street, Newcastle-upon-Tyne NE1 2PQ
Website: www.thefunpalace.co.uk
e-mail: mikeofbruvvers@hotmail.com
          Tel: 0191-261 9230

CAPITAL ARTS YOUTH THEATRE
Wyllyotts Centre, Darkes Lane
Potters Bar, Herts EN6 2HN
e-mail: capitalartstheatre@genie.co.uk
Mobile: 07885 232414   Tel/Fax: 020-8449 2342

CARIB THEATRE COMPANY
73 Lancelot Road, Wembley, Middlesex HA0 2AN
e-mail: caribtheatre@aol.com
          Tel/Fax: 020-8795 0576

CAVALCADE THEATRE COMPANY
(Touring Shows-Musicals, Pantomimes, Music Hall,
Comedy & Rock 'n' Roll)
57 Pelham Road, London SW19 1NW
Fax: 020-8540 2243   Fax: 020-8540 3513

CENTRE FOR PERFORMANCE RESEARCH
6 Science Park, Aberystwyth SY23 3AH
Website: www.thecpr.org.uk
e-mail: cprwww@aber.ac.uk
Fax: 01970 622132   Tel: 01970 622133

CHANGELING The
14 The Terrace, Rochester, Kent ME1 1XN
e-mail: mail@thechangeling.com   Tel: 01634 831957

CHANNEL THEATRE COMPANY
TIE Company
Central Studios
130 Grosvenor Place, Morgate, Kent CT9 1UY
Website: www.channel-theatre.co.uk
e-mail: info@channel-theatre.co.uk
Fax: 01843 280088   Tel: 01843 280077

CHATS PALACE ARTS CENTRE
42-44 Brooksby's Walk, Hackney, London E9 6DF
Fax: 020-8985 6878   Tel: 020-8533 0227

CHERUB COMPANY LONDON The
81 The Cut, Waterloo, London SE1 8LL
Website: www.cherub.org.uk
e-mail: visnevski@cherub.org.uk
          Tel/Fax: 020-7928 1033

CIRCUS MANIACS YOUTH CIRCUS
(International Award-Winning Youth Circus
Company)
Office 8A, The Kingswood Foundation
Britannia Road, Kingswood, Bristol BS15 8DB
e-mail: youthcircus@circusmaniacs.com
Mobile: 07977 247287   Tel/Fax: 0117-947 7042

CLEAN BREAK THEATRE COMPANY
2 Patshull Road, London NW5 2LB
e-mail: general@cleanbreak.org.uk
Fax: 020-7482 8611   Tel: 020-7482 8600

CLOSE FOR COMFORT THEATRE COMPANY
34 Boleyn Walk
Leatherhead, Surrey KT22 7HU
Website: www.hometown.aol.com/close4comf
e-mail: close4comf@aol.com   Tel: 01372 378613

COMMON PULSE THEATRE
c/o Cardiff Casting, Chapter Arts Centre
Market Road, Canton, Cardiff CF5 1QE
e-mail: admin@cardiffcasting.co.uk
Fax: 029-2023 3380   Tel: 029-2023 3321

COMPANY OF CRANKS The
1st Floor, 62 Northfield House
Frensham Street, London SE15 6TN
e-mail: mimetic@london.com   Tel: 020-7358 0571

COMPLETE WORKS THEATRE COMPANY Ltd The
12 Willowford, Bancroft Park
Milton Keynes, Bucks MK13 0RH
Website: www.tcw.org.uk
e-mail: info@tcw.org.uk   Tel: 01908 316256

CORNELIUS AND JONES ORIGINAL PRODUCTIONS
49 Carters Close, Sherington
Newport Pagnell, Bucks MK16 9NW
Website: www.corneliusjones.com
e-mail: admin@corneliusjones.com
Fax: 01908 216400   Tel: 01908 612593

CRAGRATS Ltd
The Mill, Dunford Road
Holmfirth, Huddersfield HD9 2AR
Website: www.cragrats.com
e-mail: alex@cragrats.com
Fax: 01484 686212   Tel: 01484 686451

CTC THEATRE
Arts Centre, Vane Terrace
Darlington, Co Durham DL3 7AX
Website: www.ctctheatre.org.uk
e-mail: ctc@ctctheatre.org.uk
Fax: 01325 369404   Tel: 01325 352004

CUT-CLOTH THEATRE
41 Beresford Road
London N5 2HR   Tel: 020-7503 4393

ELAN WALES
(European Live Arts Network)
Chapter, Market Road, Canton, Cardiff CF5 1QE
Website: www.elanw.demon.co.uk
e-mail: info@elan-wales.fsnet.co.uk Tel/Fax: 029-2034 5831

EMPTY SPACE THEATRE COMPANY
32 Kenbrook House
Leighton Road, London NW5 2QN
e-mail: estc@dircon.co.uk
Fax: 0870 9090103   Tel: 0870 9090102

ESCAPE ARTISTS
42 Woodlark Road, Cambridge CB3 0HS
e-mail: houdini@escapeartists.co.uk
Fax: 01223 522301   Tel: 01223 301439

EUROPEAN THEATRE COMPANY The
39 Oxford Avenue, London SW20 8LS
Website: www.europeantheatre.co.uk
e-mail: admin@europeantheatre.co.uk
Fax: 020-8544 1999   Tel: 020-8544 1994

FAMILY CURIOSO THEATRE COMPANY
334A High Road
London N22 8JW
Website: www.familycurioso.co.uk
e-mail: mail@familycurioso.co.uk   Tel: 020-8888 2095

FIGURE & GROUND
10 Cleveland Avenue
Wimbledon Chase, London SW20 9EW
e-mail: fandg@caso.clara.net   Tel: 020-8543 5939

FLOATING POINT SCIENCE THEATRE
10 Warren Drive, Chelsfield, Kent BR6 6EX
e-mail: stevemesure@ic24.net   Tel: 01689 812200

FORBIDDEN THEATRE COMPANY
Diorama Arts Centre
34 Osnaburgh Street, London NW1 3ND
Website: www.forbidden.org.uk
e-mail: info@forbidden.org.uk Tel/Fax: 020-7813 1025

FOREST FORGE THEATRE COMPANY
The Theatre Centre, Endeavour Park
Crow Arch Lane, Ringwood, Hampshire BH24 1SF
e-mail: theatre@forestforge.demon.co.uk
Fax: 01425 471158   Tel: 01425 470188

FOURSIGHT THEATRE Ltd
Newhampton Arts Centre
Dunkley Street, Wolverhampton WV1 4AN
Website: www.foursight.theatre.mcmail.com
e-mail: foursight.theatre@cwcom.net
Fax: 01902 428413   Tel: 01902 714257

FRANTIC THEATRE COMPANY
32 Woodlane
Falmouth TR11 4RF
Website: www.frantictheatre.co.uk
e-mail: frantic@btinternet.com Tel/Fax: 01326 312985

FUTURES THEATRE COMPANY
Room 9, The Albany
Douglas Way, London SE8 4AG
e-mail: futures@ukonline.co.uk
Fax: 020-8694 0289   Tel: 020-8694 8655

GALLEON THEATRE COMPANY Ltd
Greenwich Playhouse
Greenwich BR Station Forecourt
189 Greenwich High Road, London SE10 8JA
Website: www.galleontheatre.co.uk
Fax: 020-8969 2910   Tel: 020-8858 9256

GRANGE ARTS CENTRE
Rochdale Road, Oldham
Greater Manchester OL9 6EA
e-mail: joanne.draper@oldham.ac.uk
Fax: 0161-785 4263   Tel: 0161-785 4239

GREASEPAINT ANONYMOUS
4 Gallus Close, Winchmore Hill, London N21 1JR
e-mail: info@greasepaintanonymous.co.uk
Fax: 020-8882 9189   Tel: 020-8886 2263

GREENWICH & LEWISHAM'S YOUNG PEOPLES THEATRE (GYPT)
Burrage Road, London SE18 7JZ
e-mail: postbox@gypt.co.uk
Fax: 020-8317 8595   Tel: 020-8854 1316

GWENT TIE COMPANY
The Drama Centre Pen-y-pound
Abergavenny, Monmouthshire NP7 5UD
Website: www.gwenttie.co.uk
e-mail: gwenttie@aol.com
Fax: 01873 853910   Tel: 01873 853167

HACKNEY YOUNG PEOPLE'S YOUTH THEATRE
Hoxton Hall Theatre & Arts Centre
130 Hoxton Street
London N1 6SH
Website: www.hoxtonhall.co.uk
e-mail: office@hoxtonhall.co.uk
Fax: 020-7729 3815   Tel: 020-7684 0060

HALF MOON YOUNG PEOPLE'S THEATRE
43 White Horse Road, London E1 0ND
Website: www.halfmoon.org.uk
e-mail: admin@halfmoon.org.uk
Fax: 020-7709 8914   Tel: 020-7265 8138

HIJINX THEATRE
(Adults with Learning Disabilities, Community)
Bay Chambers
West Bute Street, Cardiff Bay CF10 5BB
Website: www.hijinx.org.uk
e-mail: info@hijinx.org.uk
Fax: 029-2030 0332   Tel: 029-2030 0331

HORLA
The Rose and Crown Theatre
59-61 High Street, Hampton Wick, Surrey KT1 4DG
Website: www.horla.co.uk
e-mail: info@horla.co.uk   Tel/Fax: 020-8296 0242

IMAGE MUSICAL THEATRE
23 Sedgeford Road
Shepherd's Bush, London W12 0NA
Website: www.imagemusicaltheatre.co.uk
e-mail: brian@image-theatre-co.demon.co.uk
Fax: 020-8749 9294   Tel: 020-8743 9380

IMMEDIATE THEATRE
C1/62 Beechwood Road, London E8 3DY
e-mail: immediatejo@aol.com
Fax: 020-7683 0247   Tel: 020-7683 0233

IN TOTO PRODUCTIONS
Basement Flat, 1 Montpelier Villas, Brighton BN1 3DH
e-mail: admin@intoto.freeserve.co.uk
Tel/Fax: 01273 205863

INOCENTE ART AND FILM Ltd
(Film, Multimedia, Music Videos &
two Rock 'n' Roll Musicals)
5 Denmans Lane, Lindfield, Sussex RH16 2LA
e-mail: rikki.tarascas@virginnet.com
Mobile: 07973 518132

INTERPLAY THEATRE COMPANY
Armley Ridge Road, Leeds LS12 3LE
Website: www.interplaytheatre.org
e-mail: info@interplaytheatre.org   Tel: 0113-263 8556

ISOSCELES COMEDY COMPANY
7 Amity Grove, Raynes Park, London SW20 0LQ
Website: www.isosceles.freeserve.co.uk
e-mail: patanddave@isosceles.freeserve.co.uk
Tel: 020-8946 3905

KOMEDIA
44-47 Gardner Street, Brighton BN1 1UN
Website: www.komedia.co.uk
e-mail: info@komedia.co.uk
Fax: 01273 647102   Tel: 01273 647101

LADDER TO THE MOON ENTERTAINMENT
66A St Ann's Hill, London SW18 2SB
e-mail: enquiries@laddertothemoon.co.uk
Mobile: 07711 984378

LANGUAGE ALIVE!
The Play House
Longmore Street, Birmingham B12 9ED
e-mail: theplayhouse@saqnet.co.uk
Tel/Fax: 0121-446 4301

LATCHMERE THEATRE
(Chris Fisher)
Unit 5A, Imex Business Centre
Ingate Place, London SW8 3NS
e-mail: fisherfalcon@compuserve.com
Fax: 020-7978 2631   Tel: 020-7978 2620

LITTLE ACTORS THEATRE COMPANY
12 Hardy Close, Surrey Quays, London SE16 6RT
e-mail: samanthahgiblin@hotmail.com
Fax: 0870 1645895   Tel: 020-7231 6083

LIVE THEATRE COMPANY
(New Writing)
7-8 Trinity Chare
Quayside, Newcastle-upon-Tyne NE1 3DF
Website: www.live.org.uk
e-mail: info@live.org.uk
Fax: 0191-232 2224   Tel: 0191-261 2694

LOGOS THEATRE COMPANY
48 Taybridge Road
London SW11 5PT   Tel: 020-7228 4374

LONDON ACTORS THEATRE COMPANY
Unit 5A, Imex Business Centre
Ingate Place, London SW8 3NS
e-mail: fisherfalcon@compuserve.com
Fax: 020-7978 2631   Tel: 020-7978 2620

LONDON BUBBLE THEATRE COMPANY Ltd
5 Elephant Lane, London SE16 4JD
Website: www.londonbubble.org.uk
e-mail: admin@londonbubble.org.uk
Fax: 020-7231 2366   Tel: 020-7237 4434

LSW: JUNIOR INTER-ACT
181A Faunce House
Doddington Grove, London SE17 3TB
Website: www.londonshakespeare.org.uk
e-mail: londonswo@hotmail.com
Fax: 020-7735 5911   Tel: 020-7793 9755

LSW: PRISON PROJECT
181A Faunce House
Doddington Grove, Kennington, London SE17 3TB
Website: www.londonshakespeare.org.uk
e-mail: londonswo@hotmail.com
Fax: 020-7735 5911   Tel: 020-7793 9755

LSW: SENIOR RE-ACTION
181A Faunce House
Doddington Grove, London SE17 3TB
Website: www.londonshakespeare.org.uk
e-mail: londonswo@hotmail.com
Fax: 020-7735 5911   Tel: 020-7793 9755

LUNG HAS THEATRE COMPANY
Central Hall, West Tollcross, Edinburgh EH3 9BP
e-mail: info@lunghas.co.uk
Fax: 0131-229 8965   Tel: 0131-228 8998

M6 THEATRE COMPANY
Hamer CP School
Albert Royds Street, Rochdale OL16 2SU
e-mail: info@m6theatre.freeserve.co.uk
Fax: 01706 711700   Tel: 01706 355898

MADDERMARKET THEATRE
(Resident Community Theatre Company and
Small-Scale Producing & Receiving House)
St John's Alley, Norwich NR2 1DR
Website: www.maddermarket.freeserve.co.uk
e-mail: theatre@maddermarket.freeserve.co.uk
Fax: 01603 661357   Tel: 01603 626560

MAGIC CARPET THEATRE
18 Church Street, Sutton-on-Hull HU7 4TS
Website: www.magiccarpettheatre.com
e-mail: jon@magiccarpettheatre.com
Fax: 01482 787362   Tel: 01482 709939

MAN MELA THEATRE COMPANY
(Admin Contact: Caroline Goffin)
PO Box 24987, London SE23 3XS
Website: www.man-mela.dircon.co.uk
e-mail: man-mela@dircon.co.uk
Mobile: 07973 349101   Mobile: 07966 215090

MANCHESTER ACTORS COMPANY
PO BOX 54, Manchester M60 7AB
Website: manactors@cs.com
e-mail: stephenboyes@amserve.net
Tel: 0161-227 8702

MAYA PRODUCTIONS Ltd
156 Richmond Road
London E8 3HN
e-mail: mayachris@aol.com   Tel/Fax: 020-7923 0675

MERSEYSIDE YOUNG PEOPLE'S THEATRE COMPANY
13 Hope Street, Liverpool L1 9BH
e-mail: mail@mypt.co.uk
Fax: 0151-707 9950   Tel: 0151-708 0877

MIKRON THEATRE COMPANY Ltd
(Canal Touring Nationally)
Marsden Mechanics
Peel Street, Marsden, Huddersfield HD7 6BW
Website: www.mikron.org.uk
e-mail: admin@mikron.org.uk   Tel: 01484 843701

MONTAGE THEATRE
59 Embleton Road, London SE13 7DQ
Website: www.montagetheatre.com
e-mail: info@montagetheatre.com
Tel: 020-8314 5036

MOVING THEATRE
16 Laughton Lodge
Laughton, Nr Lewes, East Sussex BN8 6BY
Website: www.movingtheatre.com
e-mail: info@movingtheatre.com
Fax: 01323 815736   Tel: 01323 815726

NATIONAL ASSOCIATION OF YOUTH THEATRES (NAYT)
Arts Centre, Vane Terrace
Darlington, County Durham DL3 7AX
Website: www.nayt.org.uk
e-mail: naytuk@aol.com
Tel: 01325 363330   Fax: 01325 363313

NATIONAL STUDENT THEATRE COMPANY
20 Lansdowne Road, London N10 2AU
Website: www.studentdrama.org.uk/nstc
e-mail: clive@nsdf.org.uk
Fax: 020-8883 7142   Tel: 020-8883 4586

NATIONAL YOUTH MUSIC THEATRE
5th Floor, The Palace Theatre
Shaftesbury Avenue, London W1D 5AY
Website: www.nymt.org.uk
e-mail: enquiries@nymt.org.uk
Fax: 020-7734 7515   Tel: 020-7734 7478

NATIONAL YOUTH THEATRE OF GREAT BRITAIN
443-445 Holloway Road, London N7 6LW
Website: www.nyt.org.uk
e-mail: info@nyt.org.uk
Fax: 020-7281 8246   Tel: 020-7281 3863

NATURAL THEATRE COMPANY
Widcombe Institute, Widcombe Hill, Bath BA2 6AA
Website: www.naturals.dircon.co.uk
e-mail: naturals@dircon.co.uk
Fax: 01225 442555   Tel: 01225 469131

NETI-NETI THEATRE COMPANY
Quintin Kynaston School
Marlborough Hill
London NW8 0NL Tel/Fax: 020-7483 4239 (Minicom)

NETTLEFOLD The
West Norwood Library Centre
1 Norwood High Street, London SE27 9JX
Fax: 020-7926 8071   Tel: 020-7926 8070

NEW PECKHAM VARIETIES@MAGIC EYE THEATRE
Havil Street, London SE5 7SD
e-mail: npv-arts@easynet.co.uk   Tel: 020-7708 5401

NEW PERSPECTIVES THEATRE COMPANY
(Touring and Community Theatre Projects)
The Old Library
Leeming Street, Mansfield, Notts NG18 1NG
Website: www.newperspectives.co.uk
e-mail: info@newperspectives.co.uk
                                    Tel: 01623 635225

NORTHERN STAGE PROJECTS
(See NORTHERN STAGE THEATRICAL
PRODUCTIONS Ltd)

NORTHERN STAGE THEATRICAL PRODUCTIONS Ltd
Newcastle Playhouse, Barras Bridge
Haymarket, Newcastle-upon-Tyne NE1 7RH
Website: www.northernstage.com
e-mail: info@northernstage.com
Fax: 0191-261 8093   Tel: 0191-232 3366

NTC TOURING THEATRE COMPANY
The Playhouse, Bondgate Without
Alnwick, Northumberland NE66 1PQ
Website: www.ntc-touringtheatre.co.uk
e-mail: admin@ntc-touringtheatre.co.uk
Fax: 01665 605837   Tel: 01665 602586

NUFFIELD THEATRE
(Touring & Projects)
University Road, Southampton SO17 1TR
e-mail: theatrefirst@nuffieldtheatre.co.uk
Fax: 023-8031 5511   Tel: 023-8034 4515

OCTOBER GALLERY The
24 Old Gloucester Street, London WC1N 3AL
Website: www.theoctobergallery.com
e-mail: octobergallery@compuserve.com
Fax: 020-7405 1851   Tel: 020-7242 7367

OLD TYME PLAYERS The
140 Manor Road
New Milton, Hants BH25 5ED
e-mail: j.sinclair@cwcom.net   Tel: 01425 612830

ONATTI THEATRE COMPANY
9 Field Close, Warwick, Warwickshire CV34 4QD
Website: www.onatti.co.uk
e-mail: info@onatti.co.uk
Fax: 0870 1643629   Tel: 01926 495220

OPEN STAGE PRODUCTIONS
49 Springfield Road, Moseley
Birmingham B13 9NN   Tel/Fax: 0121-777 9086

OXFORDSHIRE TOURING THEATRE COMPANY
Unit 1 St John Fisher School
Sandy Lane West, Oxford OX4 6LD
Website: www.ottc.org.uk
e-mail: manager@ottc.oxfordshire.co.uk
Fax: 01865 714822   Tel: 01865 778119

PANDEMONIUM TOURING PARTNERSHIP
228 Railway Street
Cardiff CF24 2NJ   Tel: 029-2047 2060

PASCAL THEATRE COMPANY
35 Flaxman Court, Flaxman Terrace
Bloomsbury, London WC1H 9AR
Website: www.pascal-theatre.com
e-mail: pascaltheatreco@aol.com
Fax: 020-7419 9798   Tel: 020-7383 0920

PAUL'S THEATRE COMPANY
Fairkytes Arts Centre
51 Billet Lane, Hornchurch, Essex RM11 1AX
e-mail: paul@the-theatreschool.fsnt.co.uk
Fax: 01708 475286   Tel: 01708 447123

PERFORMANCE PROJECT The
32 Kenbrook House, Leighton Road,
London NW5 2QN   Tel: 020-7482 1850

PHANTOM CAPTAIN THE
618B Finchley Road, London NW11 7RR
e-mail: ziph@macunlimited.net
                              Tel/Fax: 020-8455 4564

PIED PIPER COMPANY (TIE)
(In association with The Yvonne Arnaud Theatre
Guildford)
1 Lilian Place
Coxcombe Lane
Chiddingfold, Surrey GU8 4QA
e-mail: twpiedpiper@aol.com   Tel/Fax: 01428 684022

PILOT THEATRE COMPANY
(New Writing & Multi Media YPT)
Glasshoughton Cultural Centre
Redhill Avenue, Castleford
Wakefield, West Yorkshire WF10 4QH
Website: www.pilot-theatre.com
e-mail: info@pilot-theatre.com
Fax: 01977 512819   Tel: 01977 604852

PLAYTIME THEATRE COMPANY
18 Bennells Avenue, Whitstable, Kent CT5 2HP
Website: www.playtime.dircon.co.uk
e-mail: playtime@dircon.co.uk
Fax: 01227 266648   Tel: 01227 266272

PRAXIS THEATRE COMPANY Ltd
24 Wykeham Road, London NW4 2SU
e-mail: praxisco@globalnet.co.uk
                              Tel/Fax: 020-8203 1916

PRIME PRODUCTIONS
54 Hermiston Village, Currie EH14 4AQ
e-mail: mheller@primeproductions.fsnet.co.uk
                              Tel/Fax: 0131-449 4055

PROTEUS THEATRE COMPANY
Queen Mary's College
Cliddesden Road, Basingstoke
Hampshire RG21 3HF
Website: www.proteustheatre.com
e-mail: info@proteustheatre.com   Tel: 01256 354541

PUMBLECHOOK
(Singing Duo)
1 Clifford Avenue, Bletchley, Milton Keynes MK2 2LT
Website: www.cabaretuk.co.uk
e-mail: andycllrr@aol.com
Mobile: 07736 520930   Tel/Fax: 01908 374223

PURSUED BY A BEAR PRODUCTIONS
6 Glenluce Road, Blackheath, London SE3 7SB
Website: www.pbab.org
e-mail: pbab@pbab.org   Tel/Fax: 020-8480 9514

Q20 THEATRE COMPANY
19 Wellington Crescent
Shipley, West Yorks BD18 3PH
e-mail: info@q20theatre.co.uk   Tel: 01274 591417

QUAKER YOUTH THEATRE
Ground Floor, 1 The Lodge
1046 Bristol Road, Birmingham B29 6LJ
Website: www.leaveners.org.uk
e-mail: qyt@leaveners.org.uk
Fax: 0121-414 0090   Tel: 0121-414 0099

QUANTUM THEATRE FOR SCIENCE
Unit S9, The Shakespeare Centre
245A Coldharbour Lane, London SW9 8RR
Website: www.quantumtheatre.co.uk
e-mail: quantumtheatre@btinternet.com
Tel: 020-7733 8150

QUEST THEATRE COMPANY
(Artistic Director David Craik)
3C Mecklenburgh Street
Bloomsbury
London WC1N 2AH   Tel/Fax: 020-7713 0342

QUICKSILVER THEATRE
The Glasshouse, 4 Enfield Road, London N1 5AZ
Website: www.quicksilvertheatre.org.uk
e-mail: talktous@quicksilvertheatre.org
Fax: 020-7254 3119   Tel: 020-7241 2942

RED LADDER THEATRE COMPANY Ltd
3 St Peters Buildings, York Street, Leeds LS9 8AJ
Website: www.redladder.co.uk
e-mail: wendy@redladder.co.uk
Fax: 0113-245 5351   Tel: 0113-245 5311

RIDING LIGHTS THEATRE COMPANY
Friargate Theatre, Lower Friargate, York YO1 9SL
Website: www.ridinglights.org
e-mail: Info@rltc.org
Fax: 01904 651532   Tel: 01904 655317

ROSE THEATRE COMPANY The
10 Riverside Forest Row, Sussex RH18 5HB
e-mail: dan.skinner@btinternet.com
Tel/Fax: 01342 825639

ROYAL COURT YOUNG WRITERS PROGRAMME
The Site, Royal Court Theatre
Sloane Square, London SW1W 8AS
Website: www.royalcourttheatre.com
e-mail: ywp@royalcourttheatre.com
Fax: 020-7565 5001   Tel: 020-7565 5050

SALTMINE THEATRE COMPANY
St James House
Trinity Road, Dudley, West Midlands DY1 1JB
Website: www.saltmine.org
e-mail: stc@saltmine.org   Tel: 01384 454807

SCARLET THEATRE
Studio 4, The Bull
68 High Street, Barnet, Herts EN5 5SJ
Website: www.scarlettheatre.co.uk
e-mail: admin@scarlettheatre.co.uk
Fax: 020-8447 0075   Tel: 020-8441 9779

SCOTTISH YOUTH THEATRE
3rd Floor, Forsyth House
111 Union Street, Glasgow G1 3TA
Website: www.scottishyouththeatre.org
e-mail: info@scottishyouththeatre.org
Fax: 0141-221 9123   Tel: 0141-221 5127

SHARED EXPERIENCE YOUTH THEATRE
The Soho Laundry, 9 Dufours Place, London W1F 7SJ
e-mail: youththeatre@setheatre.co.uk
Fax: 020-7287 8763   Tel: 020-7434 9248

SKINNING THE CAT, CIRCUS OF THE SKY
Woolston House, 3 Tetley Street, Bradford BD1 2NP
e-mail: skats@globalnet.co.uk
Fax: 01274 770352   Tel: 01274 770300

SNAP THEATRE COMPANY
29 Raynham Road
Bishops Stortford, Herts CM23 5PE
Website: www.snaptheatre.co.uk
Fax: 01279 506694   Tel: 01279 461607

SPANNER IN THE WORKS
155 Station Road, Sidcup
Kent DA15 7AA
Website: members.netscapeonline.co.uk/spintheworks
e-mail: rapieruk@aol.com   Tel: 020-8304 7660

SPARE TYRE THEATRE COMPANY
(Community Drama & Music Projects)
Hampstead Town Hall, 213 Haverstock Hill
London NW3 4QP   Tel: 020-7419 7007

SPECTACLE THEATRE
Pontyprid College
Rhondda Campus, Llwynypia, Tonypandy CF40 2TQ
Website: www.spectacletheatre.co.uk
e-mail: info@spectacletheatre.co.uk
Fax: 01443 423080   Tel: 01443 430700

SPRINGBOARD THEATRE COMPANY
20 Lansdowne Road, London N10 2AU
e-mail: clive@nsdf.org.uk   Tel: 020-8883 4586

TAG THEATRE COMPANY
18 Albion Street, Glasgow G1 1LH
Website: www.tag-theatre.co.uk
e-mail: info@tag-theatre.co.uk
Fax: 0141-552 0666   Tel: 0141-552 4949

TARA ARTS GROUP
356 Garratt Lane, London SW18 4ES
Fax: 020-8870 9540   Tel: 020-8333 4457

THEATR NA N'OG
Unit 3, Milland Road Industrial Estate
Neath, West Glamorgan SA11 1NJ
Website: www.theatr-nanog.co.uk
e-mail: cwmni@theatr-nanog.co.uk
Fax: 01639 647941   Tel: 01639 641771

THEATR POWYS
The Drama Centre, Tremont Road
Llandrindod Wells, Powys LD1 5EB
Website: www.theatrpowys.co.uk
e-mail: theatr.powys@powys.gov.uk
Fax: 01597 824381   Tel: 01597 824444

THEATRE CENTRE
(National Touring & New Writing for
Young Audiences)
Units 7 & 8, Toynbee Workshops
3 Gunthorpe Street, London E1 7RQ
Website: www.theatre-centre.co.uk
e-mail: admin@theatre-centre.co.uk
Fax: 020-7377 1376   Tel: 020-7377 0379

THEATRE EXPRESS
(Write)
PO Box 97, Cleveleys FY5 5XA
e-mail: perform@theatre-express.com

THEATRE IN EDUCATION TOURS (TIE TOURS)
Holloway School
Hilldrop Road, Islington, London N7 0JG
Website: www.tietours.com
e-mail: tie@tietours.com
Fax: 020-7700 3697   Tel: 020-7619 9115

THEATRE OF LITERATURE The
(Dramatised Readings)
51 The Cut, London SE1 8LF
e-mail: info@calderpublications.com
Fax: 020-7928 5930   Tel: 020-7633 0599

THEATRE RE:PUBLIC
1 Mellor Road, Leicester LE3 6HN
e-mail: theatrerepublic@hotmail.com
                           Tel: 0116-233 8432

THEATRE VENTURE
(Alternative/Multimedia)
Stratford Circus, Theatre Square, London E15 1BX
e-mail: info@theatre-venture.org
Fax: 020-8519 8769   Tel: 020-8519 6678

THEATRE WORKSHOP
34 Hamilton Place, Edinburgh EH3 5AX
Fax: 0131-220 0112   Tel: 0131-225 7942

THEATRE WORKSHOP NORTH-WEST AND MIDLANDS
18 Weston Lane, Crewe, Cheshire CW2 5AN
Website: www.theatreworkshop.co.uk
e-mail: tw4kids@globalnet.co.uk
Fax: 07020 982098   Tel: 07020 962096

THIRD PARTY PRODUCTIONS Ltd
87 St Thomas' Road, Hastings, East Sussex TN34 3LD
Website: www.thirdparty.demon.co.uk
e-mail: agleave@thirdparty.demon.co.uk
                           Tel/Fax: 01424 719320

THREE COUNTIES YOUTH THEATRE
1 Clifford Avenue, Bletchley, Milton Keynes MK2 2LT
Website: www.skynary.com/lbyt
e-mail: andycllr@aol.com
Mobile: 07736 520930   Tel: 01908 374223

TIME OF OUR LIVES MUSIC THEATRE Ltd
(Formerly Gilt and Gaslight Music Theatre Ltd)
5 Monkhams Drive, Woodford Green, Essex IG8 0LG
Website: www.giltandgaslight.com
e-mail: dympna@giltandgaslight.com
                           Tel/Fax: 020-8491 6695

TITHE BARN MUSIC & DRAMA SOCIETY
Shiplake College, Henley-on-Thames RG9 4BW
Website: www.shiplake.org.uk
e-mail: tithe@shiplake.org.uk   Tel: 0118-940 2455

TRICYCLE THEATRE
269 Kilburn High Road, London NW6 7JR
Website: www.tricycle.co.uk
e-mail: admin@tricycle.co.uk
Fax: 020-7328 0795   Tel: 020-7372 6611

TROY PRODUCTIONS
17 Talbot Meadows
Talbot Village, Poole, Dorset BH12 5OG
e-mail: lulu_2013@yahoo.co.uk   Tel: 01202 780346

VOLCANO THEATRE COMPANY Ltd
176 Hanover Street, Swansea SA1 6BP
Website: www.volcanotheatre.co.uk
e-mail: volcano.tc@virgin.net
Fax: 01792 467563   Tel: 01792 472772

WAREHOUSE THEATRE COMPANY
Dingwall Road, Croydon CR0 2NF
Website: www.warehousetheatre.co.uk
e-mail: warehous@dircon.co.uk
Fax: 020-8688 6699   Tel: 020-8681 1257

WEAVER-HUGHES ENSEMBLE
565 Lordship Lane, London SE22 8LB
Website: www.weaverhughesensemble.co.uk
e-mail: ensemble@weaverhughesensemble.co.uk
                           Tel/Fax: 020-8693 5614

WEIRD SISTERS The
4 Shamrock Street
Clapham North, London SW4 6HE
e-mail: weirdsists@aol.com
Mobile: 07715 360021   Tel/Fax: 020-7720 4252

WIGAN PIER THEATRE COMPANY
The 'Way We Were' Museum
Wigan Pier
Trencherfield Mill
Wigan, Lancs WN3 4EF
Website: www.wiganpier.net
e-mail: s.aitken@wiganmbc.gov.uk   Tel: 01942 709305

WINCHESTER HAT FAIR, FESTIVAL OF STREET THEATRE
5A Jewry Street, Winchester, Hants SO23 8RZ
Website: www.hatfair.co.uk
e-mail: info@hatfair.co.uk
Fax: 01962 868957   Tel: 01962 849841

WOMEN & THEATRE BIRMINGHAM Ltd
220 Moseley Road, Highgate, Birmingham B12 0DG
e-mail: womenandtheatre@btinternet.com
Fax: 0121-446 4280   Tel: 0121-440 4203

Y TOURING THEATRE COMPANY
8-10 Lennox Road, Finsbury Park, London N4 3JQ
Website: www.ytouring.org.uk
e-mail: d.jackson@ytouring.org.uk
Fax: 020-7272 8413   Tel: 020-7272 5755

YELLOW EARTH THEATRE
Diorama Arts Centre
34 Obnaburgh Street, London NW1 3ND
Website: www.yellowearth.org
e-mail: admin@yellowearth.org
Fax: 0870 1319775   Tel: 020-7209 2326

YORICK INTERNATIONALIST THEATRE ENSEMBLE
(Yorick Theatre & Film)
4 Duval Court, 36 Bedfordbury
Covent Garden, London WC2N 4DQ
e-mail: yorick.internationalist.theatre@ukgateway.net
                           Tel/Fax: 020-7836 7637

YORKSHIRE WOMEN'S THEATRE COMPANY
(Touring Theatre in Health Education)
Host Media Centre, 21 Savile Mount, Leeds LS7 3HZ
e-mail: admin@ywtheatre.com   Tel: 0113-200 7200

YOUNG VIC COMPANY
66 The Cut, London SE1 8LZ
Website: www.youngvic.org
e-mail: info@youngvic.org
Fax: 020-7928 1585   Tel: 020-7633 0133

ZIP THEATRE
Newhampton Centre, Dunkley Street,
Wolverhampton WV1 4AN
Website: www.ziptheatre.co.uk
e-mail: cathy@ziptheatre.co.uk
Fax: 01902 572251   Tel: 01902 572250

A.R.C. ENTERTAINMENTS
10 Church Lane, Redmarshall
Stockton on Tees
Cleveland TS21 1EP
e-mail: cmlittlefair@fsbdial.co.uk   Tel: 0870 7418789

BAC
(Workshops thoughout Year & Theatre on Saturdays)
Lavender Hill, Battersea, London SW11 5TF
Website: www.bac.org.uk
e-mail: mailbox@bac.org.uk
Fax: 020-7978 5207   Tel: 020-7223 6557

BARKING DOG THEATRE COMPANY
18 Hayley Bell Gardens
Bishop's Stortford, Herts CM23 3HB
Website: www.barkingdog.co.uk
e-mail: pat@barkingdog.co.uk
Fax: 01279 465386   Tel: 01279 465550

BITESIZE THEATRE COMPANY
8 Green Meadows
New Broughton, Wrexham LL11 6SG
Website: www.bitesizetheatre.co.uk
Administrator: Bill Robertson
Fax: 01978 358315   Tel: 01978 358320

BLUE HAT PRODUCTIONS
43 Radwinter Road, Saffron Walden, Essex CB11 3HU
e-mail: sweeneybluehat@aol.com
Mobile: 07811 175351   Tel: 01799 502569

BLUNDERBUS THEATRE COMPANY
The Mick Jagger Centre
Shepherds Lane, Dartford, Kent DN1 2JZ
Website: www.blunderbus.co.uk
e-mail: admin@blunderbus.co.uk
Fax: 01322 286285   Tel: 01322 286284

BOOSTER CUSHION THEATRE COMPANY
1st Floor, Building B, Chocolate Factory
Clarendon Road, London N22 6JX
e-mail: psbct@aol.com
Fax: 020-8365 8686   Tel: 020-8888 4545

DANCE FOR EVERYONE Ltd
30 Sevington Road, London NW4 3RX
Website: www.dfe.org.uk
e-mail: orders@dfe.org.uk   Tel: 020-8202 7863

DAYLIGHT THEATRE
66 Middle Street, Stroud
Glos GL5 1EA   Tel: 01453 763808

DONNA MARIA COMPANY
16 Bell Meadow, Dulwich, London SE19 1HP
Website: www.donna-marias-world.co.uk
e-mail: info@donna-marias-world.co.uk
    Tel: 020-8670 7814

DRAGON DRAMA
(Theatre Company, Tuition, Workshops, Parties)
1B Station Road
Hampton Wick, Kingston, Surrey KT1 4HG
Website: www.dragondrama.co.uk
e-mail: dragondrama@hotmail.com
    Tel/Fax: 020-8943 1504

EUROPA CLOWN THEATRE SHOW
36 St Lukes Road, Tunbridge Wells, Kent TN4 9JH
Website: www.clownseuropa.co.uk
    Tel: 01892 537964

IMAGE MUSICAL THEATRE
23 Sedgeford Road
Shepherd's Bush, London W12 0NA
Website: www.imagemusicaltheatre.co.uk
e-mail: brianthresh@image-theatre-co.demon.uk
Fax: 020-8749 9294   Tel: 020-8743 9380

IRISH (London-Irish) YOUTH THEATRE The
St Joseph's Youth Centre
Highgate Hill, London N19 0SH
Mobile: 07956 855512   Tel/Fax: 020-8361 0678

NETTLEFOLD The
The Nettlefold
West Norwood Library Centre
1 Norwood High Street, London SE27 9JX
Fax: 020-7926 8071   Tel: 020-7926 8070

OILY CART COMPANY
Smallwood School Annexe
Smallwood Road, London SW17 0TW
Website: www.oilycart.org.uk
e-mail: oilycart@globalnet.co.uk
Fax: 020-8672 0792   Tel: 020-8672 6329

PANDEMONIUM TOURING PARTNERSHIP
228 Railway Street
Cardiff CF24 2NJ   Tel: 029-2047 2060

PARASOL THEATRE FOR CHILDREN
Artistic Director: Richard Gill
Garden House
4 Sunnyside, Wimbledon, London SW19 4SL
Fax: 020-8946 0228   Tel: 020-8946 9478

PAUL'S THEATRE COMPANY
Fairkytes Arts Centre
51 Billet Lane, Hornchurch, Essex RM11 1AX
e-mail: paul@the-theatreschool.fsnet.co.uk
Fax: 01708 475286   Tel: 01708 447123

PIED PIPER THEATRE COMPANY
(In association with The Yvonne Arnaud Theatre
Guildford)
1 Lilian Place, Coxcombe Lane
Chiddingfold, Surrey GU8 4QA
e-mail: twpiedpiper@aol.com   Tel/Fax: 01428 684022

PLAYTIME THEATRE COMPANY
18 Bennells Avenue, Whitstable, Kent CT5 2HP
Website: www.playtime.dircon.co.uk
e-mail: playtime@dircon.co.uk
Fax: 01227 266648   Tel: 01227 266272

POLKA THEATRE FOR CHILDREN
240 The Broadway, Wimbledon SW19 1SB
Website: www.polkatheatre.com
e-mail: admin@polkatheatre.com
Fax: 020-8545 8365   Tel: 020-8545 8320

Q20 THEATRE COMPANY
19 Wellington Crescent
Shipley, West Yorks BD18 3PH
e-mail: into@q20theatre.co.uk   Iel: 01274 591417

QUANTUM THEATRE FOR SCIENCE
Unit S9, The Shakespeare Centre
245A Coldharbour Lane, London SW9 8RR
Website: www.quantumtheatre.co.uk
e-mail: quantumtheatre@btinternet.com
    Tel: 020-7733 8150

QUERCUS THEATRE COMPANY
33 Broadlands Avenue
Shepperton, Middlesex TW17 9DJ
Website: www.quercustheatrecompany.org.uk
e-mail: quercus@quercustheatrecompany.org.uk
    Tel: 01932 252182

QUICKSILVER THEATRE COMPANY
(National Touring - New Writing for the under 12's)
4 Enfield Road, London N1 5AZ
Website: www.quicksilvertheatre.org.uk
e-mail: talktous@quicksilvertheatre.org
Fax: 020-7254 3119   Tel: 020-7241 2942

REDROOFS THEATRE COMPANY
The Novello Theatre, Sunninghill
Nr Ascot, Berks SL5 9NE   Tel: 01344 620881

SCOTTISH YOUTH THEATRE
3rd Floor, Forsyth House
111 Union Street, Glasgow G1 3TA
Website: www.scottishyouththeatre.org
e-mail: info@scottishyouththeatre.org
Fax: 0141-221 9123   Tel: 0141-221 5127

SEAGULL THEATRE OF THE GORGE Ltd
(Theatre in Education)
Artistic Directors: Margo Cooper & Sian Murray
16 Victoria Road, Much Wenlock
Salop TF13 6AL   Tel/Fax: 01952 727803

SHAKESPEARE 4 KIDZ THEATRE COMPANY Ltd
27 Station Road West, Oxted, Surrey RH8 9EE
Website: www.shakespeare4kidz.com
e-mail: office@shakepeare4kidz.com
Fax: 01883 730384   Tel: 01883 723444

THE GOOD THE BAD & THE CUDDLY THEATRE COMPANY
140 Manor Road, New Milton, Hants BH25 5ED
e-mail: j.sinclair@cwcom.net   Tel: 01425 612830

TICKLISH ALLSORTS SHOW
Cremyll, Marshmead Close
Clarendon, Salisbury, Wilts SP5 3DD
Website: www.ticklishallsorts.co.uk
e-mail: garynunn@lineone.net
                                Tel/Fax: 01722 711800

TIEBREAK THEATRE COMPANY
Heartsease High School
Marryat Road, Norwich NR7 9DF
Website: www.tiebreak-theatre.com
e-mail: info@tiebreak-theatre.com
Fax: 01603 435184   Tel: 01603 435209

TRICYCLE THEATRE
269 Kilburn High Road, London NW6 7JR
Website: www.tricycle.co.uk
e-mail: admin@tricycle.co.uk   Tel: 020-7372 6611

UNICORN
St Mark's Studios
Chillingworth Road, London N7 8QJ
Website: www.unicorntheatre.com
e-mail: admin@unicorntheatre.com
Fax: 020-7700 3870   Tel: 020-7700 0702

WHIRLIGIG THEATRE
(National Touring Company)
14 Belvedere Drive, Wimbledon SW19 7BY
e-mail: whirligig.theatre@virgin.net
Fax: 020-8879 7648   Tel: 020-8947 1732

Theatre - English Speaking in Europe

■ **AUSTRIA**
VIENNA
Vienna's English Theatre
English Agent: VM Theatre Productions Ltd
16 The Street, Ash
Kent CT3 2HJ   Tel/Fax: 01304 813330

■ **DENMARK**
COPENHAGEN
The English Theatre of Copenhagen
London Toast Theatre, Kochsvej 18
1812 Fred C. Copenhagen Denmark
Website: www.londontoast.dk
e-mail: mail@londontoast.dk   Tel: + 45 33 22 8686
Artistic Director: Vivienne McKee
Admin: Soren Hall

■ **FRANCE**
PARIS
ACT Company
51 rue Hoche, 92240 Malakoff, France
Website: www.actheatre.com
e-mail: andrew.wilson@wanadoo.fr
Fax: + 33 1 46 56 23 18   Tel: + 33 1 46 56 20 50
Artistic Director: Andrew Wilson
Administrator: Anne Wilson

■ **FRANCE**
PARIS
Dear Conjunction Theatre Company
6 rue Arthur Rozier, 75019, Paris
e-mail: dearconjunction@wanadoo.fr
                                Tel: +33 1 42 41 69 65
Artistic Directors: Barbara Bray, Leslie Clack,
Patricia Kessler

■ **FRANCE**
XARONVAL
Amandla Theatre Company (Bilingual Touring Company)
12 Bis Rue Nicolas Abram, 88130 Xaronval, France
e-mail: amandlatheatreco@aol.com
                    Mobile: + 33 6 86 37 48 92
Artistic Director: Caroline Benamza
Administrator: Jean-Marie Degove

■ **GERMANY**
FRANKFURT
The English Theatre
London Contact: Caroline Funnell
25 Rattray Road, London SW2 1AZ
Fax: 020-7326 1713   Tel: 020-7326 4417

■ **GERMANY**
HAMBURG
The English Theatre of Hamburg
Lerchenfeld 14, 22081 Hamburg, Germany
Website: www.englishtheatre.de
Fax: + 49 40 229 5040   Tel: + 49 40 227 7089
Contact: Robert Rumpf, Clifford Dean

■ **GERMANY**
TOURING GERMANY
White Horse Theatre
Boerdenstrasse 17
59494 Soest-Muellingsen, Germany
e-mail: theatre@whitehorse.de
Fax: + 49 29 217 6581   Tel: + 49 29 217 6488
Contact: Peter Griffith, Michael Dray

■ **HUNGARY**
BUDAPEST
Merlin International Theatre
Gerloczy Utca 4, 1052 Budapest, Hungary
Tel/Fax: + 36 1 317 9338   Tel/Fax: + 36 1 206 0904
Contact: Laszlo Magacs

■ **ICELAND**
REYKJAVIK
Light Nights - The Summer Theatre
The Travelling Theatre, Baldursgata 37, IS-101
Reykjavik, Iceland
Fax: + 354 551 5015   Tel: + 354 551 9181
Artistic Director: Kristine G Magnus

■ **NORWAY**
OSLO
The English Speaking Theatre Oslo
Jacob Aalls Gate 30, 0364 Oslo, Norway
Website: www.home.sol.no/~testo-no
e-mail: testo-no@online.no
Fax: + 47 22 46 62 49   Tel: + 47 22 46 62 48
Artistic Director: Simon Ley
Director: Kristin Zachariassen

■ **SWEDEN**
STOCKHOLM
The English Theatre Company Ltd
(TMA Member)
Nybrogatan 35, 114 39 Stockholm, Sweden
Website: www.englishtheatre.se
e-mail: etc.ltd@telia.com
Fax: + 46 8 660 1159   Tel: + 46 8 662 4133
Artistic Director: Christer Berg

■ **UNITED KINGDOM**
OXFORD
THEATRE FROM OXFORD Touring Europe and Beyond
69-71 Oxford Street
Woodstock, Oxford OX20 1TJ
Contact: Robert Southam (Write)

■ **UNITED KINGDOM**
WARWICK
Onatti Theatre Company
9 Field Close, Warwick, Warks CV34 4QD
Website: www.onatti.co.uk
e-mail: info@onatti.co.uk
Fax: 0870 1643629   Tel: 01926 495220
Contact: Andrew Bardwell, Seanna Hardaker-Jones

ADELPHI
Strand
London WC2R 0NS
Manager: 020-7836 1166
Stage Door: 020-7836 1166
Box Office: 020-7836 1166

ALBERY
85 St Martin's Lane
London WC2N 4AU
Manager: 020-7438 9700
Stage Door: 020-7438 9700
Box Office: 020-7369 1730

ALDWYCH
Aldwych
London WC2B 4DF
Manager: 020-7836 5537
Stage Door: 020-7836 5537
Box Office: 0870 4000805
Website: www.aldwychtheatre.com

ALMEIDA
Almeida Street
London N1 1TA
Manager: 020-7226 7432
Stage Door: ----------
Box Office 020-7359 4404

APOLLO
Shaftesbury Avenue
London W1D 7EZ
Manager: 020-7850 8701
Stage Door: 020-7850 8700
Box Office: 0870 8901101

APOLLO VICTORIA
17 Wilton Road
London SW1V 1LG
Manager 020-7834 6318
Stage Door: 020-7834 7231
Box Office: 0870 4000650
Website: www.ticketmaster.co.uk

ARTS THEATRE
6-7 Great Newport Street
London WC2H 7JB
Manager: 020-7836 2132
Stage Door: 020-7836 2132
Box Office: 020-7836 3334
Website: www.artstheatre.com
e-mail: info@artstheatre.com

BARBICAN
Barbican
London EC2Y 8DS
Manager: 020-7628 3351
Stage Door: 020-7628 3351
Box Office: 020-7638 8891
Website: www.barbican.org.uk

CAMBRIDGE
Earlham Street, Seven Dials
Covent Garden, London, WC2 9HU
Manager: 020-7850 8711
Stage Door: 020-7850 8710
Box Office: 020-7494 5040

CARLING APOLLO HAMMERSMITH
Queen Caroline Street
London W6 9QH
Manager: 020-8748 8660
Stage Door: --------------
Box Office: 0870 6063400

COLISEUM (English National Opera)
St Martin's Lane
London WC2N 4ES
Manager: 020-7836 0111
Stage Door: 020-7836 1416
Box Office: 020-7632 8300

COMEDY
Panton Street
London SW1Y 4DN
Manager: 020-7321 5310
Stage Door: 020-7321 5300
Box Office: 020-7369 1731

CRITERION
Piccadilly
London W1V 9LB
Manager: 020-7839 8811
Stage Door: 020-7839 8811
Box Office: 020-7413 1437

DOMINION
268-269 Tottenham Court Road
London W1T 7AQ
Manager: 020-7580 1889
Stage Door: 020-7927 0900
Box Office: 0870 6077400
Website: www.london-dominion.co.uk

Fax 7927 0995 (handwritten)

DONMAR WAREHOUSE
41 Earlham Street
London WC2H 9LX
Manager: 020-7438 9200
Stage Door: 020-7438 9200
Box Office: 020-7369 1732
Website: www.donmar-warehouse.com
e-mail: office@donmar.demon.co.uk

DUCHESS
Catherine Street
London WC2B 5LA
Manager: 020-7850 8721
Stage Door: 020-7850 8720
Box Office: 020-7850 8725

DUKE OF YORK'S
St Martin's Lane
London WC2N 4BG
Manager: 020-7836 4615
Stage Door: 020-7836 4615
Box Office: 020-7369 1791

FORTUNE
Russell Street
Covent Garden, London WC2B 5HH
Manager: 020-7836 6260
Stage Door: 020-7836 0441
Box Office: 020-7369 1737

GARRICK
Charing Cross Road
London WC2H 0HH
Manager: 020-7850 8731
Stage Door: 020-7850 8730
Box Office: 020-7494 5085

GIELGUD
Shaftesbury Avenue
London W1D 6AR
Manager: 020-7850 8741
Stage Door: 020-7850 8740
Box Office: 0870 8901105

HACKNEY EMPIRE
291 Mare Street
London E8 1EJ
Manager: 020-8510 4500
Stage Door: 020-8510 4515
Box Office: 020-8985 2424

HAMPSTEAD THEATRE
Eton Avenue, Swiss Cottage
London NW3 3EU
Manager: 020-7722 9224
Stage Door: 020-7722 1189
Box Office: 020-7722 9301
Website: www.hampstead-theatre.co.uk
e-mail: admin@hampstead-theatre.com

HER MAJESTY'S
Haymarket
London SW1Y 4QL
Manager: 020-7850 8750
Stage Door: 020-7850 8750
Box Office: 0870 8901106

LYCEUM THEATRE
21 Wellington Street
London WC2E 7RQ
Manager: 020-7420 8191
Stage Door: 020-7420 8100
Box Office: 020-7420 8114

LYRIC
Shaftesbury Avenue
London W1D 7ES
Manager: 020-7850 8761
Stage Door: 020-7850 8760
Box Office: 0870 8901107

LYRIC THEATRE HAMMERSMITH
King Street
London W6 0QL
Manager: 020-8741 0824
Stage Door: 020-8741 0824
Box Office: 020-8741 2311
Website: www.lyric.co.uk
e-mail: enquiries@lyric.co.uk

NEW AMBASSADORS
West Street
London WC2H 9ND
Manager: 020-7565 6471
Stage Door: 020-7836 4105
Box Office: 020-7369 1761

NEW LONDON
Drury Lane
London WC2B 5PW
Manager: 020-7242 9802
Stage Door: 020-7242 9802
Box Office: 020-7405 0072

OLD VIC THE
Waterloo Road
London SE1 8NB
Manager: 020-7928 2651
Stage Door: 020-7928 2651
Box Office: 020-7928 7616
Website: www.oldvictheatre.com
e-mail: old.vic@pobox.com

OPEN AIR THEATRE
Inner Circle, Regent's Park
London NW1 4NR
Manager: 020-7935 5756
Stage Door: 020-7935 5756
Box Office: 020-7486 2431

PALACE
Shaftesbury Avenue
London W1D 8AY
Manager: 020-7434 0088
Stage Door: 020-7434 0088
Box Office: 020-7434 0909
Website: www.rutheatres.com
e-mail: thepalacetheatre@hotmail.com

PALLADIUM
Argyll Street
London W1F 7TF
Manager: 020-7850 8777
Stage Door: 020-7850 8770
Box Office: 020-7494 5572

PEACOCK
(See SADLER'S WELLS in the West End)

PHOENIX
Charing Cross Road
London WC2H 0JP
Manager: 020-7438 9600
Stage Door: 020-7438 9610
Box Office: 020-7438 9605

PICCADILLY
Denman Street
London W1D 7DY
Manager: 020-7478 8810
Stage Door: 020-7478 8800
Box Office: 020-7478 8805

PLAYHOUSE
Northumberland Avenue
London WC2N 5DE
Manager: 020-7839 4292
Stage Door: 020-7839 4292
Box Office: 020-7839 4401

PRINCE EDWARD
Old Compton Street
London W1D 4HS
Manager: 020-7437 2024
Stage Door: 020-7439 3041
Box Office: 020-7447 5400
Website: www.delfont-mackintosh.com

PRINCE OF WALES
Coventry Street
London W1D 6AS
Manager: 020-7930 1867
Stage Door: 020-7930 1432
Box Office: 020-7839 5972

QUEEN'S
51 Shaftesbury Avenue
London W1D 6BA
Manager: 020-7850 8781
Stage Door: 020-7850 8780
Box Office: 020-7850 8785

Scenery contractors specialising in all aspects of
engineering, carpentry, scenic art and prop making.
Recent projects include Bombay Dreams, The King & I UK Tour,
Magna (winner of the Design Week Awards) Channel 5 and Aida.

Kimpton Walker

Theatre, Film and Television Scenery

10 Ellerslie Square
Lyham Road, London SW2 5DZ
Telephone: 020 7738 3222 Telefax: 020 7738 5517
E-mail: info@kimptonwalker.co.uk
Web Site: http://www.kimptonwalker.co.uk

ROYAL COURT THEATRE
Sloane Square
London SW1W 8AS
Manager: 020-7565 5050
Stage Door: 020-7565 5050
Box Office: 020-7565 5000
Website: www.royalcourttheatre.com
e-mail: info@royalcourttheatre.com

ROYAL NATIONAL
South Bank
London SE1 9PX
Admin: 020-7452 3333
Stage Door: 020-7452 3333
Box Office: 020-7452 3000
Website: www.nationaltheatre.org.uk

ROYAL OPERA HOUSE
Covent Garden
London WC2E 9DD
Manager: 020-7240 1200
Stage Door: ---------------
Box Office: 020-7304 4000

SADLER'S WELLS
Rosebery Avenue
London EC1R 4TN
Manager: ------------------
Stage Door: 020-7863 8198
Box Office: 020-7863 8000
Website: www.sadlerswells.com
e-mail: info@sadlerswells.com

SADLER'S WELLS IN THE WEST END
Peacock Theatre, Portugal Street
Kingsway, London WC2A 2HT
Manager: 020-7863 8204
Stage Door: 020-7863 8268
Box Office: 020-7863 8222

SAVOY
Strand
London WC2R 0ET
Manager: 020-7836 8117
Stage Door: 020-7836 8117
Box Office: 020-7836 8888

SHAFTESBURY
210 Shaftesbury Avenue
London WC2H 8DP
Manager: 020-7379 3345
Stage Door: 020-7379 3345
Box Office: 020-7379 5399
e-mail: nshaw@toc.dltentertainment.co.uk

SHAKESPEARE'S GLOBE
21 New Globe Walk
Bankside, London SE1 9DT
Manager: 020-7902 1400
Stage Door: 020-7902 1400
Box Office: 020-7401 9919
Website: www.shakespearesglobe.org
e-mail: info@shakespearesglobe.com

SOHO THEATRE
21 Dean Street
London W1D 3NE
Manager: 020-7287 5060
Stage Door: --------------------
Box Office: 020-7478 0100
Website: www.sohotheatre.com
e-mail: mail@sohotheatre.com

ST MARTIN'S
West Street
London WC2H 9NZ
Manager: 020-7497 0578
Stage Door: 020-7836 1086
Box Office: 020-7836 1443

STRAND
Aldwych, London WC2B 4LD
Manager: 020-7836 4144
Stage Door: 020-7836 4144
Box Office: 020-7930 8800

THEATRE ROYAL
(Haymarket)
London SW1Y 4HT
Manager: 020-7930 8890
Stage Door: ------------------
Box Office: 0870 9013356

THEATRE ROYAL DRURY LANE
Catherine Street
London WC2B 5JF
Manager: 020-7850-8793
Stage Door: 020-7850 8790
Box Office: 0870 8901109

UCL BLOOMSBURY
15 Gordon Street
London WC1H 0AH
Manager: 020-7679 2777
Stage Door: 020-7679 2922
Box Office: 020-7388 8822
Website: www.thebloomsbury.com
e-mail: blooms.theatre@ucl.ac.uk

VAUDEVILLE
404 Strand
London WC2R 0NH
Manager: 020-7836 1820
Stage Door: 020-7836 3191
Box Office: 020-7836 9987

VICTORIA PALACE
Victoria Street
London SW1E 5EA
Manger: 020-7828 0600
Stage Door: 020-7834 2781
Box Office: 020-7834 1317

WHITEHALL
14 Whitehall, London SW1A 2DY
Manager: 020-7321 5400
Stage Door: 020-7321 5400
Box Office: 020-7321 5405
e-mail: whitehall@theambassadors.com

WYNDHAM'S
Charing Cross Road
London WC2H 0DA
Manager: 020-7438 9700
Stage Door: 020-7438 9700
Box Office: 020-7438 9755

YOUNG VIC
66 The Cut, London SE1 8LZ
Manager: 020-7633 0133
Stage Door: ---------
Box Office: 020-7928 6363
Website: www.youngvic.org
e-mail: info@youngvic.org

Theatre - London Area, Out of London, Fringe, Club, Academy & Venues

T

ARCOLA THEATRE
(Artistic Director - Mehmet Ergen)
27 Arcola Street, Dalston
(Off Stoke Newington Road), London E8 2DJ
e-mail: info@arcolatheatre.com
Fax: 020-7503 1645
BO: 020-7503 1646   Admin: 020-7503 1645
Route: Victoria Line to Highbury & Islington, then
North London Line to Dalston Kingsland BR - 5 min
walk. Buses: 38 from West End, 149 from London
Bridge or 5, 30, 67, 76, 243

ASHCROFT THEATRE
Fairfield Halls Park Lane, Croydon CR9 1DG
Website: www.fairfield.co.uk
e-mail: dbarr@fairfield.co.uk
BO: 020-8688 9291   Admin & SD: 020-8681 0821
Route: Victoria (BR) to East Croydon then 5 min walk

BAC
Lavender Hill, London SW11 5TN
Website: www.bac.org.uk
e-mail: mailbox@bac.org.uk
Fax: 020-7978 5207
BO: 020-7223 2223   Admin: 020-7223 6557
Route: Victoria or Waterloo (BR) to Clapham
Junction then 5 min walk or Northern Line to
Clapham Common then 20 min walk

BARONS COURT THEATRE
'The Curtain's Up'
28A Comeragh Road
West Kensington, London W14 9RH
Fax: 020-7603 8935   Admin/BO: 020-8932 4747
Route: West Kensington or Barons Court tube

BECK THEATRE
Grange Road, Hayes, Middlesex UB3 2UE
BO: 020-8561 8371   Admin: 020-8561 7506
Route: Metropolitan Line to Uxbridge then bus 207
or 607 (10 min) to Theatre or Paddington (BR) to
Hayes Harlington then buses 90, H98 or 195 (10 min)

BEDLAM THEATRE
11B Bristo Place, Edinburgh EH1 1EZ
Website: www.bedlamfringe.co.uk
e-mail: info@bedlamtheatre.co.uk
Tel: 0131-225 9873

BELLAIRS PLAYHOUSE
(Guildford School of Acting)
Millmead Terrace, Guildford GU2 4YT
e-mail: enquiries@gsa.drama.ac.uk
Admin: 01483 560701

BLOOMSBURY THEATRE
15 Gordon Street, Bloomsbury, London WC1H 0AH
Website: www.thebloomsbury.com
e-mail: blooms.theatre@ucl.ac.uk
BO: 020-7388 8822   Admin: 020-7679 2777
Route: Tube to Euston, Euston Square or Warren Street

BRENTWOOD THEATRE
(Theatre Administrator Mark P. Reed)
15 Shenfield Road, Brentwood, Essex CM15 8AG
Website: www.brentwoodtheatre.freeserve.co.uk
Stage Door: 01277 226658
BO: 01277 200300   Admin/Fax: 01277 230833
Liverpool Street (BR) to Brentwood, then 15 min walk

BRIDEWELL THEATRE The
Bride Lane, Fleet Street, London EC4Y 8EQ
Website: www.bridewelltheatre.co.uk
e-mail: admin@bridewelltheatre.co.uk
Fax: 020-7583 5289
BO: 020-7936 3456   Admin: 020-7353 0259
Route: Blackfriars, St Paul's: City Thameslink. Fifteen
different bus routes

BULLION ROOM THEATRE
(Behind Hackney Empire Theatre)
117 Wilton Way, London E8 1BH
BO: 020-8985 2424   Press/Admin: 020-8510 4500

BUSH THEATRE
(Mike Bradwell)
Shepherd's Bush Green, London W12 8QD
BO: 020-7610 4224
Production: 020-8743 5050   Admin: 020-7602 3703
Route: Central Line to Shepherd's Bush or
Hammersmith & City Line to Goldhawk Road or
buses 12, 49, 94, 207 or 220

CAMDEN PEOPLE'S THEATRE
(Artistic Director - Chris Goode)
58-60 Hampstead Road, London NW1 2PY
Website: www.cpt.dircon.co.uk
e-mail: cpt@dircon.co.uk
Fax: 020-7813 3889   Tel: 020-7916 5878
Route: Victoria or Northern Line to Warren Street,
Metropolitan or Circle Line to Euston Square
(1 min walk either way)

CANAL CAFE THEATRE The
(Artistic Director - Emma Taylor)
The Bridge House
Delamere Terrace, Little Venice, London W2 6ND
Website: www.newsrevue.com
e-mail: mail@canalcafetheatre.com
Fax: 020-7266 1717
BO: 020-7289 6054   Admin: 020-7289 6056

CAPITAL ARTS THEATRE COMPANY
Capital Arts, Wyllyotts Centre
Darkes Lane, Potters Bar, Herts EN6 12HN
e-mail: capitalartstheatre@genie.co.uk
Mobile: 07885 232414   Tel/Fax: 020-8449 2342

CHANTICLEER THEATRE
(Webber Douglas Academy)
30 Clareville Street, London SW7 5AP
e-mail: webberdouglas@btclick.com
Fax: 020-7373 5639   Tel: 020-7370 4154
Route: Piccadilly, District or Circle Line to
Gloucester Road, turn right, walk for 300 yards then
turn left into Clareville Street

CHATS PALACE ARTS CENTRE
(Nick Reed)
42-44 Brooksby's Walk, Hackney, London E9 6DF
Box Office: 020-8533 0227   Admin: 020-8533 0227

CHELSEA THEATRE
(Francis Alexander)
World's End Place, King's Road, London SW10 0DR
e-mail: administration@chelseatheatre.org.uk
Fax: 020-7352 2024   Tel: 020-7352 1967
Route: District or Circle Line to Sloane Square then
short bus ride 11 or 22 down King's Road

299

CHRIST'S HOSPITAL THEATRE
(Director Jeff Mayhew)
Horsham, West Sussex RH13 7LW
e-mail: jm@christs-hospital.org.uk
BO: 01403 247434   Admin: 01403 247435

CLUB FOR ACTS & ACTORS The
(Concert Artists Association)
(Gerald Moon, Barbara Daniels)
20 Bedford Street, London WC2E 9HP
                      Admin: 020-7836 3172
Route: Piccadilly or Northern Line to Leicester
Square then few mins walk

COCHRANE THEATRE
(Deirdre Malynn)
Southampton Row, London WC1B 4AP
e-mail: cochranetheatre@linst.ac.uk
BO: 020-7269 1606   Admin: 020-7269 1600
Route: Central or Piccadilly Line to Holborn then 1
min walk

COCKPIT THEATRE
Gateforth Street, London NW8 8EH
e-mail: dave.wybrow@awc.ac.uk
Fax: 020-7258 2921
BO: 020-7258 2925   Admin: 020-7258 2920
Route: Tube to Marylebone/Edgware Road then
short walk or bus 139 to Lisson Grove & 6, 8, or 16 to
Edgware Road

CORBETT THEATRE
(East 15 Acting School)
Rectory Lane, Loughton, Essex IG10 3RY
Website: www.east15.ac.uk
e-mail: east15.acting@ukonline.co.uk
Fax: 020-8508 7521   BO & Admin: 020-8508 5983
Route: Central Line (Epping Branch) to Debden
then 6 min walk

COURTYARD THEATRE The
(June Abbott - Artistic Director,
Tim Gill - General Manager)
10 York Way, King's Cross, London N1 9AA
Website: www.thecourtyard.org.uk
e-mail: info@thecourtyard.org.uk
BO: 020-7833 0876   Admin/Fax: 020-7833 0870
Route: Side of King's Cross Station

CUSTARD FACTORY
Gibb Street, Digbeth, Birmingham B9 4AA
e-mail: custardfactory@clara.net
Fax: 0121-604 8888   Tel: 0121-693 7777

DARTFORD ORCHARD THEATRE
(Vanessa Hart)
Home Gardens, Dartford, Kent DA1 1ED
Website: www.orchardtheatre.co.uk
Fax: 01322 227122
BO: 01322 220000   Admin: 01322 220099
Route: Charing Cross (BR) to Dartford

DENCH Judi THEATRE
(See MOUNTVIEW THEATRE)

DIORAMA STUDIO THEATRE
(Mark Ross)
34 Osnaburgh Street, London NW1 3ND
Website: www.diorama-arts.org.uk
e-mail: admin@diorama-arts.org.uk
Fax: 020-7813 3116
BO: 020-7419 2000   Admin: 020-7916 5467
Route: Circle & District Line to Great Portland Street
then 1 min walk or Victoria/Northern line to Warren
Street then 5 min walk

DRILL HALL The
16 Chenies Street, London WC1E 7EX
Website: www.drillhall.co.uk
e-mail: admin@drillhall.co.uk
Fax: 020-7307 5062
BO: 020-7307 5060   Admin: 020-7307 5061
Route: Northern Line to Goodge Street then 1 min walk

EDINBURGH FESTIVAL FRINGE
180 High Street, Edinburgh EH1 1QS
Website: www.edfringe.com
e-mail: admin@edfringe.com
Fax: 0131-226 0016   Tel: 0131-226 0026

EDINBURGH UNIVERSITY THEATRE COMPANY
(See BEDLAM THEATRE)

EMBASSY THEATRE & STUDIOS
(Central School of Speech & Drama)
64 Eton Avenue, Swiss Cottage, London NW3 3HY
Website: www.cssd.ac.uk
BO: 020-7559 3935   Admin: 020-7559 3999
Route: Jubilee Line to Swiss Cottage then 1 min walk

ETCETERA THEATRE CLUB
(Kirsty Housley - Director,
Rob McIndoe - Literary Manager)
Oxford Arms
265 Camden High Street, London NW1 7BU
Website: www.etceteratheatre.com
e-mail: etceteratheatre@hotmail.com
Fax: 020-7482 0378   Admin/BO: 020-7482 4857

FINBOROUGH THEATRE
(Neil McPherson)
Finborough Arms
118 Finborough Road, London SW10 9ED
Website: www.finboroughtheatre.co.uk
e-mail: admin@finboroughtheatre.co.uk
Fax: 020-7835 1853
BO: 020-7373 3842   Admin: 020-7244 7439
Route: District or Piccadilly Line to Earls Court then
5 min walk. Buses 74, 328, C1, C3, 74 then 3 min walk

GATE THEATRE
(Erica Whyman)
Above Prince Albert Pub
11 Pembridge Road, London W11 3HQ
e-mail: gate@gatetheatre.freeserve.co.uk
Fax: 020-7221 6055
BO: 020-7229 0706   Admin: 020-7229 5387
Route: Central, Circle or District Line to Notting Hill
Gate then 1 min walk

GREENWICH PLAYHOUSE
(Alice de Sousa)
Greenwich BR Station Forecourt
189 Greenwich High Road, London SE10 8JA
Website: www.galleontheatre.co.uk
e-mail: alice@galleontheatre.co.uk
Fax: 020-8969 2910   Tel: 020-8858 9256
Route: BR from Charing Cross, Waterloo East or
London Bridge, DLR-Greenwich

GREENWICH THEATRE
(Executive Director - Hilary Strong)
Crooms Hill, Greenwich, London SE10 8ES
e-mail: info@greenwichtheatre.org.uk
Fax: 020-8858 8042
BO: 020-8858 7755   Admin: 020-8858 4447
Route: Jubilee Line (change Canary Wharf) then
DLR to Greenwich Cutty Sark, 3 minute walk or
Charing Cross (BR) to Greenwich, 5 minute walk

GUILDHALL SCHOOL OF MUSIC & DRAMA
Silk Street, Barbican, London EC2Y 8DT
e-mail: info@gsmd.ac.uk
Fax: 020-7256 9438   Tel: 020-7628 2571
Route: Hammersmith & City, Circle or
Metropolitan line to Barbican or Moorgate
(also served by Northern line) then 5 min walk

HEN & CHICKENS THEATRE
Unrestricted View, Above Hen & Chickens Theatre
Bar, 109 St Paul's Road, Islington, London N1 2NA
Website: www.henandchickens.com
e-mail: james@henandchickens.com
                        Tel: 020-7704 2001
Route: Victoria Line or Main Line to Highbury &
Islington directly opposite station

HORLA
(Artist Director - Alistair Green,
General Manger - Dave Roberts)
The Rose and Crown Theatre
59-61 High Street, Hampton Wick, Surrey KT1 4DG
Website: www.horla.co.uk
e-mail: info@horla.co.uk
BO: 020-8296 9100   Admin/Fax: 020-8296 0242

HUNT THEATRE
Felsted School, Felsted
Nr Dunmow, Essex CM6 3JG
e-mail: crsl@felsted.essex.sch.uk
Fax: 01371 822607   Tel: 01371 822600

ICA THEATRE
The Mall, London SW1Y 5AH
Fax: 020-7873 0051
BO: 020-7930 3647   Admin: 020-7930 0493
Route: Nearest stations Piccadilly & Charing Cross

JACKSONS LANE THEATRE
269A Archway Road
London N6 5AA   Tel: 020-8340 5226

JERMYN STREET THEATRE
(Administrator - Penny Horner)
16B Jermyn Street, London SW1Y 6ST
Fax: 020-7287 3232
BO: 020-7287 2875   Admin: 020-7434 1443

KING'S HEAD THEATRE
(Dan Crawford)
115 Upper Street, Islington, London N1 1QN
BO: 020-7226 1916   Admin: 020-7226 8561
Route: Northern Line to Angel then 5 min walk.
Approx halfway between Angel and Highbury &
Islington tube stations

KING'S LYNN CORN EXCHANGE
Tuesday Market Place
King's Lynn, Norfolk PE30 1JW
e-mail: entertainment_admin@west-norfolk.gov.uk
Fax: 01553 762141
BO: 01553 764864   Admin: 01553 765565

KOMEDIA
(Artistic Directors David Lavender - Theatre,
Marina Kobler - Music & Comedy)
44-47 Gardner Street, Brighton BN1 1UN
Website: www.komedia.co.uk
e-mail: info@komedia.co.uk
Fax: 01273 647102
BO: 01273 647100   Tel: 01273 647101

LANDMARK ARTS CENTRE
Ferry Road, Teddington Lock, Middlesex TW11 9NN
e-mail: landmarkz1@aol.com
Fax: 020-8977 4830   Tel: 020-8977 7558

LANDOR THEATRE The
(Artistic Directors - Linda Edwards, Robert McWhir)
70 Landor Road, London SW9 9PH
Website: www.landortheatre.co.uk
e-mail: info@landortheatre.co.uk
                        Admin/BO: 020-7737 7276
Route: Northern Line Clapham North then 2 min walk

LATCHMERE THEATRE
503 Battersea Park Road, London SW11 3BW
Website: www.latchmeretheatre.com
e-mail: latchmeretheatre@hotmail.com
BO: 020-7978 7040   Admin/Fax: 020-7978 7041
Route: Victoria or Waterloo (BR) to Clapham
Junction then 10 min walk or buses 44, 219, 319,
344, 345 or tube to South Kensington then buses 49
or 345 or Tube to Sloane Square then Bus 319

LEIGHTON BUZZARD
(Lois Wright - Development Manager)
Leighton Buzzard Theatre
Lake Street, Leighton Buzzard
Beds LU7 1RX   Tel: 01525 850290

LILIAN BAYLIS THEATRE
(Information: Sadler's Wells)
Rosebery Avenue, London EC1R 4TN
Website: www.sadlerswells.com
e-mail: info@sadlerswells.com
BO: 020-7863 8000   SD: 020-7863 8198

LIVE THEATRE The
27 Broad Chare, Quayside
Newcastle upon Tyne NE1 3DQ
Website: www.live.org.uk
e-mail: info@live.org.uk
Fax: 0191-232 2224
BO: 0191-232 1232   Admin: 0191-261 2694

MACOWAN THEATRE
(LAMDA)
1-2 Logan Place, London W8 6QN
Website: www.lamda.org.uk
Fax: 020-7370 1980
BO: 020-7244 2000   Admin: 020-7373 9883
Route: District or Piccadilly Line to Earl's Court then
6 min walk

MADDERMARKET THEATRE
(Clare Goddard - Artistic Director,
Michael Lyas - General Manager)
St John's Alley, Norwich NR2 1DR
Website: www.maddermarket.freeserve.co.uk
e-mail: theatre@maddermarket.freeserve.co.uk
Fax: 01603 661357
BO: 01603 620917　　　　　Admin: 01603 626560

MAN IN THE MOON THEATRE
392 King's Road, London SW3 5UZ
Fax: 020-7351 1873
BO: 020-7351 2876　　　　Admin: 020-7351 5701
Route: Tube to Sloane Square then short bus ride
11, 22 or 19 down King's Road or tube to South
Kensington then bus 49 or 345 to junction of
Beaufort Street & King's Road

MERMAID THEATRE
(Conference & Events Centre)
Puddle Dock
Blackfriars, London EC4V 3DB
Website: www.the-mermaid.co.uk
e-mail: info@the-mermaid.co.uk　　Tel: 020-7236 1919
Route: Tube to Blackfriars or St Paul's, buses 45 or 63
or Thameslink to Blackfriars

MILLFIELD THEATRE
Silver Street, London N18 1PJ
Website: www.millfieldtheatre.co.uk
e-mail: info@millfieldtheatre.co.uk
Fax: 020-8807 3892
BO: 020-8807 6680　　　　Admin: 020-8803 5283
Route: Liverpool Street (BR) to Silver Street or tube
to Turnpike Lane then buses 444, 144A, 217 or 231.
10 min to Cambridge roundabout

MOUNTVIEW THEATRE
104 Crouch Hill, London N8 9EA
　　　　　　　　　　　　Admin/BO: 020-8347 3601
Route: Piccadilly or Victoria Line to Finsbury Park
then W7 bus to Dickenson Road (5 min)

MYERS STUDIO THEATRE The
(Trevor Mitchell - Venues Manager)
The Epsom Playhouse
Ashley Avenue, Epsom, Surrey KT18 5AL
Website: www.epsomplayhouse.co.uk
Fax: 01372 726228
BO: 01372 742555　　　　　Tel: 01372 742226

NETHERBOW The
(Donald Smith)
43-45 High Street, Edinburgh EH1 1SR
Website: www.storytellingcentre.org.uk
　　　　　　　　　　　　Tel: 0131-556 9579

NETTLEFOLD The
West Norwood Library Centre
1 Norwood High Street, London SE27 9JX
Fax: 020-7926 8071　　　Admin/BO: 020-7926 8070
Route: Victoria, West Croydon or London Bridge
(BR) to West Norwood then 2 min walk, or tube to
Brixton then buses 196, 2 or 68

NEW END THEATRE
27 New End, Hampstead, London NW3 1JD
Fax: 020-7472 5808
BO: 020-7794 0022　　　　Admin: 020-7472 5800
Route: Northern Line to Hampstead then 2 min
walk off Heath Street

NORTHBROOK THEATRE The
Littlehampton Road, Goring-by-Sea
Worthing, West Sussex BN12 6NU
Website: www.northbrooktheatre.co.uk
e-mail: box.office@nbcol.ac.uk
Fax: 01903 606316　　　　　　BO: 01903 606162
　　　　　　　　Marketing & Publicity: 01903 606230
　　　　　　　　　　Theatre Manager: 01903 606287

NOVELLO THEATRE The
(Redroofs Theatre Company)
2 High Street, Sunninghill
Nr Ascot Berks　　　　　　　Tel: 01344 620881
Route: Waterloo (BR) to Ascot then 1 mile from
station

OLD RED LION
(Ken McClymont - Artistic Director
418 St John Street, Islington, London EC1V 4NJ
BO: 020-7837 7816　　　Admin/Fax: 020-7833 3053
Route: Northern Line to Angel then 1 min walk

ORANGE TREE
(Sam Walters - Artistic Director)
1 Clarence Street, Richmond TW9 2SA
e-mail: admin@orange-tree.demon.co.uk
Fax: 020-8332 0369
BO: 020-8940 3633　　　　Admin: 020-8940 0141
Route: District Line, Waterloo (BR) or North London
Line then virtually opposite station

OVAL HOUSE THEATRE
52-54 Kennington Oval, London SE11 5SW
Website: www.ovalhouse.com
e-mail: admin@ovalhouse.com
BO: 020-7582 7680　　　　Admin: 020-7582 0080
Route: Northern Line to Oval then 1 min walk,
Victoria Line & BR to Vauxhall then 5 min walk

PENTAMETERS
Three Horseshoes, 28 Heath Street
London NW3 6TE　　　　BO/Admin: 020-7435 3648
Route: Northern Line to Hampstead then 1 min walk

PLACE The
17 Duke's Road, London WC1H 9PY
e-mail: theatre@theplace.org.uk
BO: 020-7387 0031　　　　Admin: 020-7380 1268
Route: Northern or Victoria Lines to Euston or King's
Cross then 5 min walk (Opposite rear of St Pancras
Church)

PLEASANCE LONDON
(Christopher Richardson)
Carpenters Mews, North Road,
(Off Caledonian Road), London N7 9EF
Website: www.pleasance.co.uk
e-mail: info@pleasance.co.uk
Fax: 020-7700 7366
BO: 020-7609 1800　　　　Admin: 020-7700 6877
Route: Piccadilly Line to Caledonian Road, turn
left, walk 50 yds, turn left into North Road, 2 min
walk, buses 10, 17, 91, 259 or N91

POLISH THEATRE
Polish Social & Cultural Assoc. Ltd
238-246 King Street, London W6 0RF
BO: 020-8741 0398　　　　Admin: 020-8741 1940
Route: District Line to Ravenscourt Park, or District,
Piccadilly or Metropolitan Lines to Hammersmith
then 7 min walk. Buses 27, 267, 190, 391 or H91

POLKA THEATRE FOR CHILDREN
240 The Broadway
Wimbledon SW19 1SB
Website: www.polkatheatre.com
e-mail: info@polkatheatre.com
Fax: 020-8545 8365
BO: 020-8543 4888   Admin: 020-8545 8320
Route: Waterloo (BR) or District Line to Wimbledon
then 10 min walk. Northern Line to South
Wimbledon then 10 min walk

PRINCESS THEATRE HUNSTANTON
The Green, Hunstanton
Norfolk PE36 5AH
Fax: 01485 534463
BO: 01485 532252   Admin: 01485 535937

QUEEN'S THEATRE
(Artistic Director - Bob Carlton,
Administrator - Henrietta Duckworth)
Billet Lane, Hornchurch
Essex RM11 1QT
Website: www.queens-theatre.co.uk
e-mail: info@queens-theatre.co.uk
Fax: 01708 452348   SD: 01708 442078
BO: 01708 443333   Admin: 01708 456118
Route: District Line to Hornchurch, BR to
Romford/Gidea Park. 15 miles from West End take
Λ13, Λ1306 then A125 or A12 then A127

QUESTORS THEATRE EALING The
12 Mattock Lane
London W5 5BQ
Website: www.questors.org.uk
e-mail: enquiries@questors.org.uk
Fax: 020-8567 8736
BO: 020-8567 5184   Admin: 020-8567 0011
Route: Central or District Line to Ealing Broadway
then 5 min walk

RICHMOND THEATRE
(Karin Gartzke)
The Green, Richmond
Surrey TW9 1QJ
e-mail: richmondtheatre@theambassadors.com
Fax: 020-8948 3601
BO: 020-8940 0088   Admin & SD: 020-8940 0220
Route: 20 minutes from Waterloo
(South West Trains) or District Line or Silverlink to
Richmond then 2 min walk

RIDWARE THEATRE
(Alan & Margaret Williams)
Wheelwright's House
Pipe Ridware
Rugeley
Staffs WS15 3QL
e-mail: alan@christmas-time.com
                              Tel: 01889 504380

RIVERSIDE STUDIOS
Crisp Road
London W6 9RL
Website: www.riversidestudios.co.uk
e-mail: jonfawcett@riversidestudios.co.uk
BO: 020-8237 1111   Admin: 020-8237 1000
Route: District, Piccadilly or Hammersmith & City
Line to Hammersmith Broadway then 5 min walk.
Buses 9, 11, 27, 73, 91, 220, 283 or 295

ROSEMARY BRANCH THEATRE
2 Shepperton Road
London N1 3DT
Website: www.rosemarybranch.co.uk
e-mail: cecilia@rosemarybranch.co.uk
                              Tel: 020-7704 6665

SEVENOAKS STAG THEATRE
London Road
Sevenoaks, Kent TN13 1ZZ
Website: www.stagtheatre.co.uk
BO: 01732 450175   Admin: 01732 451548
Route: Charing Cross (BR) to Sevenoaks then 15 mins
up the hill from station

SHAW THEATRE The
The Barnard Shaw Park Plaza Hotel
100-110 Euston Road
London NW1 2AJ
e-mail: admin@shawtheatre.com
Fax: 020-7383 4158   BO: 020-7387 6864

SOHO THEATRE & WRITERS' CENTRE
21 Dean Street
London W1D 3NE
Website: www.sohotheatre.com
Fax: 020-7287 5061   Tel: 020-7287 5060
Route: Tube to Tottenham Court Road then 2nd left
up Oxford Street

SOUTH HILL PARK ARTS CENTRE
Bracknell, Berks RG12 7PA
Website: www.southillpark.org.uk
e-mail: admin@southillpark.org.uk
BO: 01344 484123   Admin & SD: 01344 484858
Route: Waterloo (BR) to Bracknell then 10 min bus
ride or taxi rank at station

SOUTH LONDON THEATRE
(Bell Theatre & Prompt Corner)
2A Norwood High Street
London SE27 9NS
Website: www.southlondontheatre.co.uk
e-mail: southlondontheatre@yahoo.co.uk
                              Tel: 020-8670 3474
Route: A) Victoria or London Bridge (BR) to West
Norwood then 2 min walk. Route B) Victoria Line to
Brixton then buses 2, 68, 196 or 322

SOUTHWARK PLAYHOUSE
(Artistic Director - Thea Sharrock
Hon. Directors - Juliet Alderdice, Tom Wilson)
62 Southwark Bridge Road
London SE1 0AS
Website: www.southwark-playhouse.co.uk
e-mail: skplay@globalnet.co.uk
BO: 020-7620 3494   Admin: 020-7652 2224
Route: Northern Line to Borough or Jubilee Line to
Southwark (BR) & London Bridge. Buses 133, 35, 344,
40, P3

STANSTED PARK
The Little Theatre
Stansted Park
Rowlands Castle
Hants PO9 6DX
Website: www.stansted.co.uk
e-mail: enquiry@stanstedpark.co.uk
Fax: 023-9241 3773   Tel: 023-9241 2265

TABARD THEATRE
(Hamish Gray - Artictic Director)
2 Bath Road, Turnham Green, London W4 1LW
e-mail: hamish.gray@btopenworld.com
BO: 020-8995 6035   Admin/Fax: 020-8994 5985
Route: District Line to Turnham Green then 1 min walk

THEATRE ROYAL STRATFORD EAST
(Philip Hedley)
Gerry Raffles Square, London E15 1BN
Website: www.stratfordeast.com
e-mail: theatreroyal@stratfordeast.com
Fax: 020-8534 8381
BO: 020-8534 0310   Admin: 020-8534 7374
Route: Central Line and Jubilee Line to Stratford then 2 min walk

THEATRO TECHNIS
(George Eugeniou)
26 Crowndale Road
London NW1   BO & Admin: 020-7387 6617
Route: Northern Line to Mornington Crescent then 3 min walk

TOWER THEATRE
(Tavistock Repertory Company)
Canonbury Place, Islington, London N1 2NQ
Website: www.towertheatre.org
BO: 020-7226 3633 (2.00pm-8.00pm)
      Admin: 020-7226 5111
Route: Victoria Line to Highbury and Islington then 5 min walk

TRICYCLE THEATRE
(Nicolas Kent - Artistic Director,
Mary Lauder - General Manager)
269 Kilburn High Road, London NW6 7JR
Website: www.tricycle.co.uk
e-mail: admin@tricycle.co.uk
Fax: 020-7328 0795
BO: 020-7328 1000   Admin: 020-7372 6611
Route: Jubilee Line to Kilburn then 5 min walk or buses 16, 189 or 32 pass the door, 98, 31, 206 & 316 pass nearby

TRON THEATRE
(Neil Murray - Administrative Director)
63 Trongate, Glasgow G1 5HB
Website: www.tron.co.uk
e-mail: neil@tron.co.uk
Fax: 0141-552 6657
BO: 0141-552 4267   Admin: 0141-552 3748

UCL BLOOMSBURY The
(See BLOOMSBURY The)

UNION THEATRE The
(Artistic Director - Sasha Regan)
204 Union Street, Southwark, London SE1 0LX
Website: www.uniontheatre.freeserve.co.uk
e-mail: sasha@uniontheatre.freeserve.co.uk
      Tel/Fax: 020-7261 9876
All Casting Enquiries - Paul Flynn
Route: Jubilee line to Southwark then 2 min walk

UPSTAIRS AT THE GATEHOUSE
(Ovation Theatre Ltd)
The Gatehouse Pub, North Road, London N6 4BD
Website: www.upstairsatthegatehouse.com
e-mail: events@ovationproductions.com
BO: 020-8340 3488   Admin: 020-8340 3477

WAREHOUSE THEATRE
(Ted Craig)
Dingwall Road, Croydon CR0 2NF
Website: www.warehousetheatre.co.uk
e-mail: warehous@dircon.co.uk
Fax: 020-8688 6699
BO: 020-8680 4060   Admin: 020-8681 1257
Adjacent to East Croydon (BR). Direct from Victoria (15 mins), Clapham Junction (10 mins) or by Thameslink from West Hampstead, Kentish Town, Kings Cross, Blackfriars & London Bridge

WATERMANS
(Jan Lennox)
40 High Street Brentford, Middlesex TW8 0DS
e-mail: enquiries@watermans.org.uk
Fax: 020-8232 1030
BO: 020-8232 1010   Admin: 020-8232 1020
Route: Buses: 237, 267, 65 or N97
Tube: Gunnersbury or South Ealing BR: Kew Bridge then 5 min walk, Gunnersbury then 10 min walk, or Brentford

WESTRIDGE OPEN CENTRE
(Showcase Window for Drawing Room Recitals)
Star Lane, Andover Road
Highclere
Nr Newbury, Berks RG20 9PJ   Tel: 01635 253322

WHITE BEAR THEATRE
(Favours New Writing)
138 Kennington Park Road, London SE11 4DJ
e-mail: mkwbear@hotmail.com
      Admin/BO: 020-7793 9193

WILTONS MUSIC HALL
Graces Alley, Off Ensign Street, London E1 8JB
e-mail: opera@broomhill.demon.co.uk
Fax: 020-7702 1414   Tel: 020-7702 9555
Route Tube: Under 10 minutes walk from Aldgate East (exit for Leman Street)/Tower Hill/Shadwell.
DLR: Shadwell and Tower Gateway. Car: Look out for the yellow AA signs to Wiltons Music Hall from the Highway, Aldgate and Tower Hill.
Buses: 100 and D3 stop three minutes walk from Theatre on Cannon Street Road

WIMBLEDON STUDIO THEATRE
(Wimbledon Theatre)
103 The Broadway, London SW19 1QG
Website: www.wimbledontheatre.com
Fax: 020-8543 6637
BO: 020-8540 0362   Admin: 020-8543 4549
Route: BR or District Line to Wimbledon BR, Tube and Tramlink, then 3 min walk. Buses 57,93,155

WIMBLEDON THEATRE
The Broadway, London SW19 1QG
Fax: 020-8543 6637
BO: 020-8540 0362   Admin: 020-8543 4549
Route: BR or District Line to Wimbledon BR and Tube, then 3 min walk. Buses 57, 93, 155

WYCOMBE SWAN
St Mary Street, High Wycombe, Bucks HP11 2XE
Website: www.wycombeswan.co.uk
e-mail: enquiries@wycombeswan.co.uk
BO: 01494 512000   Admin: 01494 514444

ABERDEEN

His Majesty's Theatre
Rosemount Viaduct, Aberdeen AB25 1GL
Box Office: 01224 641122
Stage Door: 01224 638677
Admin: 01224 637788
Website: www.hmtheatre.com
e-mail: info@hmtheatre.com

ABERYSTWYTH

Aberystwyth Arts Centre
University of Wales, Aberystwyth SY23 3DE
Box Office: 01970 623232
Stage Door: 01970 624239
Admin: 01970 622882
Website: www.aber.ac.uk/artscentre
e-mail: lla@aber.ac.uk

ASHTON-UNDER-LYNE

Tameside Hippodrome
Oldham Road
Ashton-under-Lyne OL6 7SE
Box Office: 0161-308 3223
Stage Door: ------------------
Admin: 0161-330 2095

AYR

Gaiety Theatre
Carrick Street
Ayr
KA7 1NU
Box Office: 01292 611222
Stage Door: 01292 617414
Admin: 01292 617400

BACUP

Royal Court Theatre
Rochdale Road, Bacup OL13 9NR
Box Office: 01706 874080
Stage Door: ----------------
Admin: ----------------

BASINGSTOKE

Haymarket Theatre
Wote Street
Haymarket RG21 7NW
Box Office: 01256 465566
Stage Door: 01256 323073
Admin: 01256 323073
Website: www.haymarket.org.uk
e-mail: info@haymarket.org.uk

BATH

Theatre Royal
Sawclose
Bath BA1 1ET
Box Office: 01225 448844
Stage Door: 01225 448815
Admin: 01225 448815
Website: www.theatreroyal.org.uk
e-mail: forename.surname@theatreroyal.org.uk

BELFAST

Grand Opera House
Great Victoria Street
Belfast BT2 7HR
Box Office: 028-9024 1919
Stage Door: 028-9024 0411
Admin: 028-9024 0411
Website: www.goh.co.uk
e-mail: info@goh.co.uk

BILLINGHAM

Forum Theatre
Town Centre
Billingham TS23 2LJ
Box Office: 01642 552663
Stage Door: ------------------
Admin: 01642 551389

BIRMINGHAM

Alexandra Theatre
Station Street
Birmingham B5 4DS
Box Office: 0870 6077533
Stage Door: 0121-230 9102
Admin: 0121-643 5536
Website: www.ticketmaster.co.uk

BIRMINGHAM

Hippodrome
Hurst Street
Birmingham
B5 4TB
Box Office: 0870 7301234
Stage Door: ------------------
Admin: 0870 7305555

BLACKPOOL

Opera House
Church Street
Blackpool FY1 1HW
Box Office: 01253 292029
Stage Door: 01253 625252 ext 148
Admin: 01253 625252

BLACKPOOL

Grand Theatre
33 Church Street Blackpool FY1 1HT
Box Office: 01253 290190
Stage Door: 01253 294571
Admin: 01253 290111
Website: www.blackpoolgrand.co.uk
e-mail: geninfo@blackpoolgrand.co.uk

BOURNEMOUTH

Pavilion Theatre
Westover Road Bournemouth BH1 2BX
Box Office: 01202 456456
Stage Door: 01202 451863
Admin: 01202 456400

BRADFORD

Alhambra Theatre
Morley Street
Bradford BD7 1AJ
Box Office: 01274 752000
Stage Door: 01274 752375
Admin: 01274 752375
Website: www.bradford-theatres.co.uk
e-mail: administration@ces.bradford.gov.uk

BRADFORD

Theatre in the Mill
University of Bradford
Shearbridge Road, Bradford BD7 1DP
Box Office: 01274 233200
Stage Door: ------------------
Admin: 01274 233188
Website: www.brad.ac.uk/admin/theatre
e-mail: theatre-manager@brad.ac.uk

BRIGHTON

Theatre Royal
New Road
Brighton
BN1 1SD
Box Office: 01273 328488
Stage Door: 01273 764400
Admin: 01273 764400
e-mail: brightontheatremanager@theambassadors.com

BRIGHTON

The Dome, Corn Exchange & Pavilion Theatres
29 New Road, Brighton BN1 1UG
Box Office: 01273 709709
Stage Door: 01273 695370
Admin: 01273 261501
e-mail: info@brighton-dome.org.uk

BRISTOL

Hippodrome
St Augustines Parade, Bristol BS1 4UZ
Box Office: 0870 6077500
Stage Door: 0117-927 3077
Admin: 0117-926 5524
Website: www.ticketmaster.co.uk

BROXBOURNE (Herts)

Civic Hall
High Street, Hoddesdon, Herts EN11 8BE
Box Office: 01992 441946
Stage Door: ----------------
Admin: 01992 441931
Website: www.broxbourne.gov.uk
e-mail: civic.leisure@broxbourne.gov.uk

BURY ST EDMUNDS

Theatre Royal
Westgate Street, Bury St Edmunds IP33 1QR
Box Office: 01284 769505
Stage Door: 01284 755127
Admin: 01284 755127
Website: www.theatreroyal.org
e-mail: admin@theatreroyal.org

BUXTON

Opera House
Water Street, Buxton SK17 6XN
Box Office: 0845 1272190
Stage Door: 01298 71382
Admin: 01298 72050
Website: www.buxton-opera.co.uk
e-mail: admin@buxtonopera.co.uk

CAMBERLEY

The Camberley Theatre
Knoll Road, Camberley, Surrey GU15 35Y
Box Office: 01276 707600
Stage Door: ----------------
Admin: 01276 707612
e-mail: camberleytheatre@surreyheath.gov.uk

CAMBRIDGE

Mumford Theatre
Anglia Polytechnic University
East Road, Cambridge CB1 1PT
Box Office: 01223 352932
Stage Door: 01223 352932
Admin: 01223 352932
e-mail: mumford@apu.ac.uk

CAMBRIDGE

Arts Theatre
6 St Edward's Passage, Cambridge CB2 3PJ
Box Office: 01223 503333
Stage Door: 01223 578951
Admin: 01223 578933
Website: www.cambridgeartstheatre.com
e-mail: info@cambridgeartstheatre.com

CANTERBURY

Gulbenkian Theatre
University of Kent, Canterbury CT2 7NB
Box Office: 01227 769075
Stage Door: 01227 769565
Admin: 01227 827861
Website: www.ukc.ac.uk/gulbenkian
e-mail: gulbenkian@ukc.ac.uk

CANTERBURY

The Marlowe Theatre
The Friars, Canterbury CT1 2AS
Box Office: 01227 787787
Stage Door: 01227 786867
Admin: 01227 763262
Website: www.marlowetheatre.com
e-mail: markeverett@canterbury.gov.uk

CARDIFF

New Theatre
Park Place
Cardiff CF10 3LN
Box Office: 029-2087 8889
Stage Door: 029-2087 8900
Admin: 029-2087 8787

CHELTENHAM

Everyman Theatre
Regent Street, Cheltenham GL50 1HQ
Box Office: 01242 572573
Stage Door: 01242 512515
Admin: 01242 512515
Website: www.everymantheatre.org.uk
e-mail: admin@everymantheatre.org.uk

CHICHESTER

Festival Theatre
Oaklands Park, Chichester PO19 6AP
Box Office: 01243 781312
Stage Door: 01243 784437
Admin: 01243 784437
Website: www.cft.org.uk
e-mail: admin@cft.org.uk

CRAWLEY

The Hawth
Hawth Avenue, West Sussex RH10 6YZ
Box Office: 01293 553636
Stage Door: ----------------
Admin: 01293 552941
Website: www.hawth.co.uk
e-mail: info@hawth.co.uk

CREWE

Lyceum Theatre
Heath Street
Crewe CW1 2DA
Box Office: 01270 537333
Stage Door: 01270 537336
Admin: 01270 537243

DARLINGTON

Civic Theatre
Parkgate
Darlington DL1 1RR
Box Office: 01325 486555
Stage Door: 01325 467743
Admin: 01325 468006
Website: www.darlington-arts.co.uk

DUBLIN

Gate Theatre
1 Cavendish Row, Dublin 1
Box Office: 00 353 1 8744045
Stage Door: ---------------------
Admin: 00 353 1 8744368
Website: www.gate-theatre.ie
e-mail: info@gate-theatre.ie

DUBLIN

Gaiety Theatre
South
King Street
Dublin 2
Box Office: 00 353 1 6771717
Stage Door: ---------------------
Admin: 00 353 1 6795622

DUBLIN

Olympia Theatre
72 Dame Street, Dublin 2
Box Office: 00 353 1 6793323
Stage Door: 00 353 1 6771400
Admin: 00 353 1 6725883
Website: www.mcd.ie
e-mail: aideen@olympia.ie

EASTBOURNE

Devonshire Park Theatre
Admin: Winter Garden Compton Street BN21 4BP
Box Office: 01323 412000
Stage Door: 01323 410074
Admin: 01323 415500
Website: www.eastbournetheatres.co.uk
e-mail: theatres@eastbourne.gov.uk

EASTBOURNE

Congress Theatre
Admin: Winter Garden, Eastbourne
Compton Street BN21 4BP
Box Office: 01323 412000
Stage Door: 01323 410048
Admin: 01323 415500
Website: www.eastbournetheatres.co.uk
e-mail: theatres@eastbourne.gov.uk

EDINBURGH

King's Theatre
2 Leven Street, Edinburgh EH3 9LQ
Box Office: 0131-529 6000
Stage Door: 0131-229 3416
Admin: 0131-662 1112
Website: www.eft.co.uk
e-mail: admin@eft.co.uk

EDINBURGH

Playhouse Theatre
18-22 Greenside Place, Edinburgh EH1 3AA
Box Office: 0870 6063424
Stage Door: 0131-524 3324
Admin: 0131-524 3333
Website: www.ticketmaster.co.uk

GLASGOW

King's Theatre
297 Bath Street
Glasgow
G2 4JN
Box Office: 0845 3303511
Stage Door: 0141-248 5332
Admin: 0141-287 8913

GLASGOW

Theatre Royal
282 Hope Street
Glasgow G2 3QA
Box Office: 0141-332 9000
Stage Door: 0141-332 3321
Admin: 0141-332 3321
Website: www.theareroyalglasgow.com

GRAYS THURROCK

Thameside Theatre
Orsett Road
Thurrock RM17 5DX
Box Office: 01375 383961
Stage Door: -------------
Admin: 01375 382555
Website: www.thurrock.gov.uk/theatre
e-mail: mallinson@thurrock.gov.uk

HARLOW

The Playhouse
Playhouse Square, Harlow CM20 1LS
Box Office: 01279 431945
Stage Door: ----------------
Admin: 01279 446760
Website: www.playhouseharlow.com
e-mail: philip dale@harlow.gov.uk

HARROGATE

**Harrogate
International Centre**
Kings Road
Harrogate HG1 5LA
Box Office: 01423 537230
Stage Door: 01423 537222
Admin: 01423 537200

HARROGATE

Royal Hall
Ripon Road
Harrogate
HG1 2RD
Box Office: 01423 537230
Stage Door: ----------------
Admin: 01423 537200

HASTINGS

White Rock Theatre
White
Rock
Hastings
TN34 1JX
Box Office: 01424 781000
Stage Door: 01424 434091
Admin: 01424 781010

HAYES (Middlesex)

Beck Theatre
Grange Road
Middlesex
UB3 2UE
Box Office: 020-8561 8371
Stage Door: ----------------
Admin: 020-8561 7506

HEREFORD

The Courtyard
Edgar Street
Hereford HR4 9JR
Box Office: 01432 359252
Stage Door: ----------------
Admin: 01432 346500

HIGH WYCOMBE

Wycombe Swan
St Mary Street HP11 2XE
Box Office: 01494 512000
Stage Door: 01494 514444
Admin: 01494 514444
Website: www.wycombeswan.co.uk
e-mail: enquiries@wycombeswan.co.uk

HUDDERSFIELD

(Cragrats Ltd)
The Mill, Dunford Road, Holmfirth,Huddersfield HD9 2AR
Box Office: 01484 686212
Stage Door: 01484 686451
Admin: ----------------
Website: www.cragrats.com
e-mail: jill@cragrats.com

HUDDERSFIELD

Lawrence Batley Theatre
Queen's Square
Queen Street
Huddersfield HD1 2SP
Box Office: 01484 430528
Stage Door: ----------------
Admin: 01484 425282
e-mail: theatre@lbt-uk.org

HULL

Hull Truck Theatre
Spring Street, Hull HU2 8RW
Box Office: 01482 323638
Stage Door: -------------------
Admin: 01482 224800
Website: www.hulltruck.co.uk
e-mail: admin@hulltruck.co.uk

HULL

Hull New Theatre
Kingston Square
Hull HU1 3HF
Box Office: 01482 226655
Stage Door: 01482 320244
Admin: 01482 613818
e-mail: theatre.management@hullcc.gov.uk

ILFORD

Kenneth More Theatre
Oakfield Road, Ilford IG1 1BT
Box Office:	020-8553 4466
Stage Door:	020-8553 4465
Admin:	020-8553 4464
Website:	www.kenneth-more-theatre.co.uk
e-mail:	kmtheatre@aol.com

IPSWICH

Sir John Mills Theatre (Hire Only)
Gatacre Road, Ipswich IP1 2LQ
Box Office:	01473 211498
Stage Door:	---------------
Admin:	01473 218202
Website:	www.easternangles.co.uk
e-mail:	admin@easternangles.co.uk

JERSEY

Opera House
Gloucester Street, St Helier, Jersey JE2 3QR
Box Office:	01534 511115
Stage Door:	---------------
Admin:	01534 511100
e-mail:	istephens_je@yahoo.co.uk

KIRKCALDY

Adam Smith Theatre
Bennochy Road, Kirkcaldy KY1 1ET
Box Office:	01592 412929
Stage Door:	-----------------
Admin:	01592 412567

LEEDS

City Varieties Music Hall
Swan Street, Leeds LS1 6LW
Box Office:	0113-243 0808
Stage Door:	----------------
Admin:	0113-391 7777
Website:	www.cityvarieties.co.uk
e-mail:	info@cityvarieties.co.uk

LEEDS

Grand Theatre & Opera House
46 New Briggate, Leeds LS1 6NZ
Box Office:	0113-222 6222
Stage Door:	------------------
Admin:	0113-245 6014

LICHFIELD

The Lichfield Garrick
Castle Dyke
Lichfield WS13 6HR
Box Office:	01543 308796
Stage Door:	-----------------
Admin:	01543 308797

LINCOLN

Theatre Royal
Clasketgate
Lincoln LN2 1JJ
Box Office:	01522 525555
Stage Door:	01522 523303
Admin:	01522 523303
Website:	www.theatreroyal.com

LIVERPOOL

Empire Theatre
Lime Street
Liverpool
L1 1JE
Box Office:	0870 6063536
Stage Door:	0151-708 3200
Admin:	0151-708 3200

LIVERPOOL

Neptune Theatre
Hanover Street, Liverpool L1 3DY
Box Office:	0151-709 7844
Stage Door:	0151-709 7844
Admin:	0151-709 7844
Website:	www.neptunetheatre.co.uk
e-mail:	neptune.theatre@liverpool.gov.uk

MALVERN

Malvern Theatres (Festival & Forum Theatres)
Grange Road, Malvern WR14 3HB
Box Office:	01684 892277
Stage Door:	-----------------
Admin:	01684 569256
Website:	www.malvern-theatres.co.uk
e-mail:	post@malvern-theatres.co.uk

MANCHESTER

Apollo Theatre
Ardwick Green, Manchester M12 6AP
Box Office:	0161-242 2560
Stage Door:	0161-273 2416
Admin:	0161-273 6921
Website:	www.ticketmaster.co.uk

MANCHESTER

Opera House
Quay Street, Manchester M3 3HP
Box Office:	0161-242 2509
Stage Door:	0161-834 1787
Admin:	0161-834 1787

MANCHESTER

Palace Theatre
Oxford Street
Manchester
M1 6FT
Box Office:	0161-242 2503
Stage Door:	0161-228 6255
Admin:	0161-228 6255

MARGATE

Theatre Royal
Addington Street, Margate, Kent CT9 1PW
Box Office:	01843 293877
Stage Door:	-----------------
Admin:	01843 293397

MILTON KEYNES

Milton Keynes Theatre
500 Marlborough Gate
Central Milton Keynes MK9 3NZ
Box Office:	01908 606090
Stage Door:	01908 547500
Admin:	01908 547500

NEWARK

Palace Theatre
Appletongate, Newark NG24 1JY
Box Office:	01636 655755
Stage Door:	----------------
Admin:	01636 655750
Website:	www.palacenewark.com
e-mail:	david.piper@nsdc.info

NEWCASTLE UPON TYNE

Newcastle Opera House
111 Westgate Road NE1 4AG
Box Office:	0191-232 0899
Stage Door:	0191-232 1551
Admin:	0191-261 1725
Website:	www.newcastleopera.org
e-mail:	operahouse@virgin.net

NEWCASTLE UPON TYNE

Playhouse & Gulbenkian Studio Theatre
Barras Bridge, Haymarket NE1 7RH
Box Office: 0191-232 5151
Stage Door: --------------------
Admin: 0191-232 3366
Website: www.northernstage.com
e-mail: info@northernstage.com

NEWCASTLE UPON TYNE

Theatre Royal
Grey Street NE1 6BR
Box Office: 0870 9055060
Stage Door: 0191-244 2500
Admin: 0191-232 0997

NORTHAMPTON

Northampton Theatres, The Royal & Derngate
19-21 Guildhall Road, Northampton NN1 1DP
Box Office: 01604 624811
Stage Door: 01604 626289
Admin: 01604 626222
Website: www.northamptontheatres.com
e-mail: postbox@ntt.org.uk

NORWICH

Theatre Royal
Theatre Street NR2 1RL
Box Office: 01603 630000
Stage Door: 01603 598500
Admin: 01603 598500
Website: www.theatreroyalnorwich.co.uk

NOTTINGHAM

Theatre Royal & Royal Concert Hall
Theatre Square, Nottingham NG1 5ND
Box Office: 0115-989 5555
Stage Door: 0115-989 5500
Admin: 0115-989 5500
Website: www.royalcentre-nottingham.co.uk
e-mail: enquiry@royalcentre-nottingham.co.uk

OXFORD

Apollo Theatre
George Street
Oxford OX1 2AG
Ticketmaster 0870 6063500
Stage Door: 01865 241631
Admin: 01865 243041
Website: www.ticketmaster.co.uk

OXFORD

Oxford Playhouse
Beaumont Street, Oxford OX1 2LW
Box Office: 01865 305305
Stage Door: 01865 305301
Admin: 01865 305300
Website: www.oxfordplayhouse.co.uk
e-mail: admin@oxfordplayhouse.com

PAIGNTON

Palace Theatre
Palace Avenue, Paignton TQ3 3HF
Box Office: 01803 665800
Stage Door: -----------------
Admin: 01803 558367
Website: http://palacetheatre/torbay.gov.uk
e-mail: palace.theatre@torbay.gov.uk

PLYMOUTH

Athenaeum
Derry's Cross
Plymouth PL1 2SW
Box Office: 01752 266104
Stage Door: --------------
Admin: 01752 266079

POOLE

Towngate Theatre, Poole Arts Centre
Kingland Road
Poole
Dorset BH15 1UG
Box Office: 01202 685222
Stage Door: --------------
Admin: 01202 665334

READING

The Hexagon
Queen's Walk, Reading RG1 7UA
Box Office: 0118-960 6060
Stage Door: 0118-939 0018
Admin: 0118-939 0390

RICHMOND (N Yorks)

Georgian Theatre Royal
Victoria Road
Richmond DL10 4DW
Box Office: 01748 823021
Stage Door: -----------------
Admin: 01748 823710
Website: www.georgiantheatre.com

RICHMOND (Surrey)

Richmond Theatre
The Green
Surrey TW9 1QJ
Box Office: 020-8940 0088
Stage Door: 020-8940 0220
Admin: 020-8940 0220

SHEFFIELD

Crucible, Lyceum & Crucible Studio
55 Norfolk Street
Sheffield S1 1DA
Box Office: 0114-249 6000
Stage Door: 0114-249 5999
Admin: 0114-249 5999
Website: www.sheffieldtheatres.co.uk

SOUTHAMPTON

Mayflower Theatre
Commercial Road, Southampton SO15 1GE
Box Office: 023-8071 1811
Stage Door: 023-8033 0071
Admin: 023-8071 1800
Website: www.the-mayflower.com
e-mail: info@the-mayflower.com

ST ALBANS

Abbey Theatre
Holywell Hill, Herts AL1 2DL
Box Office: 01727 857861
Stage Door: 01727 861731
Admin: 01727 847472
Website: www.abbeytheatre.org.uk
e-mail: manager@abbeytheatre.freeserve.co.uk

ST ALBANS

Alban Arena
Civic Centre, Herts AL1 3LD
Box Office: 01727 844488
Stage Door: -----------------
Admin: 01727 861078
Website: www.alban-arena.co.uk
e-mail: info@alban arena.co.uk

ST HELENS

Theatre Royal
Corporation Street
St Helens, Lancs WA10 1LQ
Box Office: 01744 756000
Stage Door: -----------------
Admin: 01744 756333

STRAFFORD

Stafford
Stafford Gatehouse Theatre
Eastgate Street, Stratford ST16 2LT
Box Office: 01785 254653
Stage Door: -------------------
Admin: 01785 253595
e-mail: gatehouse@staffordbc.gov.uk

STEVENAGE

Gordon Craig Theatre
Arts & Leisure Centre, Lytton Way SG1 1LZ
Box Office: 08700 131030
Stage Door: 01438 242629
Admin: 01438 242642
Website: www.stevenage-leisure.co.uk
e-mail: gordoncraig@stevenage-leisure.co.uk

STOCKPORT

The Peter Barkworth Theatre
Stockport College
Wellington Road
Stockport SK1 4UQ
Box Office: 0161-958 3114
Stage Door: 0161-958 3429
Admin: 0161-429 7413

STRATFORD-UPON-AVON

Royal Shakespeare Theatre
Waterside, Stratford-Upon-Avon CV37 6BB
Box Office: 01789 403403
Stage Door: 01789 296655
Admin: 01789 296655
Website: www.rsc.org.uk
e-mail: info@rsc.org.uk

STRATFORD-UPON-AVON

The Other Place
Southern Lane
Straford Upon Avon
CV37 6BH
Box Office: 0870 6091110
Stage Door: 01789 296655
Admin: 01789 296655

SUNDERLAND

Empire Theatre
High Street West
Sunderland
SR1 3EX
Box Office: 0191-514 2517
Stage Door: 0191-565 6750
Admin: 0191-510 0545

SWANAGE

Mowlem Theatre
Shore Road, Swanage BH19 1DD
Box Office: 01929 422239
Stage Door: ---------------
Admin: 01929 422229

TAMWORTH

Assembly Rooms
Corporation Street
Tamworth
B79 7BX
Box Office: 01827 709618
Stage Door: ----------------
Admin: 01827 709620

TEWKESBURY

The Roses
Sun Street, Tewkesbury, Glos GL20 5NX
Box Office: 01684 295074
Stage Door: ----------------
Admin: 01684 290734
e-mail: arts@rosestheatre.org.uk

TORQUAY

Babbacombe Theatre
Babbacombe Downs, Torquay TQ1 3LU
Box Office: 01803 328385
Stage Door: 01803 328385
Admin: 01803 322233
Website: www.babbacombe-theatre.com
e-mail: matpro@btinternet.com

TORQUAY

Princess Theatre
Torbay Road, Torquay TQ2 5EZ
Box Office: 0870 2414120
Stage Door: 01803 290068
Admin: 01803 290288
Website: www.ticketmaster.co.uk
e-mail: princess@clearchannel.co.uk

WATFORD

Palace Theatre
Clarendon Road, Watford, Herts WD17 1JZ
Box Office: 01923 225671
Stage Door: ----------------
Admin: 01923 235455
Website: www.watfordtheatre.co.uk
e-mail: enquiries@watfordtheatre.co.uk

WINCHESTER

Theatre Royal
21-23 Jewry Street
Winchester SO23 8SB
Box Office: 01962 840440
Stage Door: --------------
Admin: 01962 844600
e-mail: marketing@theatre-royal-winchester.co.uk

WOKING

New Victoria Theatre, The Ambassadors
The Peacocks Centre, Woking GU21 6GQ
Box Office: 01483 545900
Stage Door: 01483 545855
Admin: 01483 545800
Website: www.theambassadors.com/woking
e-mail: boxoffice@theambassadors.com

WOLVERHAMPTON

Grand Theatre
Lichfield Street, Wolverhampton WV1 1DE
Box Office: 01902 429212
Stage Door: 01902 573320
Admin: 01902 573300
Website: www.grandtheatre.co.uk
e-mail: marketing@grandtheatre.co.uk

WORTHING

Connaught Theatre
Union Place, Worthing BN11 1LG
Box Office: 01903 206206
Stage Door: ------------------
Admin: 01903 231799

YEOVIL

Octagon Theatre
Hendford, Yeovil, Somerset BA20 1UX
Box Office: 01935 422884
Stage Door: 01935 845926
Admin: 01935 845900
Website: www.octagon-theatre.co.uk
e-mail: octagontheatre@southsomerset.gov.uk

YORK

Grand Opera House
Cumberland Street
York YO1 9SW
Box Office: 01904 671818
Stage Door: 01904 671857
Admin: 01904 678700

For accommodation see The Good Digs Guide Listings

AUTHENTIC PUNCH & JUDY
Puppets, Booths & Presentations
(John Styles)
42 Christchurch Road
Sidcup, Kent DA15 7HQ
Website: www.johnstylesentertainer.co.uk
Tel/Fax: 020-8300 3579

BROOKER David
(Punch & Judy)
75 Northcote Road
New Malden, Surrey KT3 3HF   Tel: 020-8949 5035

BUCKLEY Simon
(Freelance Puppeteer/Presenter)
c/o Talent Artists Ltd
59 Sydner Road
London N16 7UF
Website: www.simonbuckley.co.uk
e-mail: puppet.buckley@virgin.net
Tel: 020-7923 1119

CORNELIUS & JONES
49 Carters Close, Sherington
Newport Pagnell
Bucks MK16 9NW
Website: www.corneliusjones.com
e-mail: admin@corneliusjones.com
Fax: 01908 216400   Tel: 01908 612593

DYNAMIC NEW ANIMATION
19 Royal Close
Manor Road
London N16 5SE
Website: www.dynamicnewanimation.co.uk
e-mail: dna@dynamicnewanimation.co.uk
Mobile: 07976 946003

GRIFFITHS Marc
(Ventriloquist)
The Mega Centre
Bernard Road
Sheffield S2 5BQ   Tel: 0114-272 5077

JACOLLY PUPPET THEATRE
Kirkella Road, Yelverton
West Devon PL20 6BB
Website: www.jacolly-puppets.co.uk
e-mail: theatre@jacolly-puppets.co.uk
Tel: 01822 852346

LITTLE ANGEL THEATRE
14 Dagmar Passage
Cross Street
London N1 2DN
Website: www.littleangeltheatre.com
e-mail: info@littleangeltheatre.com
Fax: 020-7359 7565   Tel: 020-7226 1787

NORWICH PUPPET THEATRE
St James, Whitefriars
Norwich NR3 1TN
Website: www.geocities.com/norwichpuppets
e-mail: norpuppet@hotmail.com
Fax: 01603 617578   Tel: 01603 615564

PARASOL PUPPET THEATRE
Garden House
4 Sunnyside
Wimbledon SW19 4SL
Fax: 020-8946 0228   Tel: 020-8946 9478

PEKKO'S PUPPETS
28 Dorset Road
London W5 4HU   Tel: 020-8579 7651

PICCOLO PUPPET COMPANY
Maythorne Higher Park Road
Braunton
North Devon EX33 2LF
e-mail: claire@active-arts.co.uk
Tel: 01271 815984   Tel: 020-8342 8555

PLAYBOARD PUPPETS
94 Ockendon Road
London N1 3NW
e-mail: thebuttonmoon@aol.com
Fax: 020-7704 1081   Tel: 020-7226 5911

POM POM PUPPETS
9 Fulham Park Gardens
London SW6 4JX
Website: www.pompompuppets.co.uk
Mobile: 07974 175247   Tel: 020-7736 6532

PROFESSOR PATTEN'S PUNCH & JUDY
(Puppetry & Magic)
14 The Crest
Goffs Oak
Herts EN7 5NP   Tel: 01707 873262

PUNCH & JUDY
(Des Turner, President Punch & Judy Fellowship)
Richmond House
2 Benington Road, Aston
Stevenage, Herts SG2 7DX
Website: www.punchandjudy.org.uk
e-mail: desturner@aol.com   Tel: 01438 880376

PUPPET CENTRE TRUST
BAC Lavender Hill
London SW11 5TN
Website: www.puppetcentre.com
e-mail: pct@puppetcentre.demon.co.uk
Fax: 020-7228 8863   Tel: 020-7228 5335

THEATR PYPEDAU SPLOTT (Splott Puppet Theatre)
Flat 2
Cog Farm House
Cog Road
Vale of Gamorgan CF64 5UD   Tel: 029-2053 0370

THE GOOD THE BAD & THE CUDDLY THEATRE COMPANY
140 Manor Road
New Milton
Hants BH25 5ED
e-mail: j.sinclair@cwcom.net   Tel: 01425 612830

TICKLISH ALLSORTS SHOW
Cremyll, Marshmead Close
Clarendon, Salisbury
Wilts SP5 3DD
Website: www.ticklishallsorts.co.uk
e-mail: garynunn@lineone.net
Tel/Fax: 01722 711800

TOPPER Chris PUPPETS
(Puppets Created & Performed)
75 Barrows Green Lane
Widnes
Cheshire WA8 3JH
Website: www.christopper-puppets.co.uk
Tel: 0151-424 8692

T

Where appropriate, Rep periods are indicated, e.g. (4 Weekly) and matinee times e.g. Th 2.30 for Thursday 2.30pm.

SD - Stage Door
BO - Box Office
TIE - Theatre in Education (For further details of TIE/YPT See Theatre - TIE/YPT Companies).

ALDEBURGH
Summer Theatre (July & August)
The Jubilee Hall
Crabbe Street, Aldeburgh IP15 5BW
Mon-Fri: 11 - 4 & Sat 11 - 2.30   BO: 01728 453007
Mon-Fri: 6 - 9 & Sat 4 - 8.30   BO: 01728 454022
Admin: (Oct-May) 020-7724 5432
Admin: (June-Sept) 01502 723077
Jill Freud

BASINGSTOKE
Haymarket Theatre Company
Wote Street, Basingstoke RG21 7NW
Fax: 01256 357130
BO: 01256 465566   Admin: 01256 323073
Website: www.haymarket.org.uk
e-mail: info@haymarket.org.uk

Theatre Director: Alasdair Ramsay
Theatre Manager: Tim Wills

BELFAST
Lyric Theatre
55 Ridgeway Street, Belfast BT9 5FB
Fax: 028-9038 1395
BO: 028-9038 1081   Tel: 028-9066 9660
Website: www.lyrictheatre.co.uk
e-mail: info@lyrictheatre.co.uk

General Manager: Mike Blair

BIRMINGHAM
Birmingham Stage Company
The Old Rep Theatre
Station Street, Birmingham B5 4DY
Fax: 0121-643 8099
BO: 0121-236 5622   Admin: 0121-643 9050
Website: www.birminghamstage.co.uk
e-mail: info@birminghamstage.net

Actor/Manager: Neal Foster
Administrator: Rebecca Shallard

London Office:
Suite 228, 162 Regent Street, London W1B 5TG
Fax: 020-7437 3395   Admin: 020-7437 3391
Website: www.birminghamstage.net
e-mail: info@birminghamstage.net

Actor/Manager: Neal Foster
Administration: Rebecca Shallard

BIRMINGHAM
Repertory Theatre
Centenary Square, Broad Street
Birmingham B1 2EP
Press Office: 0121-245 2075
BO: 0121-236 4455   Tel: 0121-245 2000
e-mail: tickets@birmingham-rep.co.uk

Artistic Director: Jonathan Church
Chief Executive: Stuart Rogers

BOLTON
Octagon Theatre
Howell Croft South, Bolton BL1 1SB
Fax: 01204 556502
BO: 01204 520661   Admin: 01204 529407

Artistic Director: Mark Babych
Executive Director: John Blackmore

BRISTOL
Theatre Royal & New Vic Studio
(3/4 Weekly) Sat 2.30pm
(Bristol Old Vic Co), King Street, Bristol BS1 4ED
Fax: 0117-949 3996
BO: 0117-987 7877   Tel: 0117-949 3993
Website: www.bristol-old-vic.co.uk
e-mail: admin@bristol-old-vic.co.uk

Executive Director: Sarah Smith

BROMLEY
Churchill Theatre (Administration)
High Street, Bromley, Kent BR1 1HA
Fax: 020-8290 6968
BO: 020-8460 6677   Tel: 020-8464 7131
Website: www.churchilltheatre.co.uk

General Manager: Lori D Dorman

CARDIFF
Sherman Theatre & Sherman Studio
Senghennydd Road CF24 4YE
Fax: 029-2064 6902
BO: 029-2064 6900   Tel: 029-2064 6901

Director: Phil Clark
General Manager: Margaret Jones

CHELMSFORD
Civic Theatre
(2 Weekly) (Oct-Mar) Sat 5pm
Fairfield Road, Chelmsford, Essex CM1 1JG
Tel: 020-8349 0802 (London)   Admin: 01245 268998

Artistic Director: John Newman (Newpalm Prods)

CHESTER
Gateway Theatre
(3-4 Weekly)
Hamilton Place, Chester, Cheshire CH1 2BH
Fax: 01244 317277
BO: 01244 340392   Admin: 01244 318603
Website: www.gateway-theatre.org.uk
e-mail: admin@gateway-theatre.org.uk

Chief Executive: Jasmine Hendry

CHICHESTER
Chichester Festival Theatre
(May-Oct & Touring) Eves 7.30pm
Thurs & Sat Mats 2.30pm
Oaklands Park, Chichester
West Sussex PO19 6AP
Fax: 01243 787288
BO: 01243 781312   SD & Admin: 01243 784437
Website: www.cft.org.uk
e-mail: admin@cft.org.uk

Artistic Director: Ruth MacKenzie
Theatre Manager: Janet Burton

CHICHESTER
Minerva Theatre at Chichester Festival Theatre
(June-Oct) Eves 7.45pm Weds & Sat Mats 2.45pm
Oaklands Park, Chichester, West Sussex PO19 6AP
Fax: 01243 787288
BO: 01243 781312   SD & Admin: 01243 784437
Website: www.cft.org.uk
e-mail: admin@cft.org.uk

Artistic Director: Ruth MacKenzie
Theatre Manager: Janet Burton

COLCHESTER
Mercury Theatre
(3-4 Weekly) Thurs & Sat Mats 2.30pm
Balkerne Gate, Colchester, Essex CO1 1PT
Fax: 01206 769607
BO: 01206 573948   Admin: 01206 577006
Website: www.mercurytheatre.co.uk
e-mail: mercury.theatre@virgin.net

Chief Executive: Dee Evans
Artistic Producer: Gregory Floy

COVENTRY
Belgrade Theatre & Belgrade Studio
(3½ Weekly) Weds 2.30pm
Belgrade Square, Coventry, Warwickshire CV1 1GS
BO: 024-7655 3055   Admin: 024-7625 6431
Website: www.belgrade.co.uk
e-mail: admin@belgrade.co.uk

Theatre Director: Bob Eaton
Associate Producer: Jane Hytch
Executive Director: David Beidas
Head of Marketing: Nancy Mules

DERBY
Derby Playhouse
(3½ Weekly)
Theatre Walk, Eagle Centre, Derby DE1 2NF
Fax: 01332 547200   SD: 01332 363271
BO: 01332 363275   Admin: 01332 363271
Website: www.derbyplayhouse.demon.co.uk
e-mail: admin@derbyplayhouse.demon.co.uk

Artistic Director: Mark Clements
Executive Director: David Edwards

DUBLIN
Abbey Theatre & Peacock Theatre
The National Theatre Society Limited
26 Lower Abbey Street, Dublin 1
Fax: 00 353 1 872 9177
BO: 00 353 1 878 7222   Admin: 00 353 1 887 2200
Website: www.abbeytheatre.ie
e-mail: mail@abbeytheatre.ie

Artistic Director: Ben Barnes
General Manager: Martin Fahy
Managing Director: Brian Jackson

DUNDEE
Dundee Repertory Theatre
Tay Square, Dundee DD1 1PB
Fax: 01382 228609
BO: 01382 223530   Admin: 01382 227684
Website: www.dundeereptheatre.co.uk

Artistic Director: Hamish Glen
Administrative Director: Joanna Reid

EDINBURGH
Royal Lyceum Theatre Company
Grindlay Street, Edinburgh EH3 9AX
Fax: 0131-228 3955
BO: 0131-248 4848   SD & Admin: 0131-248 4800
Website: www.lyceum.org.uk
e-mail: info@lyceum.org.uk

Artistic Director: Kenny Ireland

EDINBURGH
Traverse Theatre
(New Writing, Own Productions & Visiting
Companies)
Cambridge Street, Edinburgh EH1 2ED
Fax: 0131-229 8443
BO: 0131-228 1404   Admin: 0131-228 3223
Website: www.traverse.co.uk
e-mail: admin@traverse.co.uk

Artistic Director: Philip Howard
Administrative Director: Mike Griffiths

EXETER
Northcott Theatre
(3/4 Weekly)
Stocker Road, Exeter, Devon EX4 4QB
Fax: 01392 223996
BO: 01392 493493   Admin: 01392 223999
Website: www.northcott-theatre.co.uk

Artistic Director: Ben Crocker

EYE THEATRE
Eye Theatre
(4 Weekly) Sat 4.00pm
Broad Street, Eye, Suffolk IP23 7AF
Fax: 01379 871142   Tel: 01379 870519
e-mail: tomscott@eyetheatre.freeserve.co.uk

Artistic Director: Tom Scott
Associate Director: Janeena Sims

FRINTON
Frinton Summer Theatre
(July-Sept)
Ashlyns Road, Frinton, Essex
          Admin: 01255 674443 (During Season Only)

Producer: Seymour Matthews

GLASGOW
Citizens Theatre
Gorbals, Glasgow G5 9DS
Fax: 0141-429 7374
BO: 0141-429 0022   Admin: 0141-429 5561
Website: www.citz.co.uk
e-mail: anna@citz.co.uk

Artistic Director: Giles Havergal
General Manager: Anna Stapleton

GUILDFORD
Yvonne Arnaud Theatre
Millbrook, Guildford, Surrey GU1 3UX
Fax: 01483 564071
BO: 01483 440000   Admin: 01483 440077
Website: www.yvonne-arnaud.co.uk
e-mail: yat@yvonne-arnaud.co.uk

Director: James Barber

HARROGATE
Harrogate Theatre
(3-4 weekly) 2.30pm Sat
Oxford Street, Harrogate HG1 1QF
Fax: 01423 563205
BO: 01423 502116   Admin: 01423 502710
e-mail: staff.name@harrogatetheatre.demon.co.uk

Artistic Director: Rob Swain
Executive Director: Sheena Wrigley

IPSWICH
The New Wolsey Theatre
Civic Drive, Ipswich, Suffolk IP1 2AS
Admin Fax: 01473 295910   BO: 01473 295900
BO Fax: 01473 295901   Admin: 01473 295911
Website: www.wolseytheatre.co.uk

Artistic Associate: Peter Rowe
Chief Executive: Sarah Holmes
Admin e-mail: info@wolseytheatre.co.uk
BO e-mail: tickets@wolseytheatre.co.uk

KESWICK
Theatre by the Lake
Lakeside Keswick, Cumbria CA12 5DJ
Fax: 017687 74698
BO: 017687 74411   Admin: 017687 72282
Website: www.theatrebythelake.com
e-mail: enquiries@theatrebythelake.com

Artistic Director: Ian Forrest

LANCASTER
The Dukes
Moor Lane, Lancaster, Lancs LA1 1QE
Fax: 01524 598519
BO: 01524 598500   Admin: 01524 598505
Website: www.dukes-lancaster.org

Artistic Director: Ian Hastings
Chief Executive: Amanda Belcham

LEEDS
The West Yorkshire Playhouse
Inc Schools Company
Playhouse Square, Quarry Hill, Leeds LS2 7UP
Fax: 0113-213 7250
BO: 0113-213 7700   Admin: 0113-213 7800

Artistic Director (Chief Executive): Ian Brown
Managing Director: Maggie Saxon
Casting Director: Kay Magson
Producer: Paul Crewes

LEICESTER
Leicester Haymarket Theatre & Studio
Belgrave Gate, Leicester LE1 3YQ
Fax: 0116-251 3310
BO: 0116-253 9797   Admin: 0116-253 0021
Website: www.leicesterhaymarkettheatre.co.uk
e-mail: enquiry@leicesterhaymarkettheatre.org

Artistic Director: Paul Kerryson, Kully Thiarai
Chief Executive: Mandy Stewart

LIVERPOOL
Everyman and Playhouse Theatres
Everyman: 13 Hope Street, Liverpool L1 9BH,
Playhouse: Williamson Square, Liverpool L1 1EL
Fax: 0151-709 0398
BO: 0151-709 4776   Admin: 0151-708 0338
Website: www.everymanplayhouse.com
e-mail: info@everymanplayhouse.com

Director: Jo Beddoe

MANCHESTER
Contact Theatre Company
(3/4 Weekly)
Oxford Road, Manchester M15 6JA
Fax: 0161-274 0640
BO: 0161-274 0600   Admin: 0161-274 3434
Website: www.contact-theatre.org
e-mail: info@contact-theatre.org.uk

Chief Executive/Artistic Director:
John Edward McGrath

MANCHESTER
Library Theatre Company
St Peter's Square, Manchester M2 5PD
Fax: 0161-228 6481
BO: 0161-236 7110   Admin: 0161-234 1913
Website: www.libtheatreco.org.uk
e-mail: ltc@libraries.manchester.gov.uk

Artistic Director: Chris Honer
General Manager: Adrian J. P. Morgan

MANCHESTER
Royal Exchange Theatre
St Ann's Square, Manchester M2 7DH
Fax: 0161-832 0881
BO: 0161-833 9833   SD & Admin: 0161-833 9333
Website: www.royalexchange.co.uk

Artistic Directors: Braham Murray,
Gregory Hersov, Marianne Elliot
Executive Director: Patricia Weller
General Manager: Richard Morgan
Casting Director: Sophie Marshall

MILFORD HAVEN
Torch Theatre
St Peter's Road
Milford Haven, Pembrokeshire SA73 2BU
Fax: 01646 698919
BO: 01646 695267   Admin: 01646 694192
Website: www.torchtheatre.org.uk
e-mail: info@torchtheatre.co.uk

Artistic Director: Peter Doran

MOLD
Clwyd Theatr Cymru
(Repertoire, 4 Weekly, also touring)
Mold, Flintshire, North Wales CH7 1YA
Fax: 01352 701558
BO: 01352 755114   Admin: 01352 756331
Website: www.clwyd-theatr-clwyd.co.uk
e-mail: drama@celtic.co.uk

MUSSELBURGH
The Brunton Theatre
(Annual programme of theatre, dance, music,
comedy and children's work)
Ladywell Way
Musselburgh EH21 6AA
Fax: 0131-665 3665
BO: 0131-665 2240   Admin: 0131-665 9900

General Manager: Lesley Smith

NEWBURY
Watermill Theatre
(4-7 Weekly) (Feb-Jan)
Bagnor, Nr Newbury, Berks RG20 8AE
Fax: 01635 523726   SD: 01635 44532
BO: 01635 46044   Admin: 01635 45834
Website: www.watermill.org.uk
e-mail: admin@watermill.org.uk

Artistic Director: Jill Fraser

NEWCASTLE UPON TYNE
Northern Stage (Theatrical Productions) Ltd
Newcastle Playhouse
Barras Bridge, Haymarket NE1 7RH
Fax: 0191-261 8093
BO: 0191-230 5151   Admin: 0191-232 3366
Website: www.northernstage.com
e-mail: info@northernstage.com

Artistic Director: Alan Lyddiard

NEWCASTLE-UNDER-LYME
New Vic Theatre
(3-4 Weekly)
Theatre in the Round, Etruria Road,
Newcastle-under-Lyme, Staffs ST5 0JG
Fax: 01782 712885
BO: 01782 717962   Tel: 01782 717954
e-mail: victheatre@aol.com

Artistic Director: Gwenda Hughes

NORTHAMPTON
Northampton Theatres, The Royal & Derngate
Guildhall Road, Northampton, Northants NN1 1DP
BO: 01604 624811   Casting: 01604 638343
TIE: 01604 627566   Admin: 01604 626222

Acting Chief Executive: Roger Hopwood
Artistic Director: Rupert Goold
Associate Director: Simon Godwin

NOTTINGHAM
Nottingham Playhouse
(3/4 Weekly)
(Nottingham Theatre Trust Ltd)
Wellington Circus
Nottingham NG1 5AF
Fax: 0115-947 5759
BO: 0115-941 9419   Admin: 0115-947 4361

Executive Director: Stephanie Sirr
Artistic Director: Giles Croft
Roundabout TIE Director: Andrew Breakwell

OLDHAM
Coliseum Theatre
(3-4 Weekly)
Fairbottom Street, Oldham, Lancs OL1 3SW
Fax: 0161-624 5318
BO: 0161-624 2829   Admin: 0161-624 1731
Website: www.coliseum.org.uk
e-mail: mail@thecoliseum.fsnet.co.uk

Chief Executive: Kevin Shaw

PERTH
Perth Repertory Theatre
(2-3 Weekly)
185 High Street, Perth PH1 5UW
Fax: 01738 624576   SD: 01738 621435
BO: 01738 621031   Admin: 01738 472700
Website: www.perththeatre.co.uk
e-mail: info@perththeatre.co.uk

Artistic Director: Michael Winter
General Manager: Paul Hackett

PETERBOROUGH
Key Theatre
(Touring & Occasional Seasonal)
Embankment Road, Peterborough, Cambs PE1 1EF
Fax: 01733 567025   SD: 01733 565040
BO: 01733 552439   Admin: 01733 552437
e-mail: keytheatre@freenetname.co.uk

PITLOCHRY
Pitlochry Festival Theatre
Pitlochry, Perthshire PH16 5DR
Fax: 01796 484616
BO: 01796 484626   Admin: 01796 484600
Website: www.pitlochry.org.uk
e-mail: admin@pitlochry.org.uk

Chief Executive: Nikki Axford
Director of Productions: Ian Grieve

PLYMOUTH
Theatre Royal & Drum Theatre
Royal Parade, Plymouth, Devon PL1 2TR
Fax: 01752 671179   Admin: 01752 668282
e-mail: s.stokes@theatreroyal.com

Artistic Director: Simon Stokes
Chief Executive: Adrian Vinken

SALISBURY
Playhouse & Salberg Studio
(3-4 Weekly)
Malthouse Lane, Salisbury, Wilts SP2 7RA
Fax: 01722 421991
Admin: 01722 320117   BO: 01722 320333
Website: www.salisburyplayhouse.com
e-mail: info@salisburyplayhouse.com

Artistic Director: Joanna Read
Executive Director: Rebecca Morland

For accommodation see The Good Digs Guide Listings   315

SCARBOROUGH
Stephen Joseph Theatre
(Repertoire/Repertory)
Westborough, Scarborough, North Yorks YO11 1JW
Fax: 01723 360506   SD: 01723 507047
BO: 01723 370541   Admin: 01723 370540
e-mail: enquiries@sjt.uk.com

Artistic Director: Alan Ayckbourn
General Administrator: Stephen Wood

SHEFFIELD
Crucible Theatre & Studio Theatre
55 Norfolk Street, Sheffield S1 1DA
Admin Fax: 0114-249 6003
BO: 0114-249 6000   Admin: 0114-249 5999
Website: www.sheffieldtheatres.co.uk

Associate Director: Michael Grandage
Chief Executive: Grahame Morris

SIDMOUTH
Manor Pavilion
(Weekly) (July-Sept)
Manor Road, Sidmouth, Devon EX10 8RP
BO: 01395 579977 (Season Only)
     Tel: 020-7636 4343 Charles Vance

SONNING THEATRE
The Mill at Sonning Theatre
(5-6 Weekly)
Sonning Eye, Reading RG4 6TY
SD: 0118-969 5201
BO: 0118-969 8000   Admin: 0118-969 6039

Artistic Director: Sally Hughes
Assistant Administrator: Ann Seymour

SOUTHAMPTON
Nuffield Theatre
(Sept-July, Sunday Night Concerts,
Occasional Tours)
University Road, Southampton SO17 1TR
Fax: 023-8031 5511   SD: 023-8055 5414
BO: 023-8067 1771   Admin: 023-8031 5500
Website: www.nuffieldtheatre.co.uk

Artistic Director: Patrick Sandford
Administrative Director: Kate Anderson

SOUTHWOLD
Summer Theatre
(July-Sept)
St Edmund's Hall
Cumberland Road, Southwold IP18 6JP
     Admin: 020-7724 5432
e-mail: jillfreudandcompany@msn.com

Jill Freud & Company

ST ANDREWS
Byre Theatre
Abbey Street, St Andrews KY16 9LA
Fax: 01334 475370
BO: 01334 475000   Admin: 01334 476288
Website: www.byretheatre.com
e-mail: enquiries@byretheatre.com

Artistic Director: Ken Alexander
Managing Director: Tom Gardner

STRATFORD-UPON-AVON
Swan Theatre & Royal Shakespeare Theatre
Waterside
Stratford-upon-Avon CV37 6BB
Fax: 01789 294810   Admin: 01789 296655
Fax: 01789 294810   BO: 01789 403403
Website: www.rsc.org.uk
e-mail: info@rsc.org.uk

WATFORD
Palace Theatre
(3-4 Weekly) Weds 2.30pm, Sat 3pm
Clarendon Road, Watford, Herts WD17 1JZ
Fax: 01923 819664
BO: 01923 225671   Admin: 01923 235455
Website: www.watfordtheatre.co.uk
e-mail: enquiries@watfordtheatre.co.uk

Artistic Director: Lawrence Till
Administrative Director: Mary Caws
Casting: Andrea Bath

WESTCLIFF
Palace Theatre & Dixon Theatre
London Road, Westcliff-on-Sea, Essex SS0 9LA
Fax: 01702 435031
BO: 01702 342564   Admin: 01702 347816
Website: www.palacetheatrewestcliff.org.uk
e-mail: palacetheatre@hotmail.com

WINDSOR
Theatre Royal
(2-3 Weekly) (Thurs 2.30 Sat 4.45pm)
Thames Street
Windsor, Berks SL4 1PS
Fax: 01753 831673
BO: 01753 853888   Admin/SD: 01753 863444
Website: www.theatreroyalwindsor.co.uk
e-mail: info@theatreroyalwindsor.co.uk

Executive Director: Mark Piper

WORCESTER
Swan Theatre
The Moors, Worcester WR1 3EF
Fax: 01905 723738
BO: 01905 27322   Admin: 01905 726969
Website: www.worcesterswantheatre.co.uk
e-mail: swan_theatre@lineone.net

Artistic Director: Jenny Stephens
General Manager: Deborah Rees

YORK
Theatre Royal
St Leonard's Place, York YO1 7HD
Fax: 01904 611534
BO: 01904 623568   Admin: 01904 658162
Website: www.theatre-royal-york.co.uk
e-mail: admin@theatreroyalyork.fsnet.co.uk

Artistic Director: Damian Cruden
Chief Executive: Ludo Keston

6:15 THEATRE COMPANY
22 Brookfield MansionsHighgate West Hill
London N6 6AS
Website: www.six15.dircon.co.uk
e-mail: six15@dircon.co.uk
Fax: 020-8340 5696   Tel: 020-8342 8239

ACTION TRANSPORT - THE YOUNG PEOPLE'S THEATRE
Whitby Hall, Stanney Lane
Ellesmere Port, South Wirral CH65 9AE
Website: www.actiontransporttheatre.co.uk
e-mail: info@actiontransporttheatre.co.uk
Tel: 0151-357 2120

BLAH BLAH BLAH THEATRE COMPANY The
East Leeds Family Learning Centre
Brooklands View, Leeds LS14 6SA
Website: www.blahs.co.uk
e-mail: admin@blahs.co.uk
Fax: 0113-224 3685   Tel: 0113-224 3171

BLUNDERBUS THEATRE COMPANY Ltd
The Mick Jagger Centre
Shepherd's Lane, Dartford, Kent DA1 2JZ
Website: www.blunderbus.co.uk
e-mail: admin@blunderbus.co.uk
Fax: 01322 286285   Tel: 01322 286284

BORDERLINE THEATRE COMPANY
North Harbour Street, Ayr KA8 8AA
Website: www.borderlinetheatre.co.uk
e-mail: enquiries@borderlinetheatre.co.uk
Fax: 01292 263825   Tel: 01292 281010
Producer: Eddie Jackson

CHANNEL THEATRE COMPANY
TIE Company
Central Studios
130 Grosvenor Place, Margate, Kent CT9 1UY
Website: www.channel-theatre.co.uk
e-mail: info@channel-theatre.co.uk
Fax: 01843 280088   Tel: 01843 280077
Artistic Director: Philip Dart

COMPLETE WORKS THEATRE COMPANY Ltd The
12 Willowford, Bancroft Park
Milton Keynes, Bucks MK13 0RH
Website: www.tcw.org.uk
e-mail: info@tcw.org.uk   Tel: 01908 316256
Artistic Director: Phil Evans

CRAGRATS Ltd
The Mill, Dunford Road
Holmfirth, Huddersfield HD9 2AR
Website: www.cragrats.com
e-mail: jill@cragrats.com
Fax: 01484 686212   Tel: 01484 686451

CTC THEATRE
Arts Centre, Vane Terrace
Darlington, Co Durham DL3 7AX
Website: www.ctctheatre.org.uk
e-mail: ctc@ctctheatre.org.uk
Fax: 01325 369404   Tel: 01325 352004

EUROPEAN THEATRE COMPANY The
39 Oxford Avenue, London SW20 8LS
Website: www.europeantheatre.co.uk
e-mail: admin@europeantheatre.co.uk
Fax: 020-8544 1999   Tel: 020-8544 1994

GAZEBO TIE COMPANY Ltd
The Multipurpose Centre
Victoria Road, Darlaston, West Midlands WS10 8AP
Website: www.gazebotie.com
e-mail: gazebo@ukgateway.net
Tel/Fax: 0121-526 6877

JOE PUBLIC THEATRE COMPANY
(Nick Rawling), c/o New College Telford
King Street, Wellington
Telford TF1 1NY   Tel: 01952 641892

M6 THEATRE COMPANY
Hamer CP School
Albert Royds Street, Rochdale OL16 2SU
e-mail: info@m6theatre.freeserve.co.uk
Fax: 01706 711700   Tel: 01706 355898

NATIONAL TRUST THEATRE The
(TMA Member)
2 & 4 Homerton High Street
Hackney, London E9 6JQ
Website: www.smtp.ntrust.org.uk/learning
Fax: 020-8985 2343   Tel: 020-8986 0242

NEW KINETIC THEATRE FOR SCIENCE
Suite H, The Jubilee Centre
Lombard Road, Wimbledon, London SW19 3TZ
Website: www.kinetictheatre.co.uk
e-mail: sarah@kinetictheatre.co.uk
Fax: 020-8286 2645   Tel: 020-8286 2613
Contact: Dr Oliver Thalmann

NORTHAMPTON THEATRES, ROYAL THEATRE IN EDUCATION
19-21 Guildhall Road, Northampton NN1 1DP
e-mail: education@ntt.org   Tel: 01604 627566

ONATTI THEATRE COMPANY
9 Field Close, Warwick, Warwickshire CV34 4QD
Website: www.onatti.co.uk
e-mail: info@onatti.co.uk
Fax: 0870 1643629   Tel: 01926 495220
Artistic Director: Andrew Bardwell

QUANTUM THEATRE FOR SCIENCE
Unit S9, The Shakespeare Centre
245A Coldharbour Lane, London SW9 8RR
Website: www.quantumtheatre.co.uk
e-mail: quantumtheatre@btinternet.com
Tel: 020-7733 8150
Artistic Directors: Michael Whitmore, Jessica Selous

QUERCUS THEATRE COMPANY
33 Broadlands Avenue
Shepperton, Middlesex TW17 9DJ
Website: www.quercustheatrecompany.org.uk
e-mail: quercus@quercustheatrecompany.org.uk
Director: Therese Kitchin   Tel: 01932 252182

ROUNDABOUT THEATRE IN EDUCATION
Nottingham Playhouse
Wellington Circus, Nottingham NG1 5AF
e-mail: admin@roundabout.org.uk
Fax: 0115-953 9055   Tel: 0115-947 4361

SHEFFIELD THEATRES EDUCATION COMPANY
55 Norfolk Street, Sheffield S1 1DA
Website: www.sheffieldtheatres.co.uk
Fax: 0114 249 6003   Tel: 0114 249 5999
Education Administator: Sue Burley
Education Director: Karen Simpson
Youth Theatre Director: Nick Nuttgens

SNAP THEATRE COMPANY
29 Raynham Road, Bishop's Stortford, Herts CM23 5PE
Website: www.snaptheatre.co.uk
e-mail: info@snaptheatre.co.uk
Fax: 01279 506694   Tel: 01279 461607

SPECTACLE THEATRE
Pontypridd College
Rhondda Campus
Llwynypia, Tonypandy CF40 2TQ
Website: www.spectacletheatre.co.uk
e-mail: info@spectacletheatre.co.uk
Fax: 01443 423080   Tel: 01443 430700

TAG THEATRE COMPANY
18 Albion Street
Glasgow G1 1LH
Website: www.tag-theatre.co.uk
e-mail: info@tag-theatre.co.uk
Fax: 0141-552 0666   Tel: 0141-552 4949

THEATR IOLO Ltd
The Old School Building
Cefn Road
Mynachdy, Cardiff CF14 3HS
Website: www.theatriolo.com
e-mail: admin@theatriolo.com
Fax: 029-2052 2225   Tel: 029-2061 3782

TIEBREAK THEATRE COMPANY
Heartsease High School
Marryat Road
Norwich NR7 9DF
Website: www.tiebreak-theatre.com
e-mail: info@tiebreak-theatre.com
Fax: 01603 435184   Tel: 01603 435209

THEATRE IN EDUCATION TOURS (TIE TOURS)
Holloway School
Hilldrop Road, Islington, London N7 0JG
Website: www.tietours.com
e-mail: tie@tietours.com
Fax: 020-7700 3697   Tel: 020-7619 9115

WEST YORKSHIRE PLAYHOUSE SCHOOLS TOURING COMPANY
West Yorkshire Playhouse
Playhouse Square
Quarry Hill
Leeds LS2 7UP
e-mail: gail.mcintyre@wyp.co.uk   Tel: 0113-213 7800

Vehicles & Transport

ACTION CARS Ltd
(Steven Royffe)
Units 3 & 4 Rosslyn Crescent
Harrow, Middlesex HA1 2SP
Fax: 020-8861 4876   Tel: 020-8863 6889

AIRLINE CREWING SERVICES Ltd
(Celebrity Services)
12B Bridge Industrial Estate
Balcombe Road, West Sussex RH6 9HU
Fax: 01293 400508   Tel: 01293 400505

ANCHOR MARINE FILM & TELEVISION
(Boat Location, Charter, Marine Co-ordinators)
Spike Mead Farm, Poles Lane
Lowfield Heath, West Sussex RH11 0PX
e-mail: amsfilms@aol.com
Fax: 01293 551558   Tel: 01293 538188

ANGLO PACIFIC INTERNATIONAL Plc
(Freight Forwarders to the Performing Arts)
Unit 1 Bush Industrial Estate
Standard Road
North Acton, London NW10 6DF
Fax: 020-8965 4954   Tel: 020-8965 1234

AUTOMATIVE ACTION TRACKING DIVISION
(Supplier)
2 Sheffield House, Park Road
Hampton Hill
Middlesex TW12 1HA
Website: www.cameratrackingvehicle.com
Mobile: 07974 919589   Tel: 020-8977 6186

AZTEC OF BRISTOL
20 Walnut Lane
Kingswood
Bristol BS15 4JG   Tel/Fax: 0117-940 7712

BARHAM ASSOCIATES
(65 foot Classic Motor Yacht Available for Water Based Events Cowes Week etc)
6 Liberty Row, The Square
Hamble, Southampton SO31 4RR
Website: www.classicyachtcharter.co.uk
e-mail: info@classicyachtcharter.co.uk
          Tel/Fax: 023-8045 8778

BIANCHI AVIATION FILM SERVICES
(Historic & Other Aircraft)
Wycombe Air Park
Booker Nr Marlow, Bucks SL7 3DP
Fax: 01494 461236   Tel: 01494 449810

BICYCLES UNLIMITED
(D Pinkerton)
522 Holly Lane, Erdington
Birmingham B24 9LY
e-mail: pinkertn@mwfree.net   Tel: 0121-350 0685

BLUEBELL RAILWAY Plc
(Steam Locomotives, Pullman Coaches, Period Stations. Much Film Experience)
Sheffield Park Station, East Sussex TN22 3QL
Website: www.bluebell-railway.co.uk
Fax: 01825 720804   Tel: 01825 720800

BRUNEL'S THEATRICAL SERVICES
Unit 4, Crown Industrial Estate
Crown Road
Warmley, Bristol BS30 8JB
Fax: 0117-907 7856   Tel: 0117-907 7855

BUXWORTH STEAM GROUP
(Steam Driven Victorian Fairground)
Tower Farm
Boarstall Thame
Nr Aylesbury, Bucks   Tel: 01844 239302

CENTRAL FILM FACILITIES
(Film Transport/Period & Modern Vehicles for Hire)
Marshbrook Business Park
Church Stretton
Shropshire SY6 6QE
Website: www.centralfilmfacilities.com
Fax: 01694 781468   Tel: 01694 781418

CLASSIC CAR AGENCY The
(Film, Promotional, Advertising, Publicity)
PO Box 427
Dorking, Surrey RU5 6WP
Website: www.theclassiccaragency.com
e-mail: theclassiccaragency@btopenworld.com
Mobile: 07788 977655   Tel: 01306 731052

CLASSIC CAR HIRE
(Rolls Royce Phantoms, Bentleys, a Lagonda & Daimlers for hire 1920-70)
Unit 2 Hampton Court Estate
Summer Road, Thames Ditton
Surrey KT7 0RG   Tel: 020-8398 8304

CLASSIC OMNIBUS
(Vintage Open-Top Buses & Coaches)
44 Welson Road, Folkestone, Kent CT20 2NP
Website: www.opentopbus.co.uk
Fax: 01303 241245   Tel: 01303 248999

CRESTAR YACHTS Ltd
Colette Court
125 Sloane Street, London SW1X 9AU
Website: www.crestaryachts.com
e-mail: charters@crestaryachts.com
Fax: 020-7824 8691   Tel: 020-7730 9962

DEVEREUX K. W. & SONS
(Removals)
Daimler Drive, Cowpen Industrial Estate
Billingham, Cleveland TS23 4JD
e-mail: devereux@onyxnet.co.uk
Fax: 01642 566664   Tel: 01642 560854

EAST LONDON MOTORCYCLES
249 Barking Road, East Ham
London E6 1LB   Tel: 020-8472 8301

EST LTD
(Trucking - Every Size & Country)
Marshgate Sidings
Marshgate Lane, London E15 2PB
e-mail: delr@est-uk.com
Fax: 020-8522 1002   Tel: 020-8522 1000

FAHREN WIDE
(Coach Company)
15 Darwin Close, Orpington
Kent BR6 7EP   Tel: 01689 851565

FELLOWES Mark TRANSPORT SERVICES
(Transport/Personal Storage)
59 Sherbrooke Road, London SW6 7QL
Website: www.fellowesproductions.com
Mobile: 07850 332818   Tel: 020-7386 7005

FRANKIE'S YANKEES
(Classic 1950's American Cars,
Memorabilia & New Superstretch Limos)
1768-1770 Pershore Road, Birmingham B30 3BG
Fax: 0121-459 0009   Tel: 0121-445 5522

IMPACT
(Private & Contract Hire of Coaches - Terry Marley)
1 Leighton Road, Ealing, London W13 9EL
Fax: 020-8840 4880   Tel: 020-8579 9922

JASON'S LADY ROSE
(Up-market Cruising Canal Wideboat)
Opp. 42 Blomfield Road
Little Venice, London W9 2PD
Website: www.jasons.co.uk
e-mail: enquiries@jasons.co.uk
Fax: 020-7266 4332   Tel: 020-7286 3428

KEIGHLEY & WORTH VALLEY LIGHT RAILWAY Ltd
(Engines, Stations, Carriages, Props & Crew)
The Railway Station
Haworth, Keighley, West Yorkshire BD22 8NJ
Website: www.kwvr.co.uk
e-mail: admin@kwvr.co.uk
Fax: 01535 647317   Tel: 01535 645214

LUCKING G. H. & SONS
(Transporters/Storage/Stage Hands)
Commerce Road, Brentford, Middlesex TW8 8LX
Fax: 020-8569 9847   Tel: 020-8569 9030

MAINSTREAM LEISURE GROUP
(Riverboat/Canal Boat Hire)
5 The Mews
6 Putney Common, London SW15 1HL
Website: www.mainstreamleisure.co.uk
Fax: 020-8788 0073   Tel: 020-8788 2669

McNEILL BRIAN
(Vintage Truck & Coaches)
Hawk Mount
Kebcote, Todmorden, Lancs OL14 8SB
Website: www.rollingpast.com
e-mail: autotrams@currantbun.com
Fax: 01706 812292   Tel: 01706 812291

MOTORHOUSE HIRE Ltd
(Period Vehicles 1900-80)
Weston Underwood, Olney, Bucks MK46 5LD
e-mail: john@motorhouseltd.co.uk
Fax: 01234 240393   Tel: 020-7495 1618

M. V. DIXIE QUEEN
Thames Luxury Charters
5 The Mews
Putney Common, London SW15 1HL
Website: www.thamesluxurycharters.co.uk
e-mail: sales@thamesluxurycharters.co.uk
Fax: 020-8788 0072   Tel: 020-8780 1562

NATIONAL MOTOR MUSEUM
John Montagu Building
Beaulieu, Nr Brockenhurst
Hants SO42 7ZN   Tel: 01590 612345

NINE-NINE CARS Ltd
Hyde Meadow Farm, Hyde Lane, Hemel
Hempstead HP3 8SA
e-mail: sales@nineninecars.demon.co.uk
          Tel: 01923 266373

PICKFORDS REMOVALS Ltd
Heritage House, 345 Southbury Road
Enfield, Middlesex EN1 1UP
Fax: 020-8219 8001   Tel: 020-8219 8000

PLUS FILM SERVICES
(All Periods Vehicle Hire)
1 Mill House Cottages
Winchester Road
Bishop's Waltham SO32 1AH
e-mail: stephen@plusfilms.freeserve.co.uk
          Tel/Fax: 01489 895559

RADCLIFFE'S TRANSPORT
(see LUCKING G. H. & SONS)

SCOOTABOUT MOTORCYCLE HIRE CENTRE
1-3 Leeke Street, London WC1X 9HZ
Fax: 020-7833 4613   Tel: 020-7833 4607

STOKE BRUERNE BOAT COMPANY
(Passenger & Commercial Boats)
29 Main Road
Shutlanger, Northants NN12 7RU
Website: www.stokebruerneboats.co.uk
Fax: 01604 864098   Tel: 01604 862107

THAMES LUXURY CHARTERS Ltd
5 The Mews
6 Putney Common
London SW15 1HL
Website: www.thamesluxurycharters.co.uk
e-mail: sales@thamesluxurycharters.co.uk
Fax: 020 8788 0072   Tel: 020 8780 1562

TOWN TYRE SERVICES Ltd
(Tug Boat for Hire)
Valley Way
Swansea Enterprise Park
Llansamcet
Swansea SA6 8QP   Tel: 01792 773431

VINTAGE CARRIAGES TRUST
(Owners of the Museum of Rail Travel at Ingrow
Railway Centre)
Keighley
West Yorks BD22 8NJ
Website: www.vintagecarriagestrust.org
e-mail: admin@vintagecarriagestrust.org
Fax: 01535 610796   Tel: 01535 680425

VIRGIN ATLANTIC AIRWAYS
(Reservations)
The Office
Crawley Business Quarter
Manor Royal, West Sussex RH10 2NU
Fax: 01293 444123   Tel: 01293 747747

INDEX TO ADVERTISERS CONTACTS 2003

INDEX TO ADVERTISERS CONTACTS 2003